THE ARRL
ANTENNA VOL 6
COMPENDIUM

EDITOR
R. Dean Straw, N6BV

ASSISTANT EDITORS
Chuck Hutchinson, K8CH
Larry Wolfgang, WR1B

COVER DESIGN
Sue Fagan

PRODUCTION
Michelle Bloom, WB1ENT
Paul Lappen
Jodi Morin, KA1JPA

TECHNICAL ILLUSTRATIONS
Dave Pingree, N1NAS
Mike Daniels

i

Foreword

You keep asking for more articles on antennas and we're pleased to deliver them. Yes, indeed, **hams love their antennas**! From the first volume in 1989, the *ARRL Antenna Compendium* series has thanks to a cadre of loyal readers, now grown to six volumes. It has become a prestigious forum for presenting not just theoretical ideas and concepts, but also proven, practical antenna designs.

Many well-known authors have contributed articles over the years to the *Antenna Compendium* series. Volume 6 includes the work of such highly esteemed authors as Al Christman, K3LC (ex-KB8I); L. B. Cebik, W4RNL; Peter Dodd, G3LDO; Floyd Koontz, WA2WVL; Jack Kuecken, KE2QJ; Rudy Severns, N6LF; John Stanley, K4ERO; and Frank Witt, AI1H, to name only a few.

In Volume 6 you will find 43 previously unpublished articles, covering a wide range of antenna-related topics—from a thorough technical discussion by K3LC on how to use elevated radials over sloping ground, all the way to a colorful treatise on simple, practical, cheap-and-dirty multiband antennas by new *Compendium* author Jeff Brone, WB2JNA.

Are you fascinated with 10 meters? So are veteran authors L. B. Cebik, W4RNL; Andy Griffith, W4ULD, and Sam Kennedy, KT4QW. They've all contributed great articles on practical 10-meter designs.

Are you into the nitty-gritty of transmission lines? Then you're in excellent company. Frank Witt, AI1H, does his usual outstanding job exploring transmission lines in two different articles. And Wes Stewart, N7WS, and Hal Rosser, W4PMJ, have each contributed thought-provoking articles on the use (and perhaps the abuse) of open-wire ladder line from HF to VHF.

Are you a low-frequency enthusiast? Five articles are devoted to 40 to 160-meter antennas, including one by well-known Topband operator Jerry Arnold, K9AF, who describes his no-compromise 160-meter vertical. Now you know why he's so strong on Topband! Perhaps you've been hankering after some gain on 40, but you can't swing a rotary Yagi. Carrol Allen, AA2NN, describes a two-element switchable 40-meter wire beam that can be strung in the trees.

Many of you marveled at the strength of the CW signals from 6Y2A during the 1998 CQ World Wide Contest. Dean Straw, N6BV, who went along on that DXpedition, has contributed two articles describing the antennas used and the detailed planning that went into the 6Y2A DXpedition. See why Dean feels that the ante has been raised for future DXpeditions.

In short, there is something for any antenna enthusiast in this volume. Perhaps you'll be inspired to write an antenna article of your own. We'd love to see it, as we prepare next for Volume 7.

David Sumner, K1ZZ
Executive Vice President

Newington, Connecticut
August 1999

Instructions for Accompanying CD-ROM

The CD-ROM bundled in the back of this volume includes numerous data files created by the authors of *The ARRL Antenna Compendium, Vol 6* to analyze their antennas, using commercially available antenna modeling software such as *NEC2*, *NEC/Wires*, *NEC-4.1*, *EZNEC*, *EZNEC/4* and *AO*.

The ARRL does not include the modeling software itself on the CD-ROM, only data for these programs. Note also that *NEC-4.1* or *EZNEC/4* are not publicly available because of security restrictions by the US government, although certain institutions have access to this program.

Other Programs

Several authors also wrote special analysis programs for their articles. Where possible, executable versions of these are also on the CD-ROM, together with source code. Where a program can be customized by the reader, the source code is supplied in BASIC. All programs are written for the IBM PC, or fully compatible computers.

Organization of the CD-ROM

The main directory (\ACV6) of the CD-ROM contains this README.TXT file. The other data on the diskette are organized into separate subdirectories, each named using the author's amateur call sign. We suggest that you copy the contents of the CD-ROM (about 4 MB) to your hard disk so that you can access the data easily, using the procedure in the next section **Copying Files to Your Hard Disk**.

For example, the data corresponding to the article by Al Christman, K3LC, is found in the \ACV6\K3LC subdirectory, while the article by Peter Dodd, G3LDO, refers to disk files found in the \ACV6\G3LDO subdirectory. Each data file has a distinct filename extension corresponding to the antenna-analysis program in which it is used. The filename extensions on the disk are:

* *.NEC—used for the *NEC2* or *NEC4.1* program
* *.ANT—used for the *NEC/Wires* or *AO* programs by K6STI
* *.EZ—used for the *EZNEC* or *EZNEC/4* programs by W7EL
* *.BAS—BASIC source code
* *.EXE—executable file

In DOS, when you wish to examine or use a particular ASCII data file, change to the appropriate subdirectory and read the file using a word processor. The procedure is to get into the subdirectory you want using the "CD" (Change Directory) command. For example, to get into the \ACV6\K3LC subdirectory, you would type "CD \ACV6\K3LC [Enter]."

In Windows, use the *Notepad* or *Wordpad* program for navigation and for reading a file you're interested in. You can examine individual antenna data files with an *.ANT or *.NEC filename extension using any word-processing program that can handle ASCII, since each such file contains only ASCII data. The *.EZ files are binary files and can only be examined inside the *EZNEC* or *EZNEC/4* programs.

Copying Files to Your Hard Disk

You will normally copy all files to appropriate subdirectories on your hard disk so that you may examine and use the modeling files with your modeling software. Use the batch file INSTALL.BAT on the CD-ROM to copy the files and to set their attributes properly for use.

Antenna Modeling Files

A comment about the antenna modeling data files: Even if you are an experienced antenna modeler, you will gain valuable insight into how the experts work by examining their data files. Some very interesting techniques are displayed in a number of the data files, and it certainly beats typing in the data manually when you wish to see if you can possibly improve or "tweak" a design any further.

Installing the XMW Program by N6XMW

The *XMW* program is a BASIC program that will only work under the *QBASIC.EXE* program installed automatically with late versions of DOS and early versions of Windows. Later versions of Windows did not automatically install *QBASIC.EXE*, although the executable file and its help file QBASIC.HLP are located on the CD-ROM for Windows 95 or Windows 98. You can locate *QBASIC.EXE* and QBASIC.HLP using the "Find" command [Ctrl][F] from the Windows Explorer. Once you find them, copy these files to your C:\Windows\Command folder. Another source for *QBASIC.EXE* and QBASIC.HLP is on the Web at: **http://support.microsoft.com/download/support/mslfiles/Olddos.exe**.

To initialize *XMW* from the DOS prompt, you must first set up its configuration file. After getting in the N6XMW subdirectory using "CD C:\ACV6\N6XMW [Enter]," type "INIT_XMW" and answer the prompts on-screen. Then you will automatically be taken to the main *XMW* screen. In order to exit *QBASIC*, press [Ctrl-Break] simultaneously and then [ALT-X] simultaneously. The next time you want to start XMW from the N6XMW subdirectory, type "XMW [Enter]."

EZNEC and *EZNEC/4* are available from Roy Lewallen, W7EL, PO Box 6658, Beaverton, OR 97007.

Contents

10-Meter Antennas

Two Hilltoppers for 10 Meters: a Dipole in a Tube and a Beam in a Boom 1
L. B. Cebik, W4RNL
W4RNL fully describes two portable 10-meter antennas that pack up nicely
(along with a picnic basket, of course) for those hilltop recreational trips.

An Aluminum Moxon Triangle for 10 Meters 10
L. B. Cebik, W4RNL
This is one of W4RNL's favorite simple antennas. He tells you how you can build one for yourself.

The PVC Delight — A Simple 10-Meter Wire Beam 14
Andy Griffith, W4ULD
W4ULD describes a simple, inexpensive wire beam.

A Hanging 10-Meter Vertical 19
Sam Kennedy, KT4QW
For hams without a tower, but who do have at least one tree, this simple, low-cost, low-profile
radiator may be the right choice!

40, 80 and 160-Meter Antennas

Two-Element 40-Meter Switched Beam 23
Carrol Allen, AA2NN
Here's a simple two-element wire antenna that has exceptional front-to-back ratio
—and it fits in less space than you might imagine!

A No-Compromise 160-Meter Antenna 26
Jerry Arnold, K9AF
Have some land and Rohn 25 tower available? Want a $1/4$-λ vertical for 160 meters?
K9AF tells how he built his.

Dual-Mode Elevated Verticals 30
Al Christman, K3LC
Making an antenna work in the DX windows on both ends of the 80/75-meter band is not always easy to do.
K3LC describes a nifty solution to this problem for a vertical antenna with elevated radials.

The Versa Beam 34
Al Christman, K3LC
Follow along with K3LC as he systematically designs a versatile 40-meter beam.

The Optima 160/80-Meter Receive Antenna 45
Richard Marris, G2BZQ
Taking the Big Stick to Topband noise levels.

Antenna Modeling

A Matching Technique for Optimized, Broadband Yagi Antennas with Direct Coax Feed 49
Bernd von Bojon, DJ7YE
Do you want high front-to-back ratio and low SWR? DJ7YE describes an unusual broadband
10-meter antenna and describes a new Yagi matching system.

Measurements and Computations

Skywave Antenna Measurements 57
Jack Kuecken, KE2QJ
> This paper describes a system of measurement that allows you to make a realistic evaluation of antenna peformance.
> The measurement techniques set forth represent the culmination of several years of experimentation by the author.

A Remote Noise Bridge 63
Don Urbytes, W8LGV
> W8LGV tells us how he adapted a noise bridge for remote operation by using a relay.
> With his system, you don't have to remove the noise bridge to operate your station.

Multiband Antennas

The Triple S All-Band Antenna 65
George L. Bond, KF2OC
> The SSS is a bent top folded dipole on 40 through 10 meters that uses trees for support.
> On 80 meters, it operates as a $^1/_4$-λ vertical.

A Cheap-and-Dirty Multiband Antenna 68
Jeff Brone, WB2JNA
> *Real* hams don't buy those fancy commercial antennas—They make their own!

The HF Skeleton Slot Antenna 70
Peter Dodd, G3LDO
> G3LDO presents a practical new perspective on a simple, low-profile, low-angle DX antenna that
> covers the bands from 10 through 28 MHz.

Log Periodic Dipole Array Improvements 74
Carl Luetzelschwab, K9LA**10**
> K9LA analyzes his LPDA antenna and improves its performance.

Propagation and Ground Effects

The XMW Propagation-Prediction Program 77
Bill Alsup, N6XMW
> N6*XMW* describes his latest and most ambitious foray into the art and science of HF propagation predictions.

Where the Holes Are and How to Plug Them 82
Dan Handelsman, N2DT
> N2DT gets *really* serious about evaluating his terrain!

Low-Angle HF—History and Future 89
Richard Silberstein, WØYBF
> WØYBF tells the still-unfolding story about investigations into low-angle HF communications.

Using HF Propagation Predictions 101
Dean Straw, N6BV
> N6BV offers some practical tips for would-be practitioners of the art/science of HF propagation predicting,
> using examples from the 1998 6Y2A operation in the CQ World Wide CW Contest.

Quad Antennas

Monster Quads 113
Rudy Severns, N6LF
> So you're dreaming about a *really* big antenna for 40 meters? N6LF tells us about his monster
> two-element 40-meter quad, with bonus three elements on 20 and 15 meters.

Improving the CUBEX Three-Element, Five-Band Quad 119
Danny Mees, ON7NQ
> ON7NQ shows how he improved on the popular CUBEX quad.

Special Antennas

A Vertically Polarized Inverted Soffit Monopole Antenna 121
Grant Bingeman, KM5KG
    KM5KG describes his soffit-mounted broadband inverted monopole antenna. He also tells how
    to add a second inverted monopole for improved performance.

Plastic Antennas, Part Two 128
Pat Hamel, W5THT
    W5THT updates us on some very practical issues he's faced since his last article in
    The ARRL Antenna Compendium, Vol 5.

The Diamondback Antenna 130
Floyd Koontz, WA2WVL
    Like its namesake, the Diamondback can bite the DX!

The Bumbershooter 135
John Sherrick, W3HVQ
    Here is a truly amazing piece of mechanical and electrical work! W3HVQ's unique multi-band
    antenna features three-element Yagis on 40 and 30 meters, together with a log-periodic design from
    20 through 10-meter coverage—and it even folds down for protection against nasty weather.

Towers and Practical Tips

Through-the-Roof Antenna Mounting System 147
Kaz Soong, K8KS
    Ever thought about putting your antenna through your roof but were worried about trying it?
    Read how K8KS accomplished the task.

Motorizing Your Crank-Up Tower Isn't Difficult 151
Allan Fusler, KI7NF
    Allan Fusler, KI7NF, describes how he motorized his crank-up tower.

Weatherproofing Coaxial Cable 156
Jack Warren, WB4MDC
    WB4MDC shares a couple of his tricks for keeping the moisture out of the ends of his coaxial cable feed lines.

Tuners and Transmission Lines

A Remote Tunable Center-Loaded Mobile Antenna 161
Jack Kuecken, KE2QJ
    KE2QJ describes a unique and very intriguing mobile antenna.

Use Low-Loss "Window" Ladder Line for Your 2-Meter Antenna 165
Hal Rosser, W4PMJ
    Take advantage of the low-loss, low-cost, lightweight characteristics of window-line and
    twin lead to feed your 2-meter antenna.

FilTuners—**a New (Old) Approach to Antenna Matching** 168
John Stanley, K4ERO
    To be thoroughly modern in antenna tuners, you sometimes have to look back to see how and why
    the "old timers" did things the way they did them.

Balanced Transmission Lines in Current Amateur Practice 174
Wes Stewart, N7WS
    N7WS takes a hard look at ladder line in amateur applications.

Transmission Line Properties from Manufacturer's Data 179
Frank Witt, AI1H
    How to derive comprehensive information from the limited data provided by cable manufacturers.

Transmission Line Properties from Measured Data 184
Frank Witt, AI1H
    With very few measurements you can learn an enormous amount about your transmission lines.

Vertical Antennas

Elevated Radials Over Sloping Ground **189**
Al Christman, K3LC
> One important part of antenna analysis that's frequently neglected is ground slope.
> Here's a look at how to configure a single elevated vertical, a pair in a cardioid array,
> and a four-square array to meet your needs under sloping-ground conditions.

A Close Look at the Flattop Vertical Antenna **202**
Tom Kuehl, AC7A
> On 80 and 160 meters, quarter-wave verticals are 66 and 134 feet tall.
> That may pose a problem. Tom Kuehl describes the flattop vertical antenna
> that uses capacitive top loading to reduce the overall antenna height.

Broadbanding the Elevated, Inverse-Fed Ground Plane Antenna **209**
Samuel Leslie, W4PK
> N4KG's elevated ground-plane has become a popular antenna for the lower frequencies.
> W4PK offers some ideas on making it cover both CW and SSB portions of the 80-meter band.

Short Radials for Ground-Plane Antennas **212**
Rudy Severns, N6LF
> Think your elevated radials always have to be full size? N6LF lets you in on some
> great ideas to lessen the "wingspan" of radials, especially near the beach.

Antennas Here Are Some Verticals on the Beach **216**
R. Dean Straw, N6BV
> A DXpedition to Jamaica for the CQ World Wide Contest, "Field-Day" style.

VHF/UHF Antennas

The Expanded Quad (X-Q) Array for Two Meters **227**
Fred Smith, W6DV (SK)
> More about the expanded, bi-square quad antenna, with a simple, practical system.

A Portable 900-MHz Corner Reflector Antenna **230**
Jack Warren, WB4MDC
> Need an Antenna for 900 MHz that is Simple to Build and Requires Little or No Tuning?
> WB4MDC Shares His Design for a Field Day ATV-Station Antenna.

Building Log-Periodic Antennas for VHF and UHF Applications **234**
James Watterson, KBØRJG
> Commercial antennas that cover a wide portion of the VHF/UHF bands aren't inexpensive.
> KBØRJG tells you how to design and build a rugged Log-Periodic Dipole Array using
> copper tubing and brass elements.

About the American Radio Relay League

The seed for Amateur Radio was planted in the 1890s, when Guglielmo Marconi began his experiments in wireless telegraphy. Soon he was joined by dozens, then hundreds, of others who were enthusiastic about sending and receiving messages through the air—some with a commercial interest, but others solely out of a love for this new communications medium. The United States government began licensing Amateur Radio operators in 1912.

By 1914, there were thousands of Amateur Radio operators—hams—in the United States. Hiram Percy Maxim, a leading Hartford, Connecticut, inventor and industrialist saw the need for an organization to band together this fledgling group of radio experimenters. In May 1914 he founded the American Radio Relay League (ARRL) to meet that need.

Today ARRL, with approximately 170,000 members, is the largest organization of radio amateurs in the United States. The League is a not-for-profit organization that:
* promotes interest in Amateur Radio communications and experimentation
* represents US radio amateurs in legislative matters, and
* maintains fraternalism and a high standard of conduct among Amateur Radio operators.

At League headquarters in the Hartford suburb of Newington, the staff helps serve the needs of members. ARRL is also International Secretariat for the International Amateur Radio Union, which is made up of similar societies in more than 100 countries around the world.

ARRL publishes the monthly journal *QST*, as well as newsletters and many publications covering all aspects of Amateur Radio. Its headquarters station, W1AW, transmits bulletins of interest to radio amateurs and Morse code practice sessions. The League also coordinates an extensive field organization, which includes volunteers who provide technical information for radio amateurs and public-service activities. ARRL also represents US amateurs with the Federal Communications Commission and other government agencies in the US and abroad.

Membership in ARRL means much more than receiving QST each month. In addition to the services already described, ARRL offers membership services on a personal level, such as the ARRL Volunteer Examiner Coordinator Program and a QSL bureau.

Full ARRL membership (available only to licensed radio amateurs) gives you a voice in how the affairs of the organization are governed. League policy is set by a Board of Directors (one from each of 15 Divisions). Each year, half of the ARRL Board of Directors stands for election by the full members they represent. The day-to-day operation of ARRL HQ is managed by an Executive Vice President and a Chief Financial Officer.

No matter what aspect of Amateur Radio attracts you, ARRL membership is relevant and important. There would be no Amateur Radio as we know it today were it not for the ARRL. We would be happy to welcome you as a member! (An Amateur Radio license is not required for Associate Membership.) For more information about ARRL and answers to any questions you may have about Amateur Radio, write or call:

ARRL—The National Association for Amateur Radio
225 Main Street
Newington CT 06111-1494
(860) 594-0200

Prospective new amateurs call:
800-32-NEW HAM (800-326-3942)
You can also contact us via e-mail: **ead@arrl.org**
or check out our World Wide Web site: **http://www.arrl.org/**

10-Meter Antennas

Two Hilltoppers for 10 Meters:
a Dipole in a Tube and a Beam in a Boom

By L. B. Cebik, W4RNL
1434 High Mesa Drive
Knoxville, TN 37938-4443
cebik@utk.edu

Hilltopping is a popular pastime when 10 meters is open. We grab a small rig, put a portable antenna in the trunk or pickup bed and head for the highest pretty hill we can find for an afternoon of casual QSOs and sightseeing. Where hills are scarce, an open flat area will do, either on the plains or by a seashore. We can embellish the scenario with QSO party challenges, QRP trials and other activities. Whatever the exact plan, the goal is enjoyment!

Small rigs for 10 meters are plentiful. However, our antenna needs are usually not off-the-shelf items. We can press a mobile antenna into use but sometimes we want something with a bit more performance. Since we have several hours set aside for the trip, a few minutes assembly and disassembly is not much to ask in exchange for a better antenna. However, storage space during transport should be minimal.

Using readily available materials, we can have a full-sized dipole or two-element Yagi that store in packages about 5 feet long by a few inches in diameter, including some mast sections to get them about 20 feet in the air. The elements disassemble and store inside PVC tubes—hence the titles of *A Dipole in a Tube* and *A Beam in a Boom*. The tubes bundle easily with 5-foot TV mast sections using luggage straps, or in a pinch, leather dog collars. Everything is included in the package, including a small tool kit to secure the few nuts and bolts that hold things together. See **Fig 1**, a photo showing both sets of portable PVC tubes, plus tool kit and mounting mast.

The prototypes described here use different element materials. However, the two

W4RNL fully describes two portable 10-meter antennas that pack up nicely (along with a picnic basket, of course) for those hilltop recreational trips.

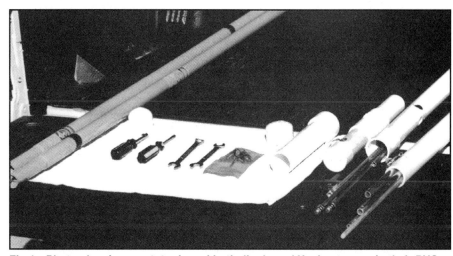

Fig 1—Photo showing mast, tools and both dipole and Yagi antennas in their PVC carrying cases laid out for assembly in back of author's pickup truck.

types are interchangeable, with only slight dimensional changes at the outer element ends. Which material you use will depend on what is available locally, as well as what you can adapt from other uses. Very little is critical, and everything is open to experi-

mentation for a better way. Even with impractical initial experiments, my total investment in these antenna prototypes is around $75 and that can be cut to about $50 for all new parts for the beam alone. Access to surplus materials and a well-stocked junk

1

box can cut the cost even further.

The Materials

Let's begin with the materials, all of which are common. However, some are easier to obtain than others.

1. **Rod Elements**: Because I had access to some aluminum rod, these formed the initial set of elements. Each element is broken in half on each side of center, with a maximum length per unit of 4.5 feet. Hence all will store inside a 5-foot length of PVC tubing.

The final version of the rod element used a $5/16$-inch diameter inner section and a $3/16$-inch diameter outer section. I experimented with $1/4$-inch diameter inner sections and found them too weak when threading was added. However, $5/16$-inch diameter rod is harder to find, since it is not a normally stocked value at either hardware depots or ham vendors. My source was a ground-plane set of radials from a defunct CB antenna.[1] With stock $3/16$ inch aluminum rods as outer sections, full size elements are easily made.

The rods require threading. Thread both ends of the inner $5/16$-inch rod. The feed-point end uses $5/16$-inch stainless steel nuts and washers. To join the inner and outer sections together, I use coupling links made from short ($1/2$ inch) sections of $1/2$-inch square aluminum stock cut from a scrap plate. A tap and die set is essential for making these elements, since the link pieces requires $5/16 \times 18$ tapping on one end and #10×24 tapping on the other. If you have access to the stock and can do the work (or have friends who can assist), the rod elements are the most compact for storage.

2. **Tube Elements**: Aluminum tubing is available from ham vendors in $1/2$ inch and $3/8$-inch diameter 6061-T6 sizes, with 0.058-inch walls. (6063-T832 would be slightly lighter, if available.) These elements nest firmly, so the inside surface of the $1/2$ inch tubes must be smooth. The cost of enough tubing to construct all of the versions of the antennas in this article is remarkably small.

The elements cut neatly with a pipe cutter, which I prefer to a hack saw to minimize deformation of the tubing. All element junctions are made with #8 stainless steel nuts and bolts through pre-drilled and thoroughly deburred holes. I avoid washers, since they tend to get lost in the hilltop grass. Although permanently installed antenna elements deserve more durable fastening for both mechanical and electrical purposes, portable antennas require quick assembly and disassembly with no deformation that will prevent storing the smaller tubing inside the larger ones and both inside a PVC tube.

I also have some scrap TV antenna elements, but I rejected them for this project. TV elements are often seamed and only approximately round, making storage a problem. They are also weak for 10-meter use.

3. **PVC**: For this project, $1/4$ inch nominal Schedule 40 PVC is the main support material. In temporary portable use, none of the concerns about UV susceptibility trouble the project and the RF characteristics are fully adequate for all phases of the project. $1/4$ inch nominal Schedule 40 PVC has dimensions closer to $1^{11}/16$-inch outside diameter and $1^3/8$-inch inside diameter. The inside diameter is just big enough to carry four $1/2$-inch diameter aluminum tubes inside, with the $3/8$-inch diameter tubes inside those.

Schedule 40 PVC is fairly hefty, but a 5-foot tube—for storage of the dipole and to make the boom of the two-element beam— is reasonably manageable. PVC is fine for a 10-meter Yagi boom; however, below about 12 meters it may add too much weight to an antenna.

In addition to the 5-foot tube sections, I use a Tee in the Yagi boom, and end caps wherever there is an open end. The caps perform two functions: they close the tubing for storage and they prevent tubing deformation under the continued weight of the elements. Although the Tee is PVC-cemented in place, the caps are only friction-fitted for regular removal and replacement.

The only other Schedule 40 $1/4$ inch fittings needed are threaded junctions. These junctions permit the dipole hub assembly and the Yagi boom to swage nicely over a standard $1/4$ inch TV mast. Although some of the gray electrical-conduit PVC materials are suitable substitutes for the Schedule 40 plumbing materials, the threaded connectors are not. They have thinner walls and a larger inside diameter that lets TV masting slide through.

4. **Miscellaneous Materials**: The antennas also require a number of common items, including male and female coax connectors (and a Tee fitting for one array), along with some coaxial cable. As mounting plates for the female connectors (1-hole SO-239s), I used a scrap length of 1×1 inch by $1/6$-inch thick aluminum L-stock. I punched the $5/8$ inch mounting holes for each bracket and then cut off a 1-inch wide section for final edge smoothing and mounting hole drilling. Two sets of #6 or #8 stainless steel nuts, bolts and lock washers mount the bracket to the tube, with the coax connector mounted last.

For each antenna I have minimized the variety of hardware necessary for assembly. The tubing versions use #8 stainless steel throughout so that a single screwdriver and a $11/32$-inch or $3/8$-inch nutdriver (depending on the specific hardware used) can be part of the dedicated portable tool kit. The rod versions require $5/16$-inch nuts and the link pieces, both of which require $1/2$-inch

wrenches. The only other tool in the kit is a bottle brush to clean the ends of the tubes for each use. The tools and a few supplies fit in a short scrap PVC tube with end caps. The hardware bag and tools are wrapped in a clean shop cloth. Besides quieting down the rattle of tools, the cloth also serves as a field drop cloth for laying out the tools and hardware.

5. **Masts**: For a 20-foot target antenna height, PVC is both heavy and a bit wobbly. Therefore, I have four 5-foot sections of TV mast. Each section locks with a tab in the next lower one. Together, they form a satisfactory hill-topping mast with the antenna on top. A variety of bracing and guying schemes can be used for temporary stability. When the wind is sufficient to threaten the antenna installation, it is usually time to go home anyway.

These notes on materials appear here at the beginning so that as you look at the simple antennas, you can be planning substitutes that you prefer—or have—or can obtain.

A Rod Dipole in a Tube

Since the elements are interchangeable, let's start with the simplest antenna, a dipole composed of aluminum rod elements that store in a PVC tube. **Fig 2** is a photo showing the assembled dipole in test position on top of the 20-foot mast. **Fig 3** shows the details of the rod-element mounting to a short (1-foot) section of PVC. The threaded $5/16$ inch rods go through the sides of the PVC tube and are locked in place with inner and outer nuts. A second set of outer nuts clamps the terminated wires from the coax connector, which is mounted on its plate and secured to the PVC hub. Leave room for the end cap on top of the PVC hub, but don't place the rod holes so far down the hub that you can't start the nut with your fingers.

If you use rods, as in this example, the overall dipole length should be about 17 feet. Allow a bit extra for trimming to per-

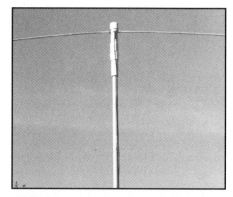

Fig 2—Photo showing rod dipole on top of field mast during tests.

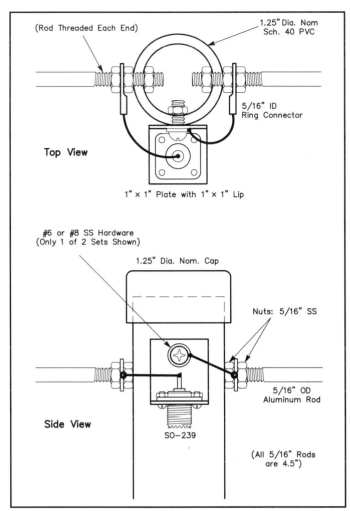

Fig 3—Details for mating the PVC hub to the 5/8-inch diameter rod and coax connector. This detail applies to both the dipole in a tube and the beam in a boom.

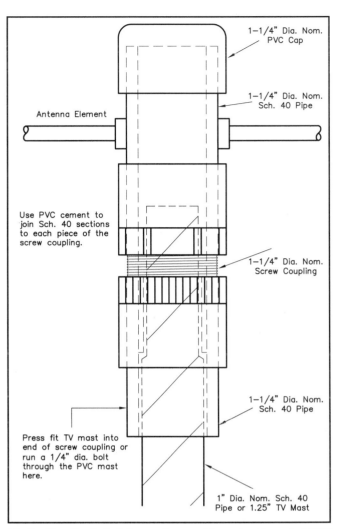

Fig 5—The dipole hub-to-mast assembly, using threaded PVC couplings.

fection. For a tubing version using 4¹/₂-foot inner sections of ¹/₂-inch diameter aluminum and ³/₈-inch diameter outer sections, the overall length should be about 16 feet, 9 inches. Leave extra for tubing overlap, since the ³/₈-inch diameter tube slides inside the large size.

Fig 4 shows the drilled-and-tapped link coupling piece for the rod elements.[2] Be sure to follow the tap manufacturer's recommended guidelines for the holes to drill before using the tap. An undersized hole may snap the tap while an oversized hole will not have secure threads. If you have not used a tap-and-die set before, it makes a good addition to the shop. Just go slowly, follow recommendations and add a drop of oil to the work every now and then. Afterwards, clean the work thoroughly to remove the lubricating oil.

The final assembly of the dipole requires a cemented Schedule 40 female threaded coupling at the bottom of the hub section. A male coupling is cemented to another section of tubing, shown as a short piece in

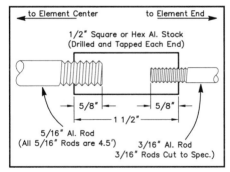

Fig 4—Details of the rod link-coupling piece.

Fig 5. The male section inside diameter is small enough to fit over the reduced diameter at the swaged end of the TV mast but will friction-fit firmly on the enlarged part of the mast.

You have a choice here. You can add a smooth PVC coupling cemented to a longer section of tubing, with a cap (cemented or

friction fit) to the far end. The coupling will then friction-fit the short tube in Fig 5 to form a storage tube for the antenna elements. Alternatively, you can make the tube section from the male coupling downward from one piece of PVC with a friction-fit cap. When in use as an antenna, the entire tube up to the male connector fits over the TV mast. **Fig 6** shows the dipole hub, with feed coax connector, after assembly.

The dipole requires about 10 minutes to set up and a similar period to disassemble and store. Everything fits inside the hub and storage tube, although the SO-239 remains attached to the outside of the hub. An old white sock covers the connector and bracket during storage and transport.

Fig 7 is a comparative SWR curve set for the two types of elements: rods and tubes. The tube version curve is slightly broader, but both versions of the antenna will cover well over the first MHz of 10 meters with under 2:1 SWR to a 50-Ω feedline, even though the resonant feedpoint impedance with the antenna at a 20-foot height is about

3

65-Ω resistive.

Tuning up the antenna calls for setting the element lengths slightly long. For the rod version, use longer outer element sections. For the tube version, with no holes drilled in the inner tubing, set the 3/8-inch section long. Using a temporary setup in the open that permits raising and lowering the antenna easily, simply trim the outer rod or slide in the 3/8-inch tubing until the SWR is lowest at your desired center frequency. Once the outer rod length is correct, smooth the edges of the trimmed end. For the 3/8-inch tubing, mark and drill the holes that align with those in the 1/2-inch tubing.

The dipole is the most flexible of the antennas in my portable collection. One 8-year-old version has traveled the Southeast on loan. The antenna has been mounted at every angle, including horizontal, from the balconies of upper-story vacation condos. RG-8X or RG-58 are suitable for short (20 feet) feedline runs. The addition of a 1:1 choke-balun (coiled coax or W2DU design) is desirable. If surroundings create a slightly high SWR, and the rig has a built-in tuner, by all means use it. Losses will be slight.

A Beam in a Boom: A Two-Element Yagi

Sometimes we want more than a dipole. A little gain and front-to-back ratio can help curb midday QRM. A two-element Yagi or similar array is usually that all we need. The dipole in a tube can easily become a beam in a boom to fill this need. Fig 8 is a photograph of the assembled two-element Yagi on its portable mounting mast.

Fig 9 shows the general outline of the beam elements, with dimensions for both the rod and the tubing versions. The 4.8-foot spacing between elements was selected for three reasons. First, it allows room for end caps using a 5-foot PVC tube length. Second, this spacing provides a very reasonable direct match to a 50-Ω feedline, while still preserving fair two-element Yagi performance. Third, it provides about the right element separation, given the element lengths shown, to allow some phasing experiments for increased antenna performance.

The dimensions in Fig 9 show the lengths of the outer sections of both tubing and rod versions of the two-element Yagi. The rod version has an overall driver length of 16.7 feet and a reflector length of 17.8 feet. The tubing version elements are slightly shorter overall: 16.4 feet and 17.7 feet. Let's build a Yagi, starting with the combination boom and storage tube.

Fig 10 reveals the simplicity of the boom design. Twin sections of Schedule 40 1 1/2-inch nominal diameter PVC join (with cement) at the center in a standard PVC Tee fitting. The distance between the centers of the element holes is 4.8 feet. A short section of PVC comes down from the Tee to a female threaded connector. A male threaded connector and short PVC section complete the assembly and swage over the support mast in the same fashion as the hub-to-mast coupling for the dipole.

Experience has taught me not to cement both boom sections until after the holes for the elements have been drilled and aligned. Place an element section through the holes at each end so that there is a reference line for aligning each element during cementing,

Fig 6—Photo close-up of dipole hub-to-mast assembly, showing coax connector and rod elements.

Fig 8—Photo of assembled two-element 10-meter portable Yagi.

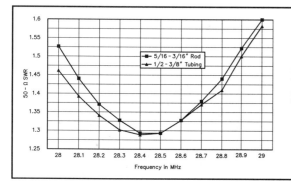

Fig 7—Comparative 50 Ω SWR curves for rod and tubing versions of the dipole in a tube, derived from NEC-4 models.

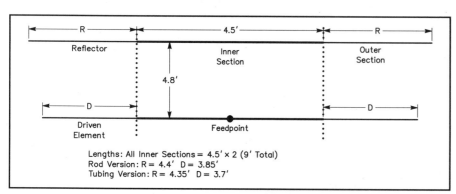

Lengths: All Inner Sections = 4.5' × 2 (9' Total)
Rod Version: R = 4.4' D = 3.85'
Tubing Version: R = 4.35' D = 3.7'

Fig 9—General outline of the two-element Yagi beam in a boom, with length dimensions for rod and tubing versions.

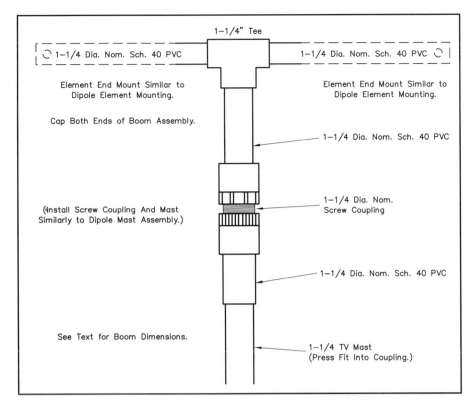

Fig 10—Boom and mast-coupling details for both parasitic and phased versions of the beam in a boom.

Labels in figure:
- 1-1/4" Tee
- 1-1/4 Dia. Nom. Sch. 40 PVC
- 1-1/4 Dia. Nom. Sch. 40 PVC
- Element End Mount Similar to Dipole Element Mounting.
- Cap Both Ends of Boom Assembly.
- Element End Mount Similar to Dipole Element Mounting.
- 1-1/4 Dia. Nom. Sch. 40 PVC
- 1-1/4 Dia. Nom. Screw Coupling
- (Install Screw Coupling And Mast Similarly to Dipole Mast Assembly.)
- 1-1/4 Dia. Nom. Sch. 40 PVC
- See Text for Boom Dimensions.
- 1-1/4 TV Mast (Press Fit Into Coupling.)

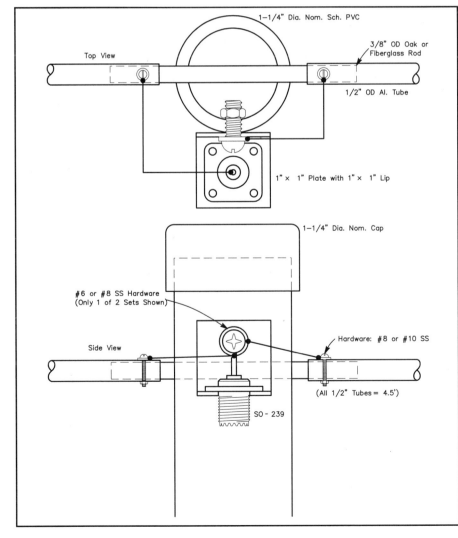

Labels in figure:
- 1-1/4" Dia. Nom. Sch. PVC
- Top View
- 3/8" OD Oak or Fiberglass Rod
- 1/2" OD Al. Tube
- 1" × 1" Plate with 1" × 1" Lip
- 1-1/4" Dia. Nom. Cap
- #6 or #8 SS Hardware (Only 1 of 2 Sets Shown)
- Side View
- Hardware: #8 or #10 SS
- (All 1/2" Tubes = 4.5')
- SO - 239

as well as to ensure that both elements are at a 90° angle to the Tee section.

I've alread described how to mount rod elements. Tube elements require a slightly different technique, as shown in **Fig 11**. The boom holes are 3/8-inch diameter. Through them, run a 2 foot (or longer) length of 3/8-inch insulated rod. Fiberglass rod is ideal, but an oak rod from the hardware depot will also work if it never gets wet.

Select two 4.5-foot lengths of 1/2-inch diameter tubing. About 1/2 inch from the end, drill a hole large enough to easily pass a #8 stainless steel bolt. Carefully deburr the hole and ensure the insulating rod will slide smoothly in the tubes. With the insulated rod marked at its center, and with the center visible through the end of the PVC boom, place the sections of tubing over the rod and press them to the PVC boom. Mark hole positions on the support rod through the element holes. If the assembly is for a dipole, align the holes as shown in the figure. If the assembly is for a Yagi, align the holes so that they are vertical when the beam is in its flat or horizontal orientation.

Drill the holes for #8 hardware and test fit the elements. The bolts should hold the element securely against the boom. Drill holes in the other ends of the 1/2-inch tubing, again cleaning the burrs and smoothing the inner surface so that the 3/8-inch diameter tubing slides easily. Don't drill the 3/8-inch tubing yet.

Allowing for 3 to 6 inches of overlap, cut the outer 3/8-inch diameter tubing for both the reflector and driver. Mark the points at which the smaller tubing should stop when sliding it into the larger tubing. Tape the elements in position temporarily.

Install the coax connector and its brackets as you did for the dipole. Be sure that the connector is below the boom and that the threaded section of the connector faces the mast, since this is the route for the system feed line. In place of a coax connector for the reflector, install a jumper across the PVC. In both cases, I used #8 ring connectors around the element bolts soldered to #12 house wiring scraps to make good connections.

Now you are ready to test the antenna. An easy tune-up technique is to resonate the

Fig 11—Details of mating the PVC hub to the 1/2-inch diameter tubing, with connecting rod and coax connector. This detail applies equally to the dipole in a tube and the beam in a boom; however, for the beam, #8 bolts should be oriented 90° from their orientation in the dipole version shown. The bolt rule is "heads up."

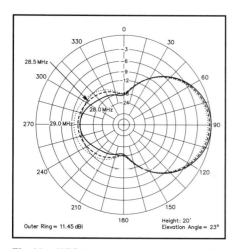

Fig 12—*NEC-4* azimuth-plane pattern for the two-element Yagi from 28 to 29 MHz, at a height of 20 feet above average ground and an elevation angle of maximum radiation of 23°.

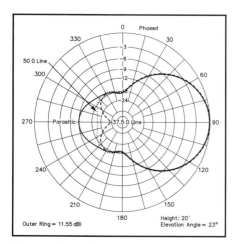

Fig 13—Comparative design frequency (28.5 MHz) *NEC-4* azimuth-plane patterns for the parasitic Yagi and for two different phased versions of the beam in a boom, at a height of 20 feet above average ground and an elevation angle of maximum radiation of 23°.

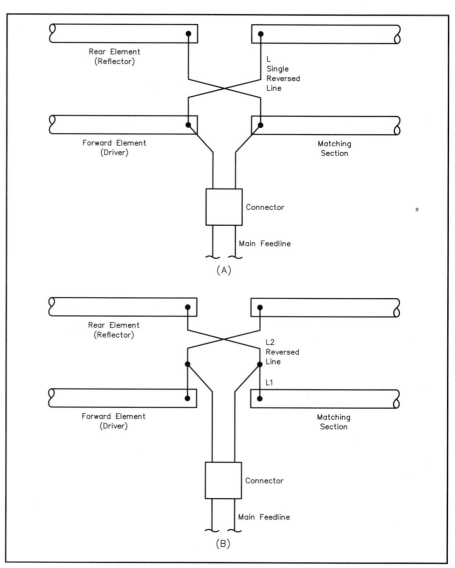

Fig 14—At A, standard ZL Special phasing, and at B, modified HB9CV phasing of the forward and rear elements of the beam in a boom.

individual elements at their independent resonant frequencies, one at a time, by feeding each as a dipole. Set the antenna at its intended use height, in my case 20 feet up. For a design frequency of 28.5 MHz, the tubing driver should be resonant at 29.1 MHz and the reflector should resonate at 27.1 MHz by itself. The rod driver should resonate at 29.0 MHz and its reflector at 27.25 MHz. With these initial positions marked, but not yet drilled, you can proceed to fine tuning.

You can check performance with local stations and take some impedance readings. Adjusting the length of the reflector affects the source resistance most strongly. Altering the length of the driven element has its strongest effect upon the feed-point reac-

tance. If you have an antenna analyzer that can read both resistance and reactance, you should seek a resistance of about 40 Ω at the design frequency with a few ohms of inductive reactance. This will provide an SWR under 2:1 across the first MHz of 10 meters and a bit higher. Finally, when you are satisfied with the performance, drill the holes.

Fig 12 shows the kind of performance you can expect with the two-element Yagi at a height of 20 feet, which yields an elevation angle of maximum radiation of about 23°. The pattern does not change enough across the span between 28 and 29 MHz to be detectable. Yet the QRM from the rear will be quieted by almost 2 S units compared to signals in the forward direction. For many types of operation, this modest gain and equally modest front-to-back ratio is ideal. Often, in net operations on 10 meters, it is useful to hear stations off the rear, so long as their check-in calls do not disrupt the con-

versation in progress. Similar thinking often applies in general contest operating.

The disassembled and nested antenna elements will fit inside the boom. I have discovered that variations in PVC sometimes allow the insulated rods to fit in the exact center of the tubing square. Other pieces of PVC may not allow the fit, and the rods must be strapped to the bundle of boom plus mast sections.

Something More: A Phased Array

I mounted some extra coax connectors on top of my boom. These are for an experimental phasing line that you may wish to use or not depending on your needs and willingness to deal with a further bit of complexity. **Fig 13** shows azimuth patterns at a 20-foot antenna height using the 28.5 MHz design frequency for the parasitic or Yagi version just described, along with two methods of phasing the elements of the array. There is

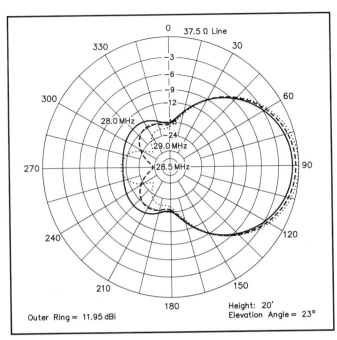

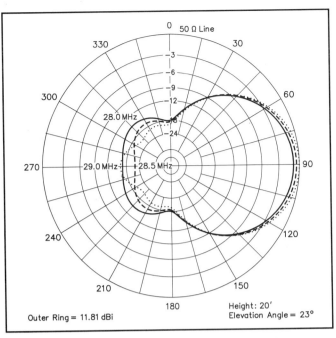

Fig 15—*NEC-4* azimuth-plane patterns for the two-element array with a single 37.5 Ω, 0.66 VF phasing line from 28 to 29 MHz, at a height of 20 feet above average ground and an elevation angle of maximum radiation of 23°.

Fig 16—*NEC-4* azimuth-plane patterns for the two-element array with a two-piece 50 Ω, 0.78 VF phasing line from 28 to 29 MHz, at a height of 20 feet above average ground and an elevation angle of maximum radiation of 23°.

some added gain (less than 0.5 dB), but a considerable increase in the front-to-back ratio. The 37.5-Ω phasing line consists of either two lengths of 75-Ω coax in parallel or two lengths of 75-Ω parallel-wire feedline. Each is connected between the forward and rear elements, with a half twist.

Despite the very nice 180° front-to-back ratio, the presence of the rear quartering lobes promises an average front-to-rear ratio of around 20 dB. The deep null occurs only over a fairly small bandwidth, and the rear lobe flattens out somewhere off the design frequency. With a mechanically simpler 50-Ω cable system, one can obtain almost the same front-to-rear ratio. The front-to-rear ratio of either phased array is a significant improvement over a raw two-element Yagi's performance. When the needs call for high rear rejection, the phased array may prove useful.

Fig 14 sketches the difference between the 37.5-Ω and 50-Ω phasing systems. In Fig 14A, I show the ZL-Special phasing system, where a single piece of 37.5-Ω transmission line goes from the forward to the rear element. (The terms *reflector* and *driven element* are no longer apt, since both elements are driven using predetermined current magnitudes and phases.) Note that a single 50-Ω line between the two elements would not provide the desired rear element current magnitude and phase.

However, something close to optimum can be achieved by using a short section of line between the feedpoint proper and the

forward element. In effect, this phasing system is a variant of the HB9CV system and is shown in Fig 14B. The difference from the original HB9CV design is that the boom is not part of the transmission line.

In terms of performance across the first MHz of 10 meters, **Fig 15** and **Fig 16** show that there is little to choose between the two systems except at frequencies very near the design frequency. Unlike the parasitic Yagi, the phased array's gain rises as the frequency increases. The source impedance for each of the phased-array arrangements is closer to 25 Ω than to 50 Ω. Therefore, lengths of 37.5-Ω cable, made from parallel sections of RG-59, provide series matching sections. The required length can be calcu-

lated from the Regier equations,[3] but given the modeling source of these antenna designs, it was simpler to try lengths until reasonable smooth SWR curves emerged.

Fig 17 shows the modeled and anticipated SWR curves for the Yagi and for the two phasing arrangements, with matching sections added to the latter.[4] Note that for the phased arrays, the SWR curve is not centered, but is shifted upward from the design frequency of 28.5 MHz. This move is intentional to provide relatively similar SWR figures at both 28 and 29 MHz. One consequence of shifting the SWR curve is that the matching sections are not a true 1/4 wavelength long, but somewhat shorter.

Fig 18 provides the transmission-line

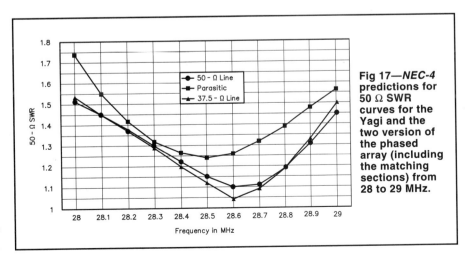

Fig 17—*NEC-4* predictions for 50 Ω SWR curves for the Yagi and the two version of the phased array (including the matching sections) from 28 to 29 MHz.

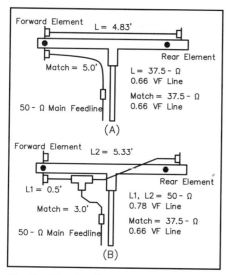

Fig 18—Phasing line lengths and line-run arrangements for each of the two phasing systems whose performance is shown in Fig 17.

Table 1

A hilltopping tool kit for the antennas discussed in this article. Omit tools that are not relevant to the antenna(s) you build.

Number	Item
2	$^{1}/_{2}$ inch open-end or combination wrenches (for rod elements)
1	$^{3}/_{16}$-inch wide flat-blade screwdriver (for tube element #8 bolts)
1	$^{11}/_{32}$ inch or $^{3}/_{8}$-inch nut driver (for tube element #8 nuts)
1	package of $^{5}/_{16}$-inch nuts (spares only; regulars stored on element)
1	package of #8 nuts and bolts (4 sets per tube element plus spares)
1	small bundle of cable ties and/or roll of electrical tape
1	towel or large shop rag
1	$^{1}/_{2}$-inch diameter bottle brush with a fairly long handle
1	Yagi reflector jumper wire (with ring connectors)
1	short length of 2-inch PVC with end caps (long enough to hold tools and supplies when wrapped in the towel)

Note: additional tools necessary for rig setup and for the preferred guying or mast bracing method are not included in this list.

lengths used for these prototypes.[5] Variations of materials and antenna dimensions will require some additional modeling and experimentation to determine what is correct for any other versions of these arrays.

Structurally, the phasing harness is simple to install. I added SO-239 connectors and brackets on the topside of the boom at each end. The rear connector routes its center conductor lead to the element half that is opposite that of the center lead to the forward element. This move effects the needed half twist. The 37.5-Ω line runs from front to rear on top of the boom. The line is just long enough to reach using parallel 75-Ω lines with a 0.66 to 0.67 velocity factor. A small cable tie holds the phasing line in place about mid-boom. (A wrap of electrical tape does the same job when I forget to renew my supply of cable ties in the tool tube.) The matching section plugs into the lower SO-239 and runs back to the mast, where a cable tie (or tape) holds it in position.

The 50-Ω, 0.78 velocity factor line system (RG-8X) can use either the upper or lower forward SO-239. I tend to use the lower coax connector and bring the cable up to the top side about half way between the front and rear connectors. Since the overall cable length is longer, I use two cable ties, one to the rear and another near the Tee connector (a UG-358, with a PL-258 double female adapter in the male Tee leg for the matching section). The requisite matching section again goes to the mast, but not against the phasing line. The velocity factor of RG-8X may not be precisely 0.78. The batch I used had a velocity factor closer to 0.73. This nearly 7% variance creates no noticeable performance difference (on the

air or in models).

For modeling aficionados who have *EZNEC*, there are modeling files on the accompanying CD-ROM.

My own habit (and you may have a better one) is to store the phasing lines and the 50-Ω main feed-line coiled neatly in an old pillowcase. This is the one "lumpy" or non-tubular portion of the entire portable antenna system. Of course, you would carry along only those parts of the particular antenna you select to build, according to your own needs.

With the added front-to-rear benefits of the phasing system, there is not much difference between the performance of the two-element phased array and a short-boom three-element beam. Three elements on an 8 foot boom would yield about an extra half dB of gain (around 7 dBi free space or about 12.5 dBi at 20 feet over average ground) and perhaps 1 to 2 dB additional front-to-rear ratio. The two-element phased array saves three feet of boom length and four lengths of tubing that would not fit into the boom anyway. The two-element array has proven quite adequate to any hilltopping I have done.

The Tool Tube

Hilltopping requires planning, and that includes having a dedicated tool kit for the antennas. Mine consists of the tools and materials in **Table 1**. These tools cover all of the versions of the antenna set, so select your tools for whatever you build. For hilltopping, I haunted tool sales to obtain inexpensive items that I could devote to the antenna. (If you raid your tool set for household jobs, something necessary will be missing when you find yourself atop the perfect hill.) I also put a dab of paint on each shank or handle to identify the tools as be-

longing in the tool tube.

The towel is my large shop rag on which I spread my tools and hardware when setting up an antenna. This rag traps loose hardware. However, I always carry extra hardware in case the hilltop grass decides to eat something made of stainless steel. Self-sealing plastic bags, salvaged from parts purchases, carry the hardware, sorted by size.

Conclusion

I have not performed precision range tests on these antennas, so I shall not guarantee that they deliver every bit of performance that the models promise. For example, phasing and matching section lines length difference of 2 inches or so appear to make little noticeable difference, even in the SWR curve. This flexibility makes construction less critical, but allows the antenna to be slightly off peak performance capability. The basic parasitic Yagi delivers gain and front-to-back ratio when compared to the dipole, and the added front-to-back ratio of the phased array is clearly noticeable.

Minor element drooping, such as seen in the photographs, has no affect on performance. I have modeled the element droop and differences show up only in the second decimal place of any performance figure. The materials I used were designed to withstand abuse that I hope I never give them. I have avoided structural materials that are only marginally adequate. Aluminum rods may be the most difficult item to find in the $^{5}/_{16}$-inch diameter. Everything else is available from ham vendors or from hardware depots.

These antennas are adaptable to a wide variety of materials. I can imagine versions of these antennas using hardwood dowels as booms and hubs. I can also imagine a metal boom for the Yagi (but not for the phased array, without considerable redesign to prevent interaction with the phasing lines). However, PVC is a highly adaptable material, a sort of "Tinkertoys for adults."

The antennas in this set of hilltoppers are full size, and give commensurate performance. They easily break down for transportation and storage into convenient packages. Bound together with luggage straps, they steal little room in the trunk or pickup bed from the picnic food and drink that add to the enjoyment of 10-meter hilltopping. They cost little to build.

Whenever the sunspots are on the rise, why not have a dipole in a tube or a beam in a boom ready to go? And don't forget to take along the rig with accessories, a picnic lunch and a friend as well.

Notes

[1] I found my first set locally at an estate sale. Henry Pollock, K4TMC, graciously donated the second set from a defunct antenna stored under his house. I am told that the rod sets are used on an Antenna Specialists CB antenna.

[2] Gerald Williamson, K5GW, of Texas Tower fame, sent me some precut $1/2$ inch square, $1^1/2$ inch long blanks cut from scrap in his home shop, thus saving me a long search. I am grateful for his help, which is proof that hams do better together than alone.

[3] For information on Regier's work, see "Series-Section Transmission-Line Impedance Matching," July 1978 QST, pp 14-16, or refer to The ARRL Antenna Book, 18th Ed., pp 26-4 to 26-5 and pp 28-12 to 28-14.

[4] Modeling for these designs was done on a combination of GNEC by Nittany Scientific and EZNEC Pro by W7EL. Both programs employ NEC-4. A version of NEC-2 (with its built-in tapered-diameter correction) or MININEC should work just as well, although MININEC will not model the transmission lines used in the phased arrays.

[5] See "When Is a Quarter Wavelength Not a Quarter Wavelength?" April 1998 AntenneX.

An Aluminum Moxon Rectangle for 10 Meters

By L. B. Cebik, W4RNL
1434 High Mesa Drive
Knoxville, TN 37938-4443
cebik@utk.edu

I occasionally receive inquiries from folks who cannot quite support the width of a 10-meter Yagi of two or three elements because obstructions restrict them to less than the 16.5 feet needed. Is there an antenna with decent performance that will fit in a space about 13 feet wide? If it can be home-built to save money and to require no complex tuning or matching system, so much the better.

In fact, there is an antenna that fits this description almost perfectly. Imagine an antenna with the gain (over real ground) of a two-element Yagi (> 11 dBi), nearly the front-to-back ratio of a three-element Yagi (> 20 dB from 28.3 to 28.5 MHz), and an SWR below 2:1 from one end of the band to the other. Also imagine that the antenna has better than 15 dB F/B all the way down to 28 MHz, and retains about 12 dB F/B at 29.7 MHz.

Imagine also that the antenna can be directly connected to 50-Ω coax (even though I always recommend a 1:1 choke or bead balun). Now imagine that you can make it yourself from hardware store materials, that it will weigh about 10 pounds including the boom (under 5 pounds without the boom), and that you can make it in your garage with no special tools. Finally, imagine that when it is done, you will still have change from a $50 bill.

Imagine no more. The antenna is the Moxon rectangle. Les Moxon, G6XN, derived the original design from VK2ABQ squares. He tunes both elements of his wire version to form a two-way, fixed-mounted beam.[1] However, we can optimize the dimensions to form an aluminum beam that is easy to rotate.[2]

Fig 1 shows a sketch, with dimensions, of my latest version. It uses hardware-store $^7/_8$ and $^3/_4$-inch diameter aluminum tubing to

form the main elements, with $^3/_4$-inch tubing for the side elements. The corners can use radius-bent tubing or be squared by making corner supports from L-stock. Cut the straight tubing at 45° end angles and use $^1/_{16}$-inch thick L-stock to fashion upper and lower supports. One- to two-inch lengths of support each way around the corner, using stainless-steel sheet-metal screws or pop rivets, solidify the corners with minimal weight. I also tried $^1/_2$-inch conduit Ls, but had to ream out the ends to accept the $^3/_4$-inch tubing.

The corners I use are $^7/_8$-inch aluminum radius-bent sections sent to me by Tom Schiller, N6BT (of Force 12), to speed up the experimentation. You can bend your own by filling the aluminum tube with sand (or cat litter) and bending it around a 6-inch or larger wheel or pulley. Work slowly. Keep the sand well packed in the tube to prevent kinking.

The combination of $^7/_8$-inch and $^3/_4$-inch aluminum tubing lets you telescope the ends into the center for a precise fit or a

center frequency adjustment. A similar advantage accrues from using 1-inch and $^7/_8$-inch hardware-store aluminum tubing. **Fig 2** is a close-up photograph of a corner assembly.

The side-to-side length is the key to centering the SWR curve for lowest reading at 28.4 to 28.5 MHz. The center frequency changes about 150 kHz for every inch of length adjustment. Hence, using the U-shaped outer ends as trombone slides will let you center the antenna anywhere in the 10-meter band. If you use slightly larger stock, say 1-inch and $^7/_8$-inch tubing, performance will change very little. With $^7/_8$-inch tubing for the outer main elements and the sides, you can weld or otherwise fasten (with Penetrox or another conductive paste) $^3/_4$-inch copper plumbing pipe Ls at the corners.

Since the end spacing and alignment is somewhat critical to the antenna's full performance, you can slide a piece of CPVC or similar lightweight, durable tubing either inside the ends or over the ends and fasten

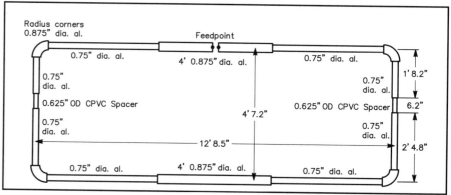

Fig 1—General outline of the 10-meter aluminum Moxon rectangle, showing tubing dimensions. See text for hardware and mounting details.

Fig 2—A close-up of the corner assembly. The 7/8-inch diameter corner piece makes a good fit over the 3/4-inch diameter straight pieces and requires only a single fastener at each end (with a light coat of "Penetrox A" at the joint).

them in place with sheet-metal screws. The rigid spacer also limits the twisting force placed on the corners. Sheet-metal screws also connect the 3/4-inch and 7/8-inch tubing together. Be sure that all hardware is stainless steel. Pop rivets will also do well, if you use sufficiently sturdy ones.

The feed-point assembly is shown in **Fig 3**. I used a very simple system. I cut one side of the driven element tubing 1 inch short at the feed point. I then cut a 2-inch section of 1/16-inch thick L stock, and cut a 5/8-inch diameter hole at one end. A chassis-mount female coax connector (with a lock washer) fits into the hole, with the

plug side pointed at the mast. Stainless-steel sheet metal screws attach the longer side of the L stock to the cut-off tube. A #14 copper wire (tinned the entire length) goes from the center pin to the other side of the feed point, where it is fastened to the tubing by a sheet-metal screw. Feel free to devise your own method of feed-point connections. After testing, but before committing the antenna to permanent installation, be sure to waterproof the rear of the coax connector as well as the coax plugs.

For element-to-boom plates, you can use any durable material. Spar varnished 3/8-inch plywood or LE plastic make good plates. About 3 by 9 inch (or longer) plates give ample room to U-bolt the elements to the plate and have room for U bolts that go over the mast. My prototype uses 1/2-inch PVC electrical conduit U straps fastened in place with #8 stainless-steel hardware. Since 7/8-inch tubing overstresses these straps, I placed an extra washer between the U strap and the plywood plate. The object is a firm grip, but not a broken strap. Two straps hold the reflector center tube in place; the driven element requires two on each side of the feed point.

As with all good antenna structures, let the elements hang under the boom. What boom? Well, you can use almost anything, from 1 1/4-inch PVC (which I had on hand) to a good grade of aluminum tubing (thicker-wall than the usual 0.055-inch hardware store variety–or two pieces nested) to a 5-foot length of spar varnished 1 1/4-inch-diameter closet rod. PVC is the heaviest, aluminum the lightest; but

at 5 feet, the boom weight is not a significant issue. Make a boom-to-mast plate similar to the boom-to-element plates, only a bit more nearly square, and you are in business.

The antenna dimensions in the drawing are given to three decimal places, being direct translations of the computer model used to generate the antenna. Try to keep the dimensions within about 1/4 inch of the drawing, and you won't be able to tell any difference in performance. Squaring the corners or missing the dimensions by a half inch will shift the performance centers by about 100 kHz at most. In most cases, you will not be aware of any difference at all. To assure that the assembly is neatly squared and close to the prescribed dimensions, you can draw the outer dimensions and center line on the shop/garage/basement floor with a marker pen and then assemble the pieces within those boundaries. As shop experts always say, measure twice, cut and assemble once.

Note that the antenna is about 12 feet, 8 inches wide and under 5 feet front-to-back, for a turning radius of about 6 feet, 8 inches. Strapped up on the side of the house, the antenna is unlikely to overhang the property line. The antenna is light enough for hand rotation, but an old TV rotator might come in handy. Because of the antenna's characteristics, you may not need to rotate it much.

The free-space azimuth patterns, shown in **Fig 4** for 28.1, 28.5, and 28.9 MHz, show the possibilities for the Moxon rectangle. Note the very broad forward lobe, almost a cardioid, giving reception and transmission

Fig 3—A close-up of the feed-point assembly, with 3/4-inch wide U-stock used for the coax receptacle. After initial tests the rear of the coax fitting, the bare wire-to-tube connection and the connector from the ferrite-bead choke balun were sealed with butylate. Experience with other outdoor uses suggests that the gray PVC half-clamps should be replaced every two to three years during routine maintenance.

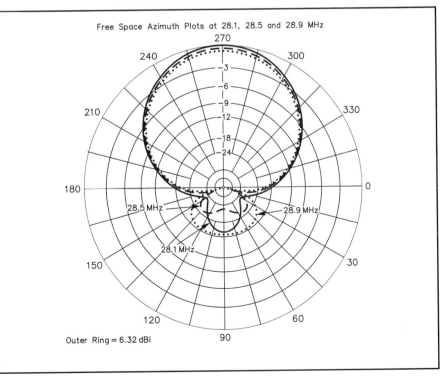

Free Space Azimuth Plots at 28.1, 28.5 and 28.9 MHz

Outer Ring = 6.32 dBi

Fig 4—Free space azimuth plots at 28.1, 28.5 and 28.9 MHz.

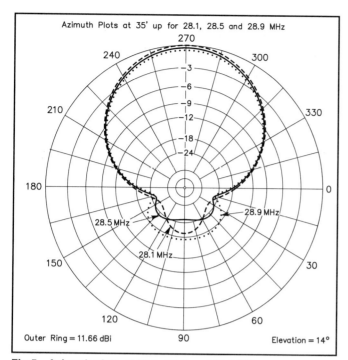

Fig 5—Azimuth plots at 28.1, 28.5 and 28.9 MHz at an elevation angle of 13° with the antenna at 35 feet.

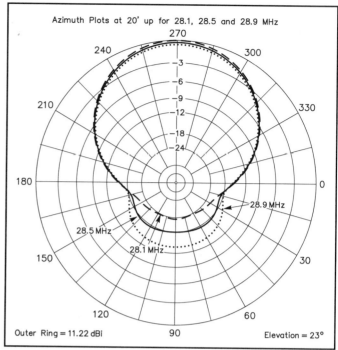

Fig 6—Azimuth plots at 28.1, 28.5, and 28.9 MHz at an elevation angle of 23° with the antenna at 20 feet.

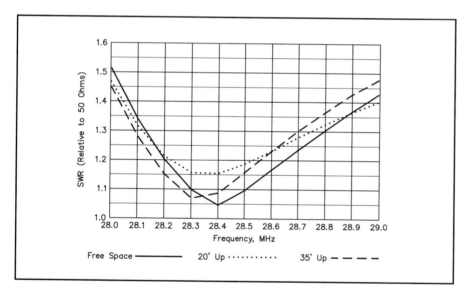

Fig 7—Computer SWR predictions for the Moxon rectangle between 28 and 29 MHz.

ground. Therefore, setting up the antenna for operation is simple.

My initial procedure was to fasten the antenna, pointed straight up, to a 20-foot mast propped up by a sturdy tripod. The reflector was no more than 5 feet above ground. I then adjusted the side-to-side length to minimize SWR at 28.450 MHz, using the trombone-slide end sections. After fastening down the sections and raising the antenna, there was no detectable change in SWR performance from the adjustment position pointing at the sky.

Fig 8 is a photograph of my antenna mounted in place on its test mast. On-the-air tests with Moxon rectangles verify that the antenna shows less than 2:1 SWR across the entire 10-meter band when the design center frequency is about 28.5 MHz. The

as wide as your peripheral vision. Behind you is silence—or at least a significant amount of silencing. The performance characteristics promise to hold up well across the most active part of 10 meters.[3]

But what about performance at real heights above real ground? At 35 feet, about one wavelength, the antenna provides most of its free-space performance across the band, as shown in **Fig 5**. At greater heights, the performance moves closer to free space. The elevation angle at 35 feet for maximum gain is 13° to 14°, similar to that of a dipole or Yagi.

Even at 20 feet up, a typical portable antenna height at 10 meters, the antenna continues to display excellent front-to-back characteristics with the gain of a typical driven element-reflector two-element Yagi (which does *not* have good front-to-back characteristics at this height—perhaps 9 or 10 dB). See **Fig 6**. The elevation angle of maximum radiation is about 23° at the $5/8$ wavelength height.

As shown in the computer projections of **Fig 7**, the Moxon rectangle is quite stable with respect to feed-point characteristics as the antenna is raised and lowered. The curves actually flatten somewhat over real

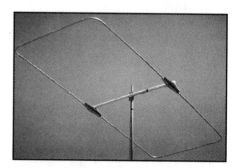

Fig 8—The completed 10-meter aluminum Moxon rectangle on its test mast. Despite some stiff breezes, the physically closed assembly has remained very stable.

gain and front-to-back ratio continue to decrease as the frequency increases, but some directionality and gain persist even at the top end of 10 meters. Local contacts confirm that the front-to-back ratio within the first megahertz of 10 meters is far superior to that of a comparable driven element-reflector two-element Yagi. I cannot measure gain, but there is no detectable difference between the Moxon and a two-element Yagi at my station.

Contrary to claims made for the VK2ABQ squares, these antennas do not like to be nested for a multiband array. Stacking requires a minimum of 10 feet between 10 and 15-meter models. However, you might consider back-to-back 10 and 15-meter antennas. Computer studies suggest that a 13-foot boom would hold both antennas, reflector-to-reflector, with minimal interaction.

The Moxon rectangle will not overpower big competition. However, it does provide wideband gain with very good directional performance and a good match to common coax for the 10-meter operator with limited space and budget. Construction is straightforward using commonly available materials. These may be enough good features to earn the antenna a place at many stations.

Notes

[1] L. A. Moxon, G6XN, *HF Antennas for All Locations* (London, RSGB: 1982), pp 67, 168, 172-175.

[2] Past versions that I built using wire elements required lots of PVC to support them. See "Modeling and Understanding Small Beams, Part 2: VK2ABQ Squares and Moxon Rectangles," Spring 1995 *Communications Quarterly*, pp 55-70. Those versions were constructed to prove the principles of the Moxon rectangle, not to produce an easy-to-build antenna.

[3] All computer plots were made with *NEC-4* using the *EZNEC Pro* software from Roy Lewallen, W7EL, PO Box 6658, Beaverton, OR 97007.

The PVC Delight–A Simple 10-Meter Wire Beam

By Andrew S. Griffith, W4ULD
203 Lord Granville Dr, Rte 2
Morehead City, NC 28557

The 10-meter band is really hopping and the DX is rolling in as Solar Cycle 23 progresses. Right now is an excellent time for Novice and Technician Plus operators to put up a 10-meter antenna and join the fun. Here is a simple rotatable beam antenna with a calculated 3-dB gain over a dipole and about 10-dB front-to-back ratio, as shown in **Fig 1**. Of course, this simple antenna does not compare with the performance of a three-element beam on a 100-foot tower, but neither do the costs compare. The beam is easy to build and is constructed of readily available materials. You can mount it on a mast and rotate it with a TV rotator, or you can suspend it from the limb of a tall tree and rotate it with a line attached to one corner. The turning

W4ULD presents a 2-element, easy-to-build, low-cost, rotatable wire beam.

radius is only 6 feet 1½ inches.

You can see the details of the PVC Delight in **Fig 2** and **Fig 3**. The beam consists of a driven element with the ends folded back and a reflector with the ends folded forward. Thus the driven element and reflector form a square horizontal loop. Insulators separate the element ends, which form the sides of the loop. A shorted stub at its center tunes the reflector. I used *EZNEC*[1] to design the antenna for a compromise among

forward gain, front-to-back ratio, and ease of matching to 50-Ω line. The impedance at the center of the driven element is about 110 Ω; that means that ¼-λ of 75-Ω line (Q section) between the feed point and a 50-Ω feedline will result in an SWR of about 1.15:1.

Construction Details

Critical dimensions are: the lengths of the elements, the length of the stub in the reflec-

Construction Materials

Assuming that one can scrounge the small pieces of exterior plywood for the hub, the beam can be constructed for about $20. The required 35 feet of #14 stranded-copper wire is available from advertisers in *QST* at about $0.14 per foot for a total cost of $4.90. Most of the other materials can be obtained from a local building-supply house or hardware store. At my location 45 feet of ¾ inch PVC pipe was $5.45, eight ¼ × 1⅛ × 2-inch-long plated U bolts were $6.56, 4 plated ¼ × 2½-inch long hex bolts with nuts and washers were $0.68, and a 1½ inch stainless steel hose clamp was $1.50. A 6-inch-long piece of aluminum strap for the mast brackets was $1 from a metal shop. Of course stainless steel hardware is preferable to plated steel. Stainless steel U bolts were priced at a total of $15.76 and stainless steel hex bolts, nuts and washers, $11.32.

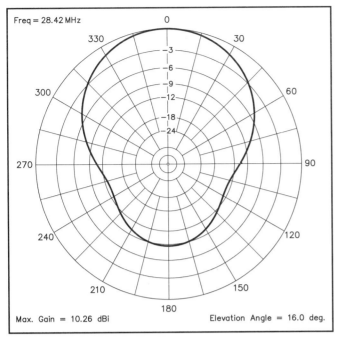

Freq = 28.42 MHz

Max. Gain = 10.26 dBi   Elevation Angle = 16.0 deg.

Fig 1—Azimuthal radiation pattern at 16° elevation angle for the PVC Delight mounted 30 feet above real ground.

The PVC Special. Top view of the hub.

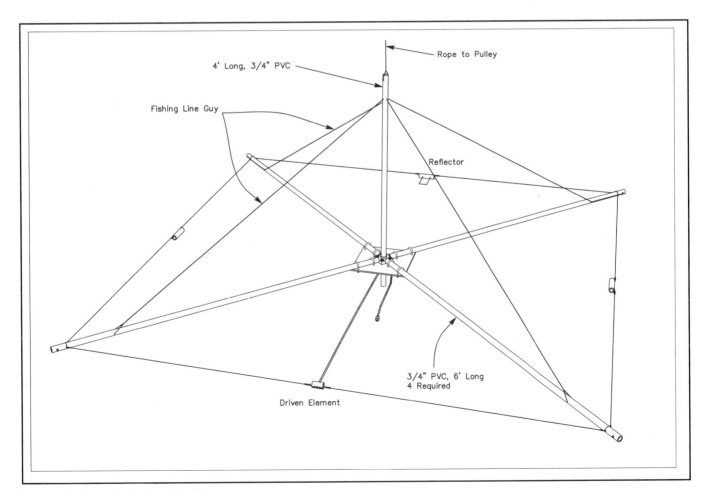

Fig 2—Angle view of the PVC Delight.

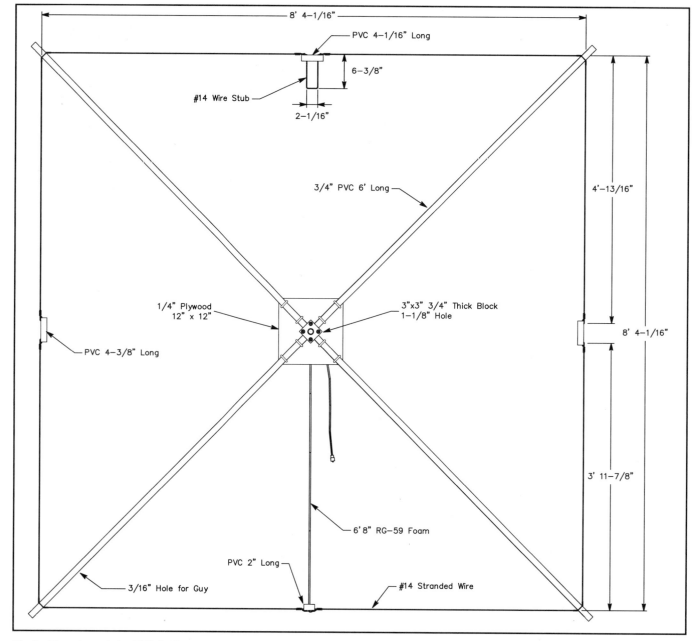

Fig 3—Top view of the PVC Delight.

tor, the length of the Q section, and the 8 feet 4¹/₁₆ inch length of each side of the square loop. There are many ways to construct a supporting framework. Some readers may devise a better construction method than my design, and that's okay. In my version, the framework consists of a hub (built of exterior plywood) to which four arms of ³/₄-inch PVC pipe (schedule 40) are attached by U bolts.

The #14 wire elements pass through holes in the ends of the arms. A 4-foot length of ³/₄-inch PVC pipe is mounted vertically in the hub and extends 42 inches above the hub. One hole near the top of this pipe is a tie point for a rope to hoist the beam into a tree. A second hole is a tie point for four guys which extend to holes near the ends of

the PVC arms. The guys are polyester fishing line and keep the arms straight and parallel to the ground. For mast mounting, pass the mast through the hub and connect to the hub by two angle brackets. Attach the angle brackets to the mast with a hose clamp.

Fig 4 shows the hub detail. It is best to cut the two 3 × 3 × ³/₄-inch blocks and attach them to the 12 × 12 × ¹/₄-inch piece of plywood before drilling the center hole through the assembly. In this way, the center hole will be perfectly aligned through the entire assembly. If you're going to hoist the beam into a tree, the center hole should be 1¹/₁₆ inches in diameter to fit the vertical support pipe. If you don't have access to a bit or hole saw for this diameter, you may use a

1¹/₈-inch bit and tape the center support pipe to fit the hole. If you plan to mount the antenna on a mast, the center hole should be 1¹/₄-inch diameter for standard TV mast. Fig 4C shows the details of the angle brackets that attach the hub to the mast. The vertical support pipe will slide into the top of the mast. You'll probably want to paint the hub and the U bolts for protection against the weather.

Fig 5 shows the details for the ends of the arms. The hub end of the arms butt against the top 3 × 3 inch block of the hub. Two ⁵/₁₆ × 1¹/₈ × 2 inch-long U bolts attach each arm to the hub. It is best to drill the holes in the arms at final assembly, which will be covered later.

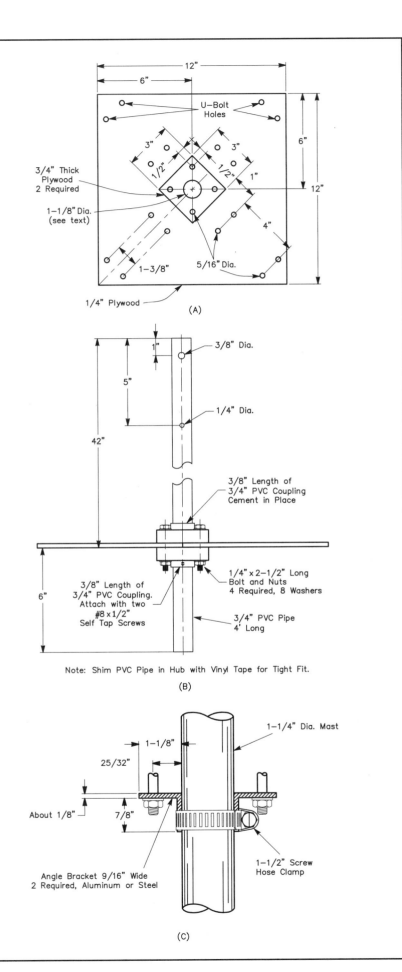

I made all insulators from ³/₄-inch PVC pipe as shown in **Fig 6**. For clarity, I've shown cross sectional views of the insulators. The Q section consists of a 6 foot 8 inch length of foam-type RG-59 coax. Measure the length from the point where the center conductor emerges from the shield at the feed point to the end of the body of the PL-259. [If you're going to use an amplifier, the Q section should be 5 feet 8⁵/₁₆ inches of RG-11A cable (solid dielectric).] In the final assembly, bring the RG-59 cable horizontally to the mast or the bottom of the vertical support and fasten it there with a hose clamp. Thus there is little stress at the feed point. Make loops at the ends of the reflector stub and the reflector wires for the self tapping screws in the stub assembly.

Assemble the hub and arms and place them on a level surface. Drill the holes in the arms for the #14 wire exactly 5 feet 10³/₄ inches from the center of the hub. Also drill the holes for the turning rope and the guys as shown in Fig 5. The guy-wire holes are not critical. Cut four 8 foot 9 inch lengths of #14 stranded copper wire to make up the two sides of the driven element and the reflector. This allows enough length to connect the wires to the insulators. Attach the wires to the feed point insulator and the stub insulator according to Fig 6A and B, respectively. Mark the wires exactly 4 feet 2¹/₃₂ inches away from the center of the feed point and stub insulators. With the marks centered in the holes in the ends of the arms, lock the wires in place by *seizing* as shown in Fig 5. Install the side insulators according to the dimensions in Fig 3. Make sure that the distance between the front and back corners is 8 feet 4¹/₁₆ in. Install the vertical support as shown in Fig 4B. Tie the four fishing-line guys between the arms and the vertical support so that the arms are straight and parallel to the ground. The beam should be ready to put up in the air.

Evaluation

As designed, the beam should resonate at about 28.6 MHz with an SWR of about 1.15:1, however, it will cover at least from 28.3 MHz to 29.0 MHz without a tuner. While the calculated front-to-back ratio is 10 dB, on-the-air checks showed a front-to-back difference of 3 S units. I could not arrange a valid comparison of forward gain compared to a dipole. I hoisted the beam

Fig 4—Details of hub construction. At A is the top view. The side view is shown at B. While the mast-mounting detail appears at C. The larger 12 × 12 piece of plywood is ¹/₄-inch-thick exterior grade, and the two smaller pieces are ³/₄-inch exterior-grade plywood.

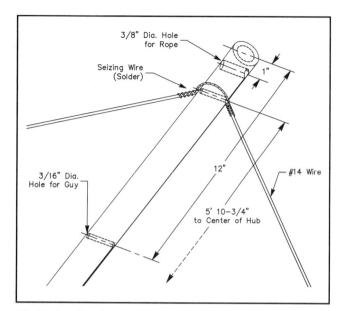

Fig 5—Details of arm showing holes for guy wires, element wires and steering rope.

The PVC Special. Bottom view of the hub showing connection to the supporting mast.

into a tall pine to about 25 feet high just in time for the 1998 CQ Worldwide CW DX Contest. I worked every station I could hear, and received 53 to 59 reports from Europe, Africa, South America, Hawaii and East Kiribati while running 100 watts. I also checked out the beam atop a 20-foot mast with similar results.

Note
[1]*EZNEC* antenna software by Roy Lewallen, W7EL, PO Box 6658, Beaverton, OR 97007.

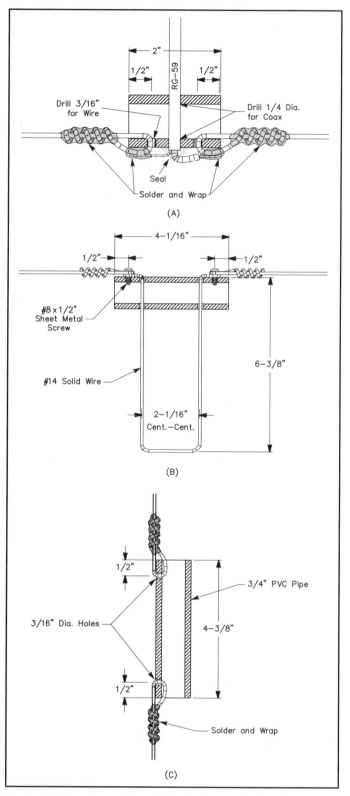

Fig 6—Details of insulators. At A, the feed-point insulator showing connection of the RG-59 used as a Q section. At B, the construction of the reflector-tuning stub, which is mounted on an insulator. At C, how the ends of the driven element and the reflector connect to the beam's side insulators.

A Hanging 10-Meter Vertical

By Sam F. Kennedy, KT4QW
57 Huxley Pl
Newport News, VA 23606

This antenna was developed to encourage and support those members of the Peninsula Amateur Radio Club of Hampton Roads, Virginia who have only phone privileges on 10 meters. Since many new hams have limited radio resources, a good, easy-to-use 10-meter antenna is a handy thing to have. In our region of Virginia, most lots have tall pines and oaks. We designed an antenna that would cover the lower part of the 10-meter band and that can be installed by simply hanging it in a tree. This article describes the theory of operation, construction and tuning of this simple antenna. Several new hams have installed and used this antenna with good results.

The antenna has omnidirectional characteristics and suits the needs of 10-meter communication for both distant and local coverage. Although I have no facilities for measuring the antenna's gain, it consistently gives more than an S unit better received signal than my reference quarter-wave vertical. A hanging vertical is not the ultimate antenna, but you will be pleased with its performance! And it doesn't need radials. The design also lends itself well to a vacation antenna.

I have constructed more than 25 antennas using this same basic design. I've found this design effective for constructing antennas for 2 through 20 meters. This article pertains only to the 10-meter model. While construction is economical and fairly easy, it is a bit tricky to tune and is a time-consuming task without an antenna analyzer such as the MFJ-259. Tune-up and test procedures are included here.

To install this antenna, you need to get a line over a high tree limb. The 1998 Edition of *The ARRL Handbook* (page 20.7) has a good description of the Wrist Rocket slingshot method of hanging things from trees. You can usually place a line over the desired tree limb within three tries. It's not a tower, but it's the next best thing!

> *For hams without a tower, but who do have at least one tree, this simple, low-cost, low-profile radiator may be the right choice!*

Theory of Operation

This antenna is electrically similar to several commercial models of fiberglass "stick" type antennas, but is packaged differently. This design provides a 50-Ω match over a reasonable bandwidth around the design frequency. SWR is typically 1.2:1 or better from 28.2 to 28.6 MHz. These antennas have been used at the 150-W level extensively, but should be able to handle 1.5 kW easily.

The antenna circuit is basically a half-wave radiator—similar to a half-wave dipole, but fed at the end rather than the center. Electrically, it is much the same as the classic J-pole antenna. The J-pole uses a quarter-wavelength shorted stub to accomplish impedance matching, whereas the hanging vertical uses an inductive link coupled to a parallel-resonant LC network. Since the significant part of the radiation from this antenna is from the half-wave section, it has no gain as over a dipole, and it gives an omnidirectional pattern.

The advantage of the hanging vertical over the J-pole is that the hanging vertical is one-third shorter than the J-pole, is much easier to weatherproof and is simpler to manage mechanically—especially as the length increases in the HF range. The hanging vertical's radiation characteristics and efficiency are approximately the same as those of a J-pole.

Fig 1 shows a schematic representation of the antenna, where C1 and L2 form a parallel-resonant circuit at the operating frequency. L1 inductively couples to the parallel-resonant circuit. C2 capacitively couples the half-wave radiating element to the parallel-resonant circuit. Capacitance and inductance values, experimentally determined, provide optimum coupling. The matching network provides a good match from the antenna's high impedance to 50 Ω.

The bottom end of the network is connected to the transmission line through a female UHF connector. Connector sealing is critical to long-term antenna reliability.

Construction

The construction sequence for the hanging vertical is as follows:

- Build the parts for the coil assembly
- Build the parts for the dual trombone tuning capacitor
- Prepare the parts for the PVC capsule
- Cut and fasten the radiator wire to the PVC capsule
- Assemble the parts
- Tune-up

The hanging vertical is constructed of widely available, low-cost materials. Although the total cost of material and parts for this project is low, the copper and PVC pipe/tubing must be purchased in minimum

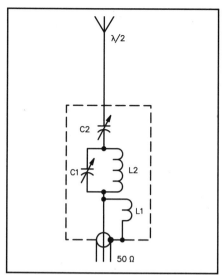

Fig 1—Schematic diagram of the hanging vertical. L1 couples energy from the antenna connector to the parallel-resonant circuit formed by C1 and L2. C2 couples RF to the radiating element. C1 and C2 are "trombone capacitors" that share a common plate, which is formed by a short section of copper pipe.

quantities, typically 5 or 10-foot sections. Unless you have access to suitable scrap materials, it makes sense to organize a club project and build several units.

Although it's not complicated, building this antenna does require basic mechanical skills as well as a general understanding of the electrical considerations. As with any project of this sort, many variations may be incorporated without degrading performance. **Fig 2** shows an overview of how the feed-point end of the antenna goes together. **Fig 3**, Fig 1 and Table 1 also help with construction.

Coil Assembly, Outer Coil

This is the larger coil, L2. Using #12 enameled copper wire, wind 17 close-spaced turns on a scrap PVC pipe as a temporary form. The outside diameter of the pipe I use is 0.625 inch. The wire measures 0.085 inch in diameter, including the enamel coating. The tuning capacitor has enough range to compensate for small variations in construction. This coil wound for the 10-meter band requires approximate 4 feet of wire; I cut 5 feet for convenience. See Fig 3 for details.

Coil Assembly, Inner Coil

This is the smaller coil, L1. Using #12 enameled copper wire, wind 7 close-spaced turns on PVC tube as a temporary form. The outside diameter of the form is 0.375 inch. Approximately 18 inches of wire is required. Cut a 24-inch length to make wind-

ing and handling easy. Note: Wind this coil in the opposite direction as the large coil (L1). Route the end back through the center of the windings. This requires a tight bend made with long-nose pliers. Wrap the pliers' gripping surfaces with a couple of layers of tape to reduce the possibility of scarring the enameled wire.

Connecting Link

To allow connection of the lower portion of L1/L2 to the tuning capacitor, fashion a piece of #12 wire in a 2.5-inch length, as shown in **Fig 4**.

Coil Spacer

Cut a piece of 0.020-inch polyethylene sheet (cut from a plastic milk jug) $1\frac{1}{2} \times 2$ inches. This spacer is later installed between L1 and L2 to assure adequate and stable spacing between them.

Scrape and Tin

Remove the enamel from the end of the wires to allow soldering during assembly. Tin these parts of the wires to allow ease of soldering later. Using a sharp pocketknife or other scraping tool, carefully remove the enamel on the magnet wire without nicking the wire. All traces of enamel must be removed from the surface to permit proper soldering.

Bend to Shape

Bend the wire parts into shapes that will allow effective assembly. Use sturdy long-nose pliers for the bending operation. Wrap the pliers gripping surfaces with a couple layers of tape to prevent damage to the wire. This operation is not critical and it can be adjusted later if necessary.

Trombone Capacitor, Outer Section

Using a hacksaw, cut a 5-inch section of $\frac{1}{2}$-inch copper water pipe, lightweight type M. (Pipe is specified in inner diameter, so the $\frac{1}{2}$-inch pipe measures 0.636 inch OD and 0.575 inch ID.) Do not use a tubing cutter to cut the pipe, as it crimps the cut inward, causing a fit problem. Debur the inside surface of the unit using a pocket knife or deburring tool. Debur the outside of the unit with a file or sandpaper. Using a propane torch or heavy duty soldering iron, flow solder down one side of this unit to prepare for soldering on the coil unit later. It helps to use a small amount of rosin (not acid) flux.

Trombone Capacitor, Inner Sections

Using a tubing cutter, cut one 2.5-inch section and one 1.5-inch section of $\frac{1}{2}$-inch soft copper tubing. Make sure you get *tubing*, and not pipe, for these pieces. The tubing fits into the outer piece with just enough clearance to accommodate the plastic di-

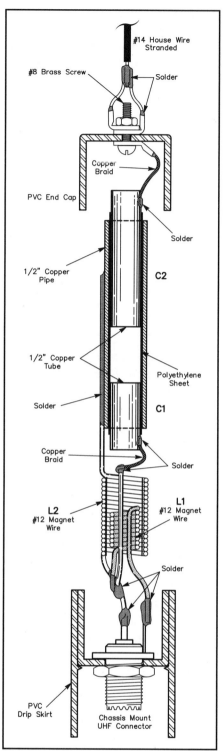

Fig 2—An overview of the feed-point assembly. The main body of the PVC pipe that encloses this assembly is omitted for clarity. L1 sits inside L2. L2 is soldered to the antenna connector at one end and to the copper pipe that makes up the common plate of C1 and C2 at the other. L1 is soldered to ground at one end and to the center conductor of the coax connector at the other. At the coax connector's center conductor, L1, L2 and a 2-inch wire are also soldered together; the 2-inch wire is routed through the center of L1 and L2 to the copper tubing that forms the inner plate of C1.

Fig 3—Coil-winding detail for the hanging 10-meter vertical. One lead of the smaller coil, L1 (at left), must be routed back through the coil body after winding is complete. *(Photos by the author.)*

Table 1

Materials

Component(s)	Description
L1	0.8 turns, #12 enameled magnet wire; coil is 0.6" outside diameter.
L2	17 turns, #12 enameled magnet wire; coil is 0.8" outside diameter
C1	1.5 inches × ¹/₂-inch copper tubing (capacitor slide)
C2	2.5 inches × ¹/₂-inch copper tubing (capacitor slide)
C1, C2	5.0 inches × ¹/₂-inch copper water pipe (lightweight type M)
C1, C2	2 × 5 × 0.02-inch polyethylene dielectric sheet (cut from milk jug)
Separator	1.5 × 2, 0.02-inch polyethylene dielectric sheet (cut from milk jug)
End Caps	³/₄-inch PVC pipe cap (2 used)
Drip Skirt	1-inch PVC pipe coupling
Barrel	³/₄-inch × 10-inch schedule 20 PVC water pipe
Connector	Female UHF chassis connector, single-hole mount
Top Screw	#8-32 × ³/₄-inch brass round head screw
Nut	#8-32 brass nut
Radiator	18 feet, #14 stranded THHN wire (vinyl insulation)
Terminal Lug	Uninsulated crimp lug for #8 screw and #14 wire (2 used)

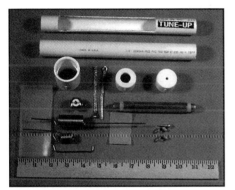

Fig 4–Part-preparation details for the 10-meter vertical. The plastic sheets, cut from a milk bottle, form the dielectric of the two-section trombone capacitor; the finished trombone-capacitor is shown in the right center of the photo. Also shown here are the coils; pre-bent coil-link wire; braid straps used for interconnection; bent solder lugs used to attach the antenna wire to the assembled matching section; and, at the top, the PVC pieces prepared for assembly. The upper section, marked TUNE UP, is used during tuning to facilitate adjusting the matching network. Then, the solid tube just below it replaces this section during final assembly.

electric. You may use a hacksaw for cutting these pieces; however, a tubing cutter works best here because it crimps the tubing inward and forms the ends to the proper shape for easy insertion into the outer piece. If you cut these pieces with a hacksaw, file or sand the outer edges to ease fitting them into the larger piece. Using a large-tip soldering iron, flow solder onto the outer surface at the end of each of these pieces to allow soldering the connecting braid to them. Tin about a ¹/₄-inch spot.

Dielectric

Using sheet-metal shears, sewing shears, or a sharp knife, carefully cut out a 2¹/₂ × 5¹/₂-inch rectangle of 0.020-inch polyethylene. This will form the dielectric between the inner and outer capacitor plates (cylinders). This dimension allows a ¹/₄-inch overlap, which will protect from arcing and will provide a firm fit between the inner pieces. This material is cut from the flat section of a clean, one-gallon plastic milk jug. To avoid melting the polyethylene dielectric, do not solder with it inserted.

Connecting Braid

Cut two 4-inch lengths of ³/₁₆-inch tinned copper braid. One piece of braid is used to connect the top slide and the other to connect the bottom slide.

Top Piece

Apply solder to one end of the braid—use just enough to keep the braid in place. Using a pointed object such as a small nail or a meter test probe, carefully separate the braid and make a hole in the braid about ¹/₄ inch back from the soldered end. Enlarge the hole until a #8 machine screw can be easily passed through. Press the braid flat and sparingly flow solder over the entire hole area. Use diagonal cutters to round the end so that a neat lug is formed. This will later be used to connect the capacitor to the radiating element.

Bottom Piece

Save this piece for use during final assembly.

PVC Outer Enclosure, Bottom End Cap

Drill a carefully centered pilot hole through the end cap using a ⁵/₃₂-inch drill bit. Carefully hold the end cap in a vise or using suitable locking pliers. Drill a ⁵/₈-inch hole using a hole cutter or wood bit. This hole is for mounting the coaxial connector.

PVC Outer Enclosure, Top End Cap

Drill a hole through the center of the end cap, using a ⁵/₃₂-inch drill bit. This hole is for the #8 brass machine screw that connects loading capacitor C2 to the radiating element. This hole is slightly undersized to cause the screw to fit tightly.

Sleeve

Using a hacksaw or hand saw, cut two 10-inch sections of ³/₄-inch schedule 20 (thin-wall) PVC pipe. Keep cuts as straight as possible at 90°. One piece will be used temporarily for tune-up, and the other for permanent assembly. Using an appropriate tool, cut an opening into the side of the tune-up section to allow access to the tuning capacitor. If you are making more than one antenna, only one tune-up section will be necessary.

Connector

Check to be sure that the connector fits properly into the bottom end cap. Make certain that the connector can be locked into position. If it becomes loose after the final assembly, you will have a difficult problem to solve.

Drip Skirt

No modification is required to this 1-inch PVC coupling. It will be glued onto the bottom end cap after final tune-up.

Radiating Element

Measure an 18-foot length of #14 stranded-copper THHN wire to form the half-wavelength radiator. The electrical length of the radiator is approximately 16.47 feet at an operating frequency of 28.4 MHz (length [feet] = 468/f [MHz]). The electri-

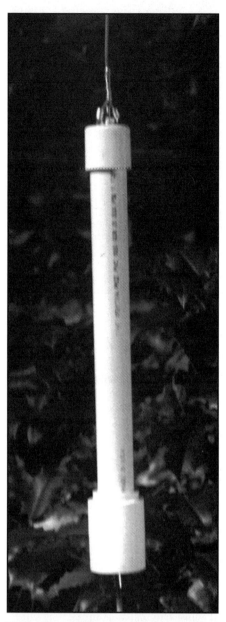

Fig 5—The finished feed-point assembly. The antenna wire is attached to the matching assembly by two solder lugs, which reduces the likelihood of flex-related failure in this connection. The large PVC pipe section, glued to the bottom of the main assembly cover pipe cap, protects the feed-line connector from rain and wind-driven moisture.

cal length is measured from the bottom of the trombone tuning capacitor to the end of the top fastening loop. Strip about 4 inches of this wire to connect it to the two terminals on the top end cap. Form a hanging loop at the top of approximately 6 to 12 inches. Twist the part of the wire that is doubled back. Note the length of the radiating element is adjusted by changing this loop. The doubled-back portion of the wire does not contribute to the electrical length.

Assembly

Slide the inner coil into the outer coil, along with the polyethylene spacer in between. Install the connecting link to the junction of the inner and outer coils at the lower end of the assembly. Using a scrap piece of fine copper wire to hold the parts in place, wrap the connection together tightly and solder it.

Using a heavy soldering iron or propane torch, solder the upper end of the larger coil to the outer part of the trombone capacitor. Make certain that the dielectric is not in place during this operation so that it won't melt.

Solder the braid sections to each of the capacitor inner slide units. The braid with the eyelet is used for the upper section, and the plain braid for the lower section.

Curl the dielectric sheet and insert it into the outer capacitor, leaving approximately $1/4$ inch exposed at each end. Slide the inner pieces into the outer pieces. Dress the lower braid for connection to the wire link. Trim and solder the lower braid.

Remove the upper tuning section from the trombone and pass the #8 brass machine screw through the eyelet. Screw it through the pilot hole (top PVC end cap). This forms a weathertight seal.

Remove the insulating plastic from the two lugs and bend the lugs as indicated in **Fig 5**. Mount them on the protruding screw using the #8 brass nut. Loop the stripped portion of the radiating wire through the two lugs, wrap, and solder. Using two lugs distributes the force over twice the area and prevents flexing that can easily break a single lug.

Solder the two lower leads from the coil assembly to the connector as indicated in Fig 1.

Tune-up

Install the coil assembly into the tune-up PVC enclosure, then install the top end cap with the radiating element attached. A press fit should be adequate to hold things together temporarily. Use tape at the pipe junctions to add strength, if necessary. Suspend the complete antenna vertically from a tree limb. Suspend the antenna so that the capsule end is at least $1/4$ λ away from any surrounding objects.

Insert the upper capacitor slide as far in as it will go without electrically shorting to the other lower section. Using an SWR analyzer, adjust the lower trombone capacitor slide until resonance is obtained, as indicated by a pronounced dip in SWR. (This is most easily done if the feed-line length is a multiple of $1/2$ λ.) If the SWR is greater than 1.2:1, adjust the two capacitors in small increments to improve the match. If not, try lengthening or shortening the radiator length by adjusting the connecting loop at the top. An SWR of 1.1:1 can usually be obtained. Note, however, that SWR changes with antenna height. If possible, check the SWR in the antenna's final position. When the antenna is tuned satisfactorily, carefully tape the connecting loop on the radiator to set its length.

Mix a small amount of epoxy and apply it to lock the lower copper slide in place. When the epoxy has hardened, carefully mark the upper capacitor slide's position so it can be reset to that point. Remove the tune-up sleeve and reinstall the coil assembly in the permanent sleeve. Glue the sleeve in the bottom end cap using PVC cement.

Install the upper copper capacitor slide, observing the depth marker applied during tune-up. Use a small amount of epoxy to stabilize this slide. (Reasonable amounts of clear epoxy do not affect antenna tuning.) Glue the top cap, with the radiating element attached, to the top of the sleeve using PVC cement.

Using a file or pocketknife, remove any protrusions from the side of the bottom end cap. Cement the 1-inch PVC pipe coupling to the bottom cap to form a drip skirt around the connector.

Your antenna is now ready for operation!

Two-Element 40-Meter Switched Beam

By Carrol Allen, AA2NN
112 Eaton's Neck Road
Northport, NY 11768

Over the years I've seen a number of designs in amateur publications for three-element switched Yagis using remote relays to short out stubs or loading inductors to convert a reflector element into a director. Here is a simple, compact two-element switched beam for 40 meters that has an exceptional front-to-back ratio.

The antenna consist of two identical horizontal dipoles spaced 22 feet at a height of 50 to 60 feet, although other heights will work with some adjustments. The outer 9.5 feet ends of each dipole are bent toward each other to cover a rectangular area that is 46.25 feet by 22 feet. The ends of the dipoles are spaced 2 feet from each other. See **Fig 1**, which shows the physical layout of the antenna.

These are dimensions for 7.2 MHz, but you can rescale linearly for other frequencies. Bringing the ends close to each other increases the coupling between the dipoles so that the current in the parasitic reflector is almost equal to the current in the driven element, yielding a front-to-back ratio approaching 30 dB.

Two identical lengths of 75-Ω coax (Belden 9290) are run to the shack or to a remote selection relay. The length of the coax is selected to provide the required loading inductance for the non-driven element. To switch directions simply interchange the feedlines. The performance is similar to a phased two-element array but saves the expense and bother of a phasing network. Two 1:1 baluns are required on each dipole to isolate the feedlines from the elements. I use a shortened quarter-wave balun that I will describe later.

A length of transmission line less than a quarter wavelength will provide an inductive reactance when the far end is shorted. The required reactance for this antenna is about +71 Ω. For 75-Ω coax this would

Here's a simple two-element wire antenna that has exceptional front-to-back ratio—and it fits in less space than you might imagine!

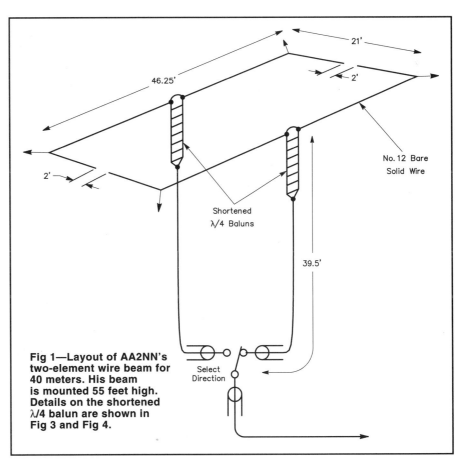

Fig 1—Layout of AA2NN's two-element wire beam for 40 meters. His beam is mounted 55 feet high. Details on the shortened λ/4 balun are shown in Fig 3 and Fig 4.

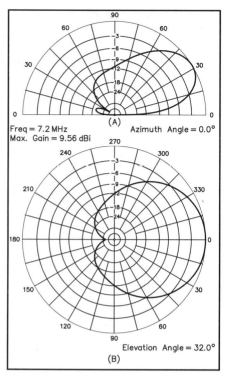

Fig 2—At A, elevation-plane response for AA2NN's two-element wire antenna at height of 55 feet over flat ground. Note the excellent front-to-back ratio of about 27 dB. At B, azimuth-plane response for antenna at an elevation angle of 32°.

Freq = 7.2 MHz
Max. Gain = 9.56 dBi
Azimuth Angle = 0.0°
Elevation Angle = 32.0°
(A)
(B)

mean a length slightly less than $\frac{1}{8}$ of a wavelength. When the velocity factor is 0.78, as with Belden 9290, this would be only 12 feet 10 inches long. A cable this long would require some sort of structure that is almost as high as the dipoles themselves to support the remote selection relay.

The line length can be increased and still provide the required inductive reactance by adding another quarter wavelength and leaving the end open-circuited, or by adding a half wavelength and shorting the end. For Belden 9290 the other two lengths are 39.5 feet and 66.1 feet respectively. I chose the 39.5-foot length since this was a convenient length to reach into the attic of the house where the remote relay was located.

The longer lines have the disadvantage of having more loss and the reactance will vary more rapidly with frequency, narrowing the antenna's bandwidth. The loss in the $\frac{3}{8}$-λ section introduces an equivalent series loss resistance of about 5 Ω. This only reduces the forward gain by about 0.34 dB. The $\frac{5}{8}$-λ line would add an additional 3 Ω.

Figs 2A and **2B** show the computer-calculated elevation and azimuth patterns for this antenna, using W7EL's *EZNEC* software. Construction is very straightforward. I used #12 solid copper with the insulation removed for low visibility. Soft-drawn copper can be stretched by about 5% before

measuring to reduce the amount of elongating with wind loading. For support I use 0.095-inch nylon *Weed Whacker* line over the top of four tall trees. The end spacers are also made from this line. Tying knots in this line is a little tricky—you should refer to any fishing book for information on tying knots in monofilament. The corners are loops made by bending the antenna wire 270° around a 3/16-inch diameter drill bit and soldering the wire to complete the closed loop. The corner loop is made to prevent slipping of the rope used to support the antenna. Note that a corner could have been made by twisting the wire into a loop at the corners, but I was concerned that this might induce stress failures.

The Shortened Quarter-Wave Balun

As mentioned earlier this antenna requires two 1:1 baluns to isolate the elements from the coax. While a toroidal or rod 1:1 balun will work fine, there is the question of the extra weight, especially if you are planning for high-power operation.

Fig 3A shows a familiar kind of λ/4 balun often used on VHF and UHF antennas. This would be 34 feet long on 40 meters and would be heavier than a ferrite-cored balun. The equivalent circuit of a λ/4 shorted transmission line is a parallel-resonant tuned circuit. The line length can be short-

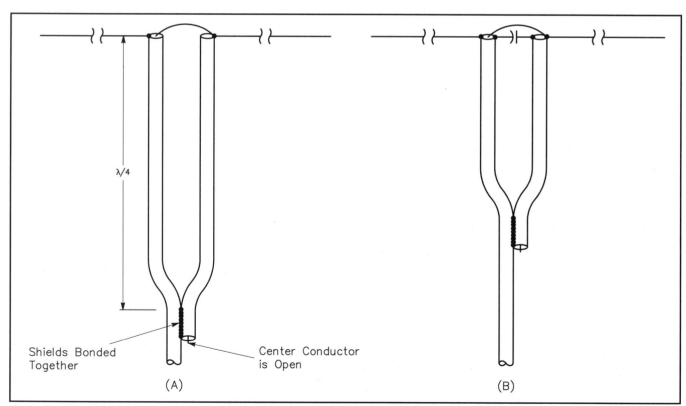

λ/4

Shields Bonded Together

Center Conductor is Open

(A)

(B)

Fig 3—Development of the traditional λ/4 balun (at A) commonly used at VHF and the shortened λ/4 balun with a capacitor across it (at B) to tune it to parallel resonance.

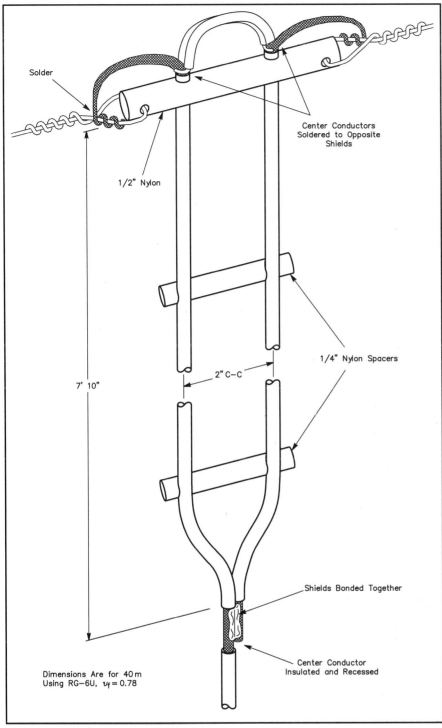

Fig 4—Diagram of AA2NN shortened λ/4 balun, which uses the capacitance of the non-fed portion on the right to tune the system to parallel resonance.

A simple solution is to use the capacitance of the non-feedline side of the balun to resonate the circuit. The exact length you end up with depends on the type of coax (capacitance per foot) and the spacing of the shields of the stub coaxes used to create the inductive part of the resonant circuit. I calculated the length for RG-6U first and then trimmed it to resonance using a grid-dip meter before connecting to a dipole. Changing the spacers' width will trim the resonant frequency, with wider spacing giving increased inductance and lowering the frequency. Being exactly resonant is not necessary, since the balun action is due to the symmetry.

One other advantage of this type of balun is it actually improves the bandwidth of series-resonant antennas as it acts as a double-tuned circuit. (See Chapter 9 of *The ARRL Antenna Book.*) Another design possibility might be to form a hairpin stub (such as used on many Yagi beams) from the coax, thereby combining the hairpin and the balun.

Fig 4 shows the completed balun. The center insulator is made from 1/2-inch nylon rod with two holes drilled for a snug fit to the coax shield after the insulation is stripped back. A couple of turns wrapped and soldered as shown prevents the coax from pulling out. After soldering all the joints I cover the ends and the bottom outer shield joint with coax seal to keep out water. The exposed braid is coated with *liquid tape* so that it doesn't act as a wick. The spacers can be made from any insulator, just as with open-wire line.

On-the-Air Performance

I installed this antenna orientated to fire east and west. This allowed me to work 40 meters at night, when the foreign broadcast AM stations were making the band unusable on a simple dipole or bidirectional W8JK antenna. Checks with stations in Australia confirmed the high front-to-back ratio predicted by *EZNEC*. Close-in stations did not exhibit this due to the high elevation angles involved. Being able to switch directions rapidly showed some interesting receive advantages. Many times signals could be heard more clearly by switching to the opposite direction due to a greater drop in noise or QRM. This was noticed mainly on close-in stations with high elevation angles.

This is a simple antenna. It doesn't take up much room and doesn't involve any expensive components. Probably the most expensive item would be the remote relay if you really wanted to use one.

ened considerably if the circuit is kept resonant by adding a parallel capacitance across the inductance formed by the shorted open-wire line of the outer conductors of the two coaxes. See Fig 3B. Of course a discrete capacitor able to handle the voltage and current with 1500 W applied power is no lightweight either.

A No-Compromise 160 Meter Antenna

By Jerry D. Arnold, K9AF
3000 West Spencer Drive
Terre Haute, IN 47802

Have some land and Rohn 25 tower available? Want a $^1/_4$-λ vertical for 160 meters? K9AF tells how he built his.

No single topic in Amateur Radio evokes as much discussion and experimentation as antennas. They are the heart of any ham's station. Over my 29 years in Amateur Radio, *QST* and other periodicals have published a wealth of information on nearly every type of antenna that can be imagined. As is the case of many hams, I have developed favorites in my radio activities—favorite mode, favorite time to operate, favorite antennas, and of course favorite band.

As I have always enjoyed a challenge, years ago I made the Top Band (160 meters) my favorite. Anyone who operates in this region of the spectrum knows the problems that arise with regard to Top-Band operation, not the least of which is the gargantuan size 160-meter antennas usually assume. Many fine articles have appeared in *QST* covering 160-meter antennas, but nearly all have been for limited space, limited effort, or other less-than-optimum performing antennas. For over a decade I was forced to employ one of those—a $^1/_4$-λ inverted L on my 37 by 125 foot city lot. While I did manage to work all states and several foreign countries, this antenna just didn't have the performance I desired.

So when I was finally able to purchase some land and build my dream house, one of my *must have* items was enough room to build a full-size 160-meter antenna. Having spent most of my working career in radio broadcasting, I know what the FCC requires for AM broadcast antennas. Using that as my guideline, I progressed with my project. I would build a full-sized $^1/_4$-λ vertical, and place it over a no-compromise radial system. The cost of the project is shown in **Table 1**.

Many AM broadcast installations use commonly available towers such as Rohn 25 or 45 as their radiating elements. And as I had a sufficient quantity of Rohn 25 sections, I built my antenna from them. The Rohn application and installation guide, recommends a concrete base no smaller than one cubic yard. So, with the help of my neighbor, K9GBO, and his transit, we first staked out the exact point for the antenna, then the points for each of the three 120°-spaced guy anchors.

I dug the tower base with nothing more than a shovel, which wasn't as much work as I had envisioned. I actually made the hole slightly larger than that recommended by the Rohn guide. The guy anchor points were another story. Rohn recommends the guy anchors be buried a minimum of three feet below grade level. I did so, but these holes required quite a bit more effort to dig. After much effort I completed the anchor holes, then installed forms made from scrap lumber to keep the concrete as close to the recom-

Table 1
Cost of the 160-meter $^1/_4$-λ Antenna *Excluding* Tower Sections

Item	Cost ($)
400 feet 8-conductor wire	90
320 feet 1-inch schedule-40 plastic pipe	82
1-inch inspection T	4
2-inch inspection T	10
500 feet RG-8 coax	160
50 Porcelain Products #502 strain insulators	158
15,000 feet #18 MTW	330
#4 and #6 bare copper wire	9
#8 wire	11
12 × 12 × 6-inch plastic box	33
Stainless steel tower hardware	20
12 galvanized turnbuckles	198
Steel for load equalizer plates	4
Ground lugs, split bolts and ground rods	31
1½" × 1½" × 48" steel angle	11
3 yards concrete	191
Galvanized hardware	13
96 Preformed Products guy grips	77
10 tons top soil	105
Misc items	16
TOTAL	1553

mended shape as possible. It took about two and one half yards of concrete to fill the tower base and the three guy anchors. After the concrete had cured, I removed the forms that were above ground, and back-filled the holes.

Next, I needed a way to get the coax and a piece of eight-conductor cable back to the shack. I borrowed a trenching machine, and dug a 4-inch-wide, 18-inch-deep trench. While I didn't have to put the coax and the eight-conductor cable in conduit, the small additional cost of schedule 40 plastic pipe is well worth it. By putting both cables in this pipe, the lives of both should be substantially extended. With K9GBO's help I threaded the two wires through all the pipe, one section at a time, glued the joints, then placed the entire pipe into the trench. Near each end of the pipe run I also included an "inspection T," with the T portion facing downward in the trench. I did this to allow any moisture that might accumulate in the pipe to drain out into the soil. I made sure to place these Ts at the low spots along the pipe's run. After back-filling the trench, my next project would be the most important: my radial ground system.

The Radial System

The FCC requires that AM broadcasters employ a minimum of 120 radials under their antennas. This was not just set down as some arbitrary figure. There are valid engineering reasons for this number of radials. Much has been written even in amateur publications as to radials, their effect, how many, above ground, on the ground, below the ground, etc. There also seems to be quite a misconception in amateur circles as to the purpose of a radial system. Many hams think it is the purpose of a radial to contact the soil. This idea has come from the common practice of burying the radials a few inches. This is not true. Radials are buried to prevent theft of the copper wire and to allow the antenna area to be mowed without mishap. (The FCC rules' "good engineering practice" phrase covers keeping the antenna lot mowed.) I know of one 160-meter operator who lays his radials on top of the ground at the beginning of each winter, then winds them up on spools the next spring. His system works very well.

One nice aspect of using 120 radials is that each radial is 3° from the adjacent ones. While I could have used a transit to determine an exact 3° spacing, I took a more simple approach. I decided where I wished to put my first radial, and drove in a temporary stake approximately 130 feet away from the tower. Then by application of simple trigonometry, I determined the distance between the *ends* of any two adjacent radials. Since I have 120 radials, equally spaced around the tower, there is 3° spacing between each 125-foot-long radial. To solve

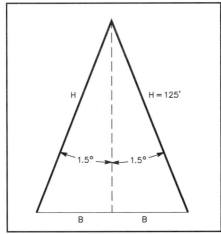

Fig 1—The distance between adjacent radials can be calculated by using trigonometry. See text for details.

the problem, I first divided the 3° angle in half to obtain a pair of right triangles as shown in **Fig 1**. The ratio of B/H is the tangent of 1.5°, and the distance between radial ends is:

$$2 \times \tan 1.5° \times 125 = 6.54 \text{ feet}$$

Measuring over 6.54 feet from my first stake, I temporarily drove in another stake. I then used a cable plow to install the radial wire a few inches below the surface. This process was repeated all the way around the circumference the circle. This was time consuming and tiring work. For the radial wire I

used 18 gauge machine tool wire (MTW), which I obtained from a local electrical supply house. The wire comes on 500-foot spools, so four radials can be cut from each spool. This wire is fairly inexpensive, and goes into the slit the cable plow dug quite nicely. After all 120 radials were installed, I drove my lawn tractor pulling a yard roller over the slits to cover over each slit, and thus prevent the radials from coming out of the ground. I attached each radial to a common ground ring near the base of the tower. I made this ring from #6 bare copper wire laid in as nearly a circular shape as I could make. Where the wire ends came together, I overlapped them a few inches, and attached them to each other using two copper split bolts. I stripped the insulation from the inner end of each radial wire and wrapped the stripped ends around the #6 ground ring several times. I then soldered them using a small torch.

At the base of the tower, I grounded each of the three legs to its own 10-foot-long ground rod. While this does little for the RF ground, it will aid in lightning protection. Each tower leg has a piece of #4 bare copper attached to it by a weatherproof clamp. The wire is then attached to its ground rod using standard ground rod clamps. Then all three rods are bonded together using another piece of #4 bare copper. This comprises the inner ring, while the previously mentioned piece of #6 comprises the outer. There are only a few feet between the two rings. I soldered additional pieces of #18 MTW

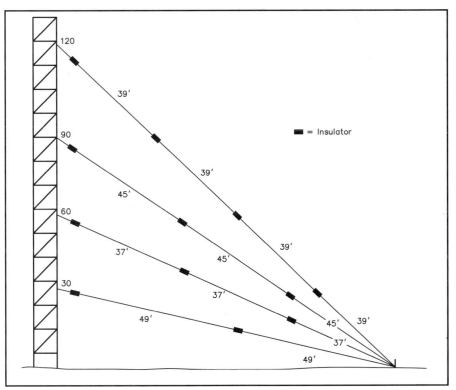

Fig 2—K9AF guyed his tower at 30, 60, 90 and 120 feet. He used insulators to break the guys into nonresonant lengths.

Fig 3—Guy grips are used to fasten insulators to guy wires.

Guy wires terminate at their lower end at equalizer plates that are attached to their respective guy anchors.

Fig 5—Photo of the tower base showing the box that houses the matching capacitor.

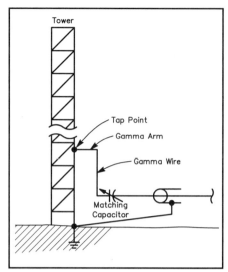

Fig 4—Diagram of the gamma match. The tower tap point must be determined experimentally. See text for details.

between the two rings, to complete the grounding system.

Since all the radial work has to be done at ground level, I was faced with the problem of making sure that where the area of the rings would be protected from my mower's blades. I quickly abandoned the idea of digging individual slits for each wire when I saw how difficult that would be. Instead, I bought 10 tons of top soil (which isn't very expensive) and used it to bury the rings. Then I raked the area smooth, and sprinkled grass seed on the soil and rolled it down. This has worked out quite well.

Installing the Tower

With my radial system completed, it was time to begin stacking tower sections. The Rohn book recommends 30-foot guy spacing for a tower of this height (130 feet). Naturally, the guys have to be broken up with insulators to insulate the antenna and to prevent interaction (See **Fig 2**). I used Porcelain Products #502 strain insulators. Instead of using thimbles and cable clamps, I chose to use Preformed Products *guy grips*. These come in a variety of sizes to accommodate nearly any size guy wire. They are easy to use, assemble much more quickly than using clamps, are galvanized so they will deteriorate at the same rate as the galvanized guy wire, and best of all, cost less than using clamps. They grip the wire in a spiral manner (see **Fig 3**). When pull is exerted on the wire, the device actually increases its hold on the wire. The harder the pull, the tighter the grip, and the grips are guaranteed to have a better tensile strength than the guy wire itself.

I stacked the sections in the conventional manner using a gin pole. It is *imperative* that the person who is on the tower has tower climbing and stacking experience in addition to a well-maintained climbing belt, hard hat, gloves and eye protection. While an error on

the ground might result in a minor annoyance, an error 100 feet in the air could result in serious injury or even death. Safety first!

When stacking the sections, every 30 feet a new set of guy wires needs to be attached. I had prepared each set of guys well in advance. I hauled each guy wire to its proper place by means of the gin pole's rope. I then attached it to the tower using a guy grip. After I attached the third guy in each set, I descended to ground level *before* tensioning those guy wires. Again, safety first! Then a quick visual inspection to ensure the tower was still plumb. When the top section was installed, I had a tower nearly 130 feet tall!

Matching

My tower can't be series fed, as is commonly done in AM-radio applications, because it is grounded for lightning protection,. One of the easiest ways to excite the antenna and match the impedance is to use a shunt feed. A shunt feed is like a gamma match you'd find on an HF or VHF Yagi. See **Fig 4**.

I constructed the gamma arm from 4 feet of $1^1/_2 \times 1^1/_2$-inch steel angle, and fastened it to the tower with two U bolts. The gamma wire is a piece of #8 wire spaced 36 inches from the

tower. The gamma wire is connected at the top to the gamma arm and at the bottom to a feedthrough insulator on the box that houses the matching capacitor. See **Fig 5**.

The tap point must be determined experimentally. I needed to find a point on the tower that yields 50-Ω resistance. Since the feed end of the gamma wire is inductively reactive, I use a series capacitor to tune out or neutralize that reactance. All that's left is 50-Ω resistive.

I tried an experimental tap at 50 feet above ground level. I pulled the wire tight between the gamma arm and the box to keep uniform spacing to the tower. I removed the 3-A fuses from their holders in the tuning box to allow a convenient place to attach the impedance meter. The one closest to the feedthrough is where I measure the impedance of the tower tap. Dan Watson, a long time friend and fellow broadcast engineer, brought his venerable General Radio 1606 RF impedance bridge to make the impedance measurements.

The tap at 50 feet resulted in a resistance value of 110 Ω (and an inductive reactance of 267 Ω) at 1.830 MHz—obviously too high. So I moved the gamma arm to a lower spot on the tower. Once I had moved the arm, I repeated the measurement. To determine the bandwidth, I made all tests at 1.800, 1.830 and 1.900 MHz. Subsequent taps and their results are documented in **Table 2**.

Once I had established the proper level (34 feet, 2 inches) for a 50-Ω (resistive) tap at 1.830 MHz, all that was left to do was to tune out the reactive component. In **Fig 6** you can see my gamma capacitor, which is a 330 pF air variable with the plate spacing adequate for transmitting at 1500 W PEP. However, 330 pF at 1.830 MHz is not quite enough capacitance to tune out the 201 Ω of

Fig 6—Photo showing inside details of the box. See text.

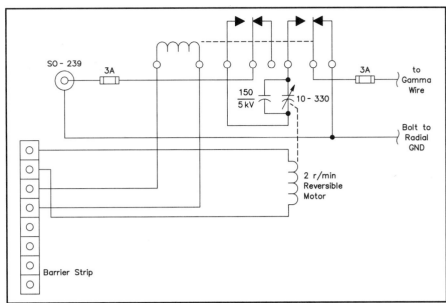

Fig 7—Diagram of the circuitry inside the tuning box.

reactance. So I connected a 150-pF 5-kV door knob capacitor in parallel with the variable to give a maximum capacitance of 480 pF, which has 181 Ω reactance at 1.830 MHz. This is slightly more capacitance than needed, and so by adjusting the variable capacitor I can QSY nearly anywhere in the band. Adjusting the variable to zero reactance at 1.830 MHz results in an impedance of slightly more than 50 Ω.

To provide a measure of lightning protection when the antenna isn't in use, I put a DPDT relay in the tuning box (see **Fig 7**). The contact rating of the relay is 10 A, so there is little danger of overloading the contacts at any amateur power level. In the normally closed position, one pole of the relay disconnects the center conductor of the RG-8 coax, and the other pole grounds the lower end of the gamma wire.

When you look at Fig 7, you might wonder why I chose to install the two 3-A fuses and holders in the RF path. This was done for two reasons: First, it affords an additional amount of lightning protection. Second, it goes back to my days of working on AM directional arrays where every tower has its own tuning network complete with a *bridge clip* that can be removed to insert a thermocouple RF ammeter to measure the RF current. By incorporating two individual 3-AG type fuse holders, I now have two places I can test the impedance of my system without having to unwire any of the circuitry. The first is immediately after the feed-through insulator, where the gamma-wire impedance measurement is made. The second is just before the SO-239 connector where I make the match measurement.

I chose to motorize the variable capacitor so I could tune it from the shack. I use a 2 rpm, 12 V dc motor, and a DPDT momentary switch in the shack to reverse the polarity of the dc going to the motor, and the direction of rotation (see **Fig 8**).

In my shack, the SWR measures 1.2:1 at 1.800 MHz, 1.0:1 at 1.830 MHz and 1.2:1 at 1.870 MHz. Above 1.900 MHz the SWR begins to rise more rapidly, but even at 1.995 MHz it is still only 2.0:1.

I made my first contact with this antenna during late summer when noise levels are seasonably high. However, the ham at the other end refused to believe I was only running 100 W! Many hams will see this article and wonder why I would spend so much time, money and effort for nothing more than a ground plane. The only answer I have is, "Because I can!" Most of the aforementioned compromise 160-meter antennas are *very* ineffective radiators, and tend to have a high take off angle. While my antenna does not have as low a take off angle as a $^5/_8$-λ vertical, the $^1/_4$ λ does a very creditable job. I am quite pleased by its performance. I have had a desire to achieve DXCC on 160 meters; this may be the antenna that will allow my dream to become reality!

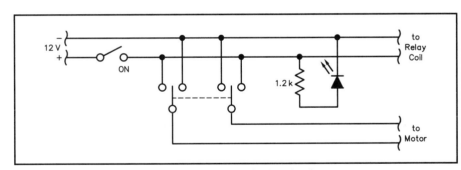

Fig 8—Diagram of the control circuit located in the shack.

Table 2
Impedance Values at Various Tap Points on the Tower

Tap Level	Impedance at 1.800 MHz	Impedance at 1.830 MHz	Impedance at 1.900 MHz
50'	126 + j 267	110 + j 267	86 + j 302
47.5'	110 + j 266	94 + j 267	74 + j 294
43.5'	99 + j 244	84+ j 252	66 + j 286
40'	73 + j 227	64 + j 233	50 + j 257
38.5'	69 + j 211	61 + j 216	46 + j 233
33'	51 + j 194	47 + j 199	36 + j 221
34.17'	52 + j 196	50 + j 201	40 + j 224

Dual-Mode Elevated Verticals

By Al Christman, K3LC
Grove City College
100 Campus Drive
Grove City, PA 16127-2104

The 80-meter band is so broad in terms of frequency that it is difficult to build an antenna that can cover both the phone and CW DX portions of the band with satisfactory SWR. This paper discusses a method for switching an elevated vertical between two different band segments using one SPST relay.

Making an antenna work in the DX windows on both ends of the 80/75-meter band is not always easy to do. K3LC describes a nifty solution to this problem for a vertical antenna with elevated radials.

Basic Concept

This antenna system utilizes a technique described in ON4UN's well-known book on low-band DXing.[1] There, John illustrates an elevated four-square 80-meter phased vertical array, composed of wire elements suspended from a central tower (ON4UN's quarter-wave transmit vertical for 160 meters). The feed points are 17 feet above ground. Interestingly, each element has only a single horizontal radial, rather than two to four as are often found with elevated verticals. The monopoles are 64 feet long, while each radial is just 61.35 feet in length, yielding resonance at 3.75 MHz. When operating on CW, a shorted stub is added to the feed end of every radial. Each stub consists of two parallel #9 AWG copper wires 7.4 feet long, spaced 8 inches apart. At each vertical monopole, a set of relay contacts at the upper end of its stub is closed for SSB, and opened to work CW, with resonance at 3505 kHz.

Design Procedure

John's clever idea clearly shows (and computer analysis confirms) that the resonant (zero-reactance) frequency of an elevated vertical antenna may be shifted by altering the length of *either* the monopole *or* the elevated radial(s). Since the radials are situated much closer to the ground, it is often easier (and safer) to adjust the length of the radials, as opposed to changing the overall height of the vertical element.

With this in mind, I created a computer model of a single elevated vertical radiator with four elevated horizontal radials, using the *EZNEC/4* computer program.[2] All conductors were #12 AWG copper, and the base of the antenna was placed 12 feet above average ground (soil conductivity = 0.005 Siemens/meter and dielectric constant = 13).

I assumed that the center of the DX phone band was at 3790 kHz and selected 3510 kHz on CW, for a median value of 3650 kHz. Then I adjusted the length of all five wires in my computer model to produce resonance at 3650 kHz. The required length for each wire was 67.25 feet, and the resulting feed-point impedance was $33.45 - j\,0.06\ \Omega$. *EZNEC/4* showed a peak gain of 0.33 dBi at a take-off angle of 22°, and the azimuthal pattern was almost perfectly circular, with the gain falling slightly to 0.31 dBi at compass angles midway between the radials.

SSB Mode

Initially, I wanted to make my reference antenna resonant at a frequency midway between the desired band segments, because I wasn't sure how the length of the vertical element would impact the SWR readings once the dual-mode design was completed (more on this later). After the antenna had been resonated at 3650 kHz, the next task

was to offset the radials slightly from their original center point, which had been directly beneath the vertical radiator. I did this to make room for the shorted stub (see **Fig 1** for a detailed drawing).

I decided to add the stub-wires to my computer model, even though I wouldn't activate them until the antenna was switched to the CW mode. Since the base of the vertical was 12 feet above ground, I made the stub wires 8 feet long, and spaced them six inches apart. When operating on SSB the stub would be shorted at its upper end, so I simulated this short-circuit with a six-inch jumper wire between the base of the vertical element and the common point where the inner ends of all four radials are joined together. I didn't bother to include the shorting bar on the stub, just the two parallel wires.

Surprisingly, these small changes at the base of the antenna necessitated a drastic shortening of the radials—to only 53.25 feet—in order to shift the resonant frequency upward from 3650 to 3790 kHz. Once I did this, an input impedance of $39.06 - j\,0.05\ \Omega$ was achieved, and the maximum gain in SSB mode was now 0.20 dBi at a 22° take-off angle. With a six-inch offset be-

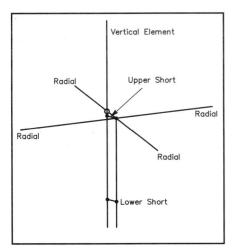

Fig 1—Close-up of the area near the feed point of a single elevated vertical antenna, showing the inner ends of the four elevated radials. These are offset slightly from the base of the vertical radiator to allow for placement of the shorted stub. The lower short (on the stub) is always present and its position sets the CW resonant frequency. The upper short consists of a closed pair of relay contacts and is present only in SSB mode (relay contacts are opened for CW).

Table 1

SWR versus Frequency for the Elevated Vertical Antenna in SSB Mode

Frequency (kHz)	SWR (50-Ω reference)
3750	1.451
3760	1.387
3770	1.335
3780	1.299
3790	1.280
3800	1.281
3810	1.301
3820	1.338
3830	1.387
3840	1.448
3850	1.516

Table 2

SWR versus Frequency for the Elevated Vertical Antenna in CW Mode

Frequency (kHz)	SWR (50-Ω reference)
3500	1.619
3510	1.599
3520	1.596
3530	1.611
3540	1.641
3550	1.690

Table 3

SWR versus Frequency for the Elevated Vertical Antenna in both CW and SSB Modes, using a 35:50-Ω un-un

Frequency (kHz)	SWR (50-Ω reference)
3500	1.162
3510	1.119
3520	1.146
3530	1.220
3540	1.312
3550	1.424
—	—
3750	1.366
3760	1.274
3770	1.195
3780	1.136
3790	1.116
3800	1.148
3810	1.212
3820	1.291
3830	1.380
3840	1.479
3850	1.582

tween the base of the monopole and the common point of the radials, the non-circularity of the azimuthal-plane radiation pattern is only 0.12 dB, which seems tolerable. The highest gain is in the direction of the offset, with the minimum (0.08 dBi) occurring in the opposite quadrant.

A frequency-sweep was carried out with *EZNEC/4* to determine the bandwidth of the antenna in SSB mode, and the results are listed in **Table 1**. Notice that the SWR (referred to 50 Ω) remains below 1.5:1 for about 100 kHz.

CW Mode

The resonance of the antenna system is moved down into the CW band by activating the stub (removing the short at its upper end) and adjusting the position of the shorting bar to achieve zero reactance at the desired frequency. With the shorting bar located 5.635 feet below the top of the stub, *EZNEC/4* predicts an input impedance of 31.28 + j 0.02 Ω at 3510 kHz. The peak gain now is 0.25 dBi (still at an elevation angle of 22°), with a non-circularity of just 0.03 dB, a negligible value. The frequency-sweep data is displayed in **Table 2**; the SWR is quite a bit higher in CW mode than on phone, which is disappointing. However, all of the numbers are well below 2:1.

The SWR on both CW and SSB can be improved by adding an "un-un" (unbalanced-to-unbalanced) transformer at the feed point of the antenna. Since the input resistances at resonance are roughly 39 and 31 Ω for the

two modes, an un-un with a 35:50-Ω ratio would be a good compromise. **Table 3** shows the results, which are certainly worth the cost of the un-un transformer. Now the SWR is below 1.12:1 at the center frequencies for both modes.

Variations

On my first attempt to model this antenna with *EZNEC/4*, I used a twelve-inch spacing between the two parallel stub-wires, but this produced a non circularity in the SSB-mode azimuthal-plane radiation pattern of fully half a decibel, which I felt was excessive. Because of this, I decreased the spacing to six inches, which yielded a pattern shape that is much more circular, as mentioned above.

Since the SWR of the dual-mode antenna (without un-un) is higher on CW than on phone, I decided to increase the length of the vertical monopole to see what effect this would have. Therefore, I added 1.75 feet to the radiator, making it 69 feet tall instead of 67.25 feet. This changed the SSB resonant frequency of the antenna, so then I had to shorten the length of the four radials to 46.65 feet to achieve resonance once again at 3790 kHz.

Now the input impedance was 43.04 + j 0.027 Ω, with a maximum gain of 0.12 dBi at a takeoff angle of 22°. The azimuthal-plane radiation pattern is very close to perfectly circular, with a minimum gain (at a 22° elevation angle) of 0.04 dBi, in the direction away from the offset.

With the stub energized, the shorting bar was then adjusted to achieve CW resonance at 3510 kHz. An active stub length of 5.80 feet yielded an input impedance of 34.35 + j 0.045 Ω, with a peak gain of 0.18 dBi at a takeoff angle of 22°. Maximum non-circularity in the azimuthal-plane radiation pattern was only 0.03 dBi. The SWR values for both modes of operation are given in **Table 4**. Note that the SWR has improved on both phone and CW, but the CW values are still a bit high, around the 1.5:1 mark. As before, an un-un (this time with a 38:50-Ω impedance ratio) at the feed point can be used in an attempt to equalize the SWR readings on the two modes, as shown in **Table 5**. Now the SWR on phone is actually slightly worse than on CW; choosing an un-un impedance-transformation ratio of 39:50 would make the phone values lower and the CW numbers higher.

A Dual-Mode Four-Square Array

The classic four-square phased-vertical array was introduced to low-band operators more than 20 years ago[3] and it continues to be widely used by DXers and contesters around the world. A simplified version of the four-square, incorporating only two elevated radials per vertical element, was

Table 4

SWR versus Frequency for the Elevated Vertical Antenna with 69-foot Radiator, in both CW and SSB Modes

Frequency (kHz)	SWR (50-Ω reference)
3500	1.476
3510	1.456
3520	1.456
3530	1.474
3540	1.510
3550	1.561
—	—
3750	1.352
3760	1.284
3770	1.226
3780	1.183
3790	1.162
3800	1.168
3810	1.198
3820	1.246
3830	1.305
3840	1.373
3850	1.446

Table 5

SWR versus Frequency for the Elevated Vertical Antenna with 69-foot Radiator, in both CW and SSB Modes, using a 38:50-Ω un-un.

Frequency (kHz)	SWR (50-Ω reference)
3500	1.146
3510	1.106
3520	1.135
3530	1.204
3540	1.292
3550	1.391
—	—
3750	1.342
3760	1.262
3770	1.193
3780	1.146
3790	1.133
3800	1.161
3810	1.216
3820	1.287
3830	1.367
3840	1.454
3850	1.549

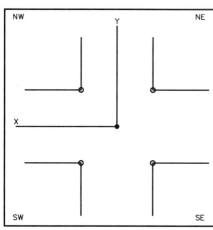

Fig 2—Plan view of the elevated dual-mode four-square array, which utilizes only two radials with each vertical element. Four shorted stubs are present but are too small to be discernible in this drawing. Each pair of radials is offset in the direction of the associated forward lobe (ie, the radials for the northeast element are offset toward the northeast from the base of the vertical radiator).

modeled using *EZNEC/4*. A plan view of this array positioned at a height of 15 feet above the ground is illustrated in **Fig 2**.

The first step in the design process would normally be to generate a computer model of a two-radial antenna resonant at 3650 kHz, midway between the center frequencies of the CW and SSB sub-bands (3510 and 3790 kHz respectively). However, many hams use the ComTek Systems hybrid unit[4] with their four-squares: Jim Miller, K4SQR, suggests a different procedure. He recommends that each full-sized element of the array be resonated at a frequency that is 100 kHz *lower* than the desired center frequency, which would be 3550 kHz for this example. The length of all three wires turned out to be 68.82 feet, producing an input impedance of 37.92 + j 0.009 Ω at 3550 kHz.

Next, I inserted a 10-foot-long stub, made from two #12 AWG copper wires spaced 6 inches apart, at the inner ends of the radial pair. Initially, the shorting bar was omitted from the *EZNEC/4* model, and the upper end of the stub was short-circuited (using a six-inch wire jumper) for SSB operation. I wanted to resonate the antenna at 3790 − 100 = 3690 kHz so the ComTek hybrid would work correctly. When each of the radials is shortened to a length of 59.8 feet, *EZNEC/4* predicts a feed point of 41.25 + j 0.024 Ω at 3690 kHz.

For CW operation, the short-circuit at the top of the stub is removed, and the adjust-

able shorting bar is moved downward along the stub until resonance is achieved at 3510 − 100 = 3410 kHz. I found that an active stub length of 7.39 feet produces an input impedance of 33.47 + j 0.031 Ω at 3410 kHz.

Don't try to improve the SWR by installing an un-un or other impedance-matching circuit at the base of the vertical element. If only a *single* antenna is contemplated, then it may be worthwhile to match the antenna impedance to 50 Ω to improve the SWR bandwidth. However, with an array like a four-square, efforts to improve the impedance match of each individual element may produce undesired consequences when these verticals are connected to the phasing/matching system, possibly generating incorrect drive-point currents.

Now at last we can create three more iden-

tical copies of our two-radial dual-mode vertical antenna to finish the construction of the entire four-square array, shown previously as Fig 2. Generally speaking, it is not a good idea to build into the model more than one vertical antenna at the start, unless *all* of the quarter-wave wires making up the other antennas are electrically isolated from one another. (If just two quarter-wave elevated radials are joined together at their inner ends, then this floating half-wave wire can interact strongly with the active antenna; simply open-circuiting the base of the vertical element is probably not sufficient.) For best accuracy, all pruning and tuning in the model should be carried out on a single,

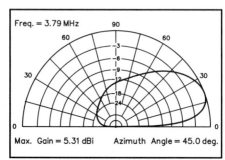

Fig 3—Elevation-plane radiation pattern for the elevated dual-mode four-square phased vertical array, in SSB mode.

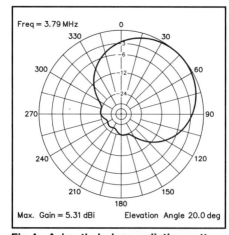

Fig 4—Azimuthal-plane radiation pattern for the elevated dual-mode four-square phased vertical array, in SSB mode.

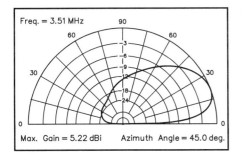

Fig 5—Elevation-plane radiation pattern for the elevated dual-mode four-square phased vertical array, in CW mode.

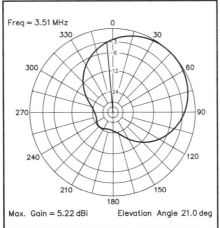

Fig 6—Azimuthal-plane radiation pattern for the elevated dual-mode four-square phased vertical array, in CW mode.

isolated vertical antenna and the other three clones should not be built into the model until all of these preliminary adjustments have been completed. This also holds true for the actual array.

When driven at 3790 kHz in the center of the 75-meter DX phone band, the elevation and azimuthal-plane radiation patterns that result are displayed in **Figs 3** and **4**. Forward gain is 5.31 dBi at a 20° elevation angle, and the front-to-back ratio at this takeoff angle is 27.37 dB. On 3510 kHz in the CW subband, the gain is slightly lower and the take-off angle a bit higher (5.22 dBi at 21°), since the physical height of the array is fixed at 15 feet. The front-to-back ratio is also not quite as good, at 24.48 dB for the 21° take-off angle. The principal-plane CW-mode ra-

diation patterns are shown in **Figs 5** and **6**.

Please be aware that the radiation patterns realized in practice may not be as good as those portrayed in the figures. It isn't possible to simulate the ComTek hybrid with *EZNEC/4*, so idealized feed-point currents are utilized in the computer model. The perfect driving-point currents assumed for the software simulation may not exist in an actual array, especially if a single set of quarter-wave 75-Ω phasing lines is used with the ComTek hybrid. Generally, these phasing lines are cut to be a quarter-wave long at the

3650 kHz center frequency, which is a compromise for both phone and CW operation. If this arrangement isn't satisfactory, it might be better to cut the phasing lines for quarter-wave resonance at 3790 kHz (SSB), and then use relays to add short extender cables to increase their electrical length to a quarter-wave at 3510 kHz (CW).

Conclusion

I've shown in this paper how to switch an elevated vertical antenna from one frequency subband to another, using a single shorted stub to effectively increase the length of several elevated radials simultaneously. Computer modeling indicates that the design can be used with an isolated vertical or with multi-element phased arrays. An actual antenna system has not been constructed by the author, although a similar elevated four square is being used successfully by John Devoldere, ON4UN, who has previously described this basic technique in the literature.

References
[1] John Devoldere, ON4UN, *Antennas and Techniques for Low-Band DXing*, second edition (Newington: ARRL, 1994).
[2] Several versions of *EZNEC* antenna-modeling software are available from Roy Lewallen, W7EL, PO Box 6658, Beaverton, OR 97007.
[3] D. Atchley, W1CF, H. Stinehelfer, ex-W2ZRS, and J. White, *"360°-Steerable Vertical Phased Arrays,"* QST, Apr 1976, pp 27-30.
[4] ComTek Systems, 11600 Hilda Court, Charlotte, NC 28226-3825.

The Versa-Beam

By Al Christman, K3LC (ex-KB8I)
Grove City College
100 Campus Drive
Grove City, PA 16127-2104

The Versa-Beam is a two-element driven array that can function as either a unidirectional or bidirectional antenna. It can beam a signal toward a specific target (like a Yagi) or it can fire in two opposite directions simultaneously (like a dipole). In addition, the unidirectional pattern can be transferred instantaneously from normal to reverse mode, enabling the operator to quickly check for both short and long-path openings at the flick of a switch. The array can be built from aluminum tubing and turned with a rotator, or it may be constructed with wires and installed as a flat-top or inverted V. In a non-rotating configuration, a pair of these antennas could be oriented at right angles to each other with minimal interaction, providing coverage of all quadrants of the globe. Two designs for 40 meters are included to illustrate the details.

One goal of this project was to design an antenna that could beam in several different directions without the need for mechanical rotation. Another objective was to create an array that would be a "step up" from a single dipole (in terms of gain and front-to-back ratio) while still including the wide-azimuth capabilities of the dipole if needed. For stateside ragchews, the bidirectional pattern of a dipole is very convenient, especially for hams who don't live along the coast-line. It can also be useful when working DX: one lobe is oriented toward the target, while energy in the rear lobe lets other operators know that the frequency is busy.

Basic Concepts

The antenna system is composed of two identical half-wave elements arranged parallel to each other, disposed either horizontally or in an inverted-V fashion. If both elements are fed with equal-amplitude in-phase currents, the resulting radiation pattern is very similar to that of a single (isolated) dipole. When one of the feed-point currents is time-delayed with respect to the other, then more signal is emitted in the direction of the lagging element. Optimization of this current phase angle yields a desirable combination of forward gain and rearward rejection. The impedance-match-

Follow along with K3LC as he systematically designs a versatile 40-meter beam.

ing/current-phasing networks can be designed without too much difficulty, using the techniques described years ago by K2BT[1] in combination with modern computer software from ON4UN.[2]

Design Procedure

Two different versions of the Versa-Beam for 40 meters will be described as examples. *EZNEC/4*[3] antenna-modeling software was used initially to create a single half-wave 40-meter dipole operating at 7150 kHz. An aluminum element with a fixed diameter of 0.75 inch was placed exactly one-half wavelength (68.781 feet) above average ground (where soil conductivity = 0.005 Siemens/meter and dielectric

constant = 13). The length of the dipole was then adjusted to achieve resonance at the desired frequency. For a half-length of 33.4 feet, the predicted feed-point impedance is $68.49 - j\,0.13\ \Omega$, while the peak forward gain is 7.56 dBi at a takeoff angle of 28°.

Spacing between the elements (boom length) is adjustable, and you could select any convenient value between $\lambda/8$ and $\lambda/4$. A $\lambda/8$-spacing is nice for cramped quarters but the input resistance of the rear element becomes quite low when the elements are mounted so close together. Spacing of $\lambda/4$ wavelength solves the low-resistance problem but is probably so large physically that it is unwieldy in many locations. Table 1 shows the results of experiments

Table 1

Gain and Front-to-back Ratio as a Function of Element Spacing and Current Phase Angle for Two-Element 40-Meter Versa-Beam Discussed in the First Example

Spacing (feet)	Phase Angle (degrees)	Gain (dBi)	Front-to-back Ratio (elevation plane, dB)
22	−130	11.36	21.26
22	−131	11.39	21.75
22	−132	11.41	21.99
22	−133	11.44	20.98
22	−131.5	11.40	22.00
23	−128	11.34	21.33
23	−129	11.37	21.80
23	−130	11.40	21.65
23	−129.5	11.38	22.04
24	−126	11.33	21.39
24	−127	11.35	21.84
24	−128	11.48	21.32
24	−127.5	11.36	21.79

Table 2

Feed-point Data for the Two Dipoles of the 40-Meter Versa-Beam Described in the First Example, in the Unidirectional Mode, for a Drive Power of 1500 W

Element #1 (Front)

$Z_{1dp} = 59.281 + j54.271 = 80.3715 \angle 42.474° \, \Omega$

$I_1 = 4.453 \angle -127° \, A$

$V_1 = I_1 Z_{1dp} = 357.89 \angle -84.53° \, V = 34.14 - j356.26 \, V$

$P_1 = 1175.6 \, W$

Element #2 (Rear)

$Z_{2dp} = 16.359 - j24.157 = 29.175 \angle -55.894° \, \Omega$

$I_2 = 4.453 \angle 0° \, A$

$V_2 = I_2 Z_{2dp} = 129.92 \angle -55.89° \, V = 72.85 - j107.57 \, V$

$P_2 = 324.4 \, W$

---

conducted on the computer using boom lengths of 22, 23, and 24 feet for a 40-meter array with a center frequency of 7150 kHz. In each case the current drive into the terminals of the rear (#2) element of the array is $1 \angle 0° \, A$.

I decided to use a boom length of 24 feet, and a current phase angle of −127° for the front element (I = 1 $\angle -127°$ A and = 1 $\angle 0°$ A). For this configuration, the peak gain in the elevation plane is 11.35 dBi at a takeoff angle of 26°, with a front-to-back ratio of 21.84 dB. In the azimuthal plane at 26°, the front-to-back ratio is 25.24 dB and the half-power beamwidth is 74.4°. **Fig 1A** is a representation of the antenna itself, while the elevation and azimuthal-plane radiation patterns are displayed in Figs 1B and 1C. With the specified current amplitudes and phase angles at the input terminals of the two dipoles, the resulting driving-point impedances are 59.28 + j 54.27 Ω for the front (#1) element and 16.36 − j 24.16 Ω for the rear (#2) element.

We can also calculate the driving-point impedances on our own, rather than relying on the answers provided by *EZNEC/4*. This is good practice, and may be helpful to review. Note that we will still use *EZNEC/4* in the procedure that follows. First we determine the input impedance at the terminals of each dipole, when the feed point of the other antenna is either opened or shorted.

At antenna #1, with element #2 open-circuited, $Z_{11} = 67.37 - j1.116 \, \Omega$; with dipole #2 short-circuited, $Z_1 = 41.66 + j37.63 \, \Omega$. At antenna #2, with element #1 open-circuited, $Z_{22} = 67.37 - j1.114 \, \Omega$; with dipole #1 short-circuited, $Z_2 = 41.66 + j37.64 \, \Omega$. (Since we are using two *identical* dipoles in the computer model, we would expect the reported values for Z_{11} and Z_{22} to be the same, as well as the answers for Z_1 and Z_2.)

It is easy to simulate open and short-circuited feed points with *EZNEC/4*. For an open-circuit, place a zero-amplitude current source at the input terminals; a zero-magnitude voltage source serves as a short-circuit.

Many of the procedures outlined below are taken from the classic series of articles on phased vertical arrays written by Forrest Gehrke, K2BT.[1] We can calculate the mutual impedance between the two dipoles, using the formula

$$Z_{12} = \pm \sqrt{Z_{22} \times (Z_{11} - Z_1)}$$

which yields $Z_{12} = \pm 55.974 \angle -28.6905° = \pm (49.102 - j \, 26.872) \, \Omega$. For the 24-foot spacing used here, the "+" sign is correct. To double-check our answer we can also determine the mutual impedance, from the perspective of the second dipole, as:

$$Z_{21} = \pm \sqrt{Z_{11} \times (Z_{22} - Z_2)}$$

and again we get the same results as for Z_{12}. Since the two antennas are identical in our idealized software model, we find that $Z_{12} = Z_{21}$. In a real-world example, things don't normally work out this well but the two values calculated for the mutual impedances should be quite similar to each other.

Now we can derive the driving-point impedances when the input currents are the desired values of $I_1 = 1 \angle -127°$ A and $I_2 = 1 \angle 0°$ A:

$$Z_{1dp} = Z_{11} + (I_2 / I_1)(Z_{12})$$
$$= 59.281 + j \, 54.271 \, \Omega$$

$$Z_{2dp} = Z_{22} + (I_1 / I_2)(Z_{21})$$
$$= 16.359 - j \, 24.157 \, \Omega$$

As we had hoped, the answers here agree very closely with the driving-point impedances already provided to us by *EZNEC/4*. For an input power (P) of 1500 watts, the actual current magnitude |I| at the feed-points of the two dipoles can be found:

$$|I| = \sqrt{P / R} = \sqrt{P / (R_{1dp} + R_{2dp})}$$

where R_{1dp} and R_{2dp} are the real parts of the two driving-point impedances calculated above (59.281 Ω and 16.359 Ω, respectively). Substituting these values of power and resistances, the magnitude of the current at the input terminals of each of the two antennas is found to be 4.453 A (rather than the nominal one ampere value assumed earlier). The power supplied to each of the dipoles is:

$$P_1 = |I_1|^2 R_{1dp} = (4.453)^2 (59.281) = 1175.6 \, W$$

$$P_2 = |I_2|^2 R_{2dp} = (4.453)^2 (16.359) = 324.4 \, W$$

Table 2 summarizes the operating parameters at the driving points of the two dipoles for this initial example. We will assume that equal lengths of lossless transmission line are connected between the antenna feed points and the tuning/matching networks. For simplicity, let's assume that the electrical length of each piece of coaxial cable is 0.5 λ. Knowing this, along with the data from Table 2, we can use ON4UN's *Low Band Software*[2] to determine the values of current, voltage, power and impedance at the input ends of these two feeders. This data is listed in **Table 3**. As expected, the impedances and power levels are unchanged, since the lines are lossless and have an electrical length of 0.5 λ. The voltage and current amplitudes are also the same as at the feed points of the elements, although both have been "rotated" through an angle of 180°, or 0.5 λ.

Now we can calculate the input voltage and resistances of the passive networks that we must use to provide the desired drive levels to the lower ends of these two transmission lines. Using coaxial cables with a characteristic impedance of = 50 Ω, the input voltage to the two networks for 1500 W is:

$$V_{in} = \sqrt{PR_0} = \sqrt{75000} = 273.86 \, V$$

The input resistances for the two networks are determined:

$$R_{1in} = (V_{in})^2 / P_1 = 75000 / 1175.6 = 63.8 \, \Omega$$

$$R_{2in} = (V_{in})^2 / P_2 = 75000 / 324.4 = 231.2 \, \Omega$$

Note that the parallel combination of R_{1in} and R_{2in} is equal to 50 Ω, which is exactly what we want because we're going to

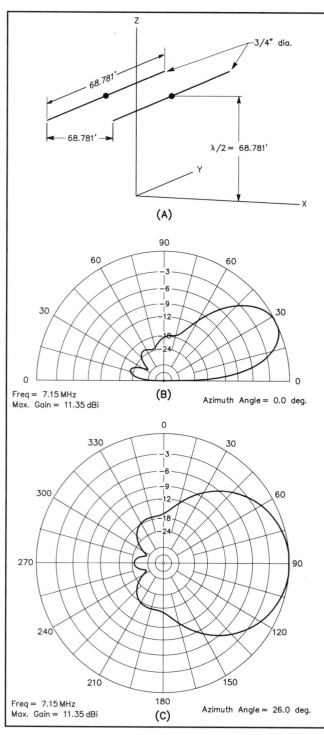

(A)

Freq = 7.15 MHz
Max. Gain = 11.35 dBi

(B)   Azimuth Angle = 0.0 deg.

Freq = 7.15 MHz
Max. Gain = 11.35 dBi

(C)   Azimuth Angle = 26.0 deg.

Fig 1—At A, perspective view of the 40-meter Versa-Beam at a height of one-half wavelength above ground. Each element is resonant at 7.15 MHz, and the spacing between elements is 24 feet. At B, elevation-plane pattern for the 40-meter Versa-Beam (with resonant elements spaced 24 feet apart) at a height of one-half wavelength, when operating in the unidirectional (Yagi) mode. At C, azimuth-plane pattern for the 40-meter Versa-Beam (with resonant elements spaced 24 feet apart) at a height of 0.5 λ, when operating in the unidirectional (Yagi) mode.

Table 3

Input Data for the Two Half-wave Lossless Transmission Lines Feeding the Dipoles of the 40-Meter Versa-Beam Described in the First Example, in the Unidirectional Mode, for a Drive Power of 1500 W

Feeder #1 (Front)
$Z_1 = 59.28 + j\,54.27\ \Omega$
$I_1 = 4.453 \angle 53°\ A$
$V_1 = 357.89 \angle 95.47°\ V$
$P_1 = 1175.6\ W$

Feeder #2 (Rear)
$Z_2 = 16.36 - j\,24.16\ \Omega$
$I_2 = 4.453 \angle 180°\ A$
$V_2 = 129.92 \angle 124.11°\ V$
$P_2 = 324.4\ W$

directly together to form a single 50-Ω feed point. Because the phase angles of the two networks aren't the same, we must insert an additional circuit in series with the network having the *smaller* phase angle (#2) to make up the difference.

Once again the *Low Band Software* comes to our rescue. I chose to use a pi-section circuit as a *line stretcher*. The characteristic impedance of this network must be 231.2 Ω (the same as R_{2in}). The input and output phase angles are 135.55° and 105.43°, respectively (phase shift = 30.12°) and the operating frequency is 7.15 MHz. The circuit to accomplish this is shown in **Fig 4**.

Fig 5 is a schematic diagram of the entire phasing/matching network needed for unidirectional (Yagi) operation of the 40-meter Versa-Beam. Swapping the transmission lines at the feeder end of the circuit reverses the direction of fire of the array.

In the bidirectional (dipole) configuration, both elements are fed with equal-amplitude, in-phase currents ($I_1 = I_2 = 1 \angle 0°\ A$). **Fig 6A** and **6B** show the elevation and azimuth-plane radiation patterns predicted by *EZNEC/4* for this situation, and the patterns really do look like those for a single conventional dipole or inverted V. The input impedances at the feed points are both the same (since the dipoles themselves are identical, as are the currents) and equal to $116.50 - j\,27.99\ \Omega$. We can check this result by using the self and mutual-impedance values derived from our previous open and short-circuit tests. The corresponding

connect the input terminals of the two networks directly in parallel at the transmitter end of the system. These last few calculations give us the final pieces of information we need in order to find the component values for the L networks we are about to design, using the *Low Band Software*:

For network #1, = 63.8 Ω, f = 7.15 MHz, and the other data is obtained from Table 3. There are four possible L-networks that we can be used in this case and all four choices

are shown in **Fig 2**. For network #2, we have = 231.2 Ω. Here there are only two circuit options for the L-network, as shown in **Fig 3**.

Notice that the input voltage *magnitude* for all six networks (in both figures) is roughly 273.86 V, although the phase angles are different. Let's select network (D) from Fig 2 and network (A) from Fig 3. We want both of the voltage amplitudes and phase angles to be identical, since we'd like to join the input ends of the two selected networks

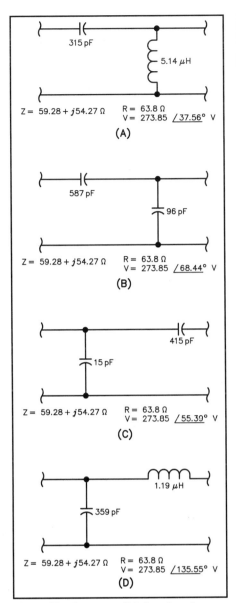

Fig 2—The four possible L networks we can use for impedance-matching purposes at the input end of feeder #1 of the first 40-meter Versa-Beam design, for unidirectional (Yagi) operation.

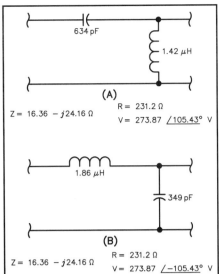

Fig 3—The two possible L-networks we can use for impedance-matching purposes at the input end of feeder #2 of the first 40-meter Versa-Beam design, for unidirectional (Yagi) operation.

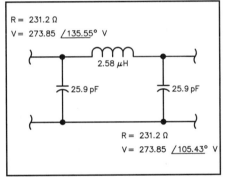

Fig 4—The pi-section line-stretcher network used for phase-shifting purposes at the input end of the feeder #2 impedance-matching network.

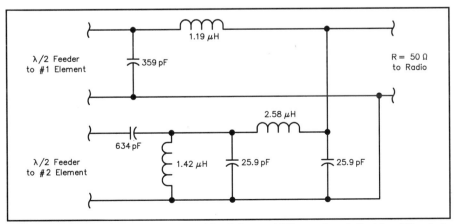

Fig 5—The complete impedance-matching/phase-shifting network that is utilized at the input ends of the two ideal (lossless) coaxial feeders of the first 40-meter Versa-Beam design for unidirectional operation.

driving-point impedances calculated by formula are:

$$Z_{1dp} = Z_{11} + \left(I_2 / I_1\right)\left(Z_{12}\right)$$

$$= 116.472 - j\,27.988\ \Omega$$

$$Z_{2dp} = Z_{22} + \left(I_1 / I_2\right)\left(Z_{21}\right)$$

$$= 116.472 - j\,27.988\ \Omega$$

As expected, the answers here agree with those already provided to us by *EZNEC/4*. When the total drive power is 1500 W, the actual current magnitude |I| at the input terminals of the two elements is:

$$|I| = \sqrt{P / R} = \sqrt{P / \left(R_{1dp} + R_{2dp}\right)}$$

where and are both 116.472 Ω. Substituting these values for power and resistance, the actual current amplitude at the input terminals of each antenna becomes 2.5376 A and the power supplied to each dipole is:

$$P_1 = P_2 = \left|I_1\right|^2 R_{1dp} = \left(2.5376\right)^2 \left(116.472\right)$$

$$= 750.0\ W$$

Table 4 summarizes the operating parameters at the driving points of the two dipoles. We can see that all of the data for both antennas is the same in the bidirectional mode. Again let's assume that an electrical half wavelength of ideal (lossless) transmission line is connected between each of the antenna feed points and the tuning/matching networks. Plugging all of the necessary data from Table 4 into ON4UN's *Low Band Software* we obtain the current, voltage, power and impedance at the input ends of these two feeders as shown in **Table 5**. As before, the impedances and power levels are unchanged, since the lines are lossless and have an electrical length of 0.5 λ. The voltage and current amplitudes are also the same as at the feed points of the elements, although their phase angles have been shifted by 180°, or one-half wavelength.

Since both feeders have the same input voltage (magnitude *and* phase) they can be connected directly in parallel with each other, with the resulting voltage remaining unchanged. The net input impedance, however, will be halved, while the total current and power will double, as displayed in **Table 6**.

We can calculate the component values for the L network needed to match the input impedance to 50 Ω, using the *Low Band Software* at f = 7.15 MHz. There are just two L network options and both are shown in **Fig 7**. Let's choose circuit (B) since the component values are smaller.

Design Procedure Using Lossy Lines

Our first example above was pretty

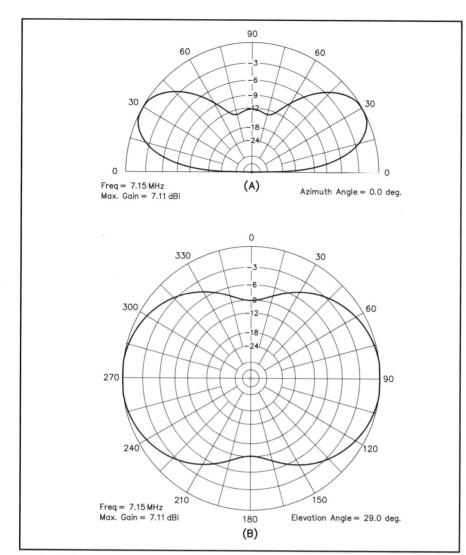

Freq = 7.15 MHz
Max. Gain = 7.11 dBi
(A)
Azimuth Angle = 0.0 deg.

Freq = 7.15 MHz
Max. Gain = 7.11 dBi
(B)
Elevation Angle = 29.0 deg.

Fig 6—At A, elevation-plane pattern for the 40-meter Versa-Beam (with resonant elements) at a height 0.5 λ, when operating in the bidirectional (dipole) mode. At B, azimuth-plane pattern for the 40-meter Versa-Beam (with resonant elements) at a height 0.5 λ, when operating in the bidirectional (dipole) mode.

Table 4

Feed-point Data for the Two Dipoles of the 40-Meter Versa-Beam Described in the First Example, in the Bidirectional Mode, for a Drive Power of 1500 W

Elements #1 and #2 (Front and Rear)

$Z_{1dp} = Z_{2dp} = 116.472 - j27.988 = 119.79\angle-13.51° \Omega$

$I_1 = I_2 = 2.5376\angle0° A$

$V_1 = V_2 = I_1 Z_{1dp} = I_2 Z_{2dp} = 303.977\angle-13.51° = 295.565 - j71.014 V$

$P_1 = P_2 = 750.0 W$

Table 5

Input Data for the Two Half-wave Lossless Transmission Lines Feeding the Dipoles of the 40-Meter Versa-Beam Described in the First Example, in the Bidirectional Mode, for a Drive Power of 1500 W.

Feeders #1 and #2 (Front and Rear)

$Z_{1in} = Z_{2in} = 116.47 - j27.99 \Omega$

$I_1 = I_2 = 2.54\angle180° A$

$V_1 = V_2 = 303.97\angle166.49° V$

$P_1 = P_2 = 750.0 W$

Table 6

Input Data for the Two Half-wave Lossless Transmission Lines Feeding the Dipoles of the 40-Meter Versa-Beam Described in the First Example, in the Bidirectional Mode, for a Drive Power of 1500 W, when Both Inputs Are Connected in Parallel

Feeders #1 and #2 Joined Together

$Z_{in} = Z_{1in}/2 = Z_{2in}/2 = 58.236 - j13.994 \Omega$

$I_{in} = I_1 + I_2 = 5.075\angle180° A$

$V_{in} = V_1 = V_2 = 303.97\angle166.49° V$

$P_{in} = P_1 + P_2 = 1500.0 W$

simple, since we pretended that the coaxial feeders had no loss. This isn't true in practice, of course, so let's carry out a second design that incorporates transmission lines with a certain amount of attenuation. In addition, we'll arbitrarily select the length of the dipoles, rather than tuning them to reso-

nance, and we'll also choose a random height above ground to simulate what would probably happen in a typical installation.

This time we'll begin with a single aluminum-tubing dipole that is exactly 70 feet long, with a diameter of $^3/_4$ inches, and we'll mount it at a height of 70 feet above average

ground. At 7.15 MHz, *EZNEC/4* tells us that the peak gain will be 7.68 dBi at a takeoff angle of 27°, while the feed-point impedance is $77.32 + j\,56.49\,\Omega$.

I have shown the results of computer-modeling studies for three different spacings and several current phase angles in **Table 7**. In each instance the current magnitude is held at 1 A for each element and the reference current phase angle is 0° for the rear (#2) dipole.

I selected a boom length of only 22 feet in this scenario (for the sake of variety) and a current phase angle of −131° for the front element. According to *EZNEC/4*, the peak gain in the elevation plane is 11.51 dBi, at an elevation angle of 26° with a front-to-back ratio of 22.42 dB. In the azimuth plane at 26° elevation, the front-to-back ratio is 25.76 dB and the half-power beamwidth is 73°. The elevation and azimuth-plane radiation patterns are shown in **Fig 8A** and **8B**. For the specified current amplitudes and phase angles at the input terminals of the two dipoles, the driving-point impedances predicted by the computer are $56.73 + j\,115.50\,\Omega$ for the front element and $18.91 + j\,27.26\,\Omega$ for the rear element. Since the

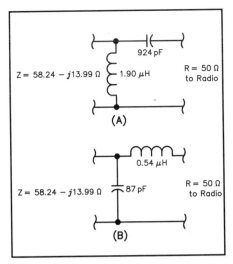

Fig 7—The two possible L networks we can use for impedance-matching purposes when the input ends of lossless (ideal) feeders #1 and #2 are connected in parallel, for bidirectional (dipole) 40-meter Versa-Beam operation.

Table 7

Gain and Front-to-back Ratio as a Function of Element Spacing and Current Phase Angle for Two-Element 40-Meter Versa-Beam Discussed in the Second Example

Spacing (feet)	Phase Angle (degrees)	Gain (dBi)	Front-to-back Ratio (elevation plane, dB)
22	−130	11.48	21.89
22	−131	11.51	22.42
22	−132	11.54	21.75
22	−133	11.56	20.76
22	−131.5	11.52	22.27
23	−128	11.47	21.98
23	−129	11.49	22.39
23	−130	11.52	21.40
23	−129.5	11.51	21.89
24	−126	11.45	22.06
24	−127	11.48	22.01
24	−128	11.50	21.07
24	−126.5	11.46	22.30

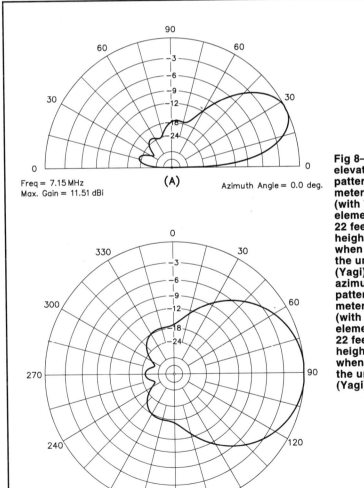

Fig 8—At A, elevation-plane pattern for the 40-meter Versa-Beam (with 70-foot elements spaced 22 feet apart) at a height of 70 feet, when operating in the unidirectional (Yagi) mode. At B, azimuth-plane pattern for the 40-meter Versa-Beam (with 70-foot elements spaced 22 feet apart) at a height of 70 feet, when operating in the unidirectional (Yagi) mode.

dipoles are non-resonant here, the driving-point reactances are different than they were in the earlier example.

With 1500 W of output power from the transmitter, the total power at the terminals of the antennas will be less than this because of line losses. To be conservative, let's assume that only one kilowatt reaches these elements. Then the current magnitude |I| at the feed points of the two dipoles will be:

$$|I| = \sqrt{P/R} = \sqrt{P/\left(R_{1dp} + R_{2dp}\right)}$$

$$= \sqrt{1000/\left(56.73 + 18.91\right)} = 3.636 \text{ A}$$

The power supplied to elements #1 and #2 is:

$$P_1 = |I_1|^2 R_{1dp} = \left(3.636\right)^2 \left(56.73\right) = 750 \text{ W}$$

$$P_2 = |I_2|^2 R_{2dp} = \left(3.636\right)^2 \left(18.91\right) = 250 \text{ W}$$

Table 8 summarizes the operating parameters at the input terminals of the two antennas in this second example, using data gleaned from the *EZNEC/4* model of the antenna.

At this point in our analysis, it may be helpful to ask the question, "What is the best way to determine the actual driving-point impedances for the dipoles in the array?" If desired, one could use computer software to predict these impedances (as I have done above) based upon the specified length and diameter of the aluminum tubing used to construct the elements, along with their spacing, height above ground and the specified input currents. However, many hams feel more confident if they use measured data, and there are several

Table 8

Feed-point Data for the Two Dipoles of the 40-Meter Versa-Beam Described in the Second Example, in the Unidirectional Mode, for an Antenna Power of 1000 W

Element #1 (Front)

$Z_{1dp} = 56.73 + j115.50 = 128.68 \angle 63.84° \, \Omega$

$I_1 = 3.636 \angle -131° \, A$

$V_1 = I_1 Z_{1dp} = 467.88 \angle -67.16° = 181.61 - j431.20 \, V$

$P_1 = 750 \, W$

Element #2 (Rear)

$Z_{2dp} = 18.91 + j27.26 = 33.18 \angle 55.25° \, \Omega$

$I_2 = 3.64 \angle 0° \, A$

$V_2 = I_2 Z_{2dp} = 120.63 \angle 55.25° = 68.76 + j99.12 \, V$

$P_2 = 250 \, W$

Table 9

Manufacturer's Data for Belden 9913 Coaxial Cable

Nominal Impedance = 50 Ω
Velocity Factor = 84% = 0.84
Attenuation = 0.1 dB/100 feet at 1 MHz
Attenuation = 0.4 dB/100 feet at 10 MHz
DC Resistance per unit length
   = 0.9 mΩ/foot
Inductance per unit length
   = 0.059 μH/foot
Capacitance per unit length
   = 24.6 pF/foot

techniques to do this.

The methods described below involve measurement of the self-impedance of each element. Then the mutual impedance between the dipoles is calculated, and (finally) the driving-point impedances are determined.

One alternative is to place an actual open or short-circuit termination directly at the feed point of the first dipole and make the corresponding impedance measurement at the terminals of the second element. A crane or other lifting device would be needed to place the operator into position and move him from one end of the boom to the other while making and recording impedance data. This procedure should yield the most accurate values for the self-impedances, but would be expensive!

A cheaper but more tedious option is to maneuver the antenna back and forth, inserting and removing short circuits at the feed points whenever necessary and making impedance measurements through a short piece of coax. With a 22-foot boom, an 11-foot length of coax would make it feasible for the operator to belt himself onto the tower near the center of the boom and make the impedance measurements using a handheld bridge. The antenna would have to be moved and reoriented each time a different termination was required, but this method would yield answers that are almost as good as those achievable with the crane method. (All of the numerical values obtained at the end of the 11-foot piece of coax would need to be "rotated" to the antenna terminals to obtain the self-impedance data, either using formulas or the *Low Band Software*.)

Yet another possibility exists: Pieces of coax that are an electrical quarter or half-wave in length (or a multiple thereof) can be connected to the dipole feed points. If the line lengths are an electrical quarter-wave

(or odd multiple thereof), then a short at the antenna terminals is simulated by an open at the input end of the feeder (and vice-versa). If the lengths of coax are an electrical half-wave (or multiple), then a short at the input end of the feeder looks like a short at the dipole terminals, and vice-versa. As mentioned above, each impedance value measured at the end of the other feeder must then be transformed to the terminals of that element. How to rotate impedances through arbitrary lengths of non-ideal feed line is our next topic of discussion.

Belden 9913 coaxial cable is often used for Amateur Radio antenna installations, so it will be pressed into service as our real (nonideal) transmission line. A telephone call to Belden (1-800-BELDEN4) yielded several important specifications that are needed to carry out the design, and this data is shown in **Table 9**. Notice that the attenuation figures were given only to the nearest 0.1 dB, which isn't very precise. Fig 26 on

page 24-16 of the 18th Edition of *The ARRL Antenna Book* is helpful and it reveals that the attenuation for 9913-type cable at 7.15 MHz is about 0.35 dB per hundred feet.[4]

In free space, the wavelength at a frequency of 7.15 MHz is 41.93 meters, or 137.57 feet. Inside the Belden 9913 coax, the wavelength is only 84% as great, or 115.56 feet. If we try to use λ/2 pieces of this cable to reach from the antenna feed points to our phasing/matching box, they will be only 57.78 feet long, which is too short to reach the ground. Three-quarter wave long cables, though, are 86.67 feet in length and this is sufficient to extend all the way from the dipole terminals to ground level, with almost 6 feet left over to allow for rotor loops.

If we use 0.75-λ cables we can make all of our open-circuit/short-circuit measurements safely from the ground. The *Low Band Software* will then allow us to transform the readings from the input ends of the lines to the feed points. Since these cables have some losses, the disadvangtage to this technique is that an open or short at the lower end of a 0.75-λ line will not transform perfectly into a simulated short or open at the feed point.

Table 10 illustrates the effects of using real (Belden 9913) versus ideal (lossless)

Table 10

Impedance Transformations Using Either Ideal or Real (Belden 9913) Coaxial Cables at 7.15 MHz

Line Length (λ)	Actual Input Impedance (Ω)	Ideal-Line Load Impedance (Theoretical) (Ω)	Lossy-Line Load Impedance (Lowband) (Ω)	Lossy-Line Load Impedance (Calculated) (Ω)
0.25	zero	infinite	4235	4244
0.25	infinite	zero	0.33	0.57
0.50	zero	zero	1.14	1.14
0.50	infinite	infinite	2680	2113
0.75	zero	infinite	1410	1410
0.75	infinite	zero	1.48	1.72

coaxial cable as an impedance transformer. For the nonideal case, I have shown the data reported by *Low Band Software* and the answers that were calculated by using the exact transmission-line formulas.[5] One limitation of the *Low Band Software* is that all impedances that are supplied to the program must be larger than zero but no greater than 9999 Ω. I used values of 0.001 Ω instead of zero, and 9999 Ω for infinity. From Table 10, we can see that a short circuit ends up looking like 1 or 2 Ω, but an open is reduced to an impedance of only a few thousand ohms. For maximum transformation accuracy, $\lambda/4$ lines should be used, because the simulated impedances are closer to the ideal values.

The characteristic impedance (also called the surge impedance) of an ideal transmission line is purely resistive, but the impedance of a nonideal (lossy) line is complex, with a large resistive component and a small amount of capacitive reactance. For maximum accuracy in our analysis, we need to find the corrected impedance for Belden 9913 coaxial cable at the design frequency of 7.15 MHz. To do this, I must introduce another equation:

$$\gamma = \alpha + j\beta$$

where

γ = propagation constant [feet^{-1}]
α = attenuation constant [Nepers/foot]
β = phase constant [radians/foot]

We can find α from the cable attenuation data (at 7.15 MHz):

$$\alpha = \frac{0.35 \text{ dB/100 feet}}{8.69 \text{ dB/Neper}} = 0.0403 \text{ Neper/100 feet}$$

$$= 0.000403 \text{ Neper/foot}$$

The phase constant β is calculated by using the velocity factor of the coax and the operating wavelength:

$$\beta = \frac{2\pi}{\lambda \times VF}$$

The wavelength λ is 137.57 feet at 7.15 MHz, and the velocity factor (VF) of Belden 9913 is 84% or 0.84; substituting these numbers into our equation yields $\beta = 0.05437$ radians/foot.

Now that we know the values for α and β, we are ready to find the actual impedance (Z_0) of Belden 9913 at the frequency of interest:

$$Z_0 = \frac{\gamma}{j\omega C} = \frac{\alpha + j\beta}{j\omega C} = \frac{\beta}{\omega C} - j\frac{\alpha}{\omega C}$$

where

ω = angular frequency = $2\pi f$ [radians/second]
f = operating frequency = 7.15 MHz
C = capacitance per unit length for Belden

9913 = 24.6 pF/foot

Plugging all the numbers into this formula, we find that $Z_0 = 49.198 \angle -0.425° = 49.197 - j\,0.365\ \Omega$ (at 7.15 MHz).

Thus, when using the *Low Band Software*, the value "49.198" should be inserted as the impedance of the transmission line, rather than "50." Those with mathematical skill or curiosity may prefer to use the actual lossy-line formulas, rather than relying on the *Low Band Software*. If so, the following two equations are of great value:

$$Z_{in} = Z_0 \left[\frac{Z_L + Z_0 \tanh(\gamma L)}{Z_0 + Z_L \tanh(\gamma L)} \right]$$

and

$$Z_L = Z_0 \left[\frac{Z_0 \tanh(\gamma L) - Z_{in}}{Z_L \tanh(\gamma L) - Z_0} \right]$$

where

Z_{in} = input impedance [Ω]
Z_L = load impedance [Ω]
tanh = the hyperbolic tangent function
L = physical length of the transmission line [feet]

Many hand-held calculators cannot perform hyperbolic trigonometric operations on complex arguments, but fortunately tanh (γL) can be rewritten in a form that is more manageable:

$$\tanh(\gamma L) = \tanh(\alpha L + j\beta L)$$

$$= \frac{\sinh 2\alpha L + j \sin 2\beta L}{\cosh 2\alpha L + j \cos 2\beta L}$$

where sinh and cosh are the hyperbolic sine and cosine functions.

Let's now assume that we are standing comfortably on the ground near the base of our tower, with two identical 70-foot-long aluminum elements (spaced 22 feet apart) darkening the sky 70 feet overhead. We've connected electrical 0.75-λ sections (physical length = 86.67 feet) of Belden 9913 coax to the dipole feed points, and the lower ends of these cables are positioned near us, along with an impedance bridge and a short that can be quickly attached or removed from a PL-259 coax connector. The ends of the coax feeders are clearly marked "#1" and "#2" so we don't confuse them.

By placing a short circuit at the lower end of feeder #2 we simulate an open circuit at the terminals of dipole #2, and we measure the input impedance at the bottom end of feed-line #1 to be $Z_{1lin} = 22.45 - j\,14.61\ \Omega$. Next we remove the short from the lower end of feeder #2 (creating an open, which is the same as placing a short at the terminals of element #2), and now the impedance measured by our bridge at the bottom end of line #1 is $Z_{lin} = 13.55 - j\,16.02\ \Omega$.

Using the *Low Band Software*, we transform these two impedances from the input ends of the lines to the load (antenna) ends, where we find:

$$Z_{11} = 76.14 + j\,54.91\ \Omega$$

$$Z_1 = 70.31 + j\,97.59\ \Omega.$$

To perform these calculations, data supplied to the *Low Band* program includes, frequency = 7.15 MHz, coax attenuation = 0.35 dB per hundred feet, coax velocity factor = 0.84, physical length of coax = 86.67 feet and coax impedance = 49.198 Ω.

For simplicity, I will assume that the results when performing the open and short-circuit tests on element #2 are the same as for #1, which means that $Z_{11} = Z_{22}$ and $Z_1 = Z_2$. Next we can calculate the mutual impedance Z_{21} (which will also be equal to Z_{12} in this case):

$$Z_{12} = Z_{21} = \pm \sqrt{Z_{22} \times (Z_{11} - Z_1)}$$

$$= \pm 63.591 \angle -23.212°\ \Omega$$

Since the "+" sign is correct for this interelement spacing, the result for the mutual impedance is:

$$Z_{12} = Z_{21} = 63.591 \angle -23.212°\ \Omega$$

$$= 58.44 - j\,25.06\ \Omega$$

With the relative dipole current amplitudes and phase angles being $I_1 = 1 \angle -131°$ A and $I_2 = 1 \angle 0°$ A respectively, the driving-point impedances are:

$$Z_{1dp} = Z_{11} + (I/I)(Z) = 56.71 + j\,115.46\ \Omega$$

$$Z_{2dp} = Z_{22} + (I_1/I_2)(Z_{21})$$

$$= 18.88 + j\,27.25\ \Omega$$

The actual current amplitude into each element is:

$$|I| = \sqrt{P / (R_{1dp} + R_{2dp})}$$

$$= \sqrt{1000 / (56.71 + 18.88)} = 3.637 \text{ A}$$

and the power supplied to the dipoles is:

$$P_1 = |I_1|^2 R_{1dp} = (3.6372)^2 (56.71) = 750 \text{ W}$$

$$P_2 = |I_2|^2 R_{2dp} = (3.6372)^2 (18.88) = 250 \text{ W}$$

for a total power of 1000 W at the antenna. All of the key parameters for the array, at the feed points, are listed in **Table 11**.

The *Low Band Software* must be used again, to transform the driving-point impedances to the values that would be observed at the input ends of our 0.75 λ sections of

Belden 9913 cable. **Table 12** shows the results. Notice that, because of the nonideal coaxial cables, a total of 1214 W (930 + 284) of power must be supplied to the input ends of the two feeders in order to yield 1000 W at the antenna terminals. Also, remember that it is the input impedances shown in this table that will be used as data for the design of the phasing/matching networks.

The input voltage for these networks is:

$$V_{in} = \sqrt{PR_0} = \sqrt{1214 \times 49.198} = 244.39 \text{ V}$$

and the corresponding input resistances are:

$$R_{1in} = \left(V_{in}\right)^2 / P_1 = 59726 / 930 = 64.22 \ \Omega$$

$$R_{2in} = \left(V_{in}\right)^2 / P_2 = 59726 / 284 = 210.30 \ \Omega$$

Note that I could have substituted a value of "50" for the desired cable impedance R_0 (in the voltage equation above) if I were using lossless 50-Ω cable for the feed line run from the matching/phasing networks back to the transmitter. However, I assumed I would just use an additional length of Belden 9913, and I already know that its characteristic resistance at 7.15 MHz really isn't 50 Ω. Thus, the parallel combination of R_{1in} and R_{2in} is equal to 49.2 Ω for this example.

As usual, the *Low Band Software* is used to generate the L-network designs. For network #1, R_{in} = 64.22 Ω, f = 7.15 MHz and the remaining data is taken from Table 12. There are two possible L networks we can use in this case, as shown in **Fig 9**. For network #2, R_{in} = 210.30 Ω, and again there are only two circuit options, both of which are displayed in **Fig 10**.

We can see that the input voltage magnitudes are all similar, although the phase angles are different. This time, let's select

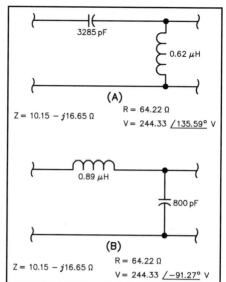

Fig 9—The two possible L-networks we can use for impedance-matching purposes at the input end of feeder #1 (Belden 9913 coax) of the second 40-meter Versa-Beam, for unidirectional (Yagi) operation.

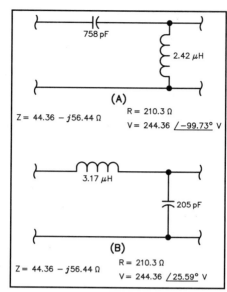

Fig 10—The two possible L-networks we can use for impedance-matching purposes at the input end of feeder #2 (Belden 9913 coax) of the second 40-meter Versa-Beam, for unidirectional (Yagi) operation.

network (B) in both Fig 9 and 10. Since the voltage phase angles are different, we need to include additional components to make up for the discrepancy. Again I will choose to utilize a pi-section circuit as a line stretcher. The characteristic impedance of this network is 64.22 Ω the input and output phase angles are 25.59° and −91.27°, respectively (phase shift = 116.86°), and the frequency is 7.15 MHz. The resulting pi-section schematic diagram is shown in **Fig 11**.

Fig 12 shows the entire phasing/matching network system that is needed for unidirectional (Yagi) operation of the 40-meter Versa-Beam with the 0.75 λ Belden 9913

transmission lines. The two shunt capacitors that are immediately adjacent to each other in the final element #1 network can be combined into a single 1364-pF unit. Swapping the cable connections at the feeder end of the circuit reverses the direction of fire of the array.

In the bidirectional (dipole) configuration, both elements are fed with equal-amplitude, in-phase currents. **Fig 13** shows the principal radiation patterns predicted by *EZNEC/4* for this situation. According to the computer software, the input impedances for the two elements are both equal to 134.6 + j 29.86 Ω. We can check this result

---

Table 11

Feed-point Data for the Two Dipoles of the 40-Meter Versa-Beam Described in the Second Example, in the Unidirectional Mode, for an Antenna Power of 1000 W

Element #1 (Front)

$Z_{1dp} = 56.71 + j115.46 = 128.635 \angle 63.841° \ \Omega$

$I_1 = 3.6372 \angle -131° \text{ A}$

$V_1 = I_1 Z_{1dp} = 467.872 \angle -67.159° = 181.62 - j431.18 \text{ V}$

$P_1 = 750 \text{ W}$

Element #2 (Rear)

$Z_{2dp} = 18.88 + j27.25 = 33.151 \angle 55.284° \ \Omega$

$I_2 = 3.6372\ 0 \text{ A}$

$V_2 = I_2 Z_{2dp} = 120.578 \angle 55.284° = 68.67 + j99.11 \text{V}$

$P_2 = 250 \text{ W}$

Table 12

Input Data for the Two Belden 9913 Transmission Lines Feeding the 40-Meter Versa-Beam Described in the Second Example, in the Unidirectional Mode, for an Antenna Power of 1000 W

Element #1 (Front)

$Z_{1in} = 10.15 - j16.65 = 19.50 \angle -58.64° \ \Omega$

$I_1 = 9.57 \angle -157.84° = -8.87 - j3.61 \text{A}$

$V_1 = I_1 Z_{1in} = 186.71 \angle 143.53° = -150.14 + j110.99 \text{ V}$

$P_1 = 930 \text{ W}$

Element #2 (Rear)

$Z_{2in} = 44.36 - j56.44 = 71.78 \angle -51.83° \ \Omega$

$I_2 = 2.53 \angle -37.07° = 2.02 - j1.52 \text{ A}$

$V_2 = I_2 Z_{2in} = 181.45 \angle -88.90° = 3.48 - j181.42 \text{ V}$

$P_2 = 284 \text{ W}$

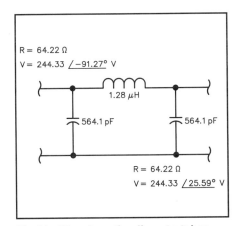

Fig 11—The pi-section line-stretcher network that is used for phase-shifting purposes at the input end of the feeder #1 impedance-matching network.

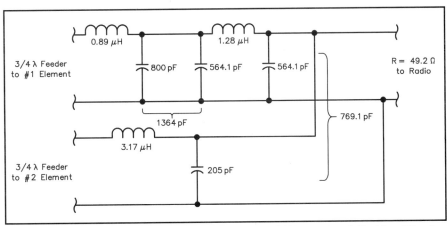

Fig 12—The complete impedance-matching/phase-shifting network that is utilized at the input ends of the two Belden 9913 coaxial feeders of the second 40-meter Versa-Beam, for unidirectional (Yagi) operation.

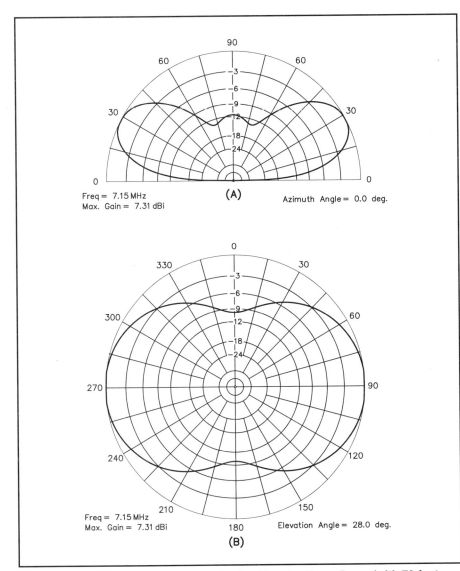

Fig 13—At A, elevation-plane pattern for the 40-meter Versa-Beam (with 70-foot elements spaced 22 feet apart) at a height of 70 feet, when operating in the bidirectional (dipole) mode. At B, azimuth-plane pattern for the 40-meter Versa-Beam (with 70-foot elements spaced 22 feet apart) at a height of 70 feet, when operating in the bidirectional (dipole) mode for Belden 9913 transmission lines.

by using the self and mutual-impedance values derived from our previous open and short-circuit tests. The corresponding driving-point impedances calculated by formula are:

$$Z_{1dp} = Z_{11} + (I_2 / I_1)(Z_{12}) = Z_{11} + Z_{12}$$

$$= (76.14 + j\,54.91) + (58.44 - j\,25.06)$$

$$= 134.58 + j\,29.85\ \Omega$$

$$Z_{2dp} = Z_{22} + (I_1 / I_2)(Z_{21}) = Z_{22} + Z_{21}$$

$$= Z_{11} + Z_{12} = \text{same as above}$$

$$= 134.58 + j\,29.85\ \Omega$$

The math is especially simple in this section. The currents are the same, so the current ratios cancel out; also $Z_{11} = Z_{22}$ and $Z_{12} = Z_{21}$. When the drive power to each element is 500 W, the actual current magnitude |I| at the input terminals of the two dipoles is:

$$|I| = \sqrt{P / R_{dp}} = \sqrt{500 / 134.58} = 1.928\ \text{A}$$

Table 13 summarizes the operating parameters at the feed points of the two dipoles, and (as before) we can see that all of the data for both antennas is the same in the bidirectional mode. Again, let us assume that an electrical 0.75 λ length of Belden 9913 transmission line is connected between each of the antenna feed points and the tuning/matching networks. Plugging the necessary data from Table 13 into ON4UN's *Low Band Software,* we obtain the current, voltage, power and impedance at the input ends of these two feeders, as shown in **Table 14.**

Since both feeders have the same input voltage magnitude and phase, they can be connected directly in parallel, with the resulting voltage remaining unchanged. The

Table 13

Feed-point Data for the Two Dipoles of the 40-Meter Versa-Beam Described in the Second Example, with Real Transmission Lines, in the Unidirectional Mode, for an Antenna Power of 1000 W

Elements #1 and #2 (Front and Rear)

$Z_{1dp} = Z_{2dp} = 134.58 + j29.85 = 137.851 \angle 12.506° \, \Omega$

$I_1 = I_2 = 1.9275 \angle 0° \, A$

$V_1 = V_2 - I_1 Z_{1dp} = I_2 Z_{2dp} = 265.707 \angle 12.506°$

$\quad = 259.40 + j57.54 \, V$

$P_1 = P_2 = 500 \, W$

Table 14

Input Data for the Two Belden 9913 Transmission Lines Feeding the 40-Meter Versa-Beam Described in the Second Example, in the Bidirectional Mode, for an Antenna Power of 1000 W

Elements #1 and 2 (Front and Rear)

$Z_{1in} = Z_{2in} = 18.64 - j3.69 = 19.00 \angle -11.21° \, \Omega$

$I_1 = I_2 = 1.17 - j5.34 = 5.47 \angle -77.64° \, A$

$V_1 = V_2 = I_1 Z_{1in} = 103.95 \angle -88.85° = 2.09 - j103.93 \, V$

$P_1 = P_2 = 558 \, W$

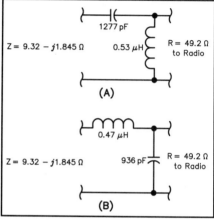

Fig 14—The two possible L-networks we can use for impedance-matching purposes when the input ends of feeders #1 and #2 (Belden 9913 coax) are connected in parallel, for bi-directional (dipole) 40-meter Versa-Beam operation.

Table 15

Input Data for the Two Belden 9913 Transmission Lines Feeding the Dipoles of the 40-Meter Versa-Beam Described in the Second Example, in the Bidirectional Mode, for an Antenna Power of 1000 W, when Both Inputs are Connected in Parallel

Feeders #1 and #2 Joined Together

$Z_{in} = Z_{1in} / 2 = Z_{2in} / 2 = 9.32 - j1.845 \, \Omega$

$I_{in} = I_1 + I_2 = 10.94 \angle -77.64° \, A$

$V_{in} = V_1 = V_2 = 103.95 \angle -88.85° \, V$

$P_{in} = P_1 + P_2 = 1116 \, W$

input impedance will be halved, while the total current and power will double, as displayed in **Table 15**.

Now we can find the component values for the L network needed to match the input impedance shown in Table 15 to 49.198 Ω, using the *Low Band Software* at f = 7.15 MHz. There are just two L-network options and both are shown in **Fig 14**. Let's choose circuit (B) since the component values are smaller. This completes the design of all the required networks for the 40-meter Versa-Beam with non ideal transmission lines.

Conclusion

This paper has described an interesting two-element antenna that can generate either a unidirectional or bidirectional radiation pattern. Examples that incorporate either perfect (lossless) or real (low-loss) transmission lines were included. Methods for determining the driving-point impedances and designing the requisite phasing/matching networks have also been discussed. Although losses in the inductors and capacitors which make up these networks are ignored in the *Low Band Software* computations, any inaccuracies caused by this assumption should be relatively small.

References

[1] Forrest Gehrke, K2BT, published a six-part series of articles entitled "Vertical Phased Arrays" in *Ham Radio*, in the issues dated May, Jun, Jul, Oct, and Dec 1983, and May 1984.

[2] The ON4UN *Low Band Software* is available from George Oliva, K2UO, 5 Windsor Drive, Eatontown, NJ 07724, or from John Devoldere, ON4UN, Poelstraat 215, B9820 Merelbeke, Belgium.

[3] *EZNEC/4* is available from Roy Lewallen, W7EL, PO Box 6658, Beaverton, OR 97007.

[4] *The ARRL Antenna Book*, 18th Edition (Newington: American Radio Relay League, 1997).

[5] *Field and Wave Electromagnetics*, Second Edition, David K. Cheng (New York: Addison-Wesley Publishing Company, 1989).

The Optima 160/80-Meter Receive Antenna

By Richard Q. Marris, G2BZQ
35 Kingswood House
Farnham Road
Slough SL2 1DA
England

Topband and noise are synonymous. As long ago as 1938, *The Admiralty Handbook of Wireless Telegraphy* concisely summarized the situation, stating:

Man-Made Noise — Atmospherics (Statics): It is well known that in spite of perfection in the propagation conditions and at the transmitter, received signals may be almost unintelligible due to noise and static, the various clicks, bangs, rumbles and crashes which often provide the background of the signal. This noise, in general, is classified into "man-made noise" and "statics," and is the noise which may disappear when the aerial is disconnected from the receiver.

Man-made noises may be due to electrical machinery of various kinds, ignition systems of cars, motors, etc.

Statics, or atmospherics, are radio waves produced by natural causes, of definite but very irregular wave form and, generally, of short duration (about 1/500 of a second). The peak voltage produced by a static signal often amounts to as much as 1.5 volts, the energy level becoming very great at the lower radio frequencies, decreasing gradually as the frequency becomes greater, and becoming quite small at VHF. The very complex wave form of an atmospheric makes it equivalent to a very large number of simple sinusoidal wave forms, with the well-known result that statics appear to be untunable noises covering up a wide frequency range.

Over the intervening 60 years, the noise problem has increased, especially in urban areas in which the majority of us live. In 1938 only the minority had cars, TVs and many of the electronic wonders of today. Computers, etc, had not been heard of. Contrast that with the present situation. So *The*

Taking the Big Stick to Topband noise levels

Admiralty Handbook statement still applies—even more so!

It is often forgotten that Topband is in the MF spectrum, and that even the 80-meter band just scrapes into the HF spectrum, which starts at 3 MHz. So high noise levels exist on 80 meters as well.

There are two main ways that noise entering the receiver input has been minimized to improve the signal-to-noise ratio. These are high-selectivity receivers, and the use of various low-noise antennas, such as loops, which also assist in reducing interference from other stations. In most implementations, a loop antenna is a few feet in diameter and located indoors. An untuned loop does not provide much signal, but a tuned, multiturn loop is another story. The enthusiast may then add a preamplifier between the loop and the receiver, overlooking the fact that modern communications receivers have plenty of RF gain. The introduction of a preamplifier may well introduce intermodulation. And, of course, as the signal is amplified, so is the noise, by the same amount.

Small, indoor rotatable loops can either be frame loops or ferrite-core loops. Frame loops can be made either as the well-known box type, or a spiral- or pancake-wound loop. The spiral loop is much more difficult to make, but is capable of very deep nulling

at 90°, if properly designed and constructed. It will outperform the box loop, with which 100% nulling cannot be achieved. Either way, the physical size, and rotation, of a frame loop can be somewhat cumbersome. Also, in some cases, house wiring forms inconvenient loops that can inductively couple into the relatively large frame loop, further degrading antenna performance.

A ferrite-core loop is comparatively small, easy to handle, and can be stored away when not in use. It also has portable uses. The popular way to make a loopstick antenna seems to be to take any old ferrite rod, add some wire turns, add a preamplifier, and hope for the best. There is a better way.

Designing a Ferrite-Core Loop

First, it's necessary to use the correct ferrite material. For 160 and 80 meters, a suitable nickel/zinc material should be used. Experiments with the available materials has narrowed the choice to the Amidon type 61 material,[1] or the MMG (UK) type F14 material.[2] MMG type F16 may be a bit better, but appears to be difficult to obtain.

Experiments I've done over the years have shown that increasing the ferrite rod diameter greatly increases sensitivity. Increased length leads to improvements in both sensitivity and directivity. Combine a large diameter and a long length, and one is well on the way toward producing an effective ferrite receiving antenna.

Suitably long, fat ferrite rods are not readily available, except made to order on a one-off basis, at an astronomical price. What to do? The tried and true Amateur Radio maxim has traditionally been that if you can't buy it, make it!

Designing the Optima 160/80-Meter Loop

The key goal is to incorporate the 160- and 80-meter bands from 1.8 to 4 MHz with some overlap, providing DX reception capability without the use of a preamplifier, and with deep nulls in the pattern for nulling interference and manmade noise.

Fig 1 shows the schematic used by many amateurs for LF, MF and lower-HF reception, often with a preamplifier. The balanced circuit shown in **Fig 2** gives far better nulls on 160 and 80 meters, with more docile handling.

The simple, somewhat unusual, balanced circuit of Fig 3 evolved from much investigation and testing using smaller rods. It consists of an 18-inch-long, 1-inch-diameter rod inside a 1½-inch-OD form. Two coils, L1 and L2, are wound on the form and resonated by a 150-pF variable capacitor, C1. L1 is wound clockwise on the form, and L2 is wound counterclockwise. Their far ends are connected to the copper base plate. The dimension between L1 and L2 is critical. Coil L3 couples the loop to the receiver via 50-Ω coaxial cable. Capacitor C2 allows fine adjustment to the loading on the selected frequency. The chassis plate is not directly grounded; the coaxial feed line is grounded at the receiver.

To achieve maximum performance, there's an air gap between the ferrite core

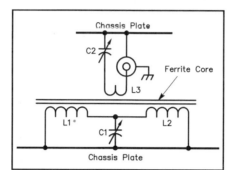

Fig 3—Schematic of the Optima 80/160-meter antenna. The base is a copper-covered plate, over which the entire antenna is mounted. C1, L1 and L2 resonate the antenna at the desired frequency, and the L3/C2 combination allow coupling energy from the loop to the receiver. The core is comprised of four 18-inch-long × ½-inch-diameter ferrite rods, glued together along their lengths to form a fat, 18-inch-long rod over which L1, L2 and L3 are wound.

C1—150-pF variable.
C2—182 pF variable with 410 pF fixed in parallel.
L1—23 turns closewound, clockwise on the core.
L2—23 turns closewound, counter-clockwise on the core.
L3—5 turns closewound at the center of the cardboard form.
See text for wire type used in L1-L3.

and L1, L2 and L3. Spacing between the wire turns is also critical. (See the next section, Construction.) Although the schematic is simple, this antenna provides excellent DX and local performance on both bands with careful construction.

Construction

The Ferrite Core

Four 18-inch-long, ½-inch-diameter ferrite rods are fabricated using Amidon 61-mix ferrite material or MMG F14 material, as shown in **Fig 4A**. After carefully cleaning the rod ends with fine sandpaper, three rods are joined end-to-end using Superglue. This effectively produces one 18-inch-long, ½-inch-diameter rod.

Two 18-inch rods are next adhered side-by-side using superglue. Repeat for the other pair. Once the adhesive has set, the two pairs of rods are then glued together to form a single rod that's 18 inches long and 1 inch square (see Fig 4B). The stage-by-stage Superglue operations must be carried out quickly and carefully, so rehearse the procedures beforehand. With Superglue, you don't get a second chance!

Amidon ½-inch rods made of mix 61 material are available direct from Amidon in small quantities, in 7½-inch and 4-inch lengths. MMG ½-inch-diameter rods are obtainable in 8 and 6-inch lengths. Rods may be cut with a hacksaw to achieve the desired 18-inch length. This could be fabricated, for example, from two 7½-inch rods and one 3-inch rod, sawed from a 4-inch piece.

After winding the coils, insert the rods into an 18-inch-long cardboard tube. I used

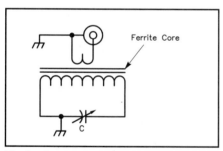

Fig 1—A conventional unbalanced loopstick, often used for VLF/LF/MF (longwave and mediumwave) reception.

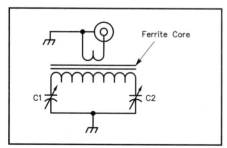

Fig 2—A conventional loopstick antenna is a balanced circuit, with two capacitors resonating the primary loop and no capacitor in the coupling-loop circuit.

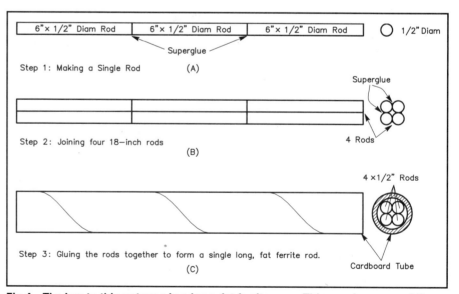

Fig 4—The key to this antenna is a long, fat ferrite core. This requires assembling several pieces of ferrite rod using Superglue into four 18-inch-long rods, then gluing them together to form a single core. The rods are then taped with several layers of wide masking tape to create an interference fit inside a cardboard tube, such as an aluminum-foil tube, over which the coils will be wound.

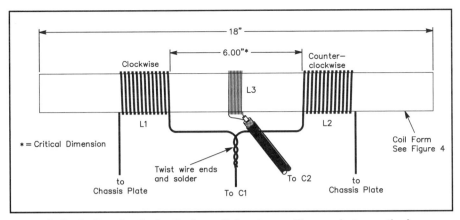

Fig 5—Coil-winding details for the loopstick antenna. The gap between the inner ends of L1 and L2 is critical to antenna operation. The inner ends of L1 and L2 are twisted and soldered together tightly against the coil form, then a single lead is carried from that point to C1. The ends of L3 are twisted together and carried to C2 over the shortest possible distance. The outer ends of L1 and L2 are dropped directly to the copper-covered base and soldered to it. The wire turns are secured to the form using Superglue.

a kitchen-foil tube, varnished before use to make it more durable. Wind three bands of wide masking tape on the 18-inch core to make it a snug fit into the cardboard tubing.

Coil Winding

Fig 5 shows the coil-winding detail. I used PVC-insulated #24 stranded-copper hookup wire with a 2.05-mm ($^5/_{64}$-inch) outer diameter. This provides an easy-to-wind, thick wire with appropriate spacing when closewound on the form.

First, wind L3 (five turns, closewound) on the center of the cardboard tubing, with tails about 12 inches long. Sleeve the long wires and glue the turns to the core with superglue. L1 and L2 are wound to a critical dimension of 6 inches apart, evenly spaced from L3. L1 is 23 turns wound closewound clockwise on the core, and terminated with a 4-inch tail.

L2 is also 23 closewound turns, but *counter-clockwise* on the core. Solder the adjacent (inner) ends of L1 and L2 are together to form a short tail for attachment. Glue the turns of these coils to the core using superglue.

The Chassis

The chassis is made of a $24 \times 4 \times ^1/_2$-inch baseboard (see **Fig 6**). This is faced with $3 \times 8 \times 4$-inch copper-clad PC boards, with the copper-clad side upward, and tacked on (end-to-end) with small wire nails. The two mating copper seams are soldered together. Copper flashing or tape could also be used to face the board, if available.

Next, two pieces of $5 \times 1^3/_4 \times ^1/_2$-inch pieces of wood are mounted vertically using metal brackets, also shown in Fig 6. The coil assembly fits between these two boards and is secured with short dowels, also as shown in Fig 6.

Resonating variable capacitor C1 has a rigid metal frame, ceramic insulated, bracketed to the chassis plate as shown in Fig 6. I used a Jackson type E 150-pF variable capacitor. C1 is fitted with an insulated extension shaft and vernier drive to allow small adjustment and marking positions for different frequencies.

The variable loading capacitor has 592 pF total capacitance (182 + 410 pF in parallel).

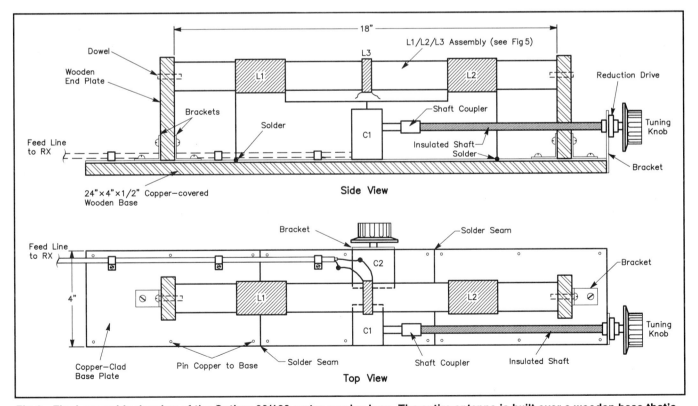

Fig 6—Final assembly drawing of the Optima 80/160-meter receive loop. The entire antenna is built over a wooden base that's covered with copper foil or unetched PC-board material, copper face up. Two end pieces secure the loop above the ground plane, where wooden dowels hold them in place. Mechanically, this antenna is a bit more complex than it is electrically, but it's still a project you can build in a weekend. Feel free to improvise on the mounting arrangement, as most dimensions aren't critical. Use wood, rather than metal, where indicated; it allows the antenna to function properly.

Any capacitance between 500 and 600 pF would do. This is bracketed to the chassis board as shown in Fig 6.

Wiring

Don't rely on mechanical joints—solder all the wire connections. Drop the outer ends of L1 and L2 directly to the chassis plate and solder them to it. The lead from the stator of C1 is soldered to the junction of the adjacent wires of L1 and L2. Solder the rotor connection to the chassis plate. The ends of coupling coil L2 go to C2 and to the coaxial feed line, respectively. The RG-58 feed line should be kept as short as possible, and routed from the L2/C2 connection along the chassis plate with cable clips.

Operation and Results

Initially set coupling capacitor C2 to about 30% meshed and bring C1 to resonance, which is indicated by a substantial increase in signal strength. Select a weak signal on the 160-meter band and adjust C2 slowly for maximum signal. As the signal gradually peaks, the bandwidth narrows. Overcoupling is indicated by widening bandwidth and a weakening signal.

The antenna is directional, especially on groundwave signals, which encompass most manmade noise and atmospherics, plus groundwave QRM. On skywave signals, the directivity is not so pronounced and appears to depend on the angle at which the signal arrives. This is more pronounced on 80 meters than on 160. Rotate the antenna to null the noise or QRM and peak the signal-to-noise ratio on the desired signal. Although the primary target for this design was low-noise DX reception on 160-meter CW, DX reception on 80 meters turns out to be most satisfactory also. I found a preamplifier unnecessary, even on weak signals. In fact, when I tried one, the result was receiver overload and intermodulation—the preamp did more harm than good.

The results I've obtained on 160 meters have been quite excellent, with transatlantic signals being received comfortably above the noise level. Rotational adjustment of the loop usually allows separating the DX signals from much of the band noise in the busy urban environment where I live.

Conclusion

This small antenna is just one of a long series of such devices that I've built, and confirms that the use of a long, fat ferrite core can pay substantial dividends with effective DX signal strengths, and much lower noise levels at MF and lower HF frequencies, than most other practical, compact, low-noise designs.

Notes
[1] Amidon, Inc, PO Box 25867, Santa Ana, CA 92799. Amidon offers fast delivery of 61-material rods in small quantities.
[2] MMG North America, 126 Pennsylvania Ave, Paterson, NJ 07503. MMG-Neosid, Icknield Way West, Letchworth, SG6 4AS, Herts, England.

A Matching Technique for Optimized, Broadband Yagi Antennas with Direct Coax Feed

By Bernd W. von Bojan, DJ7YE
Schwerzfelder Strasse 56A
52159 Roetgen
Germany

The 10-meter band, the highest and largest HF ham band (28-29.7 MHz), has a bandwidth of nearly 6%. Many commercial antenna producers are deterred by this fact and therefore divide it into lower (typically 28.0-28.8 MHz) and upper portions (28.8-29.7 MHz). This cleverly avoids many problems; the narrower the band, the simpler the antenna design. The ideal antenna would be capable of covering the complete 10-meter band with low SWR, constant forward gain, and the greatest possible F/B ratio. Furthermore, many DXers prefer a high F/B ratio to maximum forward gain, because of the better signal-to-noise ratio—the most unidirectional signal reception.

The ideal antenna's load impedance would be matched to 50-Ω coaxial cable via a simple and nearly lossless matching device to achieve an SWR at band center of 1:1, and not higher than 1.5:1 at both band edges. The free-space pattern of this idealized antenna would be free of side lobes and asymmetry. The load impedance over the whole band should result in a smoothly U-shaped, symmetrical SWR curve.

Modeling a 10-Meter, 6-Element Broadband Beam

Choosing the Characteristic Parameters

Now, let's model a beam having the above design goals in terms of the following characteristic parameters in free space:

1. Nearly constant forward gain from 28.0 to 29.7 MHz
2. Front-to-back ratio better than 20 dB
3. Boom length: 6 meters, maximum
4. Number of elements: Six (initially)
5. A clean free-space pattern
6. A smoothly varying input impedance over

Do you want high front-to-back ratio and low SWR? DJ7YE describes an unusual broadband 10-meter antenna and describes a new Yagi matching system

frequency, and low SWR
7. SWR less than 1.5:1 over the entire band for direct 50-Ω feed without the use of conventional matching devices
8. The array's weight and wind load should also be within reasonable boundaries.

Narrowband versus Broadband Performance

The US National Bureau of Standards' comprehensive research of optimized Yagi antennas with boom lengths from 0.4 to 4.2 λ yielded gain values from 7.1 to 14.2 dBd.[2] For four elements and a 0.6 λ boom, a gain of 8.1 dBd is obtained, from which follows 10.24 dBi for a gain-optimized antenna in free space. The best front-to-back ratio may be somewhere in the band at 25 to 30 dB. In many designs, these values occur only at a single frequency or a relatively small range of frequencies. In other words, the F/B undergoes an inverse U-shaped curve and rapidly drops when leaving the top toward the band edges.

Keep in mind that the optimized data are valid for at least a single frequency, but my effort is focused on modeling broadband, highest-possible F/B, lowest-possible SWR antennas over the *complete* band. Physics dictates that to this end, a certain amount of gain has to be sacrificed. Later we'll see that the gain degradation is smaller than expected, and as a result of the F/B optimizing process, the gain obtained will be "automatically" good.

The Concept of Antenna Synthesis

In selecting the boom length, the basic conditions for the layout are given. The DJ7YE antenna concept is based on the following ideas:

1. The antenna is to be built and gradually enlarged according to a modular design principle. First, the front portion will be calculated (consisting of Driven Element and three Directors) by the formulas in **Fig 1**.
2. The front part can be regarded as a complete antenna by itself. In dimensioning the front part, I have developed a logarithmic configuration according to the formula in Fig 1.
3. Next, the first Reflector will be added to

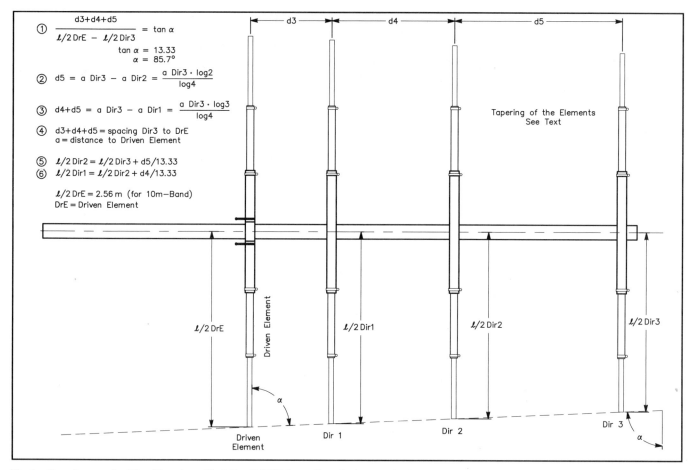

Fig 1—Development of the "front part" of the DJ7YE broadband antenna for boom lengths between 4.5 and 6 meters.

improve the directive pattern. Then, when a second Reflector is added, the front-to-back improves. For the rest, the antenna is optimized by a seventh element designed to closely interact with the driven element. This will give a broadband 50-Ω match.

According to NBS measurements, the optimum spacing between Reflector 1 (outer reflector) and the Driven Element is 0.2 λ. This means that, for a 6-meter boom length (by subtracting 0.2 λ, or 2 meters), 4 meters will remain for the front part, where the Driven Element and three Directors must be placed.

Fig 1 gives my formulas for calculating the element spacings and lengths. The angle α = 87.5°, determined by experiment, indicates how to shorten the elements proceeding from the Driven Element in the direction of Director 3. These formulas are valid for boom lengths from 4.5 to 6 meters at 28 MHz.

Half the length of the Driven Element (DE ℓ/2) is calculated by the following formula:

DE $\ell/2$ [m] = 1/4 × 300 × 0.985/midband freq (MHz) = 73.875/midband freq (MHz)

For 10 meters:

DE $\ell/2$ [m] = 73.875/28.85 = 2.56 meters

EZNEC calculations show that the length of Director 1 is comparatively critical. This element, together with the driven element, sees relatively high currents. For optimizing the antenna over the entire band, the element will have to be shortened by 1.6 %:

ℓ dir 1 = 5.00 meters − 1.6% = 4.92 meters

and $\ell/2$ dir 1 = 2.46 meters

Reflector 1 is mounted on the boom 2 meters behind the Driven Element. Its length comes from *EZNEC* simulation. Best performance occurs when the Reflector is 8% longer than the Driven Element.

Realizing 20 dB or Better Front-to-Back Ratio

For best F/B, a second Reflector (Reflector 2) is added between Reflector 1 and the Driven Element. The spacing between Reflector 2 and Driven Element is determined by *EZNEC*. For the 10-meter band, the spacing is between 0.75 and 0.80 meters for maximum F/B ratio (0.074 λ at 29.7 MHz). Although Reflector 2 considerably ameliorates front-to-back, it lowers the antenna's impedance, degrading the match to a 50-Ω feed line. However, this can be rectified by the matching technique I'll describe later.

The closer Reflector 2 approaches the Driven Element, the smaller the load impedance (at 0.75 meters on 10 meters, Z = 14 to 22 Ω). Then, the optimal length for Reflector 2 is found by *EZNEC*. Its half-length amounts to 2.71 meters (0.268 λ at 29.7 MHz).

Element Diameter

Each element has three taper diameters. The center (boom-connected) segment, 20 mm, is followed by two segments of 16 mm, joined by the outer sections telescoped to 13 mm diameter on either side. Other combinations are possible, but should be verified using *EZNEC*.

Fig 1 through **Fig 7** and **Tables 1** through **5** show some modeling results and demonstrate how the author's broadband Yagi comes into being.

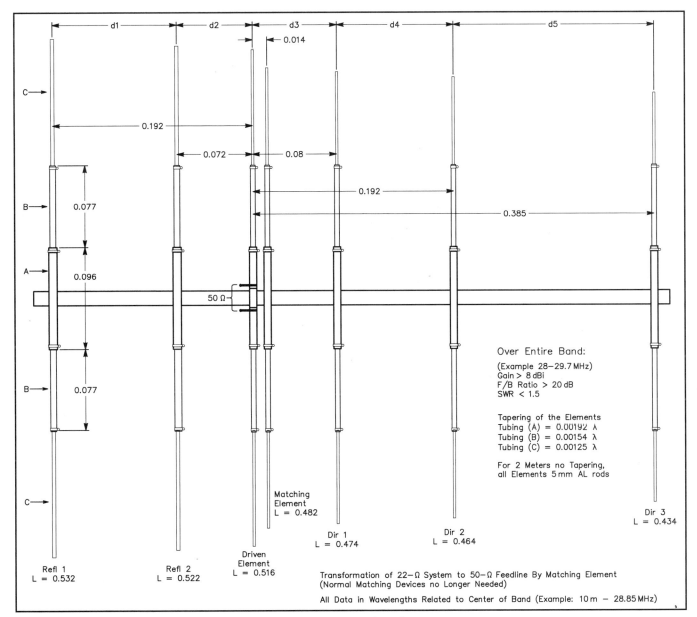

Fig 2—Six-element broadband Yagi with matching element for 50-Ω feed line.

ELECTRICAL DESIGN DETAILS

The BEAMTIME matching method: Broadband Easy Antenna Matching through Transformed Impedance by a Matching Element

I have found an easy method of bypassing the mostly tiresome procedure of connecting Yagi-type antennas to 50-Ω or 75-Ω coaxial cable. This method eliminates conventional matching devices—as well as tuner, choke and balun! Of course, ferrite beads may be used to avoid potential imbalance currents on the outer coax shielding,

Table 1

Element Lengths and Diameters of the Six-Element DJ7YE Beam with 9.1 dBi Average Gain and > 20 dB F/B Over the 10-Meter Band

Element	Length (mm)	Element-Diameter Tapering (mm)
Reflector 1	5520	20/16/13
Reflector 2	5420	20/16/13
Driven Element	5120	20/16/13
Director 1	4920	20/16/13
Director 2	4820	20/16/13
Director 3	4520	20/16/13

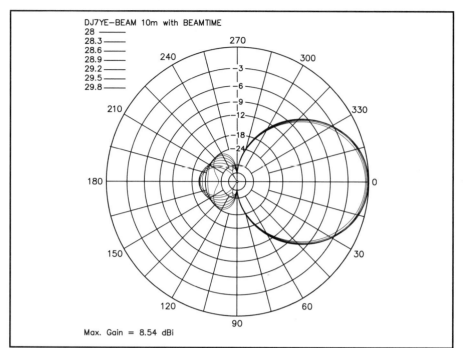

Fig 3—Seven-element DJ7YE beam with 6-meter boom; superimposed radiation patterns for the frequency range between 28.0 and 29.7 MHz (E-plane).

Table 2

Element Spacings and Taper for the Six-Element DJ7YE Beam with 9.1 dBi Average Gain and > 20 dB F/B Over the 10-Meter Band

Element Spacings and Tapering (λ at 28.85 MHz)	Tapered Element Diameters (mm)	
1.92×10^{-3}/ 1.54×10^{-3}/ 1.25×10^{-3}	20/16/13	
Spacings		
Elements	(λ at 28.85 MHz)	(mm)
Spacing Reflector 1 – Driven Element	0.192	2000
Spacing Reflector 2 – Driven Element	0.072	750
Spacing Director 1 – Driven Element	0.080	830
Spacing director 2 – Driven Element	0.192	2000
Spacing director 3 – Driven Element	0.385	4000
Total Boom Length	0.577	6000

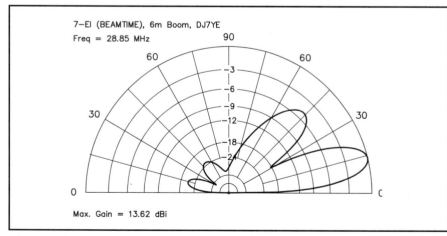

Fig 4—Elevation-plane radiation pattern of the seven-element DJ7YE beam with 6-meter boom at 10 meters above real ground (f = 28.85 MHz, calculated with *EZNEC*).

but no other method of traditional matching is required with this design method.

Adding a Seventh Element to Improve Impedance Matching

BEAMTIME raises the load impedance to the characteristic feed line impedance of 50 Ω, which is normally achieved by a matching device. The concept is to add a seventh element closely placed in front of the Driven Element, in the direction of radiation. In a particular configuration, this element performs like an upward-transformer, transforming the low impedance of about 22 Ω up to 50 Ω. Defining the length of the matching element and its location on the boom may turn out to be rather complicated, as it depends on many parameters. Furthermore, this Matching Element exerts an immediate influence on the length of the Driven Element; these two elements form a subsystem because of their interaction, and also give feedback to the rest of the antenna's elements. Once the matching dimensions are found, however, matching in its conventional sense is superfluous.

The Driven-Element length turns out to be longer than normal, and the Matching Element somewhat shorter. The Matching Element may have quite different distances from the Driven Element, depending on how the antenna is constructed.

Remodeling a Six-Element Beam Into a Seven-Element Beam

Remodeling the antenna with the Matching Element creates a seven-element Yagi with an SWR of 1.5:1 or less across the band. It is possible to bring the SWR down to 1.2:1. This great advantage results in a slight loss of forward gain, as is the case in any design optimized for wide SWR and gain bandwidths and constant F/B ratio across a large frequency span.

Adjustment of Driven and Matching Elements

First, the Driven Element was lengthened by 12 cm from its original length of 2.56 meters, to 2.68 meters per half-element. This Driven-Element length, as well as the distance of the Matching Element and its length, was remodeled by *EZNEC* simulation. Distances between 9 and 22 cm were tested more minutely. Ten cm ahead of the driven element proved optimal, but the gain went down to 7.68 dBi. A good compromise spacing is 15 cm, with the length of the Matching Element being 2.50 meters per leg. At this length the SWR dropped to 1.45:1 at 28 MHz and 1.4:1 at 29.7 MHz. In between, a broad minimum of 1.1:1 to 1.2:1 occurs.

At its center, the Matching Element should be mechanically and electrically connected to the boom. It is fastened to the

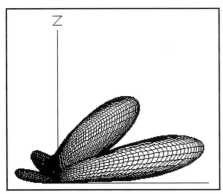

Fig 5—Three-dimensional radiation pattern of the seven-element DJ7YE beam with 6-meter boom (10 m above real ground, at 28.85 MHz, calculated with *EZNEC*).

Table 3

Computer-Modeled Performance of the Seven-Element DJ7YE Beam Designed Using BEAMTIME, with 8.3 dBi Average Gain, > 20 dB F/B, and < 1.5:1 SWR across the 10-Meter Band. All data for free space were calculated using EZNEC antenna software by W7EL.

Frequency (MHz)	Gain (dBi)	F/B (dB)	B/W (°)	SWR (50 Ω)	Impedance Z = R + j X Ω
28.000	8.16	21.38	60.8	1.45	36.62 − j 8.81
28.100	8.20	21.30	60.6	1.34	40.13 − j 8.52
28.200	8.24	21.22	60.4	1.26	42.88 − j 7.80
28.300	8.28	21.15	60.2	1.20	44.88 − j 6.86
28.400	8.31	21.09	60.0	1.16	46.17 − j 5.87
28.500	8.34	21.06	59.8	1.13	46.85 − j 4.97
28.600	8.36	21.06	59.6	1.11	47.02 − j 4.27
28.700	8.38	21.10	59.4	1.11	46.81 − j 3.82
28.800	8.39	21.21	59.2	1.11	46.33 − j 3.65
28.900	8.40	21.38	59.0	1.13	45.71 − j 3.71
29.000	8.41	21.63	58.8	1.14	45.04 − j 3.97
29.100	8.40	21.98	58.6	1.16	44.40 − j 4.32
29.200	8.39	22.45	58.4	1.18	43.80 − j 4.61
29.300	8.36	23.07	58.2	1.19	43.21 − j 4.69
29.400	8.32	23.88	58.0	1.21	42.47 − j 4.38
29.500	8.27	24.95	57.8	1.23	41.28 − j 3.59
29.600	8.19	26.39	57.6	1.28	39.22 − j 2.39
29.700	8.08	28.42	57.4	1.40	35.89 − j 1.26

Table 4

Element Spacings and Tapering for Seven-Element DJ7YE Beam Designed with BEAMTIME, Average Gain of 8.3 dBi, > 20 dB F/B and < 1.5:1 SWR over the 10-Meter Band for Direct 50-Ω Feed. (The seventh element is a matching element.)

Spacing and Tapering
Tapered Element Diameters

(λ at 28.85 MHz)	(mm)
1.92 × 10⁻³/ 1.54× 10⁻³/ 1.25 × 10⁻³	20/16/13

Spacings

Elements	(λ at 28.85 MHz)	(mm)
Spacing Reflector 1 – Driven Element	0.192	2000
Spacing Reflector 2 – Driven Element	0.072	750
Spacing Matching Element – Driven Element	0.014	150
Spacing Director 1 – Driven Element	0.080	830
Spacing Director 2 – Driven Element	0.192	2000
Spacing Director 3 – Driven Element	0.385	4000
Total Boom length	0.577	6000

Driven Element by plastic spacers to secure electrical conditions.

By the way, whether it's possible to avoid the small decrease in gain caused by the Matching Element by using other matching variants is open to question. There possibly are higher losses caused by symptoms of aging (corrosion, poor connections, detuning, etc) in mechanically complicated devices in comparison to the very simple BEAMTIME installation. Beyond that, such an easy, simple matching system would be hard to achieve otherwise. It is also well known that a "normal" matching device (ie, a gamma match) may deteriorate the antenna's radiation pattern.

Optimized Results after Application of BEAMTIME

By optimizing with BEAMTIME we get the values shown in **Table 3** and Fig 3 through Fig 5. **Fig 3** shows superimposed radiation patterns over the 10-meter band, and at a glance you may talk of an ideal diagram showing at least what has to be expected of such an antenna. Now let's have a look at the vertical radiation pattern over real ground (**Fig 4**). The main lobe has more than 14 dBi gain due to the reflections (losses are not taken into account). **Fig 5** shows the 3-D radiation pattern.

DESIGN DISCUSSION
Performance of the DJ7YE Beam

The NBS Yagi with a 1.2 λ boom and six elements delivers 12.4 dBi gain, when gain-optimized. If a double effective aperture led to a gain growth of 3 dB, theoretically hardly anything would be given away by optimizing the introduced broadband antenna matching system in having achieved 9.1 dBi in free space, along with wideband, high F/B as well as direct 50-Ω coax feed.

With regard to the forward gain degradation of 2 dB, we may speak of an obvious sacrifice of gain, of which the experts say it is to be hardly distinguished with one's ears.

What about Front-to-Back Ratio?

The diagrams in the figures clearly show well-suppressed back lobes. There are also no side lobes to be detected. The given F/B in Table 3 at 180° is still rising in direction 90° and 270° in the first half of the band, whereupon the calculated values are minimal. In the upper band portion, the back lobe, where F/B at 180° reaches 28 dB, flattens slightly and results in a small decrease of F/B at 130° and 230° off the main beam to 22.6 dB (at 29.7 MHz). The 3-dB beamwidth of radiation lies between 60.8° and 57.4°.

What Does Reflector 1 Contribute?

Reflector 1, being placed at the end of the antenna, principally has only the function of providing the desired F/B ratio at the low end of the band. Its contribution is about 1 to 2 dB. At 29.3 to 29.4 MHz, the 20 dB F/B goal is achieved without Reflector 1; however, with Reflector 1, the F/B is raised by about 3 dB in this region. At 29.7 MHz, the F/B improvement attributable to Reflector 1 is 3.8 dB. The existing high F/B of

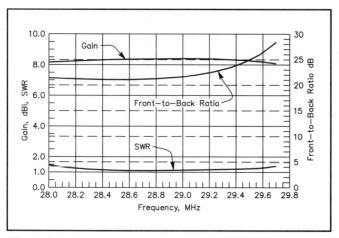

Fig 6—Gain, front-to-back ratio and SWR of the DJ7YE beam with broadband matching for 50 Ω, performed with transformed impedance by a matching element (BEAMTIME).

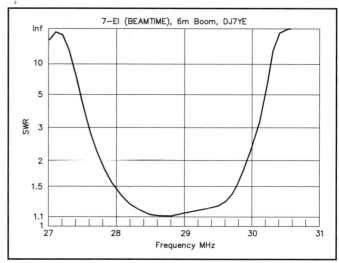

Fig 7—Bandpass characteristics of the DJ7YE beam incorporating BEAMTIME in the frequency range between 27 MHz and 31 MHz. (For antenna dimensions, see Tables 4 and 5.)

Table 5

Seven-Element DJ7YE Beam with BEAMTIME, Constant 8.3 dBi average gain, > 20 dB F/B and < 1.5:1 SWR Over the 10-Meter Band, with a 50-Ω Feeder

Element	Length (mm)	Element Diameter Tapering (mm)
Reflector 1	2 × 2760	20/16/13
Reflector 2	2 × 2710	20/16/13
Driven Element	2 × 2680	20/16/13
Matching Element	2 × 2500	20/16/13
Director 1	2 × 2460	20/16/13
Director 2	2 × 2410	20/16/13
Director 3	2 × 2260	20/16/13

Driven Element is separated in the center.

Table 6

Seven-Element DJ7YE Beam with Constant Gain for 140 to 147 MHz with F/B > 20 dB at an SWR < 1.5:1 over the Entire Band, 50-Ω Feeder

Element	Length (mm)	Element Diameter (mm)
Reflector 1	2 × 540 (540)	5
Reflector 2	2 × 530 (531)	5
Driven Element	2 × 520 (525)	5
Matching Element	2 × 480 (490)	5
Director 1	2 × 480 (482)	5
Director 2	2 × 470 (471)	5
Director 3	2 × 440 (442)	5

Data optimal for 144 to 146 MHz at maximum SWR of 1.15. Data in parentheses are optimal for 140 to 147 MHz at SWR <1.5:1. The center of Driven Element is open.

24 dB at the high edge rises above 28 dB. Therefore, Reflector 1 may be dispensable, but is certainly not useless. For amateurs limited in space, the short-boom version (4.75 meters) without Reflector 1 may be a good solution.

DATA AND INFORMATION FOR ASSEMBLY

Features of High-Performance Antenna Design

One of the most interesting results of computer simulation and optimization of high-performance Yagi antennas with four or more elements is manifested in the continuing, familiar patterns of element distribution on the boom. These patterns are relatively independent of the boom length, concerning the Reflector, Driven Element, and first Director. In every optimized antenna design, these elements are closely placed, taking not more than about 0.15 to 0.2 λ.[9]

My concept of antenna design has likewise considered the center piece consisting of Reflector 2, Driven Element, and Director 1, with a matching element needing not more than 0.15 λ extension to the boom. The spacing is rather critical.

EXPERIMENTS

Scaling the 10-Meter Model to 2 Meters

The antenna dimensions were scaled to 2 meters for testing. This was done with the rescaling function of *EZNEC,* which automatically scales the antenna to a new frequency, while the antenna dimensions—in wavelengths—are maintained.

Tables 6 and **7** show the adapted data being a proportional reduction of the

Table 7

Seven-Element DJ7YE Beam with Constant Gain for 140 to 147 MHz with > 20 dB F/B and < 1.5:1 SWR over the Entire Band, for a 50-Ω Feeder

Spacing Reflector 1 – Driven Element	390 mm (390)
Spacing Reflector 2 – Driven Element	150 mm (147)
Spacing, Matching–Element to Driven Element	17 mm – 20 mm (29)
Spacing Director 1 – Driven Element	160 mm (163)
Spacing Director 2 – Driven Element	390 mm (390)
Spacing Director 3 – Driven Element	790 mm (784)
Total Boom Length	1180 mm (1174)

Design is optimized for 144 to 146 MHz. Data in parentheses is optimized for 140 to 147 MHz.

Table 8
PV4 Original Design

Element	Spacing (λ)	Spacing (mm)	Length (λ)	Length (mm)
Reflector	0	0	2 × 0.254	2 × 5362
Driven	0.124	2618	2 × 0.238	2 × 5025
Director 1	0.324	6840	2 × 0.233	2 × 4919
Director 2	0.574	12,118	2 × 0.224	2 × 4729

PV4 Modified by BEAMTIME for 50-Ω Matching

Element	Spacing (λ)	Spacing (mm)	Length (λ)	Length (mm)
Reflector	0	0	2 × 0.254	2 × 5362
Driven	0.124	2618	2 × 0.248	2 × 5241
Matching Element	0.151-0.16	3188-3378	2 × 0.236	2 × 4991
Director 1	0.324	6840	2 × 0.233	2 × 4919
Director 2	0.574	12,118	2 × 0.224	2 × 4729

	Driven Element Length (m)	Matching Element Length (m)	Matching Element Spacing (mm)
Variant 1	2 × 5.24	2 × 4.99	570
Variant 2	2 × 5.25	2 × 5.00	670
Variant 3	2 × 5.24	2 × 4.99	760

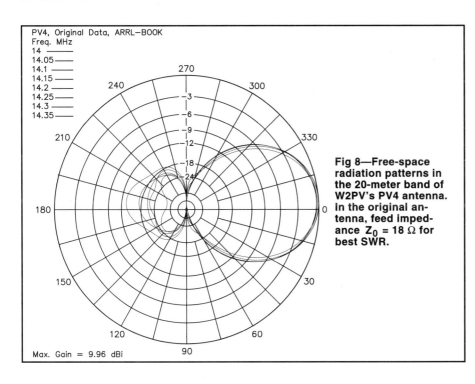

PV4, Original Data, ARRL–BOOK
Freq. MHz
14
14.05
14.1
14.15
14.2
14.25
14.3
14.35

Max. Gain = 9.96 dBi

Fig 8—Free-space radiation patterns in the 20-meter band of W2PV's PV4 antenna. In the original antenna, feed impedance $Z_0 = 18\ \Omega$ for best SWR.

10-meter, seven-element antenna using monotaper aluminum rods of 5 mm diameter for all elements. The length of the 1-inch aluminum boom is 1.3 meters.

Building and Evaluating the 2-Meter Model

After completing the modeling exercise, I set to work constructing the small, handy and compact 2-meter beam. The beam was tested in a slightly sloped meadow with the antenna completely free-standing on a wooden pole, at 2 meters above ground. Besides a problem with a 6-turn choke balun (10 cm in diameter, fastened under the boom) causing interactions with the radiating system, there were no other difficulties to overcome. During the test series with DJ2JO (far field measurements), I found no departure from the modeling predictions. RG-58 coax was connected directly to the driven element.

Impedance and SWR measurements (made using an MFJ 259 analyzer) at the input and load ends of the coax confirmed the desired 50 Ω impedance and an almost constant SWR (from 144-146 MHz) of 1.35:1. A large decrease in F/B occurred outside the given boundary frequencies (140 and 150 MHz), farther off these frequencies accompanied by a dramatic increase of backward radiation—proof of the antenna's band-pass characteristic. The calculated F/B of more than 20 dB was confirmed. Simple comparative gain measurements with the beam and a half-wave reference dipole at the testing site (both antennas same height) and a receiver with a calibrated S meter at DJ2JO's home 10 miles off the beam, showed a difference in signal strength of at least 6 dB. The values given in brackets in Tables 6 and 7 give a somewhat better gain and higher F/B (0.6 dB maximum).

Later, I built the full-scale 10-meter version and am very pleased to report that it worked exactly as computed.

MODELING OF OTHER WELL-KNOWN ANTENNAS WITH BEAMTIME

BEAMTIME with W2PV's PV4

To demonstrate the general function of BEAMTIME, let's equip the famous W2PV antenna described in *The ARRL Antenna Book*[1] with BEAMTIME and compare it with the original version. **Fig 8** and **Fig 9** show the matching effect of BEAMTIME by comparison to the original. Not only is an almost perfect 50-Ω match possible, but also an amelioration of the radiation pattern. An example in **Fig 10** shows how BEAMTIME can be used by other existing antenna systems (here "PV4").

In **Table 8,** three variants indicate how to realize a 50-Ω match. The largest bandwidth

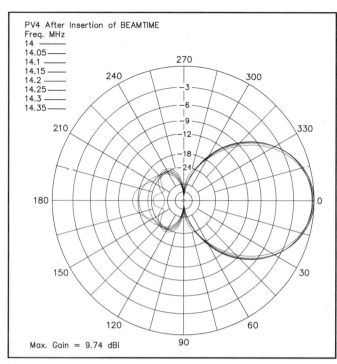

Fig 9—Free-space radiation patterns in the 20-meter band of W2PV's PV4 antenna after modification and application of BEAMTIME for 50-Ω matching. Also see Table 8.

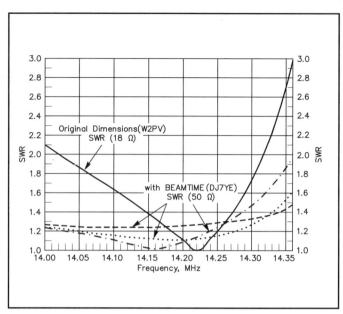

Fig 10—SWR of W2PV's PV4 antenna without matching (Z₀ = 18 Ω) and with broadband matching performed by transformed impedance with a matching element (BEAMTIME, Z₀ = 50 Ω); variants 1, 2 and 3 shown (see Table 8).

is achieved by variant 3, while the SWR rises to 1.3:1 on an average. By using BEAMTIME, the antenna gain generally decreases 0.1 to 0.2 dB at most. With variant 3, however, gain increases by a minuscule 0.01 dB at 14.35 MHz, and F/B rises 3 dB with variant 3 at 14.35 MHz.

As the data from Fig 8 and Fig 9 show, the driven element has to be lengthened by 0.01 λ per end (with respect to the original dimensions) to get a perfect match. The matching element is shortened by 0.012 λ per end in proportion to the lengthened driven element. Optimal performance can be achieved with spacings of 0.027 to 0.036 λ.

Summary and Final Remarks

Reliable antenna optimization is possible by utilizing PC antenna-analysis programs like *EZNEC*. An antenna optimized for high front-to-back ratio and low SWR over a wide range can also be designed. The gain sacrificed in the optimization process is relatively small.

BEAMTIME, a new broadband matching system with an additional element and direct 50-Ω coax feed, renders all other matching methods superfluous. BEAMTIME not only lowers SWR and creates broadband characteristics, but also improves radiation patterns. BEAMTIME can be incorporated into all existing Yagis. This new type of matching should be applicable to other antenna systems as well.

Acknowledgments

Thanks to Roy Lewallen, W7EL, for his excellent antenna-analysis PC software, *EZNEC*. Also thanks to Heinz Schifferdecker, DL7AC (SK), who helped measure the antenna impedances. Special gratitude to my old friend Ferd, DJ2JO, who translated this text to English, for his persevering assistance with the test series in the open and far-field measurements. Last but not least, thanks to Dean Straw, N6BV, who kindly checked my design using *EZNEC pro*, which uses the *NEC 4.1* core code.

Notes

1 *EZNEC* antenna software is available from Roy Lewallen, W7EL, PO Box 6658, Beaverton OR 97007; *w7el@ teleport.com.*

2 National Bureau of Standards Technical Note 688 (Boulder, CO: National Institute of Standards and Technology [formerly NBS]).

3 Professor Hidetsugu Yagi, *Proceedings of the IRE,* Vol. 16, "Beam Transmission of Ultra Short Waves," 1928.

4 J. Hall, Ed., *The ARRL Antenna Book,* 14th Edition (Newington: ARRL, 1984).

5 J. Hall, Ed., *The ARRL Antenna Book,* 16th Edition (Newington: ARRL, 1993).

6 M. Wilson, Ed., *The 1985 ARRL Handbook* (Newington: ARRL, 1984).

7 R. Schetgen, Ed., *The 1998 ARRL Handbook* (Newington: ARRL, 1997).

8 W. Maxwell, "Another Look at Reflections," *QST,* Apr, Jun, Aug and Oct 1973, Apr and Dec 1974, and Aug 1976.

9 R. D. Straw, Ed., *The ARRL Antenna Book,* 18th Edition (Newington: ARRL, 1997), chapter 11.7, Optimum Designs and Element Spacing.

Skywave Antenna Measurements

By Jack Kuecken, KE2QJ
2 Round Trail Drive
Pittsford, NY 14543

This paper describes a system of measurement that allows you to make a realistic evaluation of antenna performance.

Antenna gain measurement are usually made by comparing the signal from an antenna under test with that from a standard, or reference, antenna.[1,2] At microwave frequencies with wavelengths of centimeters or tens of centimeters it is easy to establish a path with many wavelengths' clearance from interfering objects. On line-of-sight paths, signals do not vary for hours at a time.

At VHF, where wavelengths are a meter or more, the antennas are larger and more clumsy. "Flashlight" beams that clear obstacles by many wavelengths are more difficult to achieve, and movement of objects behind or beside the antennas affects the received signal strength. The condition where more than one path exists between transmitter and receiver is called *multipath* propagation. If the effective length of one or more of the paths changes, the signals will tend to either reinforce or cancel each other. If the two signals are equal in strength they can shift from doubling the received voltage to completely cancelling it, depending on the phase difference between the signals.

On the standard broadcast band at night, stations at moderate distance will often undergo a shift from very strong to very weak in just a few seconds, cycling back and forth. This is caused by the interference between the ground wave and the sky wave. For that reason, at wavelengths longer than about 250 meters (frequencies below 1200 kHz), it is common to use antennas approximately 0.53λ in height to suppress the skywave and enhance the groundwave.

At wavelengths shorter than 160 meters, the ground wave attenuation is so large that this effect is seldom noted more than a few miles from the station. Rapid cyclic fading experienced on the HF bands is more generally due to multipath skywave propagation and polarization rotation caused by the waves passing through the ionosphere (a magnetized and ionized medium).

The HF bands are seldom as steady as

line-of-sight microwave signal paths. A short-range HF line-of-sight measurement can probably be made repeatable, subject to the movements of objects around the antenna and adjacent to the path. However, it is not very informative since it is necessarily made at a low angle, whereas the skywave path takes place at a relatively high angle and the return to Earth is also at some high angle.

Fig 1 shows that for ranges less than about

350 miles the launch angles are all above 45° for F_2 propagation.[3] Propagation on short-to-medium-range paths is frequently referred to as near-vertical-incidence (NVI) propagation. Because jungle or wooded terrain severely limits the range of ground-wave HF or line-of-sight VHF communications, this NVI propagation is widely used.[4] Hams have taken advantage of this mode for medium-range communications for years without calling it anything special.

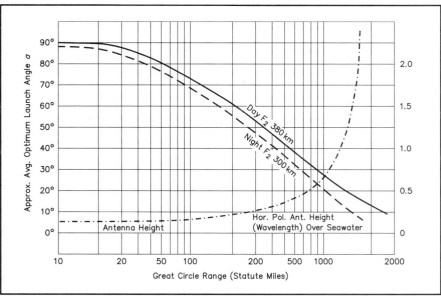

Fig 1—Optimum launch angle as a function of range for the F2 layer.

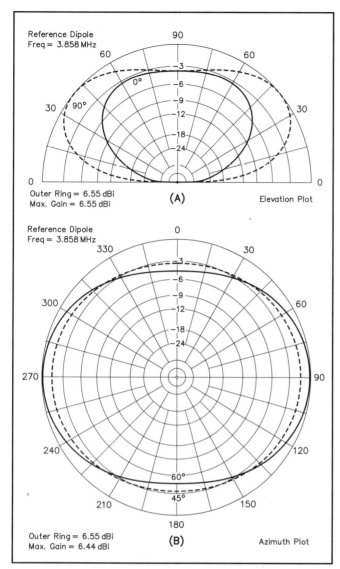

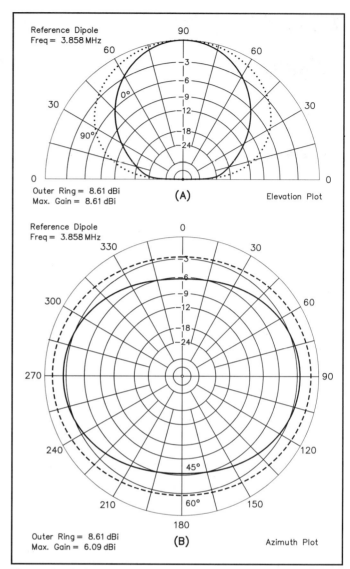

Fig 2—Radiation patterns for an 80-meter dipole installed 95.6 feet above real earth. At A, the vertical plane patterns. The solid line (marked 0°) is in the plane containing the dipole. The dotted line (marked 90°) is in the plane perpendicular to the dipole. At B, azimuthal patterns at elevation angles of 60° and 45°.

Fig 3— Radiation patterns for an 80-meter dipole installed 26 feet above real earth. At A, the vertical plane patterns. The solid line (marked 0°) is in the plane containing the dipole. The dotted line (marked 90°) is in the plane perpendicular to the dipole. At B, azimuthal patterns at elevation angles of 60° and 45°.

For HF measurements a dipole is generally used as a standard antenna. Before going further, it is worthwhile to say a few words about the radiation patterns of a dipole over Earth at angles well above the horizon. Most hams are familiar with the "doughnut" pattern of a dipole in free space. The performance of a dipole above earth is not so widely understood. The following patterns were calculated using *EZNEC*.[5] **Fig 2** shows the radiation patterns of an 80-meter half-wave dipole elevated $^3/_8$ λ (95.6 feet) above real earth. This antenna is a real "cloud warmer," but notice that the gain is nearly constant at elevations above 60° and is only down 2 dB at 45°. When we look in Fig 2B at the azimuth pattern for an elevation of 45° we note that the pattern is only

a little over 4 dB out of round. At an elevation angle of 60°, the pattern is only 2 dB out of round. The pattern is a trifle stronger in the broadside (90°) direction than in the end-fire direction (0°). There are no end-fire notches in the radiation pattern at high elevation angles. Comparing these patterns to the elevation angle chart of Fig 1 we see that the antenna is well suited to covering ranges from zero to about 400 miles at any azimuth with a nearly constant signal strength

For a temporary 75-meter reference antenna, the 95.6-foot elevation used in the previous example is not easy to obtain. What happens if the reference antenna is lowered to 26 feet? **Fig 3A** shows the elevation patterns for this lower antenna. Fig 3B shows azimuth patterns. At an elevation angle of

45°, the pattern is about 4 dB out of round. At 60°, the pattern is a little less than 2 dB out of round. At the lower height the antenna is almost omnidirectional for targets out to 300 or 400 miles. These patterns assume that a balanced feeder or a good balun is employed. If a coaxial line feed is used without a balun, the current on the outer conductor of the feed can contribute considerable asymmetry to the patterns.

WHY THE FUSS ABOUT GAIN MEASUREMENTS?

Mobile antenna are nearly always electrically small, and some form of impedance matching must be provided if any significant signal is to be radiated. The antenna couplers, loading coils and other matching arrangements are always lossy to some extent. Furthermore, the radiation patterns are often shaped by the vehicle and are not necessarily regular. This means that measurements in several directions from the vehicle are necessary if a realistic evaluation is to be made. It is the object of this paper to describe a system of measurement whereby a realistic evaluation of antenna performance can be obtained. The measurement techniques set forth represent the culmination of several years of experimentation.

HF Comparisons

Anyone who has been on the HF bands for any length of time has heard, "This is antenna A." And sometime later, "This is antenna B." Then follows the question, "Which is stronger?" If done on SSB, this evaluation usually has three strikes against it:

1. Judging the signal strength of two SSB signals is at best a haphazard proposition.
2. The time elapsed between the signals on the two antennas offers plenty of time for fading to occur.
3. If the SWR of each antenna is not matched almost perfectly the rig will adjust its power and will not deliver the same power to each antenna.

The result of such a test may satisfy the originator that B is better than A; however, the result is hardly quantitative. If the test was posed originally to find out whether a change in the feed raised the efficiency a few decibels the result would offer no real clue. A much more definitive test would result if:

1. The signal is CW where the power can be carefully monitored and controlled.
2. The switching between antennas is rapid and repetitive.
3. Both antennas are matched almost perfectly.
4. Some mechanism is used to identify which antenna is which.
5. All quantitative measurements are performed at the originating site.
6. Some mechanism is employed to reduce the effects of noise.

The following discussion will address each of these points individually.

The System

Fig 4 shows the transmit and receive setups. For transmit, a transceiver is fitted with a unit which permits the selection of either the normal microphone or a generator that supplies two tones, one at a time. A switch driver powers a PIN diode switch that selects the path for the signal and also selects which tone is applied as modulation. The tone is the mechanism by which the operator at the receiving end can identify which antenna is in use. For example, the higher pitched tone is always on when the reference antenna is connected, and the lower pitch tone is on

when the antenna under test is connected. To minimize the effects of fading or QSB, the system automatically switches between antennas every 1.5 seconds.

I've assumed that the reference antenna has a higher gain than the antenna under test. The reference antenna is fed through a calibrated high-power attenuator. (If the antenna under test has more gain than the reference antenna, the attenuator will have to be placed in that feed line.) The operator at the receiving end is asked to "eyeball" the S meter and to report whether the meter reads higher with the high pitch or with the low pitch. At the transmit end, the attenuator is adjusted until the receiving operator says the tones deflect the needle equally.

It is important to note that the receiving operator is only asked to report on which tone makes the S meter read higher. The calibration of S meters is very compressed, which makes it nearly impossible to accurately read a change of 1 or 2 dB between consecutive readings. However, a 1 dB change will make the meter visibly twitch at the switching speed used in my system. The result is that one can tell easily which tone is stronger. Similarly, the ear can scarcely discern a difference in amplitude of 1 or 2 dB so the twitching of the S meter is the most reliable guide. (The receiver AGC would have to be turned off for the "ear test.")

A word is in order here concerning the

switching speed and the tones. The switching should be at the fastest speed at which it is still possible for a typical S meter to respond and for the receiving operator to distinguish the tones. I selected a switching cycle of 1.5 seconds per tone.

The tones are F1 (the second F above middle C) for the low pitch ($\approx$698 Hz) and C2 (the second C above middle C) for the high tone ($\approx$1047 Hz). This selection is not random; the sound is very much like a European ambulance or police car. (Legend has it that someone received a PhD for the study that determined that this was the most distinctive pattern for most human ears.)

The PIN diode switch operates fast enough so that it's not necessary to unkey the transmitter as the tones change; therefore, the tone train is nearly continuous. In an earlier effort I tried mechanical switching and a CW identifier, but the periods of zero signal made the S meter needle swing wildly, making readings difficult or impossible.

To Filter or Not to Filter

In the beginning it seemed that the inclusion of a two-tone filtered voltmeter might improve the measurement and so I built one. Each passband had a bandwidth of about 100 Hz. I found that in the presence of white noise an improvement of approximately 9.25 dB in signal-to-noise ratio could be achieved. Eventually, I abandoned the fil-

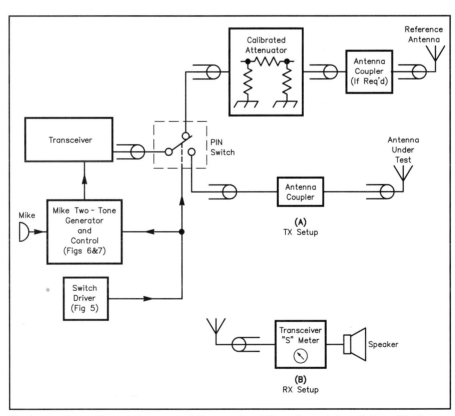

Fig 4—Configuration of the transmitting station (A), and receiving station (B). See text for details.

tered meter for the following reasons.

1. If I want the other ham to have it, I have to supply it.
2. Tuning accuracy and stability are difficult to guarantee on the other ham's rig.
3. It works only against white noise. For speech and QRM or QRN it is of little help.
4. Without this or other special equipment, I can get measurement help from any cooperative ham within communications range. Also, it is easier to get readings from a number of bearings if no special equipment is required.

The Hardware

Fig 5 shows the circuit diagram for the 100-W PIN switch and the switch driver. The PIN diodes used are Unitrode type UM4301B. These diodes are rated at 100-V breakdown (min) and have a capacitance of 2.5 pF (typ) and a series resistance of 0.3 Ω when forward biased. The "B" designation indicates axial leads. When the drive transistor Q3 or Q4 is biased off, that switch is open. When the drive transistor is on, the diode draws about 55 mA from a 12-V supply. This switch works well at the 100-W level, provided a good match is obtained on the antennas. Note that loads A and B, which represent the antenna under test and the reference antenna, must provide dc continuity for the bias current. At 1.8 MHz the switch showed 54 dB of isolation in the open condition. The isolation dropped to 39 dB at 18 and 21 MHz and rose again to 51 dB at 28 MHz. Insertion loss is relatively negligible.

The 0.01 µF capacitors have to be capable of handling the RF current, which is 1.41 A RMS at 100 W into a 50 Ω load. I used a pair of old-fashioned mica capacitors about the size of a postage stamp and 1/4 inch thick. Vitramon, among others make transmitting capacitors rated for current handling. A small dipped mica or ceramic capacitor will not stand this duty, regardless of the voltage rating.

Fig 6 shows the two-tone oscillator. (In an SSB transmitter a single tone is equivalent to CW.) Pins 4 and 10 are the reset controls of the 556 oscillator. With the switch in the ALT position, when switch drive A is high, the output of Q1 is low and the output of Q2 is high, thereby turning the LOW oscillator on. When A is low the reverse situation results and the oscillator marked HIGH is on. The control marked LEVEL is used to set the power output of the set, and the control marked BAL is used to equalize the power in the high and low tones.

Fig 7 shows the wiring for the control unit. The push-to-talk switch on the microphone is used for keying the transmitter. In the TALK position the unit operates normally. In the TEST position the transmitter is modulated by the high and low tones alternately if the LO-SCAN-HI switch is in the SCAN position. The LO and HI positions are provided for tune-up.

Setting Up

As the project progressed, it became apparent that another item would have to be standardized. The receiving operator has to determine whether the two tones are equal. There is no guarantee that the audio response of his receiver is perfectly flat. I want to determine whether any difference in received tones is due to receiver response or to differences between the antennas.

It would be nice to get a benchmark with both tones coming through the switch apparatus and the attenuator and cabling but propagating through a single antenna. A second PIN switch could be used to do that. However, that adds another switch that would not be used in the actual measurement. For that reason, I built a hybrid combiner to join the two paths into a single antenna.

Fig 8 shows the hybrid combiner transformer. (This circuit has been used in telephony since before the turn of the century.) In the hybrid-combiner circuit, A is isolated from B but sees C and D in parallel. Similarly, C is isolated from D but views A and B in series. Two separate Amidon FT82-61 ferrite cores (µ = 125) are used. Windings A and B have 6 turns and windings C and D have 9 turns. The unit shows good isolation and handles 100 W easily from 1.8 to well over 30 MHz. The windings are #22 Teflon insulated wire twisted quadrafilar. The calibration setup shown in Fig 9 wastes half of

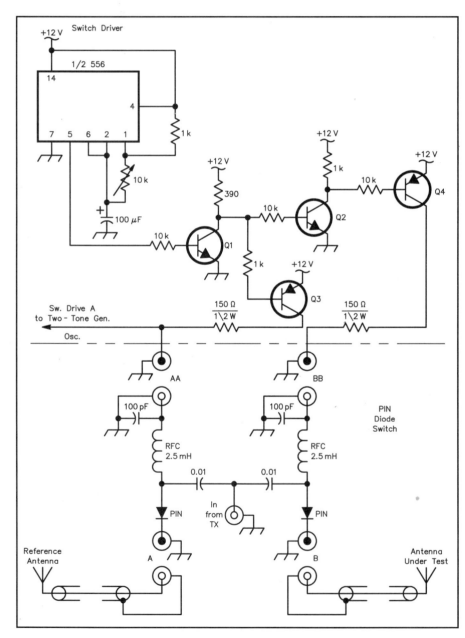

Fig 5—Circuit diagram of the 100-W PIN switch and switch driver.

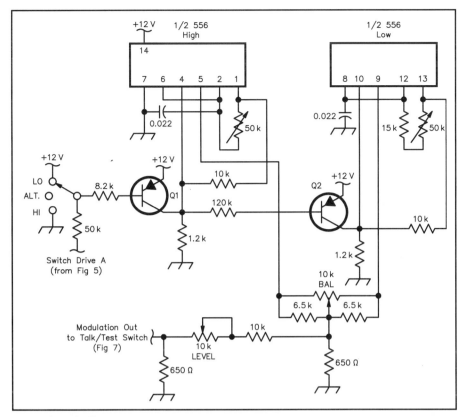

Fig 6—Circuit diagram of the two-tone generator.

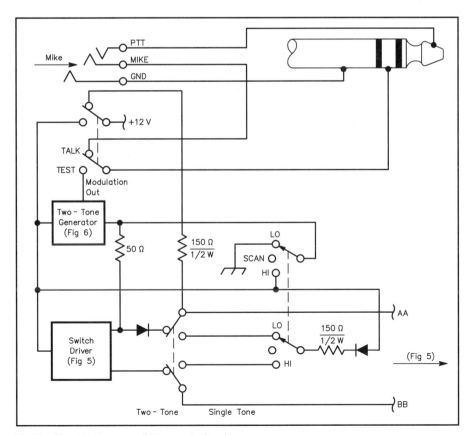

Fig 7—Circuit diagram of the control unit.

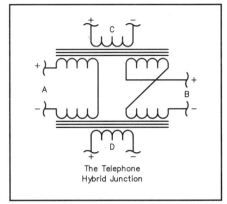

Fig 8—Diagram of the hybrid combiner transformer.

the power in the resistor at A but combines the outputs of the switch at B.

At the start of the measurement I used the two-tone test through the reference antenna using the hybrid combiner. With an operator reporting the S meter reading at the receiver end, I set the attenuator for equal strength in the low and high tones. This difference is subtracted out of the data from the two-antenna comparison. The BAL control on the two-tone generator was used to obtain equal transmitter wattmeter readings before the start of the test.

The Attenuator

The high-power attenuator is worth a few words since it is not often found around a ham shack. The attenuator is set up in binary sequence 1, 2, 4, 8 and 16 dB. Any value (in 1-dB steps) between 0 and 31 dB can be obtained. Design equations for the attenuator may be found in Reference 5, or you may use the program of *PROG-1* (included). In either event you will find that the power ratings and resistance values as shown in Table 1 are nonstandard. I use a pi-type attenuator that has equal values of input and output shunt resistors, R1 and R3, and a top (series) resistor, R2.

For example, consider the 16-dB attenuator. In this case R1 and R3 are 68.8 Ω and R1 must dissipate 36.3 W for a 50-W input. In contrast, we see that most of the power has been "burned off" by the time we reach R3 so that it dissipates only 0.9 W.

The nicest thing to use would be Carborundum resistors of these values and ratings. The 36-W Carborundum resistor would be a black cylinder about 5/8 in. diameter and 4 or 5 inches long with a 3/8 in hole through the center. The current flows through the bulk of the material and the resistor has essentially no inductance. With such resistors, and a properly designed housing, the attenuator could be made good to about 1.5 GHz. Carborundum Corp sold out of this business to a firm called Cisiwid (tel

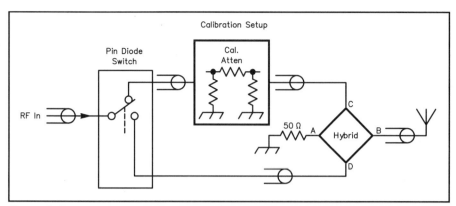

Fig 9—Calibration setup. See text for details.

Fig 10—Photo showing the system installed at KE2QJ. Above the transceiver is a directional wattmeter. To the left is the attenuator, and above that the hybrid on the left and the PIN switch on the right.

tors. The values of N in Table 1 represent the number of 2-W resistors to be paralleled. For example, the 36.3-W rating calls for at least 20 resistors of 2-W rating in parallel. Looking at the standard resistor sizes in the 5% table we find the 1500-Ω size close to our requirements. Twenty-one 1500-Ω resistors connected in parallel gives 71.42 Ω. To bring this down to 68.8 Ω, we would require a parallel resistance of:

$$(1/68.8) - (1/71.42) = 1/R$$

$$R = 1875 \ \Omega$$

We could choose either an 1800 or a 2000-Ω resistor from the standard 5% table.

These figures are only approximate. For example, the 1500-Ω resistor might actually be 1425 (-5%) or 1575 ($+5\%$). For the lowest resistance case, only 20 resistors with a 2-kΩ trim would be required. For the highest resistance case, 23 parallel resistors would give 68.5 Ω, which is close enough.

Fig 10 shows some of the principal parts of the system with the hybrid, the PIN switch, the attenuator, the directional wattmeter and the radio displayed. The two-tone generator appears in the lower right in a 2×2×5 inch box. The attenuator is electrically switched using relays to provide for future computer operation.

Conclusions

I've used this system to evaluate two mobile and two fixed antennas in the past year and a half. The measurements usually show a ±1 dB repeatability if taken during periods of low noise and low-to-moderate fading.

Table 1
Attenuator Parameters

Atten dB	R1, R3 (Ω)	P1 (W)	N1	R2 (Ω)	P2 (W)	N2	P3 (W)	N3	P_{OUT} (W)
1	870	2.88	2	5.8	5.1	3	2.3	2	39.7
2	436	5.7	3	11.6	9.1	5	3.6	2	31.5
4	221	11.3	6	24	14	7	4.5	3	19.9
8	116	21.5	11	53	17	9	3.4	2	7.9
16	68.8	36.3	20	154	12	6	0.9	1	1.3

716-286-7610). They have a $300 minimum order on each nonstandard size, however, and building the attenuator would cost significantly more than you spent on your rig!

The approach that I took was to parallel a number of 2-W carbon-composition resis-

References

[1] J. D. Kraus, *Antennas*, McGraw-Hill, 1950. Ch 15 is devoted to antenna measurements.

[2] J. D. Kraus, *Antennas*, Vol 2, McGraw Hill, 1988. Ch 18 is devoted to antenna measurements.

[3] J. A. Kuecken, *Antennas and Transmission Lines*, 2nd Ed., MFJ Enterprises. Ch 35.

[4] Jacques d'Avignon, VE3VIA. *ARRL Antenna Compendium 5*, "The NVIS Propagation and the Ham," pp 129-135.

[5] *Reference Data For Engineers*, Radio, Electronics, Computer, and Communications, 7th Ed., Howard W. Sams & Co. Ch 11, pp 11-5 and 11-6.

A Remote Noise Bridge

By Don Urbytes, W8LGV
2297 W Catalina View Drive
Tucson, AZ 85742

For many years I have used an antenna noise bridge to tune antennas, check transmission lines and also for adjusting my Transmatch. Normally, when using a noise bridge for adjusting an antenna tuner, the bridge must be inserted in the circuit to make the adjustments and then removed before transmitting. I didn't like the idea of having to change coaxial cables every time I wanted to make a noise bridge measurement, so I decided to do something about it. I designed a simple circuit that could be remotely operated and still be left in the RF circuit. Initially, I was going to build a bridge circuit and make it remotely operated.

W8LGV tells us how he adapted a noise bridge for remote operation by using a relay. With his system, you don't have to remove the noise bridge to operate your station.

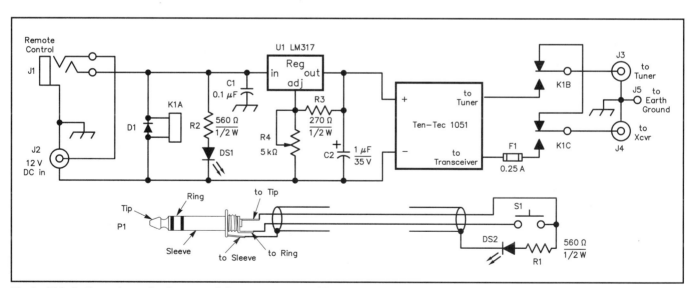

Fig 1—This is the schematic diagram of the remote-control bridge circuit. RS part numbers in parentheses are RadioShack. RSU numbers are RadioShack Unlimited, shipped directly to you.

U1—LM317 (RS 276-1778)
DS1, DS2—LED (RS 276-066)
D1—1N4002 (RSU 11929007)
R1, R2—560 Ω ½-W (RS 271-1116)
R3—270 Ω ½-W (RS 271-1112)
R4—5 kΩ potentiometer (RS 271-1714)
C1—0.1 µF, 35 V dc (RSU 11295821)
C2—1 µF, 35 V dc (RS 272-1434)

K1—Relay, 12 V dc coil (RS 275-218)
F1—Fuse, 0.25 A (RS 270-1002)
Fuse holder (RS 270-739)
S1—Push-button switch (RS 275-1556)
J1—Remote jack, ⅛-inch, 3-conductor (RS 274-24)
P1—Plug for use with remote control, ⅛-inch, 3-conductor (RS 274-284)

J2—DC jack, 5.5 mm (RS 274-1572)
P2—DC plug, 5.5mm (RS 274-1573)
J3, J4—Coax connector, SO-239 (RS 278-201)
Ten-Tec T-Kit Module Board, #1051 Transmatch Tuning Bridge
Aluminum enclosure (RS 270-238)

Then I discovered that Ten-Tec markets a line of economical kits called T-Kits.[1] One of these kits is the Transmatch Tuning Bridge, Model 1051. Priced at less than $20 for the basic kit, this seemed like a good way to go!

I decided to use this Transmatch Tuning Bridge as the basis for my remotely operated noise bridge rather than reinvent the wheel. The Ten-Tec 1051 is designed to cover a limited resistance range, and has no reactance adjustment. It provides a modulated pulse output, making it easier to recognize the null than with a simple noise bridge. I made one change on the Ten-Tec bridge, though. I replaced R12—a 100-Ω potentiometer—with a precision 50-Ω resistor. This is an optional item and does not have to be changed. All of my radios have a 50-Ω output, so I always want the antenna tuner to provide a 50-Ω match to the antenna.

If you already have a noise bridge you want to use with this remote operating circuit, you could adjust it for a 50-Ω impedance and leave it that way for normal operation. Then you can still use your noise bridge to measure antenna input impedances, design matching circuits and for other purposes.

Fig 1 shows the circuit diagram. There is nothing really critical about constructing this project except that all RF leads should be made as short as possible. I added a relay to switch the bridge into and out of the antenna circuit. When power to the relay coil is removed, the circuit switches to normal operation, removing the noise bridge from the circuit. I chose a RadioShack double-pole, double-throw type of relay with con-

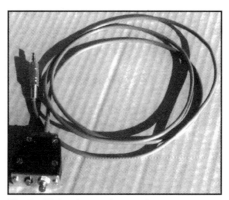

Fig 3—This photo shows the remote-control cable and push-button switch/LED control unit.

tacts rated at 10 A and a 12 V dc coil. This relay will handle the maximum transmission line current that amateurs would normally encounter. Ten-Tec recommends using fuse F1, just in case you would accidentally transmit into the bridge. An LM-317 regulates the supply voltage feeding the noise bridge and provides an adjustable output to alter the amount of noise injection. A 12 V dc wall transformer provides power and the LM 317 circuit filters the input power. Diode D1 is placed across the coil of K1 to suppress any transients when the relay is de-energized.

I located an enclosure at a local swap meet and then proceeded to mount the bridge and various components inside. See **Fig 2**. Almost any type of metal enclosure could be used to construct the remote-controlled noise bridge. I just happened to locate an aluminum enclosure that was the right size.

For the noise bridge remote control, I used a three-wire cable connected to a push-button switch and LED. I built the switch and LED into a DB-15 connector shell, and fabricated a small panel to mount the switch and LED. This arrangement is compact and the DB-15 shell provides a strain relief for the cable as well. See **Fig 3**.

Usually, I place the noise bridge behind my transceiver and out of the way. The push-button switch can be placed in any convenient location; usually it is located near the antenna tuner. Normally, I use a strip of Velcro to secure the switch/light assembly. This arrangement has worked out well, and it is very easy to relocate if needed.

To operate the noise bridge, tune your transceiver to a favorite frequency, push S1 on, and adjust R4 for about an S9 noise level on your S meter. Ten-Tec recommends setting the transceiver to the AM mode of op-

(A)

(B)

Fig 4—The completed remote control noise bridge is shown at A. The remote control cable plugs into the jack to the right of the voltage adjustment potentiometer, R4. The rear panel is shown at B. A ground connection is provided between the SO-239 coaxial connectors. The dc input connector is located below the ground terminal.

eration, but if the AM mode is not available use the LSB/USB mode. After pushing the switch on, adjust your antenna tuner for a null on the transceiver S meter. Keep adjusting the antenna tuner for the best possible, deepest null. Once this is achieved, you will be very close to a 50-Ω match to the transceiver. This may take some getting used to, but with practice you will have little difficulty. Sometimes a little tweaking will be required on the air to achieve a perfect match, but this will depend on how carefully you adjust the tuner for a null.

Whenever I match any antenna using my Kachina 505 DSP transceiver, I set the AGC time constant to a very small value. Most transceivers have an AGC time constant adjustment, which allows the S meter (or in the case of the Kachina, the vertical bar graph) to follow the Transmatch tuning.

Fig 4 shows front and back views of my bridge unit. I hope that you find this project as useful as I have over the past few years. A noise bridge eases the process of tuning your antenna tuner to the transceiver. The resulting benefit is that you won't cause any QRM while tuning your antenna.

Note
[1]Ten-Tec, Inc, 1185 Dolly Parton Parkway, Sevierville, TN 37862-3710

Fig 2—Here is a photo of the internal wiring of the remote-control bridge components. The Ten-Tec 1051 Transmatch Tuning Bridge circuit board is at the top of the photo. The relay is in the center of the unit.

Multiband Antennas

The Triple S All-Band Antenna

By George L. Bond, KF2OC
11 Trenton Rd
Fishkill, NY 12524

The slithering, sliding sloper (SSS) works well with modern transceivers. It provides a good match on all bands from 160 to 6 meters without a tuner—quite a feat. The SSS employs the concepts of the clothesline antenna that was described by Robert Victor, VA2ERY, in *QST*.[1]

The SSS is a bent top sloper that uses a tree for support (see **Fig 1**). It operates as a 66-foot sliding-feed folded dipole on 40 through 6 meters.

On 80 meters, the sliding feed is brought to the bottom of the antenna, and it is switched to operate as a $^1/_4$-λ vertical driven directly with 50-Ω coax (see **Fig 2**). I use three ground radials and two ground stakes, and the SSS provides a good match across the CW or phone portion of the band. This end-fed scheme also provides useful matches on some of the higher frequency bands.

On 160 meters, the radiator operates as a coil-loaded folded monopole. I use this configuration to step up the low radiation resistance of the short radiator. The ground resistance adds with the feed-point resistance and thus is part of the match.

Bent dipoles have been around for decades. Nizar A. Mullani, KØNM, in a recent *QST* article indicates that bending causes some reduction in the SWR bandwidth.[2] However, the folded-dipole configuration of the SSS with 12-inch wire spacing increases bandwidth.

You might think that there would be additional losses caused by the insulated antenna wire slithering through the trees and foliage. I can only say that I am unaware of any negative effects.

It seems prudent to me to limit the bend to the uppermost 30 or 35% of the antenna. Support at several points in the tree provides greater bend radius, which is probably a good thing. I prefer to limit the bend angle to about 90°; nevertheless, my SSS has a 120° bend over its last 15 or 20 feet.

> *The SSS is a bent top folded dipole on 40 through 6 meters that uses a tree for support. On 80 meters, it operates as a $^1/_4$-λ vertical.*

Construction

I built spreaders for each end of the SSS from 18 × 18-inch scrap pieces of exterior plywood (such as T111). This material is tough, and it is designed to withstand weathering. I cut and removed a U-shape with a 7.5-inch radius. Around the U, I use seven cable ties as the SSS end insulators. I mounted them as shown in **Fig 3**. Big loops in the ties permit the antenna wire to slip through when I move the feed point. This avoids the need, and cost, of using pulleys as in the clothesline antenna. Unlike pulleys, the slides offer sufficient friction to hold the sliding feed in position after I've moved it.

I've used conduit clamps to fasten a 12-inch section of garden hose to the upper spreader (see **Fig 4**). The support line runs through the hose. I split the free end of the hose, and used a cable tie to close the hose onto the line. This eases its passage through the trees. During installation, the upper spreader acts as a sled, and the hose provides the right amount of flexibility to assist in threading the sled over tree limbs and through foliage.

I built the SSS slider from $^1/_2$-inch PVC pipe (see **Fig 5**). It maintains the 12-inch spacing between the upper and lower portions of the antenna. It also acts as a feed-point insulator and strain relief point for the 300-Ω feed line.

Installation

I installed my 66-foot long SSS across the top of a 45-foot tree. That is where the slithering part comes in. That is also where the bent top develops. I use insulated wire for the dipole and it rests across the limbs and foliage of the tree. You might think that bare copper wire and ceramic insulators of the highest quality should be used. That may be ideal, but the SSS is very practical and has shown no adverse consequences of slithering and sliding the insulated sloper wires across the tree tops. If tree tops are not used, a sliding sloper or SS configuration is just fine.

It takes a little planning to install a 12-inch spaced SSS across a tree top. The plywood end spreader has been designed to assist in this task. After a single line is passed over the tree, the plywood spreader acts as a sled as it is pulled through the tree tops. It pulls a pair of nylon seine-twine lines across and through the tree tops with the desired 12-inch spacing. I use twine in place of the insulated copper to minimize weight and drag as I pull the sled across a tree. You might say the spreader acts as a sapling sled!

I favor a bow and arrow to run a line across, or through, a treetop. I suggest you use a light cotton kite string. If it gets tangled or stuck, the string will rapidly deteriorate with weathering. I prefer to use a solid fiberglass fishing arrow. Because of its weight, this type of ar-

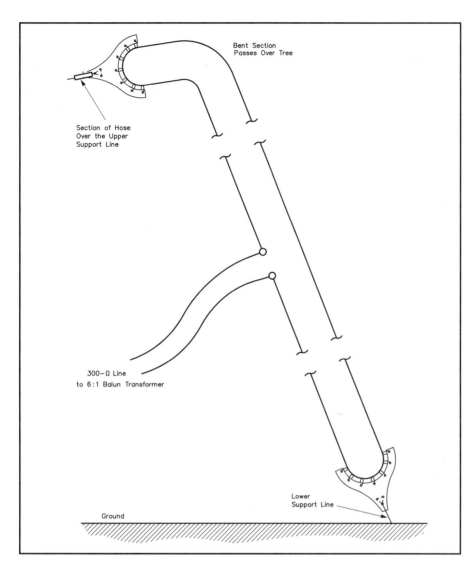

Fig 1—The SSS provides much flexibility at little cost.

Section of Hose
Over the Upper
Support Line

Bent Section
Passes Over Tree

300–Ω Line
to 6:1 Balun Transformer

Lower
Support Line

Ground

row flies slower and pulls a line better than other types. I usually shoot the arrow to a considerable height above the tree top. This helps to assure the arrow will carry the string down through any foliage that may be encountered on its return flight.

With a little practice, this approach usually works well. Consider practicing in a large open field before you try it at home. And be careful about safety! Be sure to keep all persons clear of the landing zone. If this is not one of your strong suits, seek help from a local sports or archery club.

After I pull the sled over the tree tops, I pull it down to ground level. I then use the twine to pull the top wire across the tree. Next, I thread the wire through the upper spreader and then pull it back across the tree top to complete the second side of the folded dipole.

Trees are subject to a lot of movement in the wind. I provide stress relief with a pulley and weight system at each end of the SSS. I use a pair of pulleys to support the weights for the lower spreader. This permits the low end of the SSS to be closer to the ground for efficient operation on 80 and 160 meters where I need to use a ground and radial system. The weights for the upper spreader are somewhat lighter. This assures that most movements are accommodated at the upper end. This permits the lower spreader to normally remain close to the ground, and to limit movement.

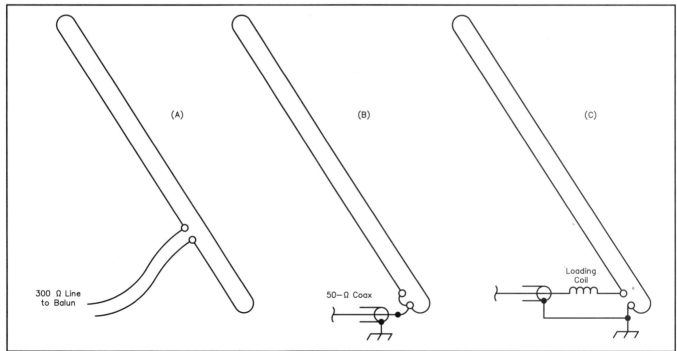

(A)

(B)

(C)

300 Ω Line
to Balun

50–Ω Coax

Loading
Coil

Fig 2—SSS feed-line connections. At A, the folded-dipole configuration. At B, the vertical configuration used on 80 meters. At C, the folded-monopole configuration used on 160 meters.

Fig 3—The lower spreader shown in its close-to-the-ground position.

Fig 4—The upper spreader. The length of garden hose is attached with conduit clamps. See text for details.

Fig 5—The slider at its midpoint position.

Adjustment

My SSS is a little shorter than the 66-foot length of the clothesline antenna. However, that's a fine starting value. The SSS slider shown in **Fig 6** provides the means of readily adjusting the radiator length. This assists in trimming and it also permits a no-tools method of shifting between the CW and phone portions of the wider bands.

The slider allows for storage of excess wire, and it has several interconnection points. Unused wire is wrapped in large loops (30 inches per turn) over the outside members or in shorter wraps (4 to 8 inches) over the closer spaced pair of members. Counting and recording the number of smaller or larger turns is a convenient means of identifying resonant locations during the tune-up process. I used an alligator clip for temporarily identifying the locations of attachment points at the resonant lengths for each desired band segment.

I soldered 8-inch drop lines at each of the resonance points, and terminated each drop line with a spade lug. I can easily connect at any particular length using a wing nut on the SSS slider. Two other wing nuts secure the connections to the 300-Ω feed line.

I use 10-24 stainless steel machine screws and wing nuts as binding posts for making slider connections. These allow me to easily change resonance points or to reconfigure the feed point as shown in Fig 2.

I use figure-eight wrapping patterns when storing excess wire on the slider. This minimizes any tendency of the wire to twist or kink. I connect both ends of the stored wire to minimize any loading effects.

The slider position tends to be somewhat more critical on the higher frequencies where the current nodes are more closely spaced. I set the slider to the midway position, and adjust for best match on 15 meters. Expect a maximum SWR of 1.3:1 across the entire band. That same position produces a good match for 40 and 18 meters as well. I marked slider positions with plastic tape on the insulation of the radiator wire. Permanent marker pen is another option.

To change the slider position, I start by pulling down on both sides of the dipole to reduce the friction in the lower spreader. Then I increase tension on one side of the

Fig 6—Details of the slider. The alligator clip in this photo was used during initial tune-up. See text for details.

dipole, which causes the slider to change position as the wire slithers through the tree and moves through the upper spreader.

Adjustment of the feed position does not affect the resonant frequency of the antenna. For that reason, you may have to adjust the antenna length as well as the feed position in order to obtain a good match on some frequencies.

Use of the end-fed configurations shown in Fig 2A and B may offer some useful choices on various bands. These may benefit from the broadband transformer matching scheme described by Thomas Kuehl, AC7A, in *QST*.[3] His article also describes the limitations of the base-loaded $1/8$-λ vertical. Despite limitations, the SSS antenna provides a fairly good starting point on the 160-meter band.

Conclusion

Good matches are available for every band and no adverse consequences are evident in using the insulated wire slithering through the tree limbs and foliage. The SSS is a natural candidate for many settings either at home or in the field. On-the-air results confirm the excellent results reported by VA2ERY in his article. My hearty thanks to him for describing the clothesline antenna. With more widespread interest, perhaps someone will develop remote control of the slide position. Meanwhile, the lowered end of the sloper brings the control within the reach of everyone!

[1]Robert Victor, VA2ERY, "The Clothesline Antenna," Jul 1998 *QST*, p 56.
[2]Nizar A. Mullani, KØNM, "The Bent Dipole," May 1997 *QST*, p 56.
[3]Thomas Kuehl, AC7A, "Build Efficient, Short Vertical Antennas," Mar 1998 *QST*, p 41.

A Cheap-and-Dirty Multiband Antenna

By Jeff Brone, WB2JNA
25 Thomas Road
Glen Burnie, MD 21060
jeffbrown.geo@yahoo.com

Here's an antenna that will work on multiple bands, costs about $10 to make (including the feed line) and takes about an hour to put together. It's great for apartment dwellers, but can also be used in a permanent installation.

Being an apartment dweller, and an incredible cheapskate, I resisted buying a multiband limited-space antenna. I knew such antennas had to be compromise propositions and I figured that I might be able to make something that would work fairly effectively on my own.

I ran across a great article by Robert H. Johns, W3JIP, in the August 1998 issue of *QST*. He detailed an end-loaded antenna (with a coil) balanced by a counterpoise. The design was a classic and I modified it to fit my limited technical and building aptitude. The result is an antenna that's so simple and easy to make, you'll hardly believe it works as well as it does.

Here's what you'll need:

- 32 feet of #14 to #18 copper wire (20 feet of it should be bare in order for winding the loading coil)
- Two "dog-bone" end insulators
- An empty two-liter soda bottle
- Two alligator clips
- 32 feet of insulated wire, such as #16 or #18 speaker wire for the counterpoise
- Coax to connect your rig to the antenna.

See **Fig 1** in the following explanation. Measure and cut off about 13 feet of wire. This will give you enough for a span of about 12 feet after you have secured each end of the wire to its insulator. Secure some more wire to the end of the left-hand insulator shown in Fig 1 and push it through the top opening of a two-liter plastic soda bottle. Push the wire through a hole you punch in the bottom of the bottle. (You can also use a short piece of wire as a "snake" through the bottle, starting at the fat end (the left-hand side in Fig 1), and then use the snake to pull a rope through the bottle to the second insulator.

Now, solder the end of a 20-foot length of bare wire to the 12-foot wire and thread the bare wire into the neck of the bottle and through a small hole you poke a few inches down from the neck. Wrap about 17 to 20 turns of the wire around the bottle to make your loading coil. Try to space the turns more or less evenly so that there is enough room for an alligator clip to fit without shorting to adjacent turns.

Use duct tape, coil dope, silicone sealant or whatever you like to hold the turns in place. Depending on how stiff the wire is, this will be, believe it or not, the hardest part of the whole project. Hang the antenna wherever it's convenient, but make sure you can easily get to the coil.

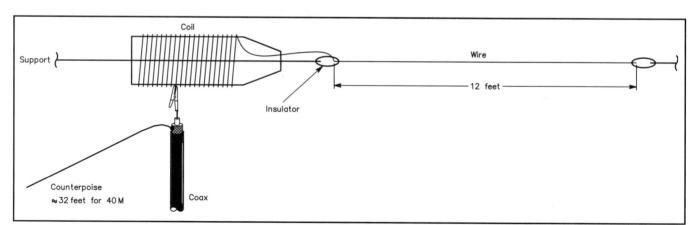

Fig 1—Layout of WB2JNA's simple and very compact multiband antenna. The coil is wound on a plastic soda bottle and the main radiator is only 12 feet long. The coax feed line uses an alligator clip for determining the appropriate tap on the loading coil, with a quarter-wave counterpoise wire from the coax shield.

Take a length of coax and solder an alligator clip to the center wire. Solder a piece of wire to the braid to be used as a counterpoise. The length of the counterpoise wire will depend on the lowest band you intend to use, so let's try 32 feet for 40 meters, the lowest band on which this particular design will work. Connect the center conductor's alligator clip to the coil, about 13 turns from the main radiating wire. Run the 32 feet of counterpoise along the floor of your apartment, on the ground or wherever you can. Keep the end away from areas where kids or pets might be able to touch it, because there is a surprising amount of RF at the end, even for QRP operation.

Connect the other end of the coax to your rig and transmit into the antenna. Try different turns of the coil with the alligator clip and experiment with the location and length (you may end up trimming some) of the counterpoise for the best SWR. That's it; you're ready for a QSO!

To use the antenna on 20 meters, connect the alligator clip about 2 to 3 turns from the front of the coil. You may want to cut the counterpoise about 16 feet in length and attach an alligator clip to its end for attaching the other 16 feet when you want to work 40 meters. Sometimes, you may also just be able to wrap the unneeded length of the counterpoise into a small coil to make it shorter, depending on the length and shortening involved.

The antenna also should work on 30 meters, though I haven't tried it there yet. As an alternative, if you shorten the 12-foot wire element to about 8 feet, you should be able to use this antenna on 20, 17, 15 and 10 meters. I found the 12-foot wire is a bit too long for 15 meters.

Of course, use an appropriate length of counterpoise wire (about a quarter wavelength or a bit less) for any band you try. You might also try soldering two counterpoise wires in parallel at the coax shield. One would be 32 feet long for 40 meters and 16 feet long for 20 meters, for example. (To determine the length in feet for a quarter wavelength, divide 234 by the desired frequency in MHz.) You may also find that if you move too far within a band, you might have to readjust the coil tap.

I use my antenna indoors (at QRP, of course, for safety) and have worked Europeans on 20 meters and 40 meter CW, and many places east of the Mississippi on 40 meters. I just hang it up in my apartment and run the counterpoise on the floor. If you can manage to put the main radiating element outside, it should work even better.

The best part about this antenna is that it takes up very little open space. The counterpoise can be laid out almost anywhere and the wire and coil only take up about 13 feet in length. I find it amazing that more hams don't try an antenna like this. Many get discouraged when they don't have room to put up a conventional dipole or a Yagi. If you like to do a lot with a little, I think you may be pleasantly surprised by this project!

The HF Skeleton Slot Antenna

By Peter Dodd, G3LDO
37 The Ridings
East Preston
West Sussex BN16 2TW
UK

This article describes the design of a five-band HF antenna for the 14, 18, 21, 24 and 28-MHz bands. It also works, with reduced gain, on the 7 and 10-MHz bands. Easy to construct and a simple design, this antenna has no traps or critical adjustments, and a turning radius of just 5 feet. It also has a much lower visual impact than a conventional multiband beam. The antenna is bidirectional and has a calculated gain, over average ground, of 8 dBi at 14 MHz and 11 dBi at 28 MHz.

> *G3LDO presents a practical new perspective on a simple, low-profile, low-angle DX antenna that covers the bands from 10 through 28 MHz.*

The Slot Antenna

The design is based on the Slot antenna normally used on the VHF and microwave frequencies and described by John Kraus, W8JK.[1] A slot antenna comprises a halfwave long slot cut in a sheet of metal as shown in **Fig 1**. When RF power is fed to a slot antenna, currents flowing from the feed point toward the ends of the slot tend to cancel, but the currents at W are in the same

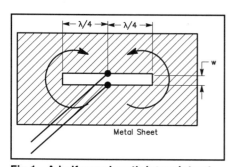

Fig 1—A half-wavelength-long slot cut in a sheet of metal radiates if RF is fed to it as shown. Radiation produced by current flowing from the feed point to the ends of the slot tends to cancel, but the currents at W are in phase, so radiation occurs. As a result, the area W radiates, hence the radiation from a vertical slot is horizontally polarized.

phase. As a result, only the area W radiates; hence the radiation from a vertical slot is horizontally polarized.

The Skeleton Slot

The skeleton slot antenna was first documented in an article by B. Sykes, G2HCG, in 1953.[2] It can best be described as a conventional slot with most of the surrounding metal sheet removed. The element is constructed from aluminum tubing and was designed as a resonant antenna for 144 MHz. See **Fig 2A**. This driven element lent itself to the design of a stacked-Yagi array, shown in **Fig 2B**, that was commercially available in the late 1950s and the 1960s. G2HCG holds a patent on this antenna.

The skeleton slot antenna was described in more detail in 1955,[3] where its application to the HF bands was discussed.

A Non-Resonant Slot For HF

The main exponent of the HF skeleton slot, other than G2HCG, is Bill Capstick, G3JYP, whose work on this antenna was first described in *Radcom* in 1969.[4] Bill recently published a construction article on

this antenna.[5] He found that the antenna also gave a good performance on several amateur bands when used with an antenna tuner. The G3JYP skeleton slot is shown in **Fig 3**.

A derivative of the skeleton slot is the Hentenna, which was developed in Japan. This is a resonant slot, fed off-center to provide a more suitable match. It also uses wire instead of tubing for the vertical elements, as described in the reference of note 1. A 50-MHz version was also published.[6]

My version of the HF skeleton slot uses a more simplified and rugged construction method, compared with G3JYP's antenna, by using wire for the vertical elements (similar to the Hentenna). I was at first concerned that this method of construction would not work because the articles referenced in notes 2 and 3 give minimum tubing diameters for the elements. However, W7EL's *EZNEC* software reassured me that this method of construction would be suitable, so I went ahead.

Construction

The antenna essentially comprises three aluminum-tubing elements fixed to the mast

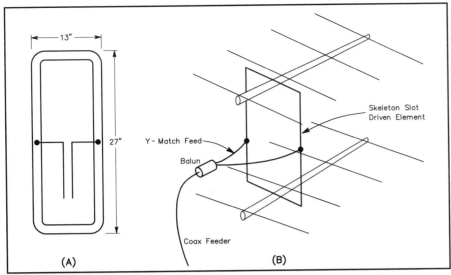

Fig 2—At A, the skeleton slot antenna as described by B. Sykes, G2HCG. The element is constructed from aluminum tubing and was designed as a resonant antenna for 144 MHz. At B, a stacked Yagi array that was marketed commercially in the late 1950s and the 1960s uses a single skeleton slot as the driven element of both arrays.

at 15-foot intervals, with the lowest element only 15 feet from the ground. The mast is an integral part of the antenna, as a boom is to a Yagi. The general construction is shown in **Fig 4.**

The center element is fed in the center with a balanced feeder. The upper and lower elements are fed at the ends by copper wire from the driven dipole. The aluminum tubing and copper wire are fixed using hose clamps. These dissimilar metal connections present no corrosion problems, even in a location like mine close to the sea, provided they are well coated with grease.

The centers of the upper and lower elements can be fixed directly to a metal grounded mast using an aluminum plate and U bolts as shown in Fig 4. I insulated the elements from the mast by using oversized U bolts and wrapping the element in an insulating material I had at hand. I did this because I wanted the option of using the antenna as top loading for a lower-frequency antenna. If you want to insulate the elements from the mast, then the method shown in Fig 4 is probably the best way. The antenna's performance on the bands it covers is unaffected by grounding or insulating the upper and lower elements. Further, the tubing and wire diameters and lengths used in this antenna are not critical.

Feeding the Slot

The antenna requires a balanced feed and is fed with 450-Ω slotted line feeder, although the feeder impedance is not critical. The feeder should be fixed on stand-off insulators about 6 inches from the mast until clear of the lower element to avoid feeder movement in the wind from affecting the impedance, although I did not do this on my experimental antenna at the time of writing.

An antenna tuner with a balanced output is required. I used a conventional Z match with two sets of balanced outputs, one ostensibly for the higher HF frequencies and the other for the lower ones. In practice, the lower frequency output worked best for all frequencies.

A more suitable tuner is one that uses a link-coupled arrangement.[7] The improved Z Match[8] also looks very suitable.

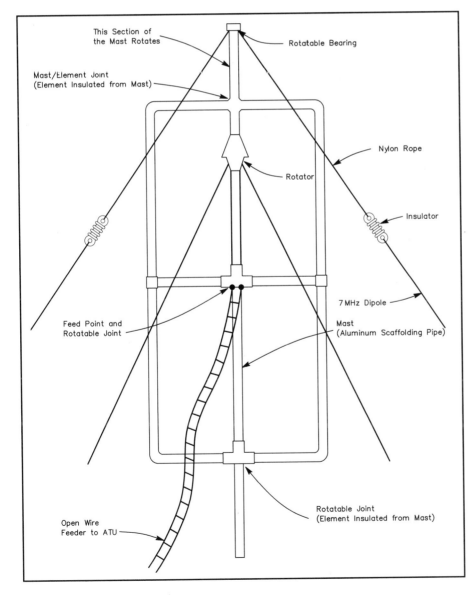

Fig 3—The G3JYP skeleton slot. All the elements are constructed from ³/₄-inch-diameter aluminum. The antenna is 10 feet wide and 30 feet high. G2HCG states that the lower element should be at least 6 feet above ground. The top section of the mast and the top element are turned with a rotator; the lower two elements, mounted on mast bearings, follow. Because the antenna is bi-directional, the antenna needs to be turned through only 180° for full azimuth coverage. *(Graphic courtesy of RSGB.)*

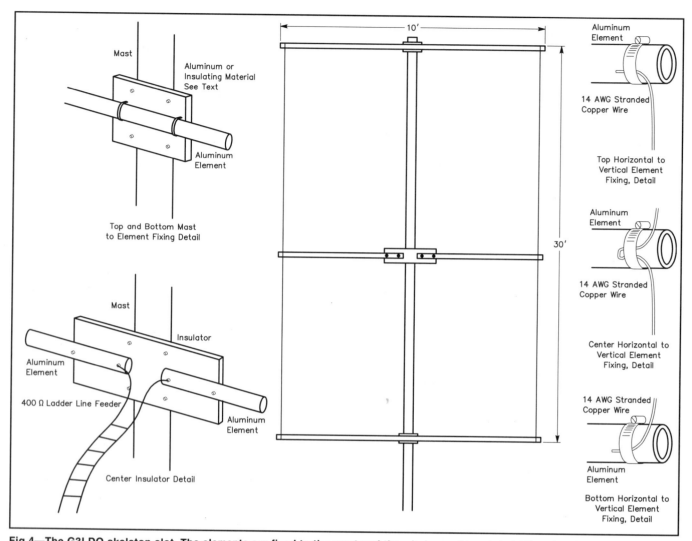

Fig 4—The G3LDO skeleton slot. The elements are fixed to the mast and the whole mast is rotated. The wire elements are fixed to the horizontal elements with hose clamps. The center insulator shown is homemade, but a commercial one would be suitable.

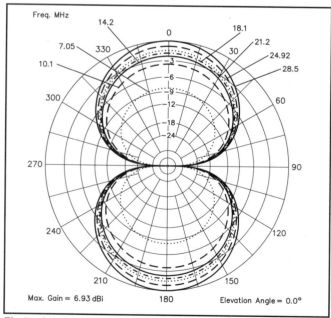

Fig 5—A free-space azimuth plot of a skeleton slot on the amateur bands from 7 to 28 MHz. A free-space plot is used to illustrate the relative gains without ground effect. To see the effect of ground, see Fig 6.

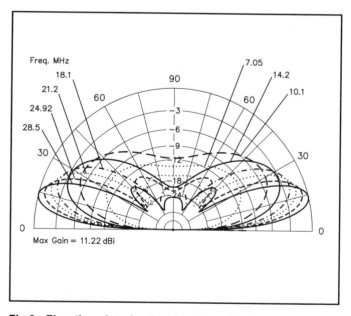

Fig 6—Elevation plot of a skeleton slot, with the lowest elements 15 feet above average ground, on the amateur bands from 7 to 28 MHz. This antenna's performance improves with increasing frequency up to 30 MHz. At 14 MHz and above, it's a low-angle radiator suitable for DX work.

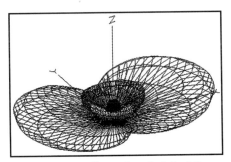

Fig 7—A three-dimensional plot of the multiband skeleton slot at 28 MHz.

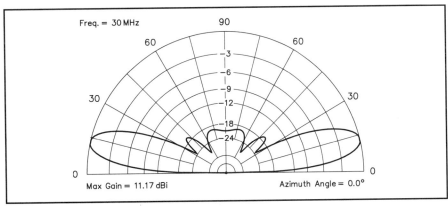

Freq. = 30 MHz

Max Gain = 11.17 dBi

Azimuth Angle = 0.0°

Fig 8—The DX potential of the skeleton slot is maximum on the 10-meter band. The cutoff frequency is around 35 MHz, above which the performance starts to deteriorate.

Performance

The predicted performance (using *EZNEC* version 2) is shown in **Fig 5,** which shows free-space azimuth plots on the bands from 7 to 28 MHz. The antenna's elevation-plane performance is shown in **Fig 6**. A three-dimensional plot of the skeleton slot at 28 MHz is shown in **Fig 7**.

The plots shown in Figs 6 and 7 are with the lower element 15 feet from the ground. Increasing the height of the lower element from 15 to 30 feet gives a calculated increase in gain (over average ground) from 9.86 dBi to 10.56 dBi at 21.2 MHz, but introduces additional high-angle lobes.

I built my slot to the size specified by Bill Capstick. These dimensions seem nearly optimum for the five higher-frequency HF bands. While the DX performance of this antenna is good up to 30 MHz, it deteriorates at frequencies higher than this, as shown in **Fig 8**. However, *EZNEC* predicts that the performance at the lower frequency

bands can be improved by increasing the slot width by about 2 feet, without having much effect on the upper cutoff frequency.

On the 21, 24 and 28-MHz bands, the antenna performs very well—particularly when conditions are marginal. Early morning contacts with the Pacific had very noticeable echoes, probably due to the antenna's bidirectional pattern.

Mast Side Mounting

Because the Skeleton Slot only has to be turned through 180° to give full azimuth coverage, it could be fixed to the side of a mast or the side of a tall, straight tree. If, however, you wanted to rotate the antenna in such an arrangement, the rotating system would require stop switches to prevent damage to the antenna.

Notes

[1] J. Kraus, *Antennas*, Second Edition, Chapter 13 (New York: McGraw-Hill, 1988).

[2] B. Sykes, "Skeleton Slot Aerials," *RSGB Bulletin* (forerunner of *Radcom*), Jan 1953.

[3] B. Sykes, "Skeleton Slot Aerial System," *The Short Wave Magazine*, Jan 1955.

[4] Technical Topics, "HF Skeleton Slot," *Radcom*, Jun 1960.

[5] B. Capstick, "The HF Skeleton Slot Antenna," *Radcom*, Jun 1996.

[6] S. Kinoshita, "The Hentenna—The Japanese 'Miracle' Wire Antenna," *The ARRL Antenna Compendium, Vol 5* (Newington: ARRL, 1995), pp 66-68.

[7] R. D. Straw, Ed., "Coupling the Transmitter to the Line," *The ARRL Antenna Book*, 18th Edition (Newington: ARRL, 1997), Chapter 25.

[8] C. A. Lofgren, "An Improved Single-Coil Z-Match," *The ARRL Antenna Compen-dium, Vol 5* (Newington: ARRL, 1995), pp 194-196.

Log-Periodic Dipole Array Improvements

By Carl Luetzelschwab, K9LA
1227 Pion Road
Fort Wayne, IN 46845-9510
k9la@gte.net

K9LA analyzes his LPDA antenna and improves its performance.

Back in the summer of 1995, I bought a Tennadyne T6 Log Periodic Dipole Array (LPDA). It covers 14 to 30 MHz with six elements on a 12-foot boom. My choice of that specific model was based solely on the wind-load capability of my 72-foot self-supporting aluminum tower. I reviewed this antenna in the Mar/Apr 1996 issue of the *National Contest Journal* (*NCJ*).

I have been very pleased with the performance, especially with the ability to QSY between 20, 17, 15, 12 and 10 meters without switching antennas. But there are some subtle performance issues with LPDAs in general, and this article describes these issues and shows how to make some performance improvements.

How Much Gain?

One of the first issues I ran into was the claimed gain of LPDAs. A plot of gain versus the LPDA parameters tau (scaling factor) and sigma (spacing factor) has been given in many antenna books and published in many articles about LPDAs. But there seems to be two versions, with one version claiming about 2 dB more gain than the other version.

After digging into all the old papers, I discovered two papers—"Comments on the Design of LPDAs" by De Vito and Stracca[1] and "A Note on the Calculation of the Gain of LPDAs" by Butson and Thompson.[2] They both claim errors had been made in the calculation of gain in the original LPDA papers by Isbell[3] and Carrel[4]—the original results were about 2 dB too optimistic. This error then propagated to many other references. Subsequently some people caught the error, and some didn't.

Table 1 is a list of references (ones I'm aware of—there may be more) in which the gain versus tau and sigma is correct. These claimed gains also agree very well with modeled results. **Table 2** is a list of references (again, ones I'm aware of) in which the gain is about 2 dB too optimistic.

The Model

To model the T6, I used K6STI's program NEC/WIRES 2.0. With its transmission line subroutine, it is a simple matter to model LPDAs. **Fig 1** shows the *NEC/Wires* file after converting the six tapered elements to $^7/_8$-inch diameter cylindrical elements.

Fig 2 shows the gain, F/B and SWR performance of the original T6. The modeled gain is free space gain compared to an iso-

---

Table 1
References with Correct Gain Values

W. Orr, *Ham Radio*, Sep 1989, p 20, Fig 4.

J. Kraus, *Antennas*, 2nd ed. (New York: McGraw-Hill, 1988), p 706, Fig 15-12.

R. Johnson, *Antenna Engineering Handbook*, 3rd ed. (New York: McGraw-Hill, 1993), p 14-38, Fig 14-34.

R. Straw, *The ARRL Antenna Book*, 17th ed. (Newington: ARRL, 1994), p 10-3, Fig 4. The 18th ed. is also correct.

J. Breakall, et al, *A New Design Method for Low Sidelobe Level LPDAs*, Applied Computational Electromagnetics Society Journal 11(2), Jul 1996, pp 100-107, Fig 2.

Table 2
References with Optimistic Gain Values

D. Isbell, "Log-Periodic Dipole Antennas," *IRE Transactions on Antennas & Propagation*, 1960, p 265, Fig 14.

R. Carrel, "The Design of Log-Periodic Dipole Antennas," *1961 IRE International Convention Record*, Part 1.

P. Rhodes, *QST*, Nov 1973, p 18, Fig 4.

P. Scholz and G. Smith, *Ham Radio*, Dec 1979, p 37, Fig 3.

L. Johnson, *Ham Radio*, May 1983, p 79, Fig 1.

D. Fink and D. Christiansen, *Electronics Engineers' Handbook*, 3rd ed. (New York: McGraw-Hill, 1989), p 18-39, Fig 18-37.

```
T6 Tennadyne LPDA
Free Space
28.3 MHz
6 wires, feet
;s = 4.346  (10-m director spacing)
;l = 7.700  (10-m director length)
10     0.000    -7.8190    0    0.0000    7.819    0    .0729
10    -1.533    -9.2630    0   -1.5330    9.2630   0    .0729
10    -3.3583  -10.9435    0   -3.3583   10.9435   0    .0729
10    -5.5417  -12.9185    0   -5.5417   12.9185   0    .0729
10    -8.3917  -15.2135    0   -8.3917    5.2135   0    .0729
10   -11.5833  -17.9940    0  -11.5833   17.9940   0    .0729
;2   -14.5833   -0.2290    0  -14.5833     .2290   0    #10 (part of shorted stub)
;10   s          -l        0     s         l       0    .0729 (10-m director)
1 source
wire 1, center
5 transmission lines
wire 1 center to wire 2 center z=150
wire 2 center to wire 3 center z=150
wire 3 center to wire 4 center z=150
wire 4 center to wire 5 center z=150
wire 5 center to wire 6 center z=150
;wire 6 center to wire 7 center z=320 untwisted short end2  (shorted stub)
0 loads

;NEC/WIRES 2.0 File
```

Fig 1—Input file for *NEC/Wires* for Tennadyne T6 LPDA. The element diameters have been standardized at 7/8 inch diameter (0.0729 feet).

tropic source, whereas the modeled F/B (at a low elevation angle) and SWR are with the T6 at 72 feet over flat ground. On the F/B and SWR plots I also included my measured data (I can't measure gain) with the T6 mounted at 72 feet. The F/B was measured with the help of Jim, KR9U, about 2 miles away, and was done using a calibrated step attenuator. The SWR was measured at the end of 80 feet of RG-8 coax with a Bird 43 wattmeter.

Note that the model is in fairly good agreement with my F/B and SWR measurements. There is some divergence in SWR at the high end of the band, so any improvements at the high end based on the model should be confirmed with measured data.

An Obvious Problem

Looking at the plots of Fig 2 shows a very troubling problem—just below the 10-meter band the pattern appears to reverse. This is best seen in the gain and F/B plots. At first I thought this might be an artificial artifact of the model, but the measured F/B (and the SWR to a certain degree) tends to confirm this anomaly. I also modeled several other generic and commercial LPDAs, and they all show the same problem.

This problem is due to the wide bandwidth of the antenna—it covers an octave, which is a 2:1 frequency ratio. Although the active region of the LPDA at the high end of the band

is in the shorter elements, the longest element at half the frequency still ends up with sufficient current (amplitude and phase) to distort the pattern. In other words, the pattern reversal occurs near twice the frequency of the lowest operating frequency.

To confirm this, I modeled the T6 without the longest element. Now both parameters do not show this significant deviation anymore. Even though the pattern reversal occurs below 10 meters, it was close enough to 10 meters for me to worry about. But eliminating the longest element was not a solution, as that degraded the performance on 20 meters.

An Answer—the Shorted Stub

In several of the early papers on LPDAs, a shorted stub was shown on the non-feed end (longest element end) of the antenna. None of these papers ever specifically said why the stub was there—there was a comment in one paper about helping performance at the low end of the band because the array was truncated so abruptly at low frequencies due to physical limitations.

I discussed this with Chuck, KA1PM, of Tennadyne, and he thought the biggest benefit of the shorted stub was to put the entire structure at DC ground, since the elements connected to the coax inner conductor would not be at ground without the stub. I thought this was a great idea, so I put a

3 foot long shorted stub at the non-feed end of my T6. I used a 6 foot long piece of rectangular aluminum bar stock (1 inch wide by 1/8 inch thick) that I bought at the local hardware store. I bent it into a long skinny U-shape, and bolted it to the non-feed end of the T6.

I also had a suspicion that this might help the high-end pattern reversal problem, as it would be changing the current in the longest element. So I re-modeled the T6 with the stub. **Fig 3** shows the resulting gain and F/B. Compare this to Fig 2. Note that there are no anomalies at the high end of the band. The performance is nice and smooth from 14 to 29 MHz.

KR9U and I again measured the F/B of the modified T6 to confirm the model, and indeed the dip in F/B just below 10 meters is no longer present with the stub. I also noted that the VSWR on 20 meters im-

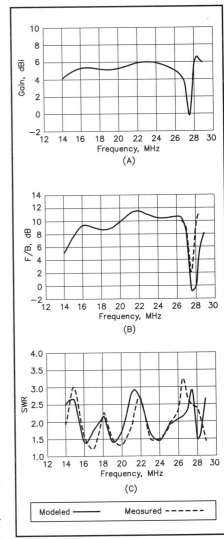

Fig 2—Graphs of computed gain, F/B and SWR for unmodified T6 antenna. The F/B and SWR curves are for antenna mounted 72 feet over flat ground, while the gain computation is for free space.

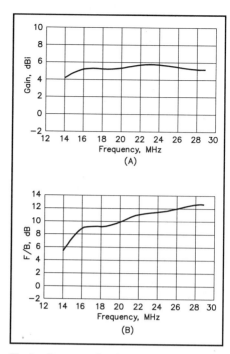

Fig 3—Computed gain and F/B for T6 modified with 3 foot long stub at longest element. The anomaly at the high-frequency end of the spectrum shown in Fig 2 has disappeared.

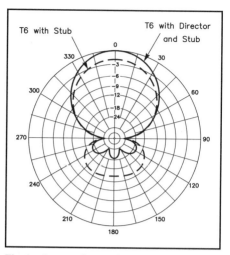

Fig 4—Comparison of pattern of T6 with stub compared to the same antenna with an additional parasitic director for 28.3 MHz. The gain and the F/B are substantially improved on this frequency.

Fig 5—Photo of modified T6 on its free-standing 72 foot high tower. The right-hand side of the boom has been extended with PVC tubing to accommodate the 10-meter director and the left-hand end of the boom holds the stub.

proved from around 2:1 without the stub to around 1.5:1 with the stub (this is also predicted in the model). This may be the performance improvement alluded to in the earlier comment about adding the stub.

10.1 MHz Operation

In his article titled "The K4EWG Log Periodic Array" that appeared in *The ARRL Antenna Compendium, Vol 3*, K4EWG shows SWR measurements for an LPDA that he designed and built. What's interesting is the SWR on 10.1 MHz is around 2:1. He states that this is due to the use of an electrical quarter-wave shorted stub for 14.1 MHz and it inductively loads the longest element, allowing 10.1-MHz operation.

Thinking this would be a great way to get 10.1-MHz capability, I modeled an electrical quarter-wave shorted stub for 14.1 MHz on my T6 in lieu of the 3-foot shorted stub described previously. But I was not able to achieve a decent SWR on 10.1 MHz, even with varying the length of the stub and its Z_0. I also modeled K4EWG's LPDA design with the longer shorted stub, but I had the same results—no decent SWR on 10.1 MHz.

I'm sure what K4EWG measured is true, so either my model is not accurate or something else came into the picture during his measurements. As for my model of K4EWG's LPDA, I did not reflect the 16-inch overlap in each half element due to his construction technique. There might be

something else coming into the picture during his measurements: the photo in his article shows that his LPDA is mounted only a few feet above a two-element 40-meter Yagi. If the SWR was measured with the 40-meter Yagi in place, perhaps coupling between these two antennas gave the 10.1-MHz SWR result, and not the stub.

Improving 10-Meter Performance

In my *NCJ* review of the T6, I said the performance of the T6 was roughly equivalent to a two-element monobander on each band. Being a 10-meter aficionado, I wondered if and by how much I could improve the performance on 10 meters by adding a parasitic director.

After more modeling efforts at 28.3 MHz,

I decided on a parasitic director 0.125 λ (52 inches) in front of the shortest element and 15.4 feet long (7/8-inch diameter cylindrical element). This combination of spacing and element length gave an increase in gain and F/B while maintaining an acceptable SWR (less than 2:1) from 28.0 to 28.6 MHz.

Fig 4 shows the comparison of the modeled azimuth patterns in free space at 28.3 MHz for the T6 as-is and for the T6 with the added 10-meter parasitic director. The extra 2 dB in gain and 10 dB more F/B was maintained from 28.0 to 28.6 MHz, so I figured this was worth a try. The model also said the SWR on 10 meters should improve.

I extended the boom of the T6 using a piece of thick-wall PVC tubing with a wooden dowel slipped inside for added strength. The added director element was a 12-foot piece of 3/4-inch aluminum tubing with 21-inch tips of 5/8-inch tubing—this came from converting the 15.4-foot cylindrical length of 7/8-inch diameter to an equivalent tapered length using the tubing sections I had laying around. **Fig 5** is a photo of the modified T6 on top of the tower at 72 feet.

KR9U and I measured the F/B across 10 meters and plotted the full azimuth pattern at 28.3 MHz on the modified T6 to verify the modeled results. The F/B definitely improved to the level expected from the model and the SWR also improved as expected. So I'm fairly confident that the gain also improved.

Summary

If you own an LPDA, I've shown two simple improvements to make it better. First, the addition of a shorted stub primarily puts the entire structure at DC ground. As an added benefit, the problem with pattern reversal at twice the lowest operating frequency is cleared up. This works on LPDAs that cover 14 to 30 MHz. I did not try this on LPDAs that cover a wider range—for example, 10 to 30 MHz. For this case, I suggest modeling it and confirming it with F/B measurements.

Second, adding a parasitic director on 10 meters significantly improves the performance. With Solar Cycle 23 on the rise, this may come in handy.

References

[1]De Vito and Stracca, "Comments on the Design of Log Periodic Dipole Antennas," *IEEE Trans Ant Propag*, May 1973.

[2]P. Butson and G. Thompson, "A Note on the Calculation of the Gain of Log-Periodic Dipole Antennas," *IEEE Trans Ant Propag*, Vol AP-24, No. 1, Jan 1976, pp 105-106.

[3]D. Isbell, "Log-Periodic Dipole Arrays," *IRE Trans Ant Propag*, Vol AP-8, No. 3, May 1960.

[4]R. Carrel, "The Design of Log-Periodic Dipole Antennas," *1961 IRE International Convention Record*, Part 1.

The XMW Propagation-Prediction Program

By William Alsup, N6XMW
1120 Ashmount Avenue
Oakland, CA 94610

X*MW* is an HF propagation-prediction program written in QBasic. The program uses a mathematical model of the earth and the ionosphere consisting of a set of equations I developed to simulate the way ionospheric propagation works. The results are reasonably accurate in my own experience and correlate reasonably (but not perfectly) with selected *IONCAP* predictions.

Based on its internal ionospheric model, *XMW* generates several display formats, including:

• A real-time, continuously updated chart showing openings from your QTH (or any other QTH) to various targets around the world based on the solar flux and K index.

• A similar chart for any given time and date, not necessarily the current time or date.

• A set of charts showing openings, strengths, takeoff angles, between any two points in the world displayed over 24 hours for any given date and set of solar flux and K index values.

• A chart showing openings between any two points in the world displayed for all 24 hours for twelve months of the year for any given solar flux and K index.

The main idea is twofold—both to help you plan in advance when to listen for DX and to alert you—real-time—about what paths (long and short) should currently be open. There are other features too.

This was a genuine learning experience for me. I did this project from scratch, writing all the code myself and developing the basic model myself. By way of background, I obtained a college degree in mathematics and engineering (but wound up becoming a

> *N6XMW describes his latest and most ambitious foray into the art and science of HF propagation predictions.*

trial lawyer). People at ARRL HQ critiqued *XMW* along the way, but all its shortcomings are strictly mine.

The lessons I learned, including some important caveats, are woven into the following description. One transcendent lesson, however, is this—every prediction program is based on a set of assumptions. And the results are only as good as the assumptions. I once regularly used *CAPMan* based on *IONCAP*, the industry standard. In my own experience, *IONCAP/CAPMan* predicted too many openings.

In turn, *XMW* is limited by the simplifying assumptions of its own algorithms. Roughly speaking, I have found that *XMW* correlates about 70% with the openings in the traditional *QST* charts and about 80% with my own actual operating experience. There is no doubt that anyone could easily find some *XMW* predictions that do not square with his or her own experience. There is also no doubt that there are equations in the literature that I missed and could have used in lieu of the homebrew substitutes actually used. With those caveats in mind, I still believe a DXer will benefit from *XMW*, a copy of which is included on the CD-ROM accompanying this volume. I would love to hear from amateurs as to how

accurate the predictions are for them and suggestions for improvement.

The Multi-Hop Model

The main engine of the program is a multi-hop model of propagation. To determine if there is a multi-hop opening, the model:

1. Finds the great-circle route between the two positions and the average *actual* height of the F layer for the path.
2. Calculates the smallest number of F-layer hops possible between the two positions.
3. Determines the angles of the hops (using the average virtual height of the path).
4. Estimates the F-layer critical frequencies at the apexes of all hops.
5. Estimates the E-layer critical frequencies for all upbound intersection points with the E layer.
6. Determines if the angle of radiation will be screened by the E layer (if so, subject to one caveat below, then the path is deemed closed).
7. Determines if the angle of radiation will reflect off the F layer at *all* apex points (if not, then the path is deemed closed).

The hop mode is open only if both steps

6 and 7 indicate the band is open. Then, the same sequence (starting with step 3) will be run for the next largest number of hops. For example, if the fewest possible hops are three, then the program will run the above steps for that assumption, and then run them for four hops, and then five, and so on, until the angle of attack to the F layer is so steep that the ray will penetrate the F layer at an apex.

An earlier version of *XMW* deemed a path to be open only if both the F layer was *ionized* enough to reflect the ray at all apexes and the E-layer was *de-ionized* enough to pass the ray at all points of intersection. This was on the theory that if the E layer screened the radiation at any point, then it would probably be E-screened at others and the signal would be too attenuated for DX, the main purpose behind the program.

I found, however, that this assumption was occasionally too restrictive and, compared to *IONCAP*, *XMW* missed some combination E and F-hop openings. This assumption was then altered so that *XMW* would now tolerate one E hop but no more. After one, any more E hops will close the path. *XMW* assumes that if the E-layer screens (that is, reflects) the ray at more than one point, then it will become so attenuated from multiple short hops that it cannot go long distances and still be heard. Since this program is directed at DX, this is a reasonable simplifying assumption. Strictly E-layer or sporadic-E openings are ignored by *XMW*. (Nor is any distinction made between the F_1 and F_2 layers.)

The foregoing only tells us whether the path is open. That is a critical issue, but even if a band is open, it does not tell us how strong a signal will be. If the path is not open, of course, it does not matter how powerful the stations involved are! Assuming that the path is open, however, the signal strength is determined by a series of factors. The starting points are the power to the antenna and the antenna gain. The program assumes 100 W to a rotatable Yagi antenna with 6 dBi gain (over isotropic) and horizontal polarization, at a height over flat ground that you specify.

The power and 6 dBi gain of the antenna are fixed and cannot be changed. You simply have to use these values as a benchmark and adjust the results for your own particular situation. The program then takes into account the following while computing signal strength on an open path.[1]

1. The signal strength varies with the distance traveled in two ways. The primary factor is simply the distance. In free space, the strength of a signal diminishes with the square of distance, but this is because the pulse is assumed to expand like an ever enlarging hollow sphere. On Earth, any received signal is instead trapped between the earth and the F layer. Rather than an ever expanding sphere, such propagation is more like a flat circle that enlarges until the antipodal equator is reached, whereupon the circle begins to shrink and ultimately converges to the antipodal point. This seems more two-dimensional, like a circular ripple caused by a stone dropped into a pond.

If a two-dimensional rather than three-dimensional model is used, the strength diminishes directly with the distance, not with the square of the distance. *XMW* uses a compromise between the two models and uses a power of 1.5. A secondary factor is antipodal focusing. This factor reduces the signal the most at the antipodal equator and increases it the most at the point of origin and the antipodal point. In this way, antipodal focusing is taken into account.

2. D and E-layer absorption reduce the signal strength. The program assumes that these are proportional to each other. During the day, they are deemed to be proportional to the critical frequency of the E layer, and proportional to the cosine of the angle of incidence to the E-layer (since the steeper the angle, the less exposure the ray will have to these layers) and inversely proportional to the square of the frequency of the radiation. This combined product is multiplied by an overall constant found, by trial and error, to match observations by N6XMW. During the night, this absorption is deemed to be zero.

Absorption in the F layer is assumed to be proportional to the sine of the angle of incidence to the F layer, to the smoothed sunspot number (times a constant), and inversely proportional to the square of the frequency, all again multiplied by a constant selected by trial and error. During the daytime, the F-layer absorption is substantially less than D/E absorption. At night, it is more (since D/E absorption is assumed to go to zero at night), although still small by absolute standards.[2] These absorptions are added and used to form a percentage, such as 21%, meaning that 21% of the signal strength is lost *per hop* on average for the path. If the average absorption per hop is 21% and there are, for example, four hops, then 79% of the signal beginning a hop survives each hop and 39% (0.79 × 0.79 × 0.79 × 0.79) of the original signal gets through.

3. Auroral absorption must be estimated. This was done by estimating the position of the auroral oval and then determining how much of the path is under its influence, weighing close encounters with the auroral oval more heavily than less-close encounters. The oval expands with the K index. Its shape varies during the Earth's rotation because the geomagnetic poles are off-axis. When the K index reaches 3, for example, all QSOs between California and Europe are very weak with the 100-W assumption. *XMW* tries to simulate the auroral oval.

4. Earth losses must be taken into account at the points where the hops bounce off the Earth. The program determines, for each touch-down point, whether the touch-down is on salt water or ground. The degree of attenuation then varies directly with the cosine of the angle of incidence to the earth, raised to a power that increases more for ground reflections than for salt water reflections. The power exponent is 5.0 for each ground reflection and 1.0 for each sea reflection. This means that paths over salt water and/or paths at very shallow angles suffer little earth reflection attenuation. Paths over ground at angles like 15°, however, will be substantially reduced after about four hops. A single touchdown over ground at 30° will reduce signal strength by one-half. The program treats all ground (as opposed to sea) the same and does not distinguish between mountains, desert, fresh water or other ground.[3]

5. Vertical focusing must also be taken into account. The higher the takeoff angle, the greater will be the vertical focusing and the lower the takeoff angle, the greater will be the vertical de-focusing. This is simply the result of the geometry of the Earth, the ionosphere and the takeoff angles. For example, if the amount of RF energy emitted between takeoff angles 1° and 2° is equal to the energy emitted between 21° and 22°, the latter, when reflected back to earth, will illuminate and be spread out over a more concentrated range (due to curvature of the Earth along the great-circle route) than the former. The longer the illuminated arc, the greater the de-focusing. The shorter the illuminated arc, the greater the focusing. See Alsup, "The HF Illumination Profile and the Bright Leading Edge of Illumination," in *The ARRL Antenna Compendium, Vol 4* at p 131.

Noise is ignored or, really, is assumed to be uniform worldwide in *XMW*. You must make mental adjustments for the impact of noise when considering circuits involving higher or lower than normal noise profiles. Noise does vary by season and position.

Now, I need to go back and discuss some more the 100-W and 6-dBi assumptions. While the program literally inputs 100 W and 6 dBi, the final results are the function of the math model and the particular coefficients used. After much trial and error, I settled on coefficients that seem to provide final results that simulate my own actual experience and the results of *IONCAP* that I sampled. While the final results are about 70% to 80% consistent with openings, they are perhaps 50% accurate for the *strength* of the openings.

So far, the discussion has been concerned with whether a path is open and with the signal strength—I have assumed no gain or loss from the vertical radiation pattern ("VRP") of the antenna. This pre-VRP calculation is useful to know in and of itself, for it tells us how good the signal is before applying the gains or losses for the vertical radiation pattern for the particular antenna/terrain in use.

Usually, however, you will want to know the impact of the VRP (which is a function of antenna height and the terrain, always assumed by *XMW* to be flat ground). For example, even a strong signal at an incoming angle of 1° is usually hard to hear because the usual VRP favors higher angles and disfavors low angles (assuming horizontally polarized antennas over flat ground). It all depends on the shape of the VRP and where the lobes and nulls are.

So, a final but optional step is to modify the pre-VRP propagation prediction using the VRP to get the final strength. For this step of the program, I assumed horizontal antennas over flat ground with perfect reflectivity. You can, however, select the antenna heights at both ends of the circuit. If you have a vertical antenna, then the NO VRP case (the same data one step before application of the vertical radiation profiles of both antennas) is the only one of interest.

To summarize for the multi-hop model built into *XMW*, the program computes each strength, for each hop configuration where the band is open. Thus, for 14 MHz between Oakland and New Zealand, we may have calculations for 3F, 4F, 5F modes, and so on, until the angle is so steep that the ray penetrates the F-layer. The average signal strength will be equal to the strongest hop mode that is open. Although the results can be presented in different analytical formats, the methodology outlined above is always followed when the multi-hop model is used. This model is used on both short and long paths.

The Chordal-Propagation Model

The multi-hop mode is the basic engine that drives all of the propagation predictions of the program—with one exception, the *chordal-propagation model*. The chordal-propagation model looks for chordal-propagation possibilities along the F layer. This is a common mode for long-path propagation, but chordal propagation can also occur on short paths.

Chordal-propagation occurs when the signal enters the F layer and rather than encountering a profile of ionization that is symmetrical on the up and down legs, it encounters an asymmetrical profile so that the down leg is bent less than the up leg. This

may occur, for example, near the grayline as the signal heads in the direction of darkness. On the up leg through the F Layer, the ray is in sunlight but as it starts to turn downward from the ionosphere, it enters the nighttime where the ionization is falling off.

The down leg is bent less than the up leg. If the gradient is strong enough, the down leg will miss the surface of the Earth, and will go straight across to another entry into the F layer, all in a straight line, and all in a *chord* along the great circle.

At the next apex in the ionosphere, the gradient may still be decreasing (in which case the next down angle will be even more oblique) or there might not be any gradient. That is, the ionization profile is symmetrical (in which case the down angle will equal the up angle). For the signal to continue at all, the ionization must be strong enough to refract the signal at each apex. Given the oblique angles in question, however, low ionization levels will work. That is a key to chordal propagation.

The process will then be repeated. The down legs will continue to "chord," to miss the Earth, and to reenter the F layer farther along the path, forming a series of chords along the great-circle route. This series of chords will continue until the ray again encounters a sufficient gradient in the *opposite* direction, such as the grayline on the other side of the Earth. Here, the original asymmetry will be reversed. The ray will enter the F layer, will encounter ever *increasing* ionization. The down leg will thus be *steeper* and, if steep enough, will return to Earth to the lucky station listening for chordal propagation. Signals will go both ways on the same path under the reciprocity principle.

The identifying feature of such chordal propagation is a U-shaped profile as the critical frequency of the F layer is traced along the entire path, with a dip near the middle and higher near the ends. There are three circumstances that typically result in a U-shaped profile:

1. The most effective is when both ends of the path are near the grayline and the rest of the path is in darkness. An example is the path from California to Poland on short-path summer evenings and long-path winter mornings.
2. One end of the path is at the grayline and the other, although in darkness, is near the magnetic equator, with its higher critical frequencies, and the rest of the path is in darkness. Example: California to Singapore on summer mornings.
3. Many polar routes, whether completely in darkness or completely in daylight (or some combination thereof), experience a weakening of the critical frequencies near the poles and thus create a U-shape. Example: Jamaica to Japan on autumn evenings.

Near-Chordal Multi-Hop Propagation

There is an intermediate case in which the gradients of a U-shaped profile are not steep enough to launch true chordal propagation, but are strong enough to reshape the intermediate hops so that more oblique angles are created to the Earth and the F layer. On the other end of the U-shaped profile, the gradient corrects the shallower angle and returns it to an angle somewhat similar to (but not necessarily the same as) the original takeoff angle. The advantage of such propagation is that it reshapes the intermediate hop geometry in favor of more oblique angles and longer spans. This results in lower reflection losses, although the losses are obviously greater than for true chordal propagation. I call this intermediate case *Near Chordal Multi-Hop Propagation*. It can occur, once again, on either long-path or short-path propagation.

How *XMW* Takes Chordal Propagation Into Account

Both true-chordal and near-chordal propagation reduce losses and increase signal strength, the former by eliminating intermediate hops altogether and the latter by reducing their number and rendering their angles more oblique. Whether short or long path, *XMW* routinely checks for a U-shape in the F layer critical frequencies along the great circle route path. If the path is U-shaped, then it is graded and given a *tilt rating*. The more pronounced the U-shape, the higher will be the tilt rating. The tilt rating is then used to reduce the number of intermediate hops and their angles. The greater the tilt rating, the greater the effect, which is always in the direction of reducing losses and in increasing the frequencies that will refract off the F layer. Trial and error was used to find coefficients that simulated my own observations.[4] The *XMW* program does not ray trace. Instead, it looks for conducive conditions and when the conducive conditions are present, adjusts the operation of the multi-hop model.

Finding The Critical Frequency

How does the program estimate the critical frequencies along the great-circle route? The basic model takes into account many variables. The answer must be computed separately for various points along the path.

The E Layer

The E-Layer Critical Frequency (at Vertical Incidence) is:

$$E_{crit} = 0.9 \times \left[(180 + 1.44 \times SSN) \times \cos \chi \right]^{0.25}$$

where χ is the Zenith angle of the sun, referenced to vertical. This formula comes from Davis's Eq 5.1, *Ionospheric Radio Propagation*, p 130 (1990).

The F Layer

There is no published formula I could find for the F layer, so I devised the following, which works well with my own observations from Oakland. At sunrise, the F layer starts with minimum ionization and builds as the sun gets higher and higher. When the sun sets, the ionization begins to fall off. The program assumes that the F-layer critical frequency rises and falls in the same general manner as a capacitor would charge and discharge but the rates of charging and discharging are a function of the season and latitude, among other factors. During daylight:

$$F_{crit} = Floor + Delta \times$$
$$\left(1 - 1/e^{Blue/TimeConAM}\right)$$

where Floor is the starting minimum critical frequency at dawn. Floor varies with the smoothed sunspot number (SSN) as well as the latitude and declination of the Earth. Specifically,

$$Floor = (5.5 + 0.01 \times SSN) \times FnMinus$$

and

$$FnMinus = \cos(Latitude \times$$
$$K_1 - Declination2)^{K_{16}}$$

Declination2 is the declination of the Earth, slightly adjusted for a seasonal lag. K_1 and K_{16} were estimated by trial and error and are set forth in the COEFFICIENTS subroutine in *XMW*. Thus, the dawn starting point is a function of the latitude and the declination as well as SSN.

Delta is the difference between the Floor and the greatest F_{crit} possible for the latitude, Declination2 and SSN. Specifically,

$$Delta = K_{10} \times FnPlus$$

where

$$FnPlus = \cos(Latitude \times K_1$$
$$+ Declination2)^{K_{15}}$$

and again the constants K_1 and K_{15} were estimated by trial and error and are in the COEFFICIENTS subroutine.

Note that FnPlus and FnMinus vary in opposite ways with the declination of the Earth. This difference is used to simulate the *winter anomaly*, whereby the peak daytime critical frequency in the winter is greater than in the summer (all other things being equal) and the dawn critical frequency is lower than in the summer.

Blue is the time elapsed since sunrise expressed in radians (with one complete 24-hour period being 2π). TimeConAM is a time constant for the quickness (or slowness) of the build-up in the mornings. In the summer, this number is larger than in the winter, so that the build-up is slower (and vice versa). So this time constant is really a variable and it varies with the portion of a 24-hour day that the latitude in question is in daylight.

During the night:

$$F_{crit} = Dusk \times \left(1 - 1/e^{Black/TimeConPM}\right)$$

where Dusk is the last daylight F_{crit} before sunset. Black is the time elapsed since sunset expressed in radians (with one complete 24-hour period being 2π).

TimeConPM is a time constant that increases in the summer and decreases in the winter. Note: For both TimeConAM and TimeConPM there is also a slight enhancement of the steepness of the build-up or falloff as the SSN gets greater and greater (and vice versa).

In the afternoon, *XMW* makes a small adjustment to simulate a slight and steady fall-off in the critical frequency (see the FCRIT.CENTER subroutine). At all times, there are further adjustments made to increase the critical frequency somewhat just above and just below the magnetic equator, including a further increment there when the K index rises. The maximum increase will be at 20° on either side of the magnetic equator. At night, to make sure that the critical frequency will end up back where it started at dawn, a curve is imposed from the known midnight value to the known dawn value. Finally, from *The ARRL Antenna Book* comes the conversion from SSN to Solar Flux:

$$SSN = 33.52 \times (85.12 + Flux)^{0.5} - 408.99$$

Significantly, the foregoing formulas give the critical frequency *at vertical incidence*. Higher and higher frequencies can be reflected as the angle of entry into the ionosphere becomes more oblique. The relationship used for the F layer is MUF = F_{crit}/sin (UpAng) where UpAng is the angle of entry into the F layer. Note that UpAng is not the same thing as the takeoff angle at the antenna. UpAng is always larger, given the curvature of the Earth. For the E Layer, $E_{MUF} = E_{crit}$/sin (UpAngE). (UpAngE for the E layer will be less than the UpAng for the F layer, given their differences in height.) The foregoing is an overall description of the equations used.

Finding the Virtual Height of the F Layer

The program generally assumes that the average *actual* height of the centerline of the F layer is 190 miles, that it decreases more and more as we close in on the daytime in the dead of winter, and that it rises more and more as we close in on the daytimes in the middle of summer.

More specifically, the height center is a function of the thermal condition of the atmosphere. That, in turn, is a function of the season and the latitude. In the summers, there is a thermal expansion of the atmosphere. The height of the ionized regions rise as the atmosphere and ionosphere expand. In the winters, there is a contraction and there is a greater density of ions created by the sun's radiation.

At dusk, for all seasons, the electrons and ions begin to recombine. In the winter, the recombination rate is much faster, given the closer proximity of the electrons and ions. As a result, the F-layer center decays to its 190-mile standard quickly. In the summers, the electrons and ions are a further apart and it takes longer for them to recombine. *XMW* simulates this pattern. The height is also enhanced just above and below the magnetic equator with the maximum boost at 20° above and below the magnetic equator.

The *virtual* height is the height of the intersection of the extensions of the straight line portions of the up and down legs of a hop. This intersection will always be higher than the actual refraction turn-around point within the F layer. The virtual height will often be entirely above the F layer. The virtual height is a convenient way to determine the overall geometry of the hop because it allows you to use straight lines from the surface of the Earth to the apex of the virtual height.

In *XMW*, the virtual height for a given hop is found by starting with the actual height of the F layer (take 200 miles as an example) and increasing it slightly as the frequency goes up (because the higher the frequency, the longer it will take to turn the ray around), decreasing it slightly as the ionization goes up (for the opposite reason) and decreasing it with the distance covered by the hop (the shorter the hop, the steeper the up and down legs will be). Thus, *XMW* uses the following relationship:

$$Virtual\ Height = Actual\ Height \times$$
$$(1 + Increment)$$

where
$$Increment = 0.02 \times (Freq/F_{crit}) \times$$
$$(0.6/Angle)$$

where F_{crit} is the critical frequency at vertical incidence and Angle is the angle subtended by the distance of a single hop, as measured from the center of the Earth (in radians).

Thus, if the Actual Height is 200 miles and the frequency is 14 MHz and the F_{crit} is 7 MHz and Angle = 8° or 0.14 radians (about

560 miles per hop), then the Virtual Height will be

$$200 \times (1 + 0.02 \times 14/7 \times 0.6/0.14)$$
$$= 234 \text{ miles.}$$

Admittedly, this equation is homebrew but it seems to capture the general effect of the variables. In general, during the daytime in winter, the effect is that the takeoff angles go down for the same number of hops and the entry angle also goes down, thus increasing the MUF, and vice versa.

The program does not calculate the virtual height for each hop individually. Instead, it finds the *average* Actual Height (of the centerline) and the average Fcrit for all apexes along the circuit, and then calculates an average Virtual Height for the overall circuit.

Once the virtual height is known, the HOPDIMENSIONS subroutine in *XMW* calculates the angles of entry into the F and E layers (UpAng and UpAngE) and the takeoff angles from the Earth. UpAng and UpAngE are needed to find whether the angle will be so steep that it pierces the layers. This calculation to determine whether the ray penetrates the F layer is *not* made on an average basis but is tested hop-by-hop, using the critical frequencies of the actual location of the apex in the F layer or passage through the E layer. (From the 31 samples

of E and F ionization taken along the route, HOPDIMENSIONS selects those closest to the location in question.)

We have now covered a summary of the theory of operation. Now, let's review the way you can put *XMW* to use. The installation steps are on the CD accompanying this book in a plain text file called XMWGUIDE.TXT. Once you've installed the program, you can enter *XMW* from your root directory to start using *XMW*.

Have fun and please be sure to drop me a note with comments and observations about the program. [*XMW* is part of an integrated package of logging, QSLing and propagation-prediction programs created by N6XMW. Contact him directly for information on the complete package.—*Ed.*]

Notes and References
[1] For vertical antennas, you can elect to see the signal strengths before application of any vertical radiation pattern. While this will not show the effect of the antenna, it will show the ambient signal strength seen by an isotropic antenna. If you are using a vertical antenna, then you have to adjust using your own judgment. *XMW* does not yet simulate the radiation profile of a vertical antenna.

[2] Why should absorption in the D/E layers be proportional to the cosine of the angle of incidence but absorption in the F layer proportional to sine of the angle of incidence? The difference lies in the fact that the case we care about is where the ray penetrates the D/E layers but does not penetrate the F layer. Take the case of a shallow angle that nonetheless pierces the E layer. It will spend a lot of time in the D/E layers (thus cosine is indicated to increase absorption) and spend less time in the F layer, since the turn-around will take less time (thus the sine is indicated to decrease absorption).

[3] The program distinguishes between land and sea as follows. For each touchdown point, its latitude is rounded to the nearest half degree. A file is consulted that corresponds to that nearest half degree. This file (and all such files) start at 180° West longitude, the middle of the Pacific Ocean. The file contains the longitudes of all borders of land/sea along that latitude, starting at the 180° point and moving eastward. The program consults the file until it first finds a border that exceeds the touchdown point in question. The character of the land/sea just before this border then represents the character of the touchdown point.

[4] The program rates U-shapes as follows: a deep bowl is rated higher than a shallower one. A steep gradient at the ends is rated higher than more gentle gradients at the ends. A longer span of the U-shape, end-to-end, is rated higher than a path that has a shorter U-shaped span. The program then lowers the angles and intermediate hop numbers accordingly.

Where the Holes Are and How to Plug Them

By Dan Handelsman, N2DT
16 Attitash
Chappaqua, NY 10514

Introduction

All hams (especially DXers) long for the perfect QTH. They dream of hilltops first but if a hill isn't available, they'll dream of large expanses of conductive, flat ground. However, the majority of us never get to buy that perfect QTH, since other matters intrude, such as family, job and expense.

So, if your QTH is like mine—neither on the top of an unobstructed hill nor on the prairie over farmland—you will have reflections and diffractions that alter your antenna radiation pattern. These may be minimal or severe, but until the advent of terrain-modeling programs we could only guess at was happening to our signals. The real-world elevation patterns are never the same as those in *The ARRL Handbook* or in any antenna book.[1] Nonetheless, most of us assume wrongly that the pattern for flat earth should hold true for our particular installations.

My QTH

I have been a ham since 1957 but have always had poor QTHs prior to moving to my present QTH in 1975. One of the considerations for choosing it was how good it would be for ham radio, although this was a relatively minor consideration—the family came first. Still, I was delighted that for the first time I was located on a hilltop. I figured that the ridges and lines of hills in the distance were too far away to affect my signal and they never entered my stream of consciousness. How wrong I was.

I began DXing earnestly in 1977 with my new Extra Class call sign. As with most new DXers, by the word "earnestly" I actually mean "obsessively." I eventually worked them all but found that some headings on various bands were extremely good while others were quite the opposite. Initially, when I was using my first antenna, a two-element quad at 50 feet in a topped-off oak tree, I blamed the antenna and my lack of expertise.

N2DT gets really serious about evaluating his terrain!

The first DXpedition I attempted to work—Clipperton in 1978—should have taught me a lesson early on but didn't. I worked them only on 20 meters. I shouted and keyed my brains out but got nowhere on 10 and 15 meters.

Eventually I acquired more expertise and graduated to a 70-foot tower and a KLM KT34-XA at 70 feet and a KLM two-element 40-meter Yagi at 90 feet. I then started logging not only signal strengths but paths and solar conditions. I began to get a feel for DX that I could work on the proverbial "first call" and for those countries where I knew I would have to persevere, and maybe eventually work with difficulty. A pattern started to emerge on the 10 to 40-meter bands. I wasn't active on 80 meters for many years.

I discovered the right combination for contesting—I only operated on 10 and 40 meters. I chose those bands because I got my most consistent results and could compete better against the big multi-multis there. While I did pretty well, I still didn't understand why I had *holes* in some directions and *whispering galleries* in others—where it seemed I could work the DX with a loaded coat hanger. I didn't understand the inconsistent propagation until recently, when I examined the local terrain with two terrain-modeling programs.[2]

This article is to tell you what I found out about the effects of my local terrain on propagation and the remedies that I used to overcome the holes. First, I will discuss the idiosyncratic propagation at this QTH, showing you where the difficult and the easy

paths are. Then I will analyze the terrain and its effects on my signals and, lastly, I will show how I attempted to overcome the weaknesses.

Where the Propagation Holes Are

I had several difficult propagation paths based on experience. One was the hole to the southwest toward Oceania. This was most evident on 10, 15 and 40 meters. My easiest QSOs and strongest signal reports from Jarvis, Wake, and Macquarie were all on 20 meters. I had to work very hard to make QSOs with that part of the world on 10 and 15 meters. If the long path was open, things became a lot easier.

Another problem area was coverage to the southeast. For example, during one 10-meter contest I had difficulty working ZD8 and other DX in that direction. The little guys with small tribanders on 50-foot towers were having no trouble and I couldn't understand why I was.

There was also a narrow path over central Africa that gave me trouble. This ranged from 3C on the west coast to C9 and 5R8 on the east. The difficulty was not to the same degree as that of the southwestern path and was highly variable. Some days things went well and some days resulted in long periods of frustration.

My Good Propagation Paths

With the exception of the poor paths discussed above, paths to the rest of the world ranged from very good to exceptional. The latter included beam headings of 0° to 30°

encompassing Central Asia, Asiatic SSRs and the northern Indian Ocean. Other good paths were toward Europe and the Middle East, South America, JA and the northern Pacific, and the gray-line and long paths that lay to the southeast. Unlike the short path into the South Pacific, the long path over Europe was tremendous.

To illustrate some of these exceptional paths I will give you some 10-meter examples. In 1981, at the peak of that solar cycle, I noticed that I could work the southeastern 10-meter longpath into Asia and VK6 with ease. The heading was somewhere between 140° and 160°. For almost three years, I worked JA and VK6 long path in the early morning and on the short path in the evening. I had no trouble running JAs in contests.

I also had almost daily contact over two years during the fall-spring seasons with Frank, VK9NYG, a novice on Cocos Keeling, who was running low power. He came in on a heading of about 20° and on some days no one else could hear him—some of my friends thought I was talking to myself. I worked him sometimes on as little as 1 W, and occasionally on both long and short paths at the same time. One time I heard echoes on his signal because of simultaneous reception on both paths.

The northwest direction toward JA and the European paths were also exceptional from my QTH, and I began to understand why it was easy to have good runs in the DX contests into the most heavily populated areas of amateurs. These results held for all the bands.

An Early Solution

My ZD8 problem led to the wrong conclusion, but the right solution. I thought that I was having difficulty because my takeoff angle was too low because my antenna was too high—the effective height above ground in that direction was 140 feet because of the hill. After reading Les Moxon's book on antennas[3] and the influence of terrain on their radiation pattern, I wrote a computer program to calculate the takeoff angles of antennas placed down the slope of a hill. I then hung a three-element 10-meter beam, pointed to the southeast, from a tree near the bottom of the hill. The antenna was about 20 feet above the slope of the hill and about 40 feet above the far ground. It got out like gangbusters towards ZD8 and other areas to the southeast. Signal strengths were much higher than on the high antenna. I thought I fixed my low-angle problem and thought about placing an echelon of small beams at various heights along the slope of the hill and facing different directions to the east and southeast.

Where the DX is Coming From

Two things happened recently that made me curious about the great propagation in some directions and the holes in others. First, I saw the light after reading N6BV, Dean Straw's chapter in *The ARRL Antenna Book*[4] on the arrival angles of DX on the HF bands. To my surprise, the arrival angles on virtually all the bands and from all points on the compass were low, much lower than I expected. For the most part they were below 10°.

The second thing that happened was *YT*.[5] This is N6BV's computer program that analyzes terrain and its effects on propagation. I also bought *TA*,[6] another 2-dimensional terrain analysis program based on the same algorithm but with a slightly different format. After playing with both programs I found that my initial assumptions about arrival angles and antenna height were often wrong. Surprisingly, I found that sometimes *lower antennas had lower takeoff angles*. This appeared to be due to diffraction by the ridge of hills to the east of me. What I also learned was that terrain up to 2 miles distant from an antenna can influence my elevation pattern.

I then decided to systematically (OK, obsessively) model the 360° azimuth surrounding my QTH in 10° (sometimes 5°) increments to see what was happening to my signal. I taped two USGS[7] topographical maps of my area together, drew circles with radii of one and two miles around my antenna and plotted every hill and valley. The results were both surprising and revealing.

My QTH

If you look at the topo map of the area surrounding my QTH you will find that it is a glacial landscape composed of parallel ridges and valleys heading north and south. You see a sharp drop-off in elevation to the whole eastern hemisphere. My elevation is 470 feet above sea level (ASL) and the antenna height is at 540 feet. The plateau to the east below my antenna is at 400 feet and the effective height, I thought, of the antenna was 140 feet.

To the east, there is an almost parallel ridge of hills going north-south anywhere from 1500 to 2500 feet away and another ridge at 5000 to 7000 feet in distance. The near ridge varies in elevation between 480 and 600 feet and the far ridge has peaks at over 700 feet. Because of the drop-off beneath my antenna and the flat plateau of marshland until the ridge, it is not surprising that I thought my problems were due to too much of a good thing and that my takeoff angle was too low.

Fig 1 is a plot of the terrain at a heading of 110° toward ZD8, where I have had problems communicating. While the terrain does drop off quickly from the tower base, which is at 470 feet ASL, within a half mile the land rises up to 600 feet. And at a distance of a mile, the land is almost 675 feet high. The angle from

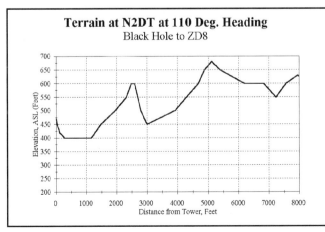

Fig 1—Terrain profile from N2DT's QTH in the direction of ZD8 (from USGS topographic map). The terrain peaks at roughly one-half and one mile create problems for signals launched in this direction.

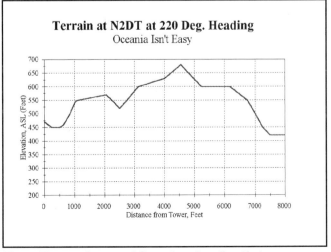

Fig 2—The terrain toward Oceania, a heading that causes major problems for N2DT.

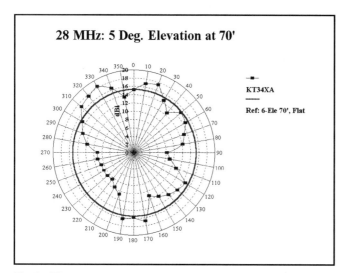

Fig 3—The computed 360° response of a 70-foot high KT34XA Yagi on 28 MHz, at a 5° elevation angle launched from N2DT's tower, compared to the response for a six-element reference Yagi mounted 70 feet above flat ground.

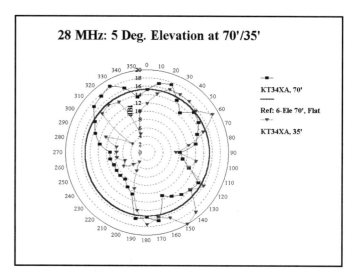

Fig 4—The same response for 70-foot 28-MHz Yagi as in Fig 3, except that the response for an identical 35-foot high Yagi is overlaid for comparison. Surprisingly, the lower antenna has better gain in some directions than the higher one.

my antenna at 540 feet ASL (70 foot tower plus 470 feet above sea level) to the 600-foot peak one-half mile away is about 1.4°, effectively blocking direct signals below this elevation angle. (Note that the different scales for X and Y in Fig 1 exaggerate the steepness of this angle, making the terrain look more severe than it really is.)

Towards the west, about 2500 to 3000 feet away, there is another valley and then another ridge that reaches up to 680 feet in altitude. The ridges and valleys continue to alternate until one reaches the Hudson River, which is about 6 miles to the west.

The southwest is my major problem heading. There is rising terrain in that direction, punctuated by hills with heights up to 670 feet. After close examination of the topographic map I began to see why I was hav-

ing trouble getting out. **Fig 2** depicts the terrain at a beam heading of 220° towards Oceania.

My Terrain and its Effects on Propagation

Because of the fact that almost all DX propagation occurs at 10° or lower, I used this angle as the high reference in my antenna comparisons. The low reference angle I used was 5°, since it is frequently encountered and I found that it was consistent with lower-angle propagation. That is, antennas with good gain at 5° were also good at even lower-elevation angles.

The antennas I used for modeling were equivalent to my KLM KT34-XA tribander in gain. On 10 meters I used a high-gain six-element Yagi on a 29 foot boom, which was

almost equivalent in gain to my tribander with a 32-foot boom. The model antennas for 15 and 20 meters were the five-element monoband HyGain HG-155 and HG-205CA. On 40 meters I used a two-element Yagi model similar to mine. For reference antennas, I used the same models, but placed them over flat terrain.

The antenna heights I used for reference were 70 and 35 feet on 10 to 20 meters and 90 feet on 40 meters. I arrived at the 35-foot height because it was the best compromise for the lower antenna height in a two antenna stack[8] on the three high bands.

Results of Terrain Modeling— Filling the Holes

What I propose to do is give you an overview of the propagation around the circle sur-

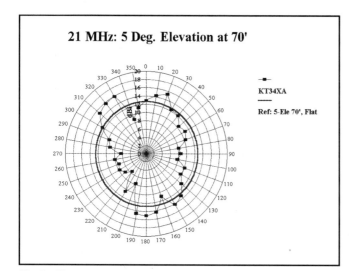

Fig 5—The computed 360° response of a 70-foot high KT34XA Yagi on 21 MHz, at a 5° elevation angle launched from N2DT's tower, compared to the response for a five-element reference Yagi mounted 70 feet above flat ground.

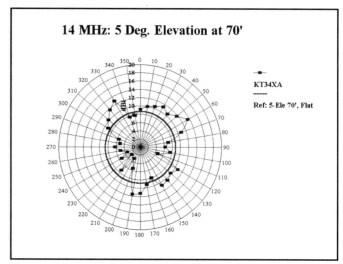

Fig 6—The computed 360° response of a 70-foot high KT34XA Yagi on 14 MHz, at a 5° elevation angle launched from N2DT's tower, compared to the response for a five-element reference Yagi mounted 70 feet above flat ground.

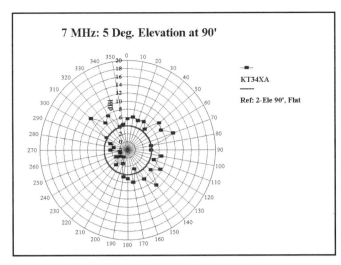

Fig 7—The computed 360° response of a 90-foot high two-element 7 MHz Yagi, at a 5° elevation angle launched from N2DT's tower, compared to the response for a two-element reference Yagi mounted 90 feet above flat ground.

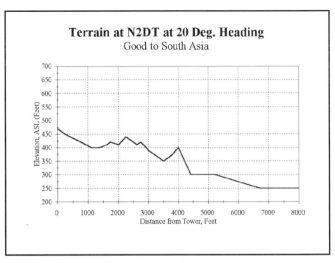

Fig 8—The terrain towards South Asia at a beam heading of 20°. This direction plays very well for N2DT!

rounding my antenna and then analyze in detail a sample of three directions that exhibit exceptional propagation, and then three directions that present problems on all bands. In each case, I used the *TA* program to compute the gain at a 5° elevation angle[9] and in each case I compared the response with that for a reference antenna over flat ground.

Fig 3 gives you an idea of what propagation is like, at an elevation angle of 5° degrees, in the 360° surrounding my QTH. The results are consistent and show minima around 45°, 70° to 110° and the whole southwestern quadrant. The maxima are in the general headings of 0° to 40°, 120° to 150°, 170°

to 190° and 300° to 340° degrees. On Fig 3 I've overlaid an excellent reference antenna, a six-element 10-meter Yagi at 70 feet over flat ground. I did most of my modeling at 28 MHz and in the rest of this article I will only make comments if the propagation on the other bands shows something different.

In General

Fig 4 is a bit more complicated to read, since it overlays the gain patterns at 5° elevation for 10-meter Yagis at 70 and 35 feet. What is really interesting here is that the lower antenna has better low-angle gain to many parts of the world than the higher one.

For example, calculations show that my 35-foot high antenna beats out my 70-foot high antenna by about 4 dB at a 60° heading, and by 8 dB at a 150° heading. The computations proved to me what I already knew—that my little three-element Yagi at the bottom of the hill had a better signal to the southeast than the bigger and higher one.

Fig 5 through **7** show the patterns at 5° elevation for my 15, 20 and 40-meter antennas. There are similarities in all quadrants to the results for 10 meters. This is better-than-average gain to the northwest, northeast, southeast and the south and worse-than-average gain to the southwest

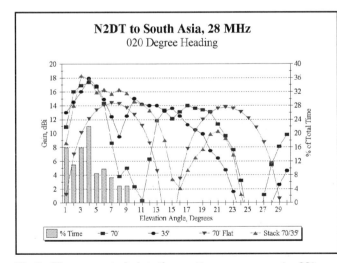

Fig 9—The computed elevation-pattern response at a 20° beam heading for a 70-foot high Yagi, a 35-foot high Yagi and the two in a stack at 70/35 feet, compared with a single Yagi at 70 feet over flat ground. The elevation-angle statistics from the 18th Edition of *The ARRL Antenna Book* are overlaid on this plot to show what angles are required to cover South Asia over the whole solar cycle. The peak angle is 4°, occurring 22% of the all the times when the 28-MHz band is open on this path.

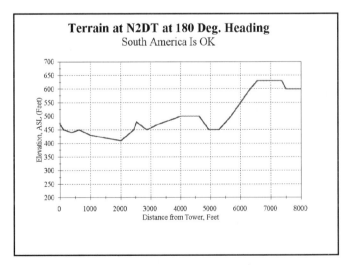

Fig 10—The terrain towards South America from N2DT, at a heading of 180°. This terrain is rather benign, with the peak at 7000 feet from the tower far enough away and low enough so that it doesn't drastically affect the launch pattern.

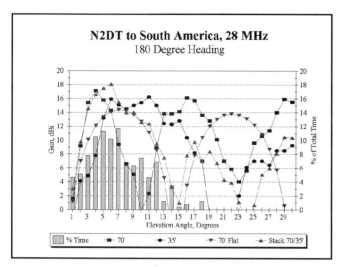

Fig 11—The computed elevation-pattern response for 70 and 35-foot high antennas at N2DT in the direction of South America. While the pattern isn't quite as good as that in Fig 9 towards South Asia, it is still excellent. For those times when the angles are higher than 8°, the antenna at 35 feet would be the best performer, better even than the stack at 70/35 feet.

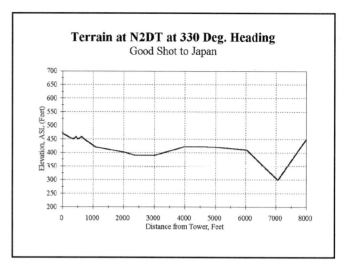

Fig 12—The terrain towards Japan from N2DT, at a heading of 330°. This is another really excellent direction for him.

and in the gaps mentioned above.

The "Good, the Bad and the Ugly" Headings

I chose three representative good headings to analyze further because they feature different terrains and different resulting effects on radiation. These are at beam headings of 20°, 180° and 330°. I will show you the terrain profile and then the takeoff patterns for individual antennas at 35 and 70 feet, plus the stacked-Yagi patterns.

20° Heading to South Asia

Fig 8 shows the terrain profile at a 20° heading. The terrain is a general downward

slope extending out to 7000 feet. The antenna elevation profiles in Fig 9 show exceptional low-angle gains for both the 35 and 70-foot heights. They are better than that of the reference Yagi at 70 feet over flat ground. Notice that the most frequent arrival angle is 4° for signals from this direction, statistically speaking, of course.

180° Heading to South America

My terrain to the south is shown in Fig 10, which shows the altitude to be lower than my antenna at 540 feet, up to a distance of a mile from the tower. Thereafter the land rises and peaks at 630 feet at a distance of 6500 feet. The elevation pattern in Fig 11

shows that there are effects due to diffractions at the nearby low hills and at the distant ones. The net effect is that there is a peak in gain of about 5 dB for my 70-foot antenna compared to the reference antenna over flat ground. There is also a good fill above about 6° for the low antenna. You can see what the diffractions do—they fill in the nulls in the elevation pattern. The stack of both antennas at 35 and 70 feet interacts in a complicated way with the diffracted and direct waves, but still is superior to the single reference over flat ground for the whole range of elevation angles of interest, from 1° to about 14°. What is clear from Fig 11 is that there is no single best antenna

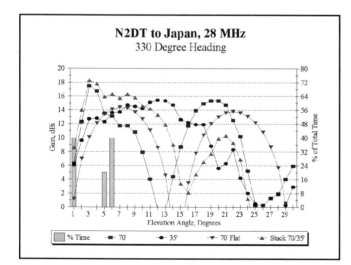

Fig 13—The computed 28-MHz elevation response in the direction of Japan from N2DT's QTH. The stack at 70/35 feet is the best performer on this path, although the single 70-foot high Yagi is not very far behind over the range of elevation angles necessary on this path.

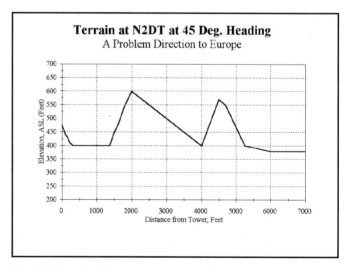

Fig 14—Despite his generally excellent response to Europe, N2DT found that at a heading of 45° he has a significant hill that can cause a problem.

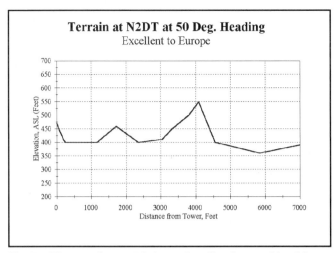

Fig 15—The terrain at a 50° beam heading is considerably more benign than at 45° shown in Fig 14.

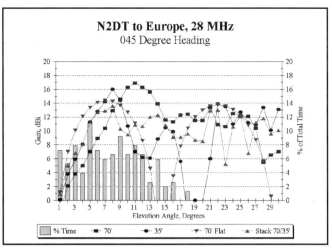

Fig 16—The computed elevation response at a 45° heading into Europe from N2DT. At all angles lower than about 9°, all his antennas are down some compared to the single 70-foot high reference Yagi over flat ground. This doesn't seem to be a major problem in practice, because he does well into Europe.

that covers all the arrival angles from South America. At any point in time, the high antenna, the low one or the stack of both can be the most effective.

330° Heading to Japan

My terrain in **Fig 12** at a 330° heading to Japan shows a general drop off in elevation until 7000 feet, and then rises to a peak of 500 feet beyond 8000 feet in distance. **Fig 13** shows the computed elevation response of the separate antennas and the two together in a stack. The statistical range of elevation angles on 10 meters to Japan from the East Coast is narrow, from 1° to only 6°.

The stack is better than either antenna by itself, but the 70-foot antenna holds it own very well over the necessary range of elevation angles.

The bad holes in coverage that showed up on all bands were at 45° and 80° to 110°. The really ugly hole was in the southwest quadrant. There were idiosyncratic holes on 15 meters at a heading of 270° and on 20 meters at 280°.

45° Heading

The 45° hole is one I never really noticed since the gains on either side of it are exceptional toward Europe. The 45° heading is

characterized by a hill that is higher than the others on the ridge. The terrain at a beam heading of 45° is shown in **Fig 14**, and **Fig 15** shows my terrain at a 50° heading. At 45° the hill shows a sharp rise at 2000 feet distance to an altitude of 600 feet, and there is another but lower peak 4500 feet away.

Note that the first peak is only 60 feet above the height of the antenna. **Fig 16** shows what happens to signals along this 45° heading. The nose of the vertical lobe is raised up and the low angles are skimmed off. The low antenna at 35 feet outperforms the high one at 70 feet for angles below 9° and curiously, the 75/35-foot stack is actu-

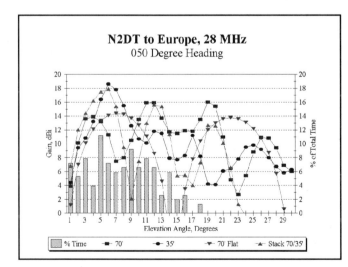

Fig 17—The computed elevation response at a 50° heading into Europe on 28 MHz. The 35-foot high lower antenna is nominally better than the 70-foot one or the stack over the relatively wide range of statistical elevation angles required on this path over all times of the 11-year solar cycle. There are times, however, at angles higher than about 9° where the 70-foot antenna's second lobe gives the best performance. At times like those when the higher antenna is dominant, you might mistakenly believe that the optimum angle is low, when it is in actuality high.

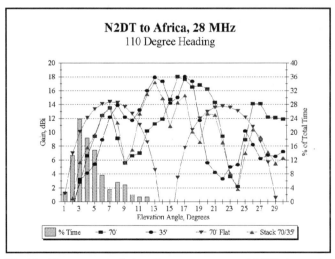

Fig 18—The computed elevation response on 28 MHz towards Africa, one of N2DT's problem directions. The operator down in the flat land will do better than N2DT on his hill in this direction.

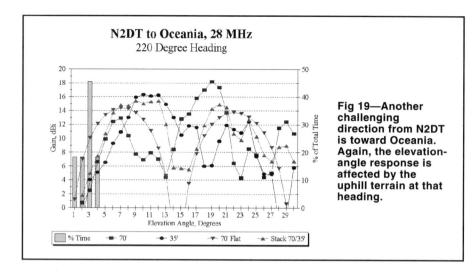

N2DT to Oceania, 28 MHz
220 Degree Heading

Fig 19—Another challenging direction from N2DT is toward Oceania. Again, the elevation-angle response is affected by the uphill terrain at that heading.

ally inferior to the 35-foot antenna by itself under these conditions.

Fig 17 shows the elevation pattern for a 50° beam heading on 10 meters. The stack at 35 and 70 feet is superior to either antenna by itself for angles lower than 6° elevation, but the 35-foot high antenna by itself is superior to the stack from 6° to 9°, while the 70-foot antenna dominates at angles higher than 10°. The peaks in the distance beyond one-half mile are apparently still getting into the diffraction act. For the path to Europe, the range of elevation angles is rather broad, from a low of 1° to a high of 18° (where the percentage of time is only 1% of all the times the 10-meter band is open to Europe over the whole solar cycle). Various antennas at various heights will be dominant at different times in the cycle, but the 35-foot high antenna is nominally the best for all times.

110° Heading to Africa

This is my ZD8 hole and is representative of the problems in the 80° to 110° sector. The terrain in Fig 1 shows a peak at 2500 feet and another, higher one, at 1 mile. The near peak is only 60 feet higher than my antenna but the low-angle degrees are chopped off, as you can see in **Fig 18**. The most common arrival angle at this heading from southern Africa is very low, at 3°, and all my antennas are disadvantaged at this angle compared to the reference

antenna over flat land. Other than putting the antenna very high, so that it can look over the top of the distant peaks, there's not much I can do in this direction. For example, raising the tower to 130 feet would net me about 4 dB more gain at 3° in this direction, leaving me still just about 3 dB down compared to the reference antenna!

220° Heading to Oceania

This "ugly" heading is representative of what happens at 200° to 270°. The terrain shown in Fig 2 rises continually, punctuated by peaks to a distance of 4500 feet. The elevation pattern is shown in **Fig 19** for this beam heading. At the peak statistical angle of 3° the 70-foot antenna is down about 8 dB compared to the reference Yagi 70-feet over flat ground. The stack has little effect on the low-angle gain because the low antenna is effectively shielded by the hills in the terrain profile. Fortunately for me, there is little DX in this direction! If you look at a polar-projection map centered on New York the quadrant to Oceania contains few countries.

Summary

Terrain modeling has brought a new dimension to DXing. Before these techniques became available we had some general feelings about what was happening to our signals but no clues about why things happened, nor how to improve the situation.

Since virtually no one lives on a flat antenna range our signals are significantly affected by the surrounding terrain.

Going bigger and higher is not a universal solution, since there are many instances where a low antenna can outperform a high one. Also we have no way to guess at how the hills and valleys affect our signals, for better or worse, and how much advantage a stack could give us. In certain directions either the high antenna, the low antenna or the stack provide more low-angle gain and the only way to know this is by terrain modeling. The only conclusion I can reach about the performance of a stack is that there is no advantage if the low antenna outperforms the higher one.

What I have shown in this article is the effect of the terrain surrounding my QTH and what measures I took to improve my signal. As far as I am concerned, the conclusions I came to after doing the modeling seem to be valid, in that they bear out observations I have made over 21 years of DXing. They confirm solutions I made empirically to improve my signal. There is no reason why all of us, with some patience and persistence, cannot put these terrain modeling programs to work to our advantage!

Notes and References

[1]*The ARRL Handbook*, 1999 Edition (Newington: ARRL, 1998). See also, *The ARRL Antenna Book*, 18th Edition (Newington: ARRL, 1997), edited by R. Dean Straw, N6BV.

[2]The programs are *YT*, by N6BV, bundled with *The ARRL Antenna Book*, and *TA* by Brian Beezley, K6STI. Beezley is no longer marketing his programs actively to amateurs.

[3]L. Moxon, *HF Antennas for All Locations* (Bath: RSGB, 1982). Available from ARRL Publication Sales.

[4]*The ARRL Antenna Book*, 18th Edition (Newington: ARRL, 1997), pp 23-24 and 23-25.

[5]See Note 2 above.

[6]Ibid.

[7]US Geologic Survey, 1:24000 topographical maps of the US.

[8]N6BV suggested stacked antennas as a solution in some directions when I sent him copies of my terrain profiles.

[9]The gains used in the figures are taken from *TA* and *YT* elevation patterns.

Low-Angle HF—History and Future

By Richard Silberstein, WØYBF
3915 Pleasant Ridge Road
Boulder, CO 80301-1717

Introduction

Anyone who has listened to small yachts communicating all over the Pacific on the 14-MHz maritime-mobile nets, or who has worked DX using vertical monopoles on seaside beaches, or who has used any antennas on favorable high sites realizes that low-angle HF propagation can often achieve spectacular results.

Most professional research on low-angle communications appears to have ceased by the late 1960s because of shortage of funds, caused largely by the advent of satellite communications. For the same reason many fine internal research reports were never submitted for publication in professional journals. However, amateurs have already done much to fill the void in low-angle and angle-control applied research, and the future holds the promise of more exciting investigations.

Low Angles

The following is a very brief explanation of why low-angle modes can improve ionospheric communication. **Fig 1** (adapted from Utlaut, 1962)[1] shows that HF ionospheric propagation in uncomplicated cases takes place using one or more hop modes. Combinations of reflections by different ionospheric layers can exist. There can be, on long-distance paths, propagation by a number of hops with high elevation angles ψ and a smaller number of low-angle hops at the same time.

In Fig 1 large elevation angles ψ coincide with small angles ϕ between the ray and a normal to the reflecting region at the ionosphere. As the angle ψ decreases towards the horizon at the transmitting site, ϕ increases up in the ionosphere. For a given frequency and ionospheric layer height, a larger angle ϕ requires less ionization to sustain refraction, and hence propagation over a given ground distance. Since they require lower levels of ionization, lower-angle modes can provide longer periods of

useful propagation compared to higher-angle modes.

Fig 1 also shows that for high elevation angles there can be a "skip zone" because of insufficient ionization for reflection. For example, angle Ψ_1 returns no signal until it bounces off the Earth's surface some 2700 km away from the transmitter. In Fig 1 any energy radiated at an angle higher than Ψ_1 shoots right through the ionosphere out into space. Lower angle Ψ_2 manages to return some signal at about 1700 km from the transmitter because it is reflected off a lower layer in the ionosphere.

The problem of exploiting low takeoff angles becomes one of designing, constructing and locating antenna systems that can radiate and receive efficiently at low elevation angles (and even negative angles with respect to the horizon at the transmitter). The goal is to have enough HF energy to

overcome atmospheric and industrial noise as well as the receiver noise floor, besides overcoming the absorption of energy in the lower ionospheric layers.

A History of Low Angle and Related Techniques

Many experiments with vertical polarization and high antennas have provided great thrills to many hams. However, no experiment that depends upon rapidly varying parameters (such as ionospheric propagation) can offer valid conclusions without comparisons with alternative methods, which must occur as nearly simultaneously as possible.

Early 1920s

In December 1921, in what may have been the greatest achievement by the ARRL, the first successful large-scale amateur transatlantic tests were performed (see

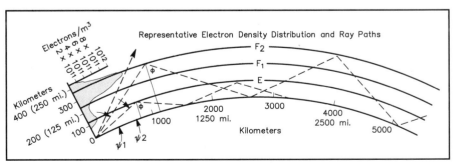

Fig 1—Idealized multihop propagation with curved Earth and ionosphere. (From Utlaut, 1962, Fig 1)

Kelley and Hudson,[2] 1996, and Warner, 1922).[3] The best reception was of 1BCG using vertical polarization, but a question remains about whether 1BCG was near enough to Long Island Sound and had a sufficiently unobstructed path to salt water for good low-angle propagation in the direction of Androssen, Scotland, where the receiver was located. The Beverage antenna used for reception in Scotland performed best on vertically polarized signals over poor soil, for which the beach at Androssen was well qualified. We'll be looking into the question of polarization often in this article.

From the Late 1920s to World War II

AT&T's Bell Laboratories performed many low-angle HF experiments (Potter and Friis, 1932)[4] during this period. Instrumentation was very good in these experiments. There were some comparisons of horizontal and vertical polarization, but only in 15-minute samples of each. At the time there was relatively little knowledge of the ionosphere, so important interpretations of adverse results were not made. Fresnel zones were not mentioned.

A later choice for telephone communications with England was 24 in-line horizontally polarized rhombics (the MUSA) over a salt marsh with vertical-angle control (Polkinghorn, 1940).[5] It is questionable how much of value was achieved with this array beyond the successful relaying of a live broadcast of the abdication address of King Edward VIII. Since salt marsh is almost as good as sea water for low-angle propagation modes using vertical polarization, perhaps the polarization choice for the MUSA array was wrong!

World War II and After

In 1943, Dr Newbern Smith, ex-3QY, National Bureau of Standards, overcame poor HF communication with a US air base in Iceland by installing a vertically polarized half-rhombic antenna by the sea near Reykjavik.

Beginning in the late 1950s Soviet and Chinese HF broadcast stations achieved phenomenal results for reception at great distances and even during some types of ionospheric disturbances. One antenna array was thought to be in Bulgaria and another at a high mountain site, probably in Asia. Angle-control was probably used, being derived from distance obtained by observing backscatter from audio peaks (Bain, 1963).[6]

An experiment by a US contractor on the East Coast of the United States utilized a high mountain for reception of CW test transmissions from Asia and achieved spectacular results near 7 MHz. However, a comparison reception site had serious problems and the quality of the Fresnel zones near the mountain were questioned. At that time,

satellite relays were beginning to replace HF systems, so the project was discontinued. I was a contract manager for the US Army at that time.

Dr H. Brueckmann of the US Army Signal Corps (later the US Army Electronics Laboratory) developed a 24-element vertically polarized broadband HF array, which was built on a slope in Maryland and oriented toward Germany. Pulsed signals at 13.560 MHz were provided by Dr Walter Dieminger, DL6DS, then director of the Max Planck Institute for Aeronomy. At that time I held the call WA2UZO, and I operated the angle-control equipment to demonstrate the importance of angle control in reducing multipath distortion, which constrained the maximum speed of digital communication (Brueckmann and Silberstein, 1963).[7]

Dr W. F. Utlaut (Utlaut, 1961)[8] performed tests of long-distance HF reception with horizontally polarized antennas at various heights over some very long paths, showing low-angle advantages. However, there were no comparisons made with other low-angle methods. Fading rates were not considered to be excessive, although the narrow lobes of high antennas could possibly cause fading problems with changes in the ionosphere.

In 1962 and 1963, Dr O. G. Villard, Jr, W6QYT,[9] ran tests using horizontally polarized antennas over some very long paths, showing low-angle advantages at high antenna heights, but did not make comparisons with vertical monopoles utilizing sea water foregrounds, even though a favorable site might have been available.

In 1962, I conducted tests by contacting DX stations in the 14-MHz band from the westernmost point on the island of Kauai, Hawaii, known then as the Barking Sands area (now part of the Pacific Missile Range). I made almost instant comparisons of vertical versus horizontal polarization for paths with all-ocean foregrounds to DX stations located mostly to the southwest of Kauai, and for paths with mostly all-land foregrounds to California and New Jersey. The vertically polarized antenna was a monopole with a low, elevated-radial ground plane on the beach. The horizontally polarized antenna was a multiple W8JK array about 40 feet high, oriented for a northeast and southwest maximum. This was later replaced with a horizontal doublet in the same orientation.

Fig 2 shows the monopole with the small island of Niihau in the background. **Fig 3** shows more details of the monopole with its elevated ground-plane radials. **Fig 4** shows the late Fred Dickson (then K2HJU, and later W7LBH) with an assistant making tests of the multiple W8JK array. **Fig 5** shows some propagation paths from the experimental site.

The vertical monopole was nearly always

best for an all-seawater foreground, and the horizontal antenna was nearly always best for the all-land foreground directions. The foreground over land was flat within about 20 feet for the first 10,000 feet in the northeasterly direction, but beyond there were high ridges and deep valleys across the path.

In one interesting case, signals from Guam went from 6 dB worse to 20 dB better

Fig 2—WØYBF's improvised 20-meter monopole at the edge of the beach at Barking Sands. The outline of the island of Niihau shows to the left on the horizon.

Fig 3—Close-up photo of monopole, showing gamma matching section and elevated ground-plane radials.

Fig 4—Fred Dickson, then K2HJU, standing, offers suggestions as a helper adjusts the feed line to a multiple W8JK antenna at Barking Sands, Kauai.

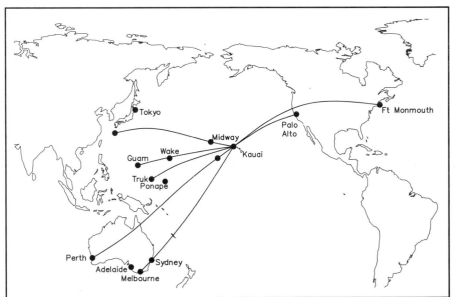

Fig 5—Great-circle paths from Kauai, Hawaii.

on the monopole compared to the doublet as the sun went down over the path. This might indicate that the higher-angle modes failed, leaving only a lower-angle mode.

In 1978 I went around South America on a ship and achieved surprising results with QRP equipment and a vertical monopole.[10] However, no direct comparisons with horizontal-antenna performance could be made. One item of note is that some vertical whips had been installed for the ship's communications on the lower HF marine bands. The operators discontinued use of them because of reception of atmospherics from tropical thunderstorms, for which good propagation of vertically polarized ocean ground wave could be blamed.

Some Pertinent Facts About the Ionosphere

The 1993 Edition of *The ARRL Handbook*

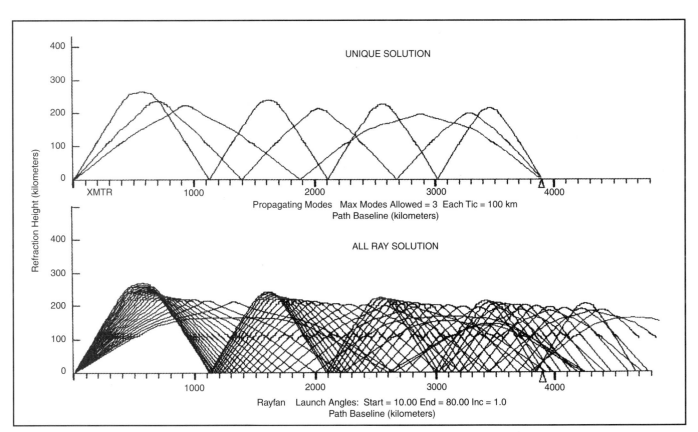

Fig 6—Ray trace of 14.0-MHz signals over the Hawaii to California path at 1800 UTC on Feb 21, 1973 (courtesy Naval Ocean Systems Center).

and also the 17th Edition of *The ARRL Antenna Book* provide rather good coverage of the role of the ionosphere as a medium of propagation of HF radio signals. Yet sometimes one wishes for just a little more explanation. However, if everyone's curiosity were satisfied, a "handbook" would become too large to carry on the back of an elephant! For those with a serious interest in the professional aspects of radio sky-wave propagation and who lean toward mathematical physics, I highly suggest a textbook like that of Ken Davies.[11] Then there are literature searches by the Internet, which can yield pertinent material rapidly if you know how to interrogate the system.

Since there are some simple features of propagation by means of the ionosphere that are pertinent to using low-angle HF modes, but which may not be obvious in published material, it is appropriate to discuss them here.

A computer output that shows how propagation modes behave in an ideal case appears as Fig 5 in Chapter 22 of the 1993 *ARRL Handbook*, reproduced here as **Fig 6**. This illustrates a ray trace of a 14-MHz signal propagated between Hawaii and San Francisco at 1800 UTC on Feb 23, 1973. This considers only the F_2 layer and assumes that it is uniform over the entire path. The distance was 2434 miles (3894 km). Fig 6 shows 2, 3 and 4-hop modes as being possible under those assumed conditions. Note that skip zones also appear.

What is not considered in Fig 6 is that some modes could be combinations of F-layer and E-layer hops. At this relatively short total distance it is also reasonable to assume that there are no departures from the great-circle azimuth.

Fig 7 (reproduced from Fig 6 in Chapter 22 of the 1993 *ARRL Handbook*) shows the classical form of a ionospheric sounder pattern for six F_2-layer hops. The sounder is

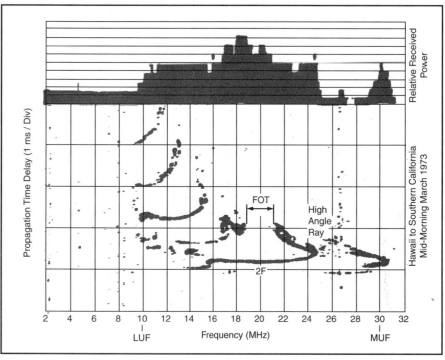

Fig 7—HF oblique sounder ionogram. This shows a typical chirpsounder measurement on a 2500-mile path during midmorning in Mar 1973 from Hawaii to Southern California.

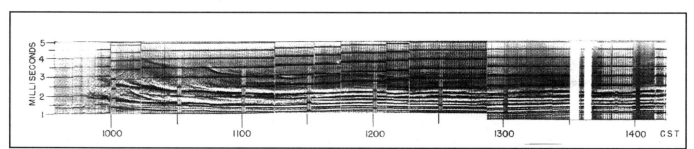

Fig 8—Oblique-incidence sunrise ionospheric sounder record, at Maui, Hawaii, for 20.1 MHz pulses from Sterling, VA, Oct 30, 1956 (from Fig 7, 1958 article by R. Silberstein).

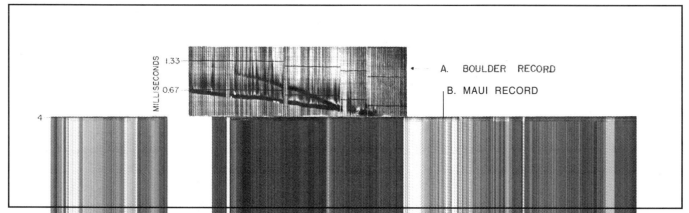

Fig 9—Oblique incidence ionospheric sounder records, Oct 25, 1956. At A, from Boulder, CO, and at B, from Maui, Hawaii (from Fig 5, 1958 article by R. Silberstein).

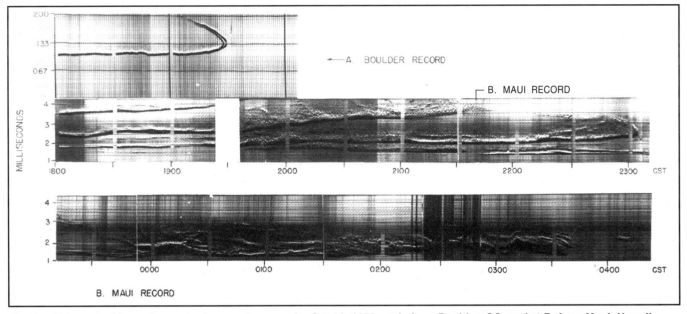

Fig 10—Oblique-incidence ionospheric sounder records, Oct 26, 1956: at A, from Boulder, CO, and at B, from Maui, Hawaii (from Fig 6, 1958 article by R. Silberstein).

an oblique-incidence system, which sweeps the frequency using pulse transmissions at one end and a synchronized receiver at the other end of the same circuit.

It is interesting to compare the computed results using ray-tracing techniques on this relatively short-distance path between Hawaii and California with actual ionogram results for a longer-distance path, this time from Sterling, Virginia, to Maui, Hawaii. This longer path is 4779 miles (7647 km) long.[12] **Figs 8**, **9** and **10**, reproduced from figures in my original 1958 report, show simultaneously recorded ionospheric sounder data and backscatter data yielding information about the most-probable propagation modes of 20.1-MHz pulses from Sterling recorded at Kihei, Maui, and at Boulder, Colorado. The ionograms show relative delay times for arriving pulses as the time of day advanced and as the ionization level changed at various reflecting regions along the path. The longer the multipath trajectory, the longer the delay.

Failure times for the recorded modes did not always agree with what was inferred from simultaneous vertical-incidence sounder data and backscatter data that were also recorded. Some of the substantial differences between the pulse recordings at several different times of day and the departures of the recorded results from ideal theoretical patterns suggested that at times when regular ionization on a longer path might have caused path failure, non-great-circle modes would appear. We saw this in a later experiment in 1965.[13]

At this point you might question the relevance of some of the above experimental results in cases where low-angle performance was not examined as a separate topic

and particularly where wave polarization was not considered. However, this material is relevant because it shows the mode structure of ionospherically propagated signals and their complexity and variability.

What is not generally realized is that polarization of received HF DX signals does not at any one moment depend solely on the polarization at the transmitting site. Briefly, this fact is due to the effect of the Earth's magnetic field on oscillating electrons in the ionosphere and the orientation of the geomagnetic field relative to the propagation path. The efficiency of launching and receiving DX radio waves at or near the Earth's surface at a given elevation angle will depend on polarization as well as the ground constants and the height of the antenna. However, the ionosphere itself will produce signals with mixed polarizations, as a signal is affected by the geomagnetic field. Signals of each polarization will then fade in a largely uncorrelated manner.

A final point worth mentioning is that for HF DX paths it is generally correct to assume reciprocity of modes. The ionosphere will in general have the same effect on a signal transmitted in either direction along a path, although Davies has pointed out non-reciprocity of polarization fading patterns, suggesting that polarization diversity reception can sometimes help fading. What will usually differ at each end of a path will be the quality of reception, since this is affected by interference plus atmospheric and man-made noises.

The Antenna and Its Environment

What follows is a description of a relatively simple method to determine the radiation patterns of small antennas by means of what is sometimes called *the two-ray optical method*. A flat Earth with uniform ground constants is assumed. **Fig 11** is a detailed version of Fig 1, from Chapter 3 of the 17th Edition of *The ARRL Antenna Book*.

The point A represents the location of the antenna at height h above ground. Using the theory of images, a point B is placed at a

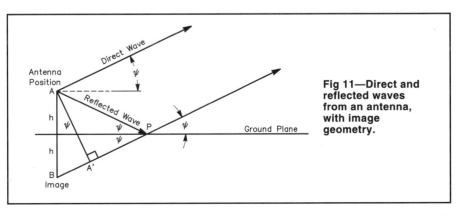

Fig 11—Direct and reflected waves from an antenna, with image geometry.

93

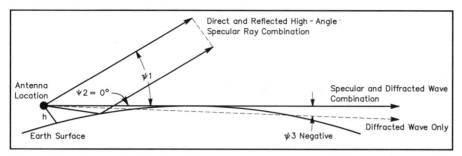

Fig 12—Breakdown of optical ray theory as elevation angle of skywave is lowered.

depth h below the ground. A direct wave radiates toward the ionosphere from A at elevation angle ψ. There is also a reflected wave from point P at the same elevation angle. Since AP is equal to BP and AA′ is at right angles to the emitted wave, then the path PA is longer than A′P by BA′, but

$$BA' = 2h \sin \psi \qquad (Eq\ 1)$$

which causes the reflected wave to be earlier in phase by an angle of

$$\frac{2\pi}{\lambda} 2h \sin \psi = \frac{4\pi}{\lambda} h \sin \psi,\ in\ radians$$
$$(Eq\ 2)$$

A reflection coefficient R_H or R_V accounts for the phase shift and attenuation of the reflected wave produced by the ground constants and horizontal or vertical polarization. The technique for deriving R_H and R_V is explained in part in the reference text by Jordan and Balmain.[14]

Starting with the well-known free-space radiation pattern of an antenna, a relative strength in the far field for each polarization, E_{OH} or E_{OV} can be multiplied by a factor to produce a radiation pattern formed by the combination of the direct and reflected rays, as follows, using exponential notation.

Since $Ae^{j\theta} = A \cos \theta + j \sin \theta$, dropping the first term,

$$E_H = E_{OH} (1 + R_H\ e^{\frac{-j4\pi th}{\lambda}} \sin \psi) \qquad (Eq\ 3)$$

and similarly

$$E_V = E_{OV} (1 + R_V\ e^{\frac{-j4\pi th}{\lambda}} \sin \psi) \qquad (Eq\ 4)$$

The expression in parentheses in Eq 3 and Eq 4 is known as the *propagation factor*, or the *reflection factor* or the *cutback factor*. The first designation will be used here. The propagation factor itself is a vector quantity dependent upon frequency and ground constants, as well as on the elevation angle. If you plot this, you will see a lobe structure.

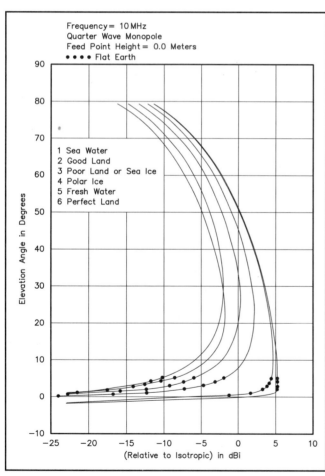

Fig 13—Vertical radiation pattern of a quarter-wave grounded antenna with perfect counterpoise on various kinds of ground. The frequency is 10 MHz.

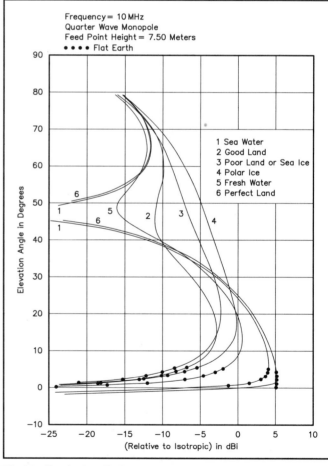

Fig 14—Vertical radiation pattern of a quarter-wave antenna with perfect counterpoise located λ/4 above various types of ground. The frequency is 10 MHz. Note the deep nulls in the elevation pattern for seawater and perfect land between about 40° to 55° in elevation. These nulls are "filled in" when the ground is not perfectly conductive (or close to that in the case of sea water).

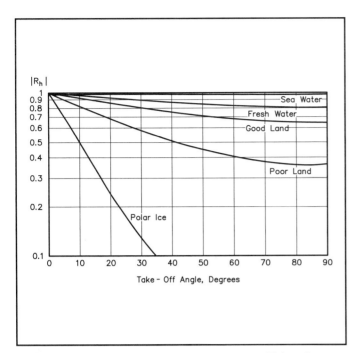

Fig 15—Amplitude of the ground-reflection coefficient for horizontal polarization, RH, for various types of ground. The frequency is 10 MHz.

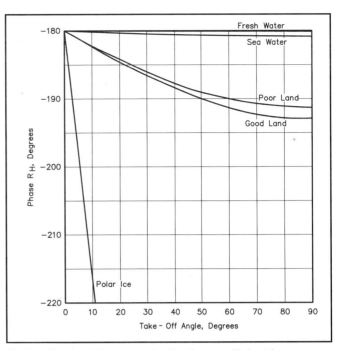

Fig 16—Phase of the ground-reflection coefficient for horizontal polarization, RH, for various types of ground. The frequency is 10 MHz.

An elementary idea of how these lobes are formed may be gained from considering reflections from an ideal, perfect ground. Then R_H reduces to –1 and R_V reduces to +1. It should be evident that in Eq 3 the propagation factor reduces to zero for an elevation angle of 0° for horizontal polarization, and in Eq 4, the propagation factor maximizes at 2.0 at 0° for vertical polarization. From the exponent of e in both Eq 3 and Eq 4 it is evident that as the elevation angle ψ is raised, maxima and minima appear. In this simple perfect-ground case, angles for maximum of one polarization produce a minimum for the other. Besides, as the height term h in the exponent increases in both equations, more and narrower lobes are formed within any range of elevation angles, with the lower lobes becoming increasingly lower.

Returning to the real world, with its non-perfect ground, however, brings us to the conclusion that the propagation factor must be modified to obtain an antenna pattern. Having been multiplied by the free-space radiation pattern in Eq 3 and Eq 4, the propagation factor must also be adjusted for the antenna impedance and current distribution that the actual antenna would have at the actual operating position. Large antennas can produce special problems, particularly if the ground under them varies in conductivity or if it isn't flat.

For vertical polarization the Brewster angle of geometric optics is very important. In radio this is an elevation angle sometimes

called the *pseudo Brewster angle*, or PBA. It is an elevation angle around which the phase and amplitude of R_V change rapidly and is generally high for "poorer" ground. It is only 0.8° for sea water and zero for a perfect reflector. Antenna pattern distortion can be seen near the PBA in *The ARRL Antenna Book* in Fig 14 on p 3-10, and in some figures in Berry and Chrisman.[15] Graphs showing the changes of amplitude and phase of R_H and R_V appear in both books. The Brewster-angle phenomenon also makes Fresnel zones for vertical polarization difficult to define precisely.

Of importance to the user interested in obtaining the most out of low elevation angles is the fact that even over flat local terrain the simple two-ray concept derived from geometric optics begins to break down as the elevation angle is lowered beyond about 1 or 2°, when diffraction by the Earth's curvature begin to take over. **Fig 12** is a simplified illustration of what happens. At moderately high elevation angles both the direct and the reflected optical ray combine into a sky wave.

At lower angles the reflected optical ray becomes mixed with diffracted waves. At $\psi = 0°$, as shown, there are probably no direct and reflected waves but a mixture of rays and diffracted waves that reach the ionosphere and produce long sky-wave hops. Finally, as ψ goes into the negative region, some diffracted waves producing very long hops with usable signal strength can exist.

The behavior of diffracted waves can be analyzed using complicated mathematical procedures described as *wave solutions*, or full-wave solutions. Such procedures have been published at least since 1909 and are an important component of standard broadcast-band ground waves. Different authors use different mathematical approaches.

Most equations are not "closed form" but must be solved for variable parameters that must be calculated separately. Even so, certain approximations have to be made to obtain solutions over certain ranges of parameters. Berry carefully checked his results over different ranges using the methods of other researchers.

Berry produced many useful graphs of calculated antenna patterns for different heights, polarizations and ground constants. He also gave explanations of how one can safely use his information in particular cases. Unfortunately, the graphs had to be in polar coordinates because the crowding of the lobes as height is increased would have made the use of rectangular coordinates impossible. The patterns represent full-wave solutions, but in cases where the flat-Earth optical solution differs appreciably at low angles, this is shown by plotted points. **Figs 13** and **14** from Berry show how a good ground enhances the low-angle performance of a simple vertical monopole, and how poor ground erases that advantage.

Fresnel zones for ground reflection are another important aspect of the environment

95

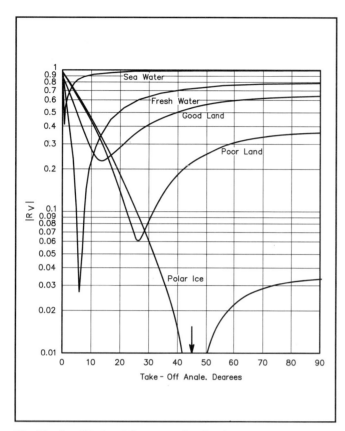

Fig 17—Amplitude of the ground-reflection coefficient for vertical polarization, R_V, for various types of ground. The frequency is 10 MHz.

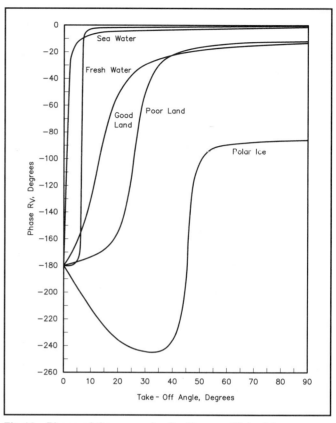

Fig 18—Phase of the ground-reflection coefficient for vertical polarization, R_V, for various types of ground. The frequency is 10 MHz.

since radio waves are not optical and therefore the reflecting region on the ground is not a small as a doormat, or even a football field. A frequently quoted report by Norton and Omberg[16] treats only a flat Earth and does not consider ground constants.

Simple Fresnel zones are reflecting regions on the Earth's surface that are ahead of the antenna structure. They are an adaptation of optical theory but can become very complicated in real situations. In accordance with formulas based on Huygen's Principle, each Fresnel zone is a region in which wavelets from the antenna are reflected obliquely at phase shifts over a range of 180°. The first Fresnel zone for a perfectly conducting Earth produces phase shifts relatively from 0° to 180° and is an ellipse, with its major axis along the direction of propagation. The minor axis crosses at the point at which reflection is shown in ray theory. The second Fresnel zone produces phase shifts from 180° to 360°. Its inner boundary is the outer boundary of the first zone and its outer boundary is another ellipse. In the ideal case it can be shown that contributions from all zones except the first cancel, leaving only the first Fresnel zone for consideration.

In a case of a real ground having finite values of conductivity and dielectric constant, the reflection coefficient R produces

amplitude and phase changes as the elevation angle changes. It should be evident from **Figs 15** and **16** that for horizontal polarization in the region of specular reflection, amplitude and phase changes are very small over a large range of elevation angles. Thus, relatively easy calculations of Fresnel zones are possible for horizontal polarization. However, for vertical polarization, **Figs 17** and **18** (from Figures 8.1 and 8.2 of Berry and Chrisman) show that there are rapid changes of amplitude and phase even in the specular reflection region, evident in the mathematics of the Brewster-angle phenomenon.

Figs 15 and 16 show these variations with elevation angle. One can conclude that Fresnel zones for vertical polarization, even in the case of specular reflection, are hard to define. Salt and fresh water appear to be exceptions above about 10°, with minor changes in amplitude and phase shown for the higher angles.

For angles below about 2°, for both polarizations, as reflected waves become increasingly more diffracted as the elevation angle is lowered into the negative region, it may be in any real situation almost impossible to define Fresnel zones in simple terms, especially considering that the generic direct wave vanishes as implied in Fig 12. For a large ocean foreground there is

no need to know Fresnel zone sizes, since the salt water acts almost like perfectly conducting ground, at least in good weather.

Both Utlaut and Berry treat obstructions in the Fresnel zones. Utlaut shows curves of Fresnel zone dimensions for the horizontal case and discusses compromises when ideal zones are not available. Les Moxon, G6XN, favors vertical polarization and has treated Fresnel zones perhaps more than other Amateur Radio author has.[17]

Modern Achievements in Better Utilization of the Ionosphere

Perhaps the most important advances as far as the amateur is concerned are the design and construction of antenna systems such as the stacked triband Yagi arrays built by Dean Straw, N6BV, and Fred Hopengarten, K1VR, reported in Feb 1994 *QST* and then in *The ARRL Antenna Book*, starting with the 17th Edition. There arrays were designed using Method-of-Moment computer programs.

The vertically stacked arrays have the advantage of using a relatively small horizontal space, and the vertical separation between antennas is large enough to minimize the effects of the induction fields between them. The use of the same length of feed line for each tribander in the array appears to be well justified since the authors point out that the lower angles are the important ones for DX. Not pointed out by the authors is the fortunate fact that for stacked antennas the phase differences between the transmitted as well as the received waves at each antenna in the array diminish as the elevation angle decreases, making it not essential to use separate phasing lines to each. The opposite is the case for an end-fire array on a flat or sloping plane, such as AT&T's MUSA or Brueckmann's ISCAN arrays.

Other advantages to stacked Yagis include diversity (which decreases the effect of signal fading), the fact that each major lobe covers a wide range of elevation angles, and pattern changes can be made by simple switching. However, one disadvantage to some designs of stacked Yagi arrays include azimuth response broadening for the rearward lobes, which can increase reception of QRM, QRN and industrial noise.

Amateur arrays need not be as complicated as stacked tribanders or monobanders to achieve some improvement in elevation-angle usage. Switching between two optimally placed simple antennas should produce improved performance at different times of day, depending on circumstances.

In England an antenna of intermediate complexity called the *skeleton slot* has become popular. When oriented in a vertical configuration, the skeleton slot takes up little space and works well on several amateur HF bands. At its design frequency it can be regarded as a stacked array. Two widely spread open-wire, low-loss parallel vertical conductors are fed in the middle with a balanced line and are shunted at the top and bottom to form two horizontal radiating elements, one element being stacked above the other with a separation of a little less than a quarter wavelength. The assembly is lightweight and low-cost and can be easily repaired if blown down. All vertical currents almost cancel. Bill Capstick, G3JYP, describes a rotatable skeleton slot with an interesting computer-derived elevation-angle pattern on 21 MHz, showing good low-angle response with no deep nulls.[18]

Software for Antenna and Propagation Analysis

Propagation Analysis

A parallel accomplishment in amateur and professional circles over the last decade has been the development of software for computation of ionospheric behavior. These programs often allow the performance of realistic antennas to be modeled as well. The ionospheric-assessment programs consider a vast number of different parameters. The original mainframe *IONCAP* program has been simplified and made more "user friendly" in a number of different implementations sold commercially and is even available for free on the Internet as *VOACAP*, a version of *IONCAP* customized by the engineers at Voice of America.

Tables naming the various programs and outlining what they can and can't do appear in both *The ARRL Antenna Book* and *The ARRL Handbook* in their chapters on propagation.[19,20] Since software can be expected to change rapidly in the commercial world, I advise readers to watch advertisements in various radio-amateur journals to keep up with their evolution.

Elevation-Angle Analysis

Great effort was put into putting many tables and graphs of statistical elevation angles by N6BV in the 17th and 18th Editions of *The ARRL Antenna Book*.[21] The *IONCAP* program was used to predict the percentage of time of optimum propagation for the HF amateur frequencies, covering all months over the full range of smoothed sunspot numbers, for a large number of DX paths. N6BV is careful to mention the complexities of the ionosphere, which even *IONCAP* can never handle completely.

A study of records like those in Figs 8, 9 and 10 show the tremendous variability of the ionosphere from day-to-day over DX paths. I wish that I could see some instantaneous records of the actual elevation angles as a refinement of the techniques I used on Kauai in 1962. That would give me a direct reality check compared to what the software predicts on a post-event basis, some 37 years later!

I'd also like to see the above *Antenna Book* graphs and tables reworked for those amateurs and international broadcasters who would benefit from listings of elevation angles. The range of elevation angles would be those necessary to provide communication over certain paths under widely varying ionospheric conditions. The connection with the ability to radiate very low elevation angles, of course, is what I have been most interested in over the years. Long ago an Australian amateur reported that his ability to contact the US began 4 hours earlier after he installed a vertical antenna overlooking the ocean. Such an installation can give excellent coverage of both very low and medium elevation angles.

In Chapter 23 of the 17th Edition of *The ARRL Antenna Book*, Figs 24 and 25 show on the computed graphs that on certain paths, at certain times of the day, relatively high-angle modes are sometimes superior to low-angle modes, and that this occurs more at high levels of solar sunspot activity. I sometimes noted the same thing on the 20-meter Guam-to-Kauai path. Greater absorption of a low-angle wave can occur, because it spends more time in the lower (more lossy) ionospheric layers.

Another possibility is that the higher-angle mode is a Pedersen ray. And there is also the possibility of a true ducting mode. Or there might be propagation between the E layer and the equatorial bulge in the F2 layer, creating what is known as a *chordal hop*.

Software for Antenna Analysis

Several popular programs for antenna analysis are derived from the mainframe *NEC-2* program, developed at various US government laboratories over the last 20 years. This program analyzes antennas best over flat earth. It takes into account ground constants, polarization and Fresnel zones in the far field. One of the most popular commercial implementations is *EZNEC* by Roy Lewallen, W7EL.

There are also several commercial ray-tracing programs available to analyze local terrain and the effect it has on the launch of HF signals for skywave propagation through the ionosphere. Brian Beezley, K6STI, markets *TA* (Terrain Analysis) and the ARRL includes the program *YT* (Yagi Terrain analysis) by Dean Straw, N6BV, with the software provided in the 18th Edition of *The ARRL Antenna Book*. Both programs use the Uniform Theory of Diffraction (UTD) to ray trace a signal traveling over actual terrain profiles created by the user from USGS topographic maps. *TA* can analyze either horizontally or vertically polarized antennas.

YT is more specialized, in that it considers only horizontally polarized Yagis, in vertical stacks of up to four antennas. *YT* can also compare the ray-traced patterns with the statistical elevation-angles required for operator-selected paths around the world. The operator can change the height of the horizontally polarized Yagi (or multiple Yagis in a stack) to see how the far-field elevation pattern changes. I understand that modern hams not only are scouting for real estate located on hilltops—they're now looking for locations on the *right* sort of hills, the ones with really favorable terrains in important DX directions!

Choice of Methods and Sites for Achieving Low-Angle DX Advantages

So what are some possible methods to go about achieving low elevation angle take-offs from your antennas?

Vertical Antennas

A vertically polarized antenna with a salt-water or salt-marsh foreground is in many ways the best method, but it is obviously limited in choice. Salt marsh may in fact be better than salt water is because large ocean areas subjected to severe storms may spoil the nearby Fresnel zones. This may never have been formally studied.

Fig 19 is a set of simple curves depicting

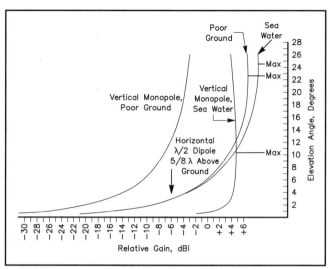

Fig 19—Relative gains of antennas at low elevation angles, derived from optical two-ray solution.

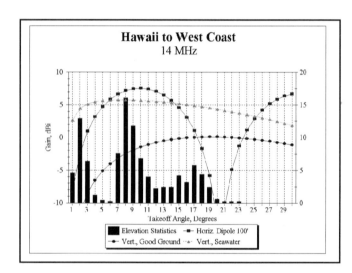

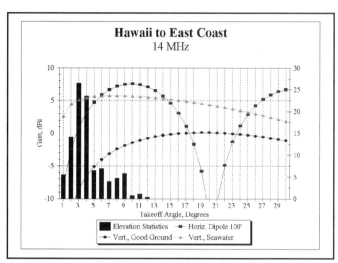

Fig 20—Graph showing elevation-pattern responses on 14 MHz for three types of antennas. These patterns are compared to the elevation-angle statistics for the Hawaii to the US East Coast (Boston, MA). The elevation-angle statistics cover the complete solar cycle, for all months, all hours. The vertical antenna located over seawater has a distinct advantage on this path—at 3° elevation it is 4 dB stronger than a horizontal dipole mounted 100 feet over flat ground with good conductivity. The vertical antenna placed over "good ground" is at a severe disadvantage compared to either of the two other antennas. In short, there's nothing like a vertical over salt water for a simple installation that can perform well! (Elevation-angle statistics from private correspondence with N6BV, ARRL HQ.) The right-hand Y axis is the percentage of times the band is open at each elevation angle.

Fig 21—Similar comparison as shown in Fig 20, but this time for the path from Hawaii to the US West Coast (San Francisco, CA). Here, the angles rise to 8° during the middle of the typical opening, but the band opens and closes at very low elevation angles.

the possible gain of a vertical monopole at ground level over sea water and over poor soil. The performance of a horizontal doublet ⁵/₈λ above flat ground is shown for comparison. Computations were done using ray theory. The relative insensitivity of horizontal polarization to most ground constants below an elevation angle of 10° appears quite obvious. For vertical polarization you can see the greatly inferior performance of the monopole over poor soil. However, over seawater at 2° the far-field elevation pattern is 15 dB better than the doublet over most grounds. And this is before considering the advantages of longer hops at lower launch angles. These can dominate when there is insufficient ionization in the ionosphere to support high-angle modes. Diffraction theory shows that even more advantage exists at lower angles than 2°. Ground-wave reception of atmospherics and noise is a negative, however, of vertical antennas.

High Horizontal Antennas

The main advantage of horizontal polarization may be an easy choice of sites and easier construction of arrays. As antenna height increases, the lowest elevation lobe goes lower, and the lobes become narrower as their number increases. The same is true for vertical polarization over seawater except that maxima and minima occur at different elevation angles. Berry states that a quarter-wave monopole over seawater is better than a half-wave dipole at very low angles unless the dipole is mounted more than 5 λ above the sea—but then it may have nulls in its elevation pattern at desirable launch angles.

Fig 20 uses the results from the *YT* program for three simple 20-meter antennas: a horizontally polarized dipole 100 feet above flat ground, a vertical dipole over seawater and a vertical dipole over "good" ground (conductivity of 5 mS/m and a di-

electric constant of 13). For comparison, the elevation-angle statistics for the path from Hawaii to the East Coast are overlaid on the elevation-patterns for the three antennas. The predominant takeoff angle on this path is 3°, occurring about 27% of all the times when the 20-meter band is open.

At the 3° takeoff angle, the vertical located over seawater is some 4 dB stronger than the 100 foot high dipole, and more than 15 dB better than a vertical over "good" ground. For contrast, look at **Fig 21**, which shows the same antennas graphed with elevation-angle statistics for the Hawaii-to-West Coast path. Now, the predominant takeoff angle is 8°, occurring some 16% of the time the band is open and the high dipole is 2 dB better than the sea-water vertical. This amount of difference would be difficult to detect due to the fading characteristics typical of HF propagation. During the time needed to switch between the two an-

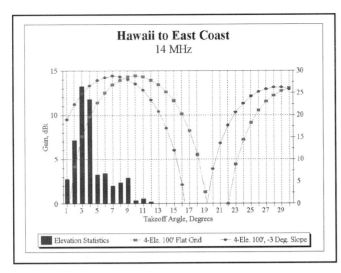

Fig 22—Elevation patterns for two more ambitious antenna installations. They both feature four-element Yagis on 100 foot towers, but one is located on flat ground, while the other has a foreground with a −3° slope. The slope effectively shifts the peak response down from 10° over flat ground to 7° over the sloping foreground, just as you would expect.

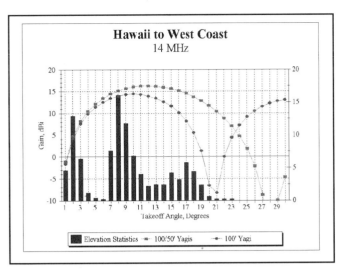

Fig 23—Graph showing elevation response for two different antenna systems mounted over flat ground. The stack of two four-element Yagis at 100 and 50 feet has more gain over a wider elevation-angle "window" of useful elevation angles than does the single Yagi at 100 feet. For example, where the single Yagi has a deep null at 20°, the stack still has over 10 dBi of gain. At the peak statistical elevation angle, 8°, the stack has about a 1 dB advantage.

tennas the signal difference would likely change due to the fading.

Note that the secondary elevation-angle peak in Fig 21 is very low, at 2°. This angle is prevalent at the opening and closing of the band. In between the Hawaiian morning opening and the West Coast afternoon closing, the takeoff angle rises to the 8° average.

The optimum elevation angles changes depending on ionospheric fluctuations. The modern development of stacked Yagis overcomes some of the objections to single-height horizontal antennas, yet the simplicity of the monopole by the beach cannot be denied!

Long Terrain Slopes for Low-Angle Response

The method is tantamount to tilting a large region at one azimuth.[4] It is best at only one azimuth but has the advantage of shorter Fresnel zones, although what lies beyond is still an issue. **Fig 22** illustrates a more grandiose antenna setup in *YT*. The antennas are assumed to be four-element Yagis, 100 feet high, where each Yagi has 8 dBi of free-space gain.

The first Yagi is located over flat ground, while the second Yagi in Fig 22 is located at the edge of a long −3° slope. The peak in the far-field elevation pattern has shifted downward 3°, exactly as you would expect. The gain difference at a takeoff angle of 3° is about 7 dB, a quite substantial amount for a fairly small slope. Terrain can make a profound difference for DXing at low elevation angles.

Knife-Edge Diffraction and Similar Phenomena

Knife-edge diffraction of radio waves was perhaps first studied by Selvidge[22] on VHF frequencies, then in Japan and later in Alaska.[23] In view of outstanding DX results by various amateurs located behind hills it would seem that with the greater distances to the "knife edge" required by the knife-edge diffraction equations of optics, comparable results at low angles could be obtained.

A roughly similar phenomenon was observed by H. V. Cottony, an antenna research scientist. In a case of unusually strong signals from the US received in the Philippines, the signal strength was attributed to a mountain east of the receiving station.[24] Amateurs who obtain good DX results in spite of a hill in the direction of their beam orientation may be experiencing favorable diffraction by the hill.

Very Large Ground Mats

Very large ground mats have been used to some extent in the military, but the cost of land, material and labor would be excessive for any amateur!

Angle Control of Arrays

For some of the methods mentioned above, angle control would make it possible to optimize signals over a wide range of ionospheric conditions. Amateurs with switchable stacks have experimented with controlling their takeoff angles. Most operators tend to leave the stacks in the circuit all the time, rather than selecting individual

antennas in the stack. This is because the wider elevation window covered by the stack compensates for changing conditions automatically.

Fig 23 shows the elevation patterns for a single 100 foot high four-element Yagi over flat ground compared to a stack of two of the same Yagis at 100 and 50 feet over flat ground. At the relatively high elevation angle of 17° (which occurs some 6% of the time), the stack is some 8 dB stronger than the single antenna. Note that the single antenna at 17° is experiencing a null in its pattern, which is deepest at just above the 20° elevation angle. The stack is superior to the single antenna at all the angles of interest on this path.

Future for Amateurs in Experimentation and theory

With the demise of funding for professional research in HF low-angle and angle-control techniques, some amateurs have performed excellent work in design and construction of antennas for optimizing elevation-angle usage. Computer software used by amateurs has largely evolved from government development of comprehensive programs for ionospheric usage (*IONCAP*) and antenna design and analysis (*NEC*), started when HF ionospheric communication for commercial, broadcasting and military use was of prime importance.

Since those days, these programs have been modified and improved by skilled radio amateurs for sale or distribution to HF amateurs who desire top performance. ARRL has pioneered in the publication of ionospheric prediction data.

As in any scientific field, much more work always needs to be done. Below are a few suggestions.

• Make real-time comparisons of performances of different antennas with different elevation-angle patterns, for selected DX paths, months and times of day to check computer-generated optimum-angle data. Antenna patterns themselves could be checked independently by modeling antenna and terrain, or even measuring using airplanes or balloons. Such techniques have been used before, but obtaining valid results especially at low angles could be difficult.

• Rework computer data to show times of day when low elevation angles are virtually the only means of HF communication to specific DX areas.

• Study ducting in the ionosphere to determine if it is taking place and is a consistent mode of propagation. Early ducting tests were done using backscatter of pulsed emissions. CW pulses with fast break-in operation can be used to produce backscatter reflections. The starting pulse could trigger a sweep with time calibration marks, yielding mode structure information. One problem would be the relatively narrow passbands of SSB transceivers, resulting in a lack of resolution of fine details.

• For a simple experiment, compare the performance of two stacked dipoles with that of stacked Yagis or of the vertical skeleton-slot antenna.

Acknowledgments

I wish to acknowledge the cooperation and help of the late Frederic H. Dickson, K2HJU (later W7LBH), who was in charge of a US Government project on the island of Kauai when time became available for the previously unplanned 14-MHz antenna-polarization DX tests.

In determining the location of the antennas many years later, the help of Dean Okayama, Engineer-in-charge of nearby station WWVH, was of great value. He made available old aerial photographs, contour maps, and the personal judgment of a friend who was familiar with the beach, with regard to photographs of the antennas used in the original experiment.

References

Unfortunately, excellent reports by highly qualified research personnel sometimes haven't been published in technical or professional literature because of a change in topic emphasis or a lack of time and funds.

Several reports listed below may be hard to find but in the case of a few internal, but unpublished, reports it may be possible to obtain reprints. After all, unclassified US Government reports are in the *public domain* and there should be no problem about making copies. Particularly, the Berry and Chrisman report may be available in many libraries. You may be able to see a copy of the Utlaut report at the library of the National Institute of Standards and Technology (NIST) at 325 Broadway, Boulder, CO 80303.

Notes

[1] W. Utlaut, "Siting Criteria for HF Communication Centers," NBS Technical Note No. 139 (PB 161640), US Dept of Commerce, National Bureau of Standards, Apr 1962.

[2] B. Kelley (W2ICE) and D. Hudson (KA1TZR), "Hams Span the Atlantic on Shortwave," *QST*, Dec 1996.

[3] K. Warner, "The Story of the Trans-atlantics," *QST*, Feb 1922, pp 7-14.

[4] R. Potter and H. Friis, "Some Effects of Topography and Ground on Short-Wave Reception," *Proc IRE 20*, Apr 1932.

[5] F. Polkinghorn, "A Single-Sideband MUSA System for Commercial Operation on Transatlantic Radiotelephone Circuits," *Proc. IRE 27*, Apr 1940, pp 157-170.

[6] W. Bain, "Abnormal Signal Strength from Soviet Transmitters," Page Communication Engineers, Inc (Northrup Corp), Report PCE R-1152-0034A, for Ninth National Communications Symposium, 9 Oct 1963.

[7] H. Brueckmann and R. Silberstein, "HF Propagation Tests of ISCAN," *IEEE Trans Ant Propag*, AP-11, Jul 1963.

[8] W. Utlaut, "Effect of Antenna Radiation Angle Upon HF Radio Signals Propagated Over Long Distances," *Journal of Research of the National Bureau of Standards 65D* (Radio Propagation), No. 2, Mar-Apr 1961, pp 167-174.

[9] M. Epstein, V. Frank, G. Barry and O. Villard, Jr (W6QYT), "A Comparison of Long-Distance HF Radio Signal Reception at High and Low Receiving Sites," *Radio Science* (New Series), No. 7, Jul 1966, pp 751-762.

[10] R. Silberstein, WØYBF, "DXing from a Deck Chair," *Ham Radio Horizons*, Aug 1979, pp 12-20.

[11] K. Davies, *Ionospheric Radio*, No. 31 of IEE Electromagnetic Wave Series (London: P. Peregrinus, 1990).

[12] R. Silberstein, "A Long-Distance Pulse-Propagation Experiment on 20.1 Megacycles," *Journal of Geophysical Research 63*, No. 3, Sep 1958, pp 445-466.

[13] R. Silberstein and F. Dickson, "Great-Circle and Deviated-Path Observations on CW Signals Using a Simple Technique," *IEEE Trans Ant Propag*, AP-13, Jan 1965, p 52.

[14] E. Jordan and K. Balmain, "Electromagnetic Waves and Radiating Systems," 2nd Ed. (New York: Prentice-Hall, 1968).

[15] L. Berry and M. Chrisman, "Linear High-Frequency Antennas Over a Finitely Conducting Spherical Earth," *ITSA No. 8*, US Dept of Commerce, Environmental Sciences Services Administration, Sep 1966.

[16] K. Norton and A. Omberg, "The Maximum Range of a Radar Set," *Proc IRE 35*, Jan 1947, pp 4-24.

[17] L. Moxon (G6XN), *HF Antennas for All Locations*, 2nd Ed. (London: RSGB, 1993).

[18] B. Capstick (G3JYP), "The HF Slot Antenna," *Radio Communication*, Jun 1996.

[19] *The ARRL Handbook*, 1995 and later Editions (Newington: ARRL), Chap 22.

[20] *The ARRL Antenna Book*, 17th and 18th Editions (Newington: ARRL, 1994, 1997), Chap 23.

[21] *The ARRL Antenna Book*, 18th Ed (Newington: ARRL, 1997) pp 23-20 to 23-29.

[22] H. Selvidge, "Diffraction Measurements at Ultra High Frequencies," *Proc IRE 29*, Jan 1941, pp 10-16.

[23] F. Dickson (K2HJU, W7LBH), J. Egli, J. Herbstreit (WØDW), G. Wickizer, "Large Reductions of VHF Transmission Loss and Fading by the Presence of a Mountain Obstacle in Beyond Line-of-Sight Paths," *Proc IRE 41*, Aug 1953.

[24] H. Leighton and R. Sodergren, "Semi-Annual Report to Voice of America," NBS Report 8226, Jul 1963-Mar 1964. Note contribution by H. Cottony.

Using HF Propagation Predictions

By R. Dean Straw, N6BV

Senior Assistant Technical Editor, ARRL
5328 Fulton Street
San Francisco, CA 94121

Have you ever planned on traveling to a distant land to operate a DXpedition or a contest and wondered: "When are the bands going to be open from down there?" And have you then mused: "How loud am I going to be if I put up such and such an antenna?" or "How loud will I be into Europe or Japan compared to the signals from New England or from Los Angeles?"

Or have you ever considered raising the tower at your home station, say, 20 feet higher? Would that really open up another layer of DX, as you've heard some of your buddies say it did for them? Or have you wondered whether your Saturday morning schedule with your brother Charlie in Boise would be better on 20 or 15 meters, or perhaps in the afternoon rather than in the morning?

It wasn't too long ago that the answers to these questions would have been a matter of pure gut feel and long-term experience "on the bands." Nowadays, you can call on modeling programs that scientifically explore many possibilities on the computer screen, well before you commit time and money to that new skywire or before going off on a DXpedition. It all starts with knowledge of what the ionosphere is doing or will be doing.

Some Personal Background

I've been fascinated by the HF bands for the almost 40 years I've been a ham (first call: WH6DKD in 1959). I've spent a great deal of time and effort building HF antennas and have operated many thousands of hours in contests and in casual operating. Over the last several decades, I've been interested in one particular aspect of HF radio: *system design*. By this I mean the process by which a ham can scientifically exploit the properties of the ionosphere and his local environment in order to put the loudest signal possible into distant (and nearby) areas of the world. And let me be candid—my main motivation has been to increase my contest scores!

> *N6BV offers some practical tips for would-be practitioners of the art/science of HF propagation predicting, using examples from the 1998 6Y2A operation in the CQ World Wide CW Contest.*

I became motivated to write this article because of two recent events. The first was that I discovered a sneaky bug in one of my software programs. The second was that I was privileged to be part of a multi-talented team at a major DXpedition to Jamaica, 6Y2A, for the 1998 CQ World Wide CW Contest.

Hedging your Bets

The scientists who write propagation-prediction programs carefully couch their computations in terms of *statistics*. *Webster's II New Riverside University Dictionary* defines a statistic as: "An estimate of a parameter, as of the population mean or variance, obtained from a sample." Therein lies the essential clue to how we should view a statistical entity. It is an extrapolation from a smaller sample of data, with a certain percentage of confidence stated for it.

For example, a hypothetical ionospheric scientist might state that one minute ago, when he directed his swept-frequency ionospheric sounder to ping the ionosphere, the maximum frequency that returned an echo from the F_2 layer directly overhead might be, say, 10.1 MHz. Now he's been doing this for many years, and he knows that 90% of the time he tried this—at the same time and same day of the year and at the same level of solar activity—the maximum frequency was this value, provided that there wasn't a geomagnetic storm in progress. And he'll only know that there was a geomagnetic storm from indirect data—perhaps even that no echo came back at all!

Our scientist extrapolates from this measured data and states that he is 90% confident that the ionosphere will return an echo at 10.1 MHz, provided of course that all conditions are the same as previously stated. However, he's a responsible ionospheric scientist and will definitely *not* say that he is 100% certain that this will happen, even if the day is the same, the geomagnetic indices are exactly the same and the time of day is the same. Our scientist knows all too well that the ionosphere is like the weather in New England—wait a minute and it'll change!

I use the words *long-term prediction* to mean a forecast for an interval that spans at least several 11-year solar cycles. This interval of time is sufficiently long to give a very broad-brush view of how the ionosphere acts and is particularly useful for designing effective antenna systems that are intended to stay up in the air for long periods of time. In other words, if you know the overall range of elevation angles that occur 99.9% of the time for a particular path and a particular frequency, then building an antenna system that covers this range of angles effectively will ensure that *you* have done everything with hardware that you can do to make a QSO. Now it comes down to factors beyond your control—how good the operator is at the other end of the circuit; how bad the power-line noise is at his receiver; how many stronger, nearby stations are calling in a pileup; what kind of thunderstorm is or isn't happening while you are calling, etc.

I call *short-term predictions* ones that cover at least a month's worth of time; for example, a forecast spanning plus/minus two weeks about the middle of a particular month. Short-term forecasts are particularly useful for contest or DXpedition planning. Data from short-term forecasts are useful for strategy decisions before a contest, never forgetting that the successful operators will change strategy whenever they detect that the conditions have changed.

Long-Term Statistical Elevation-Angle Data

The 17th Edition of *The ARRL Antenna Book* first appeared in July 1994. Chapter 23 (Radio Wave Propagation) contained abbreviated statistical tables of elevation angles needed for 10 US transmitting sites to important geographic areas throughout the world, with detailed data files on the diskette bundled with the book. The statistical elevation-angle data replaced a skimpy set of data that had been in the *Antenna Book* for many years, data that had been measured during the low point of solar Cycle 17 in 1934, for a single path from New Jersey to Slough, England. The 18th Edition of *The ARRL Antenna Book* contained even more statistical data on elevation angles.

The detailed *Antenna Book* data were generated using the *IONCAP* computer program, a program that had (at the time of the 17th Edition) been a work-in-progress for about 25 years by several agencies of the US government. *IONCAP* is still being worked on, sporadically, through a later offshoot and improvement called *VOACAP*, a product of engineers working for VOA, the Voice of America. Unfortunately, funding for further development of *VOACAP* is scarce or nonexistent and the program is being maintained through the personal dedication of a single engineer, Greg Hand, at NTIA/ITS (the National Telecommunications and Information Administration, Institute of Telecommunications Studies, a part of the US Department of Commerce) in Boulder, Colorado. You can visit their web site at: **http://elbert. its.bldrdoc.gov/hf.html**.

Statistical Elevation-Angle Methodology

The procedure used to generate the 1994 statistical elevation-angle data was to generate huge databases using *IONCAP*'s

"Method 25," the so-called "all-mode" method. The antennas I originally used for each end of each circuit were 100-foot-high flat-top dipoles over flat ground for frequencies from 3.5 to 10.5 MHz, three-element Yagis at 100 feet above flat ground from 10.5 to 20 MHz, and four-element Yagis at 60 feet above flat ground from 20 to 30 MHz.

Like any horizontally polarized antennas, these had nulls in the elevation pattern, but attempts on my part to use theoretical antennas without any nulls (that is, "isotropic" antennas in *IONCAP*) had resulted in very strange and unbelievable numbers on some paths. It turns out that a number of factors had conspired to fool me. In my defense, so to speak, I will say that the documentation for *IONCAP* leaves a *lot* to be desired and about the only practical way to find how things work in the program is to rigorously and systematically experiment with things, to see what changes.

I did the elevation-angle computations using very large batch files that automatically generated input data files for *IONCAP* for various levels of solar activity throughout the months of the year. After much number crunching, the output files are automatically parsed and placed in huge databases, showing each and every mode, the predicted signal strength, the elevation angle and the reliability for paths from the chosen transmitting site to locations all around the world. At one time, there was a computer at HQ dedicated to making these *IONCAP* computations day and night. Even now, using a 233-MHz Pentium PC from my home office, a full set of computations for one transmitting site takes about 2.5 hours of number crunching.

When *VOACAP* first appeared in 1993, it incorporated a number of improvements over the *IONCAP* core program. The engineers at VOA had found a number of small errors in *IONCAP*. These small errors added up to create some substantial errors for certain paths and certain conditions. Another thing recommending the *VOACAP* program was that it was compiled for a 32-bit processor and ran significantly faster than did the 16-bit DOS version of *IONCAP*. Unfortunately, *VOACAP* was designed to be an interactive *Windows* program, and until late in 1998, it was not suited to working with massive batch files.

For this reason, I turned to another 32-bit implementation of the basic *IONCAP* computing engine, *CAPMAN*, which proved to be a well-done, robust program. But it too had some foibles that made it less than satisfactory for handling huge batch files, including the designed-in refusal to use the all-mode Method 25 for paths longer than 10,000 km.

A Sneaky Software Bug

In early 1998 some knowledgeable

friends began to question my use of "standard," real-world antennas for the generation of statistical elevation-angle data. They preferred to use isotropic antenna types, because by definition these did not have any nulls in their elevation patterns. I took their concerns to heart and began to explore why my previous attempts at using isotropic antennas had failed. I found that an almost seven-year-old portion of my code that did statistical computations for the percentage of time a particular angle is open to the target destination was not doing what I thought it was doing.

The logic I *thought* I had implemented was to count all instances of a received signal greater than 1 dBµV occurring for each elevation angle from 1 to 70°, over all hours/dates in the gigantic database. I then compared this number to the sum total of all instances to compute the percentage at each angle. What my program was doing internally, however, was determining the strongest signal—and from that, the most prevalent angle—for each hour/date. It was in essence discarding all other modes/angles other than the strongest mode for that particular hour/date. Horror of horrors, from a statistical point of view!

When I tried to employ isotropic antennas using this flawed internal logic, the program would naturally choose the strongest signal at the most-likely elevation angle, which would usually be the lowest possible angle, using the mode with the lowest number of hops. Thus the statistics for isotropic antennas would bunch up badly at extremely low angles, with very little statistical "scatter" at higher angles/modes.

When I corrected the algorithm to do what it should have been doing all along, I could finally use isotropic antenna models. Or rather, I could use a hypothetical "isotropic antenna with gain" that would simulate the gain of a horizontal Yagi, without the deleterious effects of nulls in the elevation pattern. This was done for 1500 W of transmitter power. I then tailored the internal decision points in my statistical program (in terms of dBµV and computed reliability) for the various amateur bands.

Next, I got hold of Greg Hand at NTIA/ITS and asked him to make modifications to *VOACAP* that would allow it to work properly in my peculiar multi-step batch mode. Greg was very accommodating and within several days I had a version of *VOACAP* that worked fine for my application. Then I turned my computer loose for about a week of concentrated number crunching for 96 different QTHs around the world, more than had been available previously in the old database supplied on the diskette with the 18th Edition of *The ARRL Antenna Book*.

The result was a set of "enhanced" elevation-angle statistics that inherently (in retrospect, anyway) looked more plausible and realistic. Interestingly enough, higher angles that might have fallen into nulls using the standard antenna patterns were only marginally more evident in the new statistics. What this meant, of course, was that higher angles are still not that dominant a phenomenon on HF propagation paths.

Further, the overall range of elevation angles did not change that much from the old numbers that first appeared in 1994. It's true that the prevailing angles showing up in the new statistics files are generally lower than previously determined, but the end user must realize that in order to use these really low elevation angles, it is *mandatory* for you to have antennas that work well down at these angles. Only those amateurs lucky enough to live on either steep mountains or on saltwater marshes could really exploit these kinds of low elevation angles that are statistically most likely.

Fig 1 contrasts the old and the new enhanced elevation-angle statistics from Boston to London for all levels of solar activity on 20 meters. In the new statistical data, the peak angle has shifted down to 5° for almost 13% of all the times the band is open to Europe, while it was 11° at 18% in the old data set. Bear in mind that 5° is an angle that would require a 200-foot-high Yagi for best performance. This 200-foot-high Yagi would, however, have inferior

performance at higher angles because of its deep null at 10°, where the new statistics show that the band is open some 10% of the time. Overall, an operator with a single Yagi at 100 feet would be better able to cover all the required angles on the 20-meter path from Boston to Europe. Of course, a vertical stack of Yagis would do even better, since it would have a wider elevation window of coverage.

Confidence in the Long-Term Numbers

User confidence in long-term elevation-angle statistics generated using a computer model like *IONCAP* is only as good as his/her confidence in how well the short-term predictions model reality. And for confidence in any modeling program *validation* is required. The fact that programs like *IONCAP* have been under almost continuous development and improvement for 30 years by government scientists is certainly reassuring. These scientists have access to a wealth of data from observatories throughout the world.

Aside from hiring a professionally calibrated antenna range to actually measure incoming elevation angles over a full 11-year solar cycle, the most viable way in amateurs can validate prediction programs is by doing "post-prediction" evaluations. That is, we can take our log data and compare it with what the computer program say *should have happened* under the then-exist-

ing solar-terrestrial conditions.

Through the rest of this article I'll try to show that the computer programs do indeed produce believable results for monthly signal-strength predictions, and hence they should be fine for the longer-term statistics also. Yes, I will admit that does sound a bit like backing into the truth!

Short-Term Propagation Predictions

To do short-term, monthly predictions, I use the *CAPMAN* program. This is because I can access the updated 32-bit computing engine in *CAPMAN* directly under *Windows 95*—which was needed because of its superior memory-handling—and *CAPMAN* works on both of my computers. For some reason the batch mode in *VOACAP* refuses to work properly on my 100-MHz Pentium, while it works fine on the 233-MHz Pentium. Since I do most batch-file processing on the older computer, leaving it running for days (or even weeks), I decided to use *CAPMAN* for short-term propagation predictions. (For those of you familiar with *CAPMAN*'s annoying "beep" after it finishes a computation, the ability to disable the internal speaker was very necessary to keep peace in the house, literally.)

Like the long-term elevation-angle statistics computed using Method 25 in *VOACAP*, I use *CAPMAN* with gigantic batch files to control the processing:

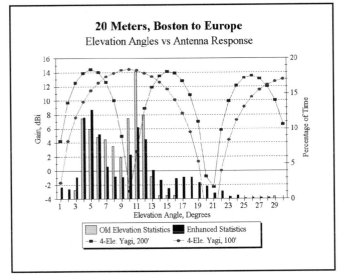

Fig 1—Contrast between the old and enhanced elevation-angle statistics for the path from Boston to all of Europe on 20 meters (from *The ARRL Antenna Book*, 18th Edition). The enhanced elevation-angle statistics cover about the same range of angles (1° to 28°) as do the old statistics (3° to 29°), but the peak percentages are at lower angles due to the assumption of "isotropic" antennas for the enhanced data. The enhanced data yields a 5° peak, at 12.5% of the time, versus 11° at 18% for the older numbers. Overlaid on the elevation statistics for reference are the responses for two large 20-meter horizontally polarized antennas: four-element Yagis at 100 feet and 200 feet over flat ground. Note that the 200-foot-high Yagi would be required to exploit the really low elevation angles in the enhanced statistical database.

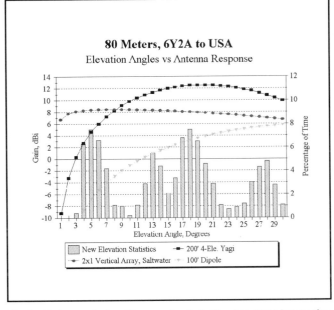

Fig 2—Enhanced elevation-angle statistics for Jamaica to the USA on 80 meters. The range of angles is large because the USA represents a big target area from Jamaica, from nearby Miami, Florida, to the westernmost tip of Washington State. Note the flat elevation response of a vertical array over seawater. At low takeoff angles it has a considerable advantage even compared to a 200-foot-high four-element 80-meter Yagi, something very few of us have up in the air. For reference, a 100-foot-high dipole over flat ground is also shown. While this is in reality a pretty good antenna, it pales in comparison to the verticals on the beach!

- For each of the 12 months in the year
- For six levels of solar activity, ranging from Very Low to Ultra High
- For 40 target QTHs throughout the world, located in each of the 40 CQ Zones.
- For what we amateurs call "short path" and "long path" headings

The batch files are as large as 400 kB in size, since they might control more than 5760 individual *CAPMAN* computations for a single transmitting site. The results are all parsed and automatically combined into very large databases for additional processing.

I use a special combination of Method 21 (the so-called "forced long path" method) and Method 22 ("forced short path") in *CAPMAN* to generate the short-term monthly predictions. The terms "long path" and "short path" used by *IONCAP* engineers has long confused radio amateurs, who are accustomed to think of a "long path" as being "the long-way-around" the globe.

IONCAP (and its derivatives *CAPMAN* and *VOACAP*) use the term "long path" to mean a path that is more than 10,000 km long. A "short path" to *IONCAP* is one that is shorter than that. Inside the programs, the short-path method uses an algorithm that "quasi ray-traces" through the model ionosphere, which is generated using parameters imbedded in *IONCAP*'s long-term monthly database. This database contains ionospheric data for almost three complete solar cycles.

Inside the long-path model, a so-called "two control-point" algorithm is used. To quote from the instruction manual, *A Guide to VOACAP*, concerning the long-path model:

The long path method does not predict normal modes, but indicates which layer, F2, F1 or E, is the most likely entry (transmit) and exit (receive) region for the ionospheric circuit. The IONCAP long path method does not force continuity with the short path model and the two methods can give considerably different predictions for the same circuit.

... An ionosphere, reflectrix, and ray set tables are calculated at points 2,000 kilometers from each end of the path, rather than at a single controlling point as in the short path model. [This is the reason this method is referred to as a "two-point" model.—N6BV]

... For long paths several physical phenomena can occur which do not exist on short paths. At about 10,000 km, the energy from the transmitter has propagated one fourth the way around the world. At this point and beyond, until the antipode is reached, the energy converges into smaller and smaller annular rings, each having greater energy density. To account for this signal build up, a convergence factor is introduced, which maximizes at 15 dB at the

antipode and then begins to decrease at greater distances.

... On extremely long range paths more and more energy is scattered away from the distinct reflection points of the normal ray path until the scatter mechanism becomes dominant. Energy can become ducted (guided between layers) or it can be chordal (reflected such that it travels on a path which does not come back to earth until it is reflected from the ionosphere a second or more times). The ionospheric absorption for the optimum rays at the end of the path are averaged.

The portions of the path that undergo either the normal D-E absorption or the more exotic modes of propagation discussed above are determined by calculating the E-layer penetration frequencies 1,000 km from each end of the path and at the mid-point.

Thus, when expressed in plain English, the so-called long-path method in *IONCAP* (and *CAPMAN* and *VOACAP*) is a sort of catchall. It can take into account antipodal focusing, chordal hops and ducted modes, without necessarily announcing them explicitly to the end user. The basic two-point methodology has been employed by other computer programs and is computationally much less intensive than rigorous ray-tracing, such as might be used in a more modern program like *PROPLAB PRO*. However, the signal-level numbers produced by *IONCAP* have been calibrated internally over the years to reflect actual experience, whatever the actual propagation mechanism actually happens to be for a particular path and time.

Comparing the reported signal levels for the *IONCAP* long-path method to those generated by the short-path method does give different values at ranges from about 7,000 to 10,000 km. It should be noted that *VOACAP* engineers look on a difference of 6 dB as a pretty big deal, while we hams are not fazed by such differences at all! The engineers at VOA devised a simple mathematical smoothing algorithm to force convergence of the signal levels calculated using the two different methodologies. This is described in the *VOACAP* on-screen documentation, under: **Help, General, Documents, Method 30**, which states in part:

"In VOACAP, the user can request area coverage plots using Methods 20, 21 or 22. Method 20 may produce 'cliffs' or strange looking coverage plots at the discontinuity occurring at 10,000 km. Method 21, the long path method, produces unrealistic coverage plots at the shorter distances where the ray hops should occur. Significant errors occur in the regions of mode transitions (e.g. between the 1F2 and the 2F2). Method 22, the short path method, may produce overly pessimistic performance estimates at the distances beyond the third ionospheric hop."

I incorporated the "Method 30" smoothing algorithm into my batch and program files. For each path from the transmitting site to a receiving QTH (in one of the 40 Zones), the Great Circle distance is computed. If the distance is less than 7000 km, only Method 22 is invoked. If the distance is between 7,000 and 10,000 km, then both Methods 22 and 21 are invoked. For distances greater than 10,000 km, only Method 21 is used. Then the resulting outputs from each Method (where both are used) are compared, smoothed if necessary and then compared to a separate calculation done for what we hams call the "long-path" azimuth. The strongest signal of these long or short path computations is chosen for display.

This sounds like it is hideously complicated, and it is! It took several years to perfect this methodology. So, you ask: "Does it work?"

Validation Needed

I have examined a number of contest logs to see how closely the computer program would post-predict QSOs found in those logs. Computerized logs from major DX contests are particularly useful because the activity is worldwide, with large volumes of QSOs made by the larger stations. Of particular interest are the so-called "multi-multi" stations, which have multiple operators simultaneously operating multiple transmitters on multiple frequencies. In previous articles in *QST* I have shown comparisons between the computer predictions and the reality of what actually happened in several such contests· and I argued that these represent validations for what the programs predict. My participation in the 1998 6Y2A multi-multi operation from Jamaica during the CQ World Wide CW contest in November 1998 provided a wonderful opportunity for another first-hand attempt at validation of propagation predictions.

The crew at 6Y2A appears to have set a new world's record in the multi-multi category, with almost 18,000 QSOs after about 1000 duplicate QSOs were removed. This provides a good-sized database from which comparisons and validations can be made to convince you that "the proof is in the pudding."

Elevation Angles for Jamaica

Fig 2 shows an example of the use of long-term elevation angles from Jamaica to all across the USA on 80 meters. The elevation-plane responses for some representative types of antennas are overlaid with the needed angles for comparison. The patterns for all antennas shown in this article were computed using *NEC-4.1*.

I confess: I put the 4-element Yagi at 200 feet in Fig 2 for dramatic effect. It shows just how heroic an effort you would have to go through to mount a horizontally polarized antenna high enough so that it would be a real "killer" antenna on 80 meters. This antenna would indeed be quite a performer, but it would also be a gargantuan project for a 10-day DXpedition to install (not to mention that we'd have to put up antennas for five other bands too).

A simple two-element 80-meter vertical parasitic array would be quite competitive with the monster Yagi, provided that it is installed "on the beach" very near salt water. Verticals do very well when surrounded by salt water. For comparison purposes, a flat-top dipole at a height of 100 feet is also shown in Fig 2. It would be considerably down from the two-element vertical array on the beach.

Note that the range of angles needed on 80 meters into the whole USA ranges from a low of 3° to a high that goes beyond 30°, with predominant angles at 5° and 18°, each occurring 7.5% of the time the band is open. These angles represent all the angles necessary on this path—for all months of the year and for all levels of solar activity in an 11-year solar cycle. This is exactly what I mean by "long-term statistics." All the antennas used at 6Y2A are described in detail in my other article in this book: "Antennas Here are Some Verticals on the Beach..." That article deals in considerable detail with the matching of antenna response patterns with the elevation angles needed for the Jamaica to the world on all the HF bands.

I want to emphasize that the angles needed from Jamaica to reach DX stations around the world are not only low angles—although low angles are extremely important. Higher angles all the way up to 30° elevation are important to cover all target QTHs also. The response of vertical arrays located right down on the ocean approximates rather well the response of the perfectly theoretical isotropic radiator used to compute the enhanced elevation-angle statistics.

If we wanted to be successful on the 6Y2A DXpedition, we knew we needed we needed to be loud everywhere. The vertical arrays we chose to mount down on the beach were a key ingredient in this successful enterprise.

Fig 3 shows a comparison of the hour-by-hour QSO rates for 1997 (6Y4A) and 1998 (6Y2A). The antennas for all bands in 1998 except for 40 meters were larger than in 1997, and the level of solar activity was also quite a bit higher. These factors translated into higher QSO rates and a total of about 3000 more QSOs for the whole contest.

Strategic Concerns

In the CQ World Wide DX Contest, a QTH like Jamaica, counted as part of the North American continent, is at a disadvantage compared to stations located on other continents. In this contest, a contact between two stations in North America is worth two points, while a contact between North America and another continent (such as Europe or Asia) is worth three points. Since Jamaica is close to the US mainland, signals from the USA are very strong—and vice versa, of course. As described in the other article, we designed the main antennas for the higher frequency bands with nulls on the USA to level the playing field for the Europeans. You should recognize that Europeans represent not only three points per QSO, but there are many country multipliers on the European continent.

Who then would really be our "competition" working into Europe, other than the Europeans themselves, who at the start of the contest would busily be working each other for points and lots of country multipliers? We determined that the main competition would come from stateside stations, particularly those on the upper East Coast, since they enjoy a propagation advantage to Europe because of their proximity. A station in Boston is about 3500 miles from Paris, while Jamaica is about 4800 miles away from Paris.

It's true that from 6Y we have a path that takes our signal on a somewhat more southerly route compared to a W1 signal. This more southerly path keeps our signals a bit further away from the effects of the auroral oval on the way to Europe. Granted, this might make a difference when conditions were disturbed by a geomagnetic disturbance, but nobody was hoping for that to occur! We needed to be loud for other reasons.

80 Meters

Fig 4 shows an 80-meter comparison between computed signals from Boston (W1) and Jamaica to Europe, overlaying the QSO rate for 6Y2A into Europe. The W1 is

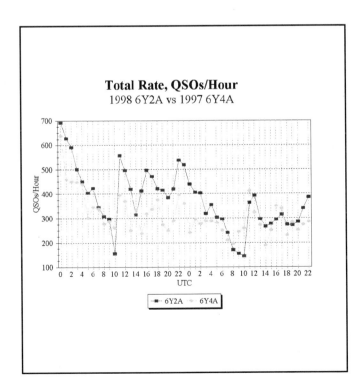

Fig 3—Comparison of total QSOs per hour rate for 1998 6Y2A DXpedition to that for the 1997 6Y4A operation. The sunspot conditions were notably better in 1998 than in 1997.

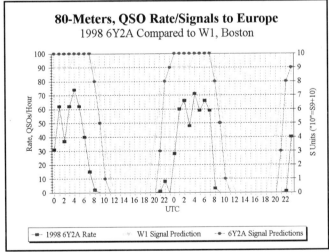

Fig 4—80-meter rate into Europe for the 1998 6Y2A operation, compared to *IONCAP* signal-level predictions from Jamaica. Also shown is the predicted signal strength in Europe for a large station in Boston, Massachusetts. This signal-strength comparison validates our pre-contest assumption that we needed to put an S9 into Europe in order to be able to control the huge pileups and to be heard over the strong East Coast stations. Indeed, when our signal went over S9 in Europe at about 23 UTC, the rate jumped dramatically. As expected, the rate shrank to nothing after European sunrise, dropping on the first night from 40 per hour at 06 UTC down to 2 per hour at 08 UTC when our predicted strength was only S8.

assumed to be running 1500 W into a 100-foot-high dipole over flat ground. The signal level for 6Y2A is computed using 1500 W into a two-by-one vertical array on the beach. Note that the calibration of the right-hand Y-axis is a little odd in that signals over S9 are labeled "10," meaning that they are more than 10 dB over S9. This graphing technique compresses the data for really high-level signals, but when you're S9 + 10 dB on 80 meters and you're operating from the Caribbean, you're already strong enough to be effective! John Dorr, K1AR, is fond of saying words to the effect: "Who cares if you're 20 dB over S9 and I'm only 16 dB over S9?" (The actual peak predicted signal strength from 6Y2A to London was S9 +16 dB on 80 meters.)

Because of the performance expected from our antennas right on the beach, we knew we would be stronger into Europe than a W1 with a 100-foot-high dipole and a kilowatt, a pretty decent station on that band. Besides, the 6Y2A call sign would have some advantage over a "garden-variety" W1. We thus felt that we should be able to hold our own against the majority of stateside stations on 80 meters, providing that the Europeans could hear us over the din of other Europeans calling us in the pileups. And believe me, the pileups were awesome at times.

A quick VOACAP run shows that on 80 meters a YU in Belgrade, Yugoslavia, using 50 W into a 50-foot-high dipole over flat ground, would be S9 + 13 dB in London. Unless our signal was close to this level, a relatively small European station could keep all the others in Europe from hearing us come back to them. We figured that we had to have a minimum signal of about S9 to be able to control the 80-meter European pileups—as best anyone can "control" an unruly pileup of Europeans desperate for a Caribbean contact on 80 meters, that is.

At this point, some of you may well be saying: "I've got to be S9 +10 dB to work anyone?" My point is that you must have a strong signal if you want to run big rates in a contest. A smaller signal can still make lots of QSOs, especially if you can spread the pileup in frequency. For example, you might have people call 1 kHz up, or 2 (or even 5) kHz up or down from your transmitting frequency. That kind of strategy is not very likely to work in a contest, however, where every 250-Hz slot is already occupied by a big CW station calling CQ!

Fig 5 is a printout for 80 meters of a customized propagation-prediction run I made for the 6Y2A operation, using the vertical gain arrays we planned to install on the beach front in Jamaica. This table is very

---

80 Meters: 6Y2A, Nov., Jamaica (Kingston), for SSN = High, Sigs in S-Units for verticals.

Zone		00	01	02	03	04	05	06	07	08	09	10	11	12	13	14	15	16	17	18	19	20	21	22	23
KL7 =	01	3	6	8	9	9	9	9	9	9	9	9	9	9	8	2	-	-	-	-	-	-	-	-	-
VO2 =	02	9+	9+	9+	9+	9+	9+	9+	9+	9+	9+	9+	9	6	-	-	-	-	-	-	-	-	5	9	9+
W6 =	03	6	8	9+	9+	9+	9+	9+	9+	9+	9+	9+	9+	9	6	1	-	-	-	-	-	-	-	-	2
W0 =	04	9+	9+	9+	9+	9+	9+	9+	9+	9+	9+	9+	9+	9+	8	1	-	-	-	-	-	-	-	7	9+
W3 =	05	9+	9+	9+	9+	9+	9+	9+	9+	9+	9+	9+	9+	9+	6	-	-	-	-	-	-	-	8	9+	9+
XE1 =	06	9+	9+	9+	9+	9+	9+	9+	9+	9+	9+	9+	9+	9+	8	-	-	-	-	-	-	-	-	5	9
TI =	07	9+	9+	9+	9+	9+	9+	9+	9+	9+	9+	9+	9+	9+	9	4	-	-	-	-	-	1	8	9+	9+
VP2 =	08	9+	9+	9+	9+	9+	9+	9+	9+	9+	9+	9+	9+	9+	6	1	-	-	-	1	6	9+	9+	9+
P4 =	09	9+	9+	9+	9+	9+	9+	9+	9+	9+	9+	9+	9+	9	4	-	-	-	-	-	1	7	9+	9+	9+
HC =	10	9+	9+	9+	9+	9+	9+	9+	9+	9+	9+	9+	9+	9	3	-	-	-	-	-	-	-	2	9	9+
PY1 =	11	8	8	8	8	8	9	9	8	8	6	1	-	-	-	-	-	-	-	-	-	-	2	6
CE =	12	8	8	8	9	9	9	9	9	9	8	6	1	-	-	-	-	-	-	-	-	-	-	4
LU =	13	7	8	8	8	8	8	9	8	8	6	3	-	-	-	-	-	-	-	-	-	-	-	5
G =	14	9+	9+	9+	9+	9+	9+	9+	9+	8	5	1	-	-	-	-	-	-	-	-	-	-	3	8	9
I =	15	9	9	9	9+	9	9	9	8	1	-	-	-	-	-	-	-	-	-	-	-	-	1	8	9
UA3 =	16	9	9	9	9	9	9	-	-	-	-	-	-	-	-	-	-	-	-	-	-	-	-	7	9
UN =	17	8	4	1	-	-	-	-	-	-	-	-	-	-	-	-	-	-	-	-	-	-	-	1	3
UA9 =	18	1	-	-	-	-	-	-	-	-	-	-	-	-	-	-	-	-	-	-	-	-	-	-	6
UA0 =	19	-	-	-	-	-	-	-	1	8	8	5	1	-	-	-	-	-	-	-	-	-	-	-	6
4X =	20	9	9	9	8	8	1	-	-	-	-	-	-	-	-	-	-	-	-	-	-	-	-	2	8
HZ =	21	8	8	8	1	-	-	-	-	-	-	-	-	-	-	-	-	-	-	-	-	-	-	1	4
VU =	22	6	1	-	-	-	-	-	-	-	-	-	-	-	-	-	-	-	-	-	-	-	-	-	2
JT =	23	-	-	-	-	-	-	-	-	1	-	-	-	-	-	-	-	-	-	-	-	-	-	-	-
VS6 =	24	-	-	-	-	-	-	-	-	1	-	-	-	-	-	-	-	-	-	-	-	-	-	-	-
JA1 =	25	-	-	-	-	-	-	-	1	8	8	5	1	-	-	-	-	-	-	-	-	-	-	-	-
HS =	26	-	-	-	-	-	-	-	-	-	-	-	-	-	-	-	-	-	-	-	-	-	-	-	-
DU =	27	-	-	-	-	-	-	-	-	2	2	-	-	-	-	-	-	-	-	-	-	-	-	-	-
YB =	28	-	-	-	-	-	-	-	-	-	-	-	-	-	-	-	-	-	-	-	-	-	-	-	-
VK6 =	29	-	-	-	-	-	-	-	-	-	-	-	-	-	-	-	-	-	-	-	-	-	-	-	-
VK3 =	30	-	-	-	-	-	-	-	-	-	4	1	-	-	-	-	-	-	-	-	-	-	-	-	-
KH6 =	31	-	-	-	6	8	9	9	9	9	9	9	9	7	-	-	-	-	-	-	-	-	-	-	-
KH8 =	32	-	-	-	-	-	8	8	9	9	9	8	-	-	-	-	-	-	-	-	-	-	-	-	-
CN =	33	8	8	8	9+	8	9+	9+	9+	4	1	-	-	-	-	-	-	-	-	-	-	-	1	7	9
SU =	34	9	9	9	9	8	1	-	-	-	-	-	-	-	-	-	-	-	-	-	-	-	-	2	8
6W =	35	8	9	9	8	8	8	9+	9+	6	2	-	-	-	-	-	-	-	-	-	-	-	-	6	8
D2 =	36	9	9	9	9	8	1	-	-	-	-	-	-	-	-	-	-	-	-	-	-	-	-	1	8
5Z =	37	8	8	8	5	-	-	-	-	-	-	-	-	-	-	-	-	-	-	-	-	-	-	-	3
ZS6 =	38	6	8	8	1	-	-	-	-	-	-	-	-	-	-	-	-	-	-	-	-	-	-	-	3
FR =	39	6	1	-	-	-	-	-	-	-	-	-	-	-	-	-	-	-	-	-	-	-	-	-	2
FJL =	40	8	8	9	9	9	8	9	9	8	8	7	5	1	-	-	-	-	-	-	-	-	-	4	7
Zone		00	01	02	03	04	05	06	07	08	09	10	11	12	13	14	15	16	17	18	19	20	21	22	23

UTC -->   * = Longpath

Expected signal levels using 1500 W and vertical array (4 dBi) at transmitter, over saltwater.

Fig 5—Printout of customized propagation-prediction page for 80 meters from 6Y2A, using the vertical arrays actually used in the 1998 DXpedition. The page is laid out with the UTC time on the horizontal axis and receiving locations in each of the 40 CQ Zones on the vertical axis. The numbers shown in the matrix are the predicted signals strengths in S-units.

similar to the 70,000 pages of such tables included with the CD-ROM version of the 18th Edition of *The ARRL Antenna Book*. These tables were computed using my standard antenna types, but the signal levels can be extrapolated for different antennas.

We expected to be able to control the pileups, since for most of the opening into Zone 14 we would be at least S9 + 10 dB, with S9 signals into the rest of the European continent. For several days before the contest we tested the station and consistently received tremendous reports into Europe. We were also strong into the USA as well, for we had another gain array of verticals pointed in that direction. As the main 80-meter operator, I figured that this was going to be fun!

The analysis above gave us the assurance that we could plunk down almost anywhere in the 80-meter band and be able to hold our own into Europe. K2KW, the mastermind behind the 6Y2A operation, suggested that we hang out down near the bottom edge of the band, where people would be able to find us quickly as they starting tuning from the bottom upwards. More importantly, this is where only Extra Class US stations could legally operate. Sorry, non-Extra US stations, but while it may sound cruel, the strategy does work. Fewer US stations calling would allow the weaker Europeans to come through, and they were worth three points each.

Fig 4 also shows the 6Y2A hourly rates into Europe. During the time the band was open, we had steady rates hovering around 60 per hour into Europe. In 1998 we had a dedicated reflector/driver pair of verticals

directed at Europe and another pair directed at the USA, while in 1997 the 80-meter station had a compromise single reflector/ driver pair aimed due North. On the first night I stayed on 3500.5 kHz for the first six and three-quarters hours, before moving up to 3543.0 kHz to pick up many Advanced and General class US stations—after the main European runs had dried up, of course.

Fig 6 shows predicted signal strengths into the USA and into Japan, overlaying the hourly rates into these target areas. The predictions said that the USA would be easy to work anytime during the hours of darkness, while JAs proved to be possible, but not easy, to work from 6Y2A. The prediction was that our signal would peak only S8 in Japan. The peak rate into JA was only 20, much less than in 1997, when the peak rate was 100. It's not at all clear to me whether the lower rate was due to the higher level of solar activity, where stations would stay on the higher bands for longer periods of time rather than moving down to 80 meters, or whether it was due to predicted signals less than S9, as they had been predicted in 1997. I certainly tried every frequency combination I knew where the Japanese can hear foreign stations. Interestingly, the few Japanese stations worked were quite loud and clear; there just weren't many of them.

There are many factors that enter into whether, or whether not, a QSO is made. As mentioned previously, one thing that might diminish the number of European or Japanese contacts from 6Y2A is that US stations will be much louder than even the strongest

of Europeans or Japanese. In the "feeding frenzy" at the beginning of a contest all the big-gun US stations are picking off multipliers left and right. Once the initial surge of very strong US stations dies down, the Europeans could come to the head of the pack. Late in the night, when many USA operators are sleeping, the JAs are able to make it through the curtain of loud W stations.

A *VOACAP* computation for a 100-W station in Philadelphia using a 50-foot-high dipole shows that his signal would be S9 + 3 dB in Jamaica. A bigger station in Philadelphia with 1500 W and a 100-foot dipole would be S9 + 22 dB in Jamaica. By comparison, a large German station would be about S9 in Jamaica if he had a 1500-W transmitter and a 100-foot-high dipole. It's not too hard to tell who would come through first in a pileup at the start of a contest on 80 meters.

The azimuthal pattern on a single "two-by-one" reflector/driver array is down only about 5 dB on US signals when the array is pointing into Europe. Perhaps we need to be more ambitious in the future, with a two-by-two 80-meter array pointed into Europe to null out the US signals on the order of 20 dB, just like on the higher bands.

In the final analysis, I believe the 6Y2A operation validates the propagation predictions made beforehand for 80 meters. Our prediction that we needed an S9 signal in Europe to keep up a good rate seemed to be validated. The rate at the evening opening doesn't rise to more than 20 per hour until 23 UTC, when the predicted level rises to

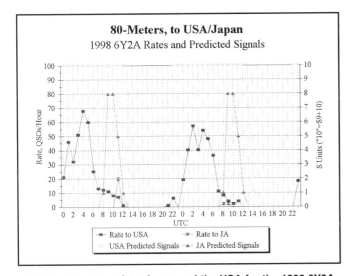

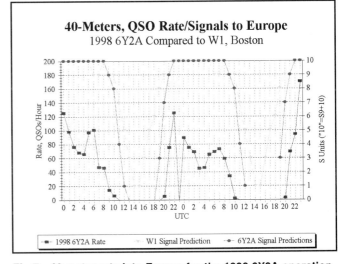

Fig 6—80-meter rate into Japan and the USA for the 1998 6Y2A operation, compared to *IONCAP* signal-level predictions for Jamaica. The rate into Japan on 80 meters in 1998 was a considerable disappointment compared to 1997, when more than 360 JA stations were worked on 80 meters. We suspect that the JA stations were working DX late in their afternoon on 10 and 15 meters in 1998, since the sunspots were so much higher in 1998 than in 1997. They were having too much fun to consider going down to 80 meters to snag any Caribbean stations at sunset.

Fig 7—40-meter rate into Europe for the 1998 6Y2A operation, compared to *IONCAP* signal-level predictions from Jamaica. This band was open somewhere for about 18 hours each day from Jamaica. Again, the rate went up dramatically once the signal strength in the target receiving area rose to S9 or higher. Only with that kind of signal strength could the massive pileups be kept under some semblance of control. Note that a W1 in Boston would be able to work into Europe about a hour earlier than we could from Jamaica.

S9 for all Zones in Europe. I could hear Europeans weakly as early as 1930 UTC, but we couldn't get their attention until several hours later, when they would sometimes come back with a question mark. An hour after that we were running our brains out, with huge pileups.

40 Meters

A similar propagation analysis on 40 meters using a vertical two-element reflector/driver array showed that we would very strong in Western Europe (peaking at S9 + 20 dB), stronger than any stateside competitors using a kilowatt and a 100-foot-high dipole. See **Fig 7**, which shows that the 6Y2A 40-meter signal would be as loud or louder than the W1 signal into Europe from 21 UTC on through 09 UTC, an interval of 13 hours. That's a lot of time to make lots of QSOs. Just like on 80 meters, there is a distinct falloff in QSOs in the early morning hours from 02 to 04 UTC in Zone 14, followed by a peak in rate around Eastern European sunrise from 05 to 06 UTC. And just like 80 meters, we couldn't get a good rate into Europe started until our signal strength was S9 or greater.

Dave Patton, W9QA, was the 40-meter 6Y2A operator, and he had rates close to or higher than 200/hour for the first four hours of the contest. From that evidence, I would hazard a guess that we were loud, just as *CAPMAN* predicted.

In the afternoon opening on 40 meters into Europe, the rate climbed to 60 per hour at 21 UTC only after the predicted signal strength went over S9. Again, it seems that it takes an S9 or stronger signal on 40 meters to attract and then control the pileups. Just

for reference, the prototypical 50-W YU station with a 50-foot-high dipole would be S9 + 13 dB in London on 40 meters too. So a station outside of Europe has to have a pretty substantial signal on 40 meters to make its presence felt there.

Into Japan, **Fig 8** shows a predicted level of S9 for five hours a day on 40 meters. While the JA QSO rates didn't equal those into Europe, they averaged about 50 to 60 per hour when the band was open after Europe had closed up around 08 UTC, through until 12 UTC. There were 564 QSOs in Asia on 40 meters in 1998, compared with 510 in 1997.

20 Meters

The 20-meter band is a lot more complicated than either 80 or 40 meters. There are also more stations available to work on this band. At the High level of solar activity we experienced from 6Y2A in November 1998, the band is open to somewhere in the world for 24 hours a day. **Fig 9** shows the calculated signal levels into Europe for a W1 station in Boston, using a three-element Yagi 100 feet over flat ground. This is contrasted with the signal level for the 6Y2A "two-by-two" vertical array on the beach in Jamaica. The 20-meter band closes to Europe from Jamaica only for about two hours a day.

The European QSO rate at 6Y2A on 20 meters is overlaid on Fig 9 as well. There is a steep drop in the 6Y2A rate for roughly four hours, between about 12 to 15 UTC. Our signal strengths predicted for that time frame vary from S9 down to S7. Part of the reason for the rate drop is that the W1 in Boston will be considerably louder in Europe during that time, at S9 + 10 dB most of

the time. Again, our old rule-of-thumb seems to hold true: Big rates require signals that are at least S9 on the 20-meter band.

However, it is not always brute signal strength (or lack thereof) that strictly determines the QSO rate. The simple fact of the matter is that the 15-meter band opens wide into Europe about 10 UTC, and following that within about an hour is the 10-meter opening, which comes alive into Europe from North America at about 11 UTC. Few contest operators stay on 20 meters, battling it out with big multi-multi stations there when they can be running at good rates themselves on 15 or 10 meters! As I say, 20 meters is a complicated band.

Fig 10 shows the 20-meter page from the customized propagation prediction for 6Y2A. As I stated previously, at a High level of solar activity the 20-meter band is open to somewhere 24 hours a day. This prediction shows that on 20 meters there are some long-path openings (indicated by asterisks), where the predicted signal strengths are greater than for the short-path heading. For example, look at Zone 29. There are a number of asterisks showing for this Zone. All three Zone 29 stations worked in 1998 were worked late in the afternoon with the beam heading toward Europe. Weaker VK3s in Zone 30 also came through on the European heading in the late afternoon at 6Y2A.

Fig 11 shows how the predicted signal strength varies with time into Japan and the USA on 20 meters. 6Y2A could be expected to put S8 or higher levels of signals into Japan for about 19 hours of the day, provided of course that the antennas were directed in that direction. Remember, the

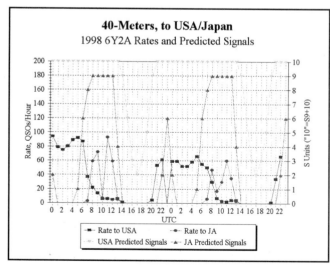

40-Meters, to USA/Japan
1998 6Y2A Rates and Predicted Signals

Fig 8—40-meter rate into Japan and the USA for the 1998 6Y2A operation, compared to *IONCAP* signal-level predictions from Jamaica.

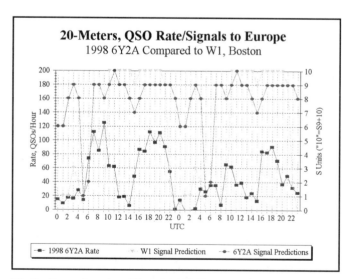

20-Meters, QSO Rate/Signals to Europe
1998 6Y2A Compared to W1, Boston

Fig 9—From Jamaica, 20 meters during a period of very high solar conditions is a 24-hour QSO party to somewhere in the world! The 20-meter band is "closed" to Europe (that is, with signals less than S8) only two hours a day.

20 Meters: 6Y2A, Nov., Jamaica (Kingston), for SSN = High, Sigs in S-Units for verticals.

Zone	00	01	02	03	04	05	06	07	08	09	10	11	12	13	14	15	16	17	18	19	20	21	22	23
KL7 = 01	9+	9+	9+	9	9	7	2	1	2	3	1	1	-	-	-	-	8	9	8	8	9	9	9+	9+
VO2 = 02	9+	9	5	2	2	4	4	9	9+	9	9	8	9+	9+	9+	9	9	9	9+	9+	9+	9+	9+	9+
W6 = 03	9+	9+	6	8	9	9	8	8	9	9	5	-	2	2	9+	9+	9	8	5	8	8	9	9+	9+
W0 = 04	9+	9+	9+	9+	9+	9+	9+	9+	9+	9+	9	9+	9+	9+	9+	9+	9+	9+	9+	9+	9+	9+	9+	9+
W3 = 05	9	4	9+	9+	9+	9+	9+	9+	9+	8	8	9+	9+	9+	9+	9+	9+	9+	9+	9+	9+	9+	9+	9+
XE1 = 06	9+	9+	9	8	9	9+	9+	9+	9+	9+	8	9+	1	9+	9+	9+	9+	9+	9+	9+	9+	9+	9+	9+
TI = 07	9+	9+	9+	9+	9	6	1	3	7	9	9+	9+	9+	9+	9+	9+	9+	9+	9+	9+	9+	9+	9+	9+
VP2 = 08	9+	9+	9+	9+	9+	9	9	8	2	1	1	9+	9+	9+	9+	9+	9+	9+	9+	9+	9+	9+	9+	9+
P4 = 09	9+	9+	9+	9+	9+	9	8	3	-	1	5	9	9+	9+	9+	9+	9+	9+	9+	9+	9+	9+	9+	9+
HC = 10	9+	9+	9+	9+	9+	9+	9+	9+	9	9	9	9+	9+	9+	9+	9+	9+	9+	9+	9+	9+	9+	9+	9+
PY1 = 11	9+	9+	9+	9+	9+	9+	9+	9+	9+	5	2	9	9+	9	7	4	2	2	4	2	7	9	9+	9+
CE = 12	9+	9+	9+	9+	9+	9+	9+	9+	9+	9	8	9	9+	9	8	7	5	4	4	6	8	9	9+	9+
LU = 13	9+	9+	9+	9+	9+	9+	9+	9+	9+	6	9	9	8	6	3	3	3	4	6	8	9	9+	9+	9+
G = 14	4	4	6	8	8	1	-	-	8	8	8	9+	9	8	7	6	8	9	9	9	9	8	9	6
I = 15	6	6	8	9	7	-	2	9	9	7	9	9	7	6	5	4	5	7	8	9	9	9	9	8
UA3 = 16	1	6	6	4	-	-	9	8	9	8	9	9	9	8	7	6	7	8	4	-	-	-	-	1
UN = 17	6	6	7	9+	9	9	9	8	7	6	8	9	8	7	6	4	1	1	1	4	6	7	7	6
UA9 = 18	9	9	9	9+	9	9	9	9	9	9	8	9	9	8	4	2	2	2	4	5	7	6	6	7
UA0 = 19	9	9	9	9	9	9	9	9	9+	9	4	-	-	1	5	3	-	-	-	1	8	8	9	9
4X = 20	9+	9+	9+	9	8	9+	9+	9	7	7	7	6	4	2	2	3	4	5	7	9	9	9	9+	9+
HZ = 21	9+	9+	9	9	9+	9	9	8	5	5	5	4	3	3	2	2	4	5	7	8	9	9	9	9+
VU = 22	9	9	9	9	7	8	2	1	-	6	8	8	7	6	2	2	1	-	1	5	8	9	9	8
JT = 23	9+	9	9	8	9	8	9	9+	9	8	9	8	2	1	1	2	2	3	3	1	1	6		
VS6 = 24	9	8	7	2	1	1	2	7	9	8	7	9	9+	9	8	3	1	1	1	1	1	9	9	
JA1 = 25	8	7	8	8	8	6	9	9	9+	9	9	1	1	2	5	4	1	-	-	2	7	8	8	8
HS = 26	9	9	8	2	-	-	-	1	6	6	6	9	9	8	3	1	1	2	4	7	4	3	9	
DU = 27	7	6	2	-	-	-	2	8	9	9	8	9	9+	9	5	2	1	1	3	2	8	8	8*	
YB = 28	8	7	1	-	-	-	-	8	6	4	7	9+	9	8	3	1	-	1	2	8	8	8	9	
VK6 = 29	5*	1*	-	-	-	-	1	4	8	9	8	9	9	8	7	2*	1*	2*	3*	3*	5*	5*	8	8*
VK3 = 30	-	-	-	1	1	7	8	9	9+	9	7	7	9	9	8	4	1	-	-	-	1*	2*	3*	3*
KH6 = 31	8	9	9+	9+	9+	9+	9	9+	9+	9+	9	9	9	6	-	7	8	4	2	2	2	3	4	6
KH8 = 32	1	5	9	9	9+	9+	9+	9+	9+	9+	8	4	9+	9+	9	8	5	2	-	-	-	-	-	-
CN = 33	9	-	9	9	9	9	-	-	-	8	9	9+	9	4	4	5	5	9	9	9	9+	9+	9+	9+
SU = 34	9+	9+	9+	9+	9	8	9+	9+	9	7	7	6	5	4	3	2	2	3	5	7	9	9+	9+	9+
6W = 35	9+	9+	9+	9+	9+	9+	8	1	3	8	9+	9	7	4	1	1	3	5	8	9	9+	9+	9+	9+
D2 = 36	9+	9+	9+	9+	9+	9+	9+	9	4	5	4	1	-	-	-	1	1	3	6	8	9	9+	9+	9+
5Z = 37	9+	9+	9+	9+	9+	9	9	7	2	-	-	-	-	2*	1	1	1	4	6	8	9	9+	9+	9+
ZS6 = 38	9+	9+	9+	9+	9+	9+	9	7	2	-	-	-	-	-	-	-	1	3	7	9	9	9+	9+	9+
FR = 39	9+	9+	9	9+	9	8	1	-	-	-	-	-	1*	2*	3*	1*	-	-	1	4	9	9	9+	9+
FJL = 40	9	9+	9	9	9	9	9	8	7	5	5	9	9	8	8	7	7	8	9	9	9	9	9	
Zone	00	01	02	03	04	05	06	07	08	09	10	11	12	13	14	15	16	17	18	19	20	21	22	23

UTC -->   * = Longpath

Expected signal levels using 1500 W and vertical array (9 dBi) at transmitter, over saltwater.

Fig 10—Printout of customized propagation prediction page for 20 meters from 6Y2A, using the vertical arrays used in the 1998 DXpedition. This kind of information was helpful to schedule QSOs for rare zones on the other bands after the 20-meter operator had made a QSO. Many rare stations were moved from one band to another in the course of the contest, boosting the 6Y2A multiplier score considerably.

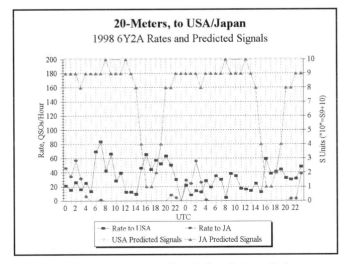

20-Meters, to USA/Japan
1998 6Y2A Rates and Predicted Signals

Fig 11—QSO rate versus predicted signal strength from Jamaica to Japan and the USA on 20 meters. QSOs were made into some areas of the USA for all 48 hours of the contest!

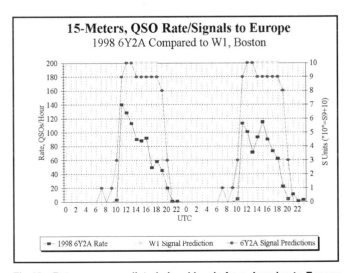

15-Meters, QSO Rate/Signals to Europe
1998 6Y2A Compared to W1, Boston

Fig 12—Rate versus predicted signal levels from Jamaica to Europe on 15 meters. Once the 15-meter band opened in the Jamaican morning with S9 or better signals, the rate rose dramatically. The IONCAP predictions are well validated by the actual QSO results.

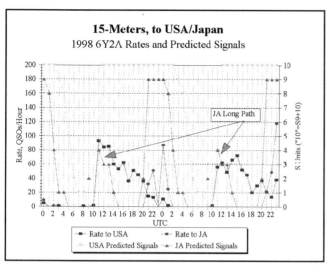

15-Meters, to USA/Japan
1998 6Y2A Rates and Predicted Signals

JA Long Path

- Rate to USA
- Rate to JA
- USA Predicted Signals
- JA Predicted Signals

Fig 13—Rate versus predicted signal levels from Jamaica to the USA and Japan on 15 meters. Note the early-morning openings predicted to Japan about 11 to 13 UTC. These were long-path openings, but we couldn't take advantage of them because of the steep cliffs behind the beach-front QTH in Jamaica. That was the compromise we had to live with in order to have direct over-the-ocean, short-path shots into Europe, the USA and Japan!

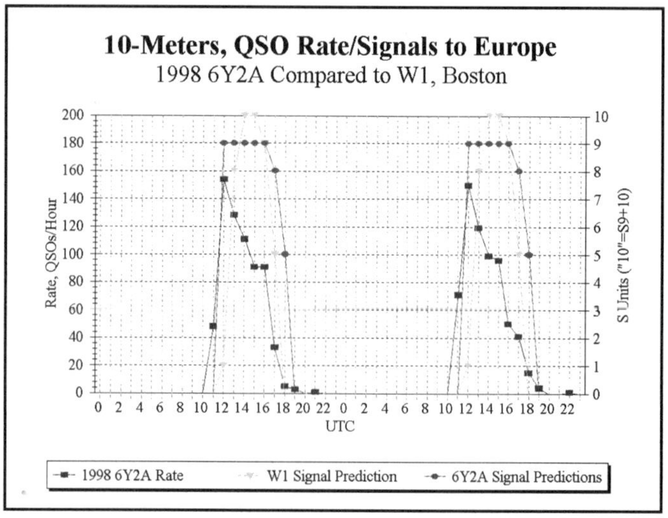

10-Meters, QSO Rate/Signals to Europe
1998 6Y2A Compared to W1, Boston

- 1998 6Y2A Rate
- W1 Signal Prediction
- 6Y2A Signal Predictions

Fig 14— Rate versus predicted signal levels from Jamaica to all of Europe on 10 meters. As many people have observed before: "There's no meters like 10 meters." The 10-meter operator had several exhilarating 150+ hour rates into Europe, while achieving almost 100 per hour into the USA simultaneously. He reported that the S-meter rarely went below S9 + 20 dB.

main European array had a null towards the USA and hence to JA.

The signals into the USA were predicted to be equal to or higher than S9 for all 24 hours of the day. Even during the prime European running hours, with the European two-by-two array in use, strong USA signals could and did work us on 20 meters during 47 of the 48 hours in the contest.

15 Meters

During a high level of solar activity in November from the Caribbean, working Europe on 15 meters is a matter of maximizing the rate, once the band opens about 10 UTC. **Fig 12** shows predicted signal strengths from both W1 and 6Y2A on this band into Europe. The W1 actually has a stronger signal for five hours during the opening because of the higher gain of the four-element Yagi at 60 feet used by the program for W1 compared to the vertical two-by-two array at 6Y2A. This didn't seem to hinder the peak rate achieved on 15 meters into Europe (140 per hour), falling below 100 per hour only after 13 UTC. I'm sure this dip occurred because most single operators were moving up to 10 meters around that time, not because the 6Y2A signal level drops to only S9!

Despite the allure of 10 meters, the shape of the 15-meter QSO rate curve compares favorably with the shape of the predicted signal strength curve for levels higher than about S8. It would appear that the band "pops open wide" when signals go above that level, into Europe anyway. **Fig 13** shows the predicted signals and resulting

rates for the USA and Japan on 15 meters. Here, S9 levels are apparently necessary for either the USA or the JA rate to go up dramatically.

You will note in Fig 13 two relatively weak long-path openings predicted for 15 meters to the Far East during the European run between 11 to 14 UTC. Unfortunately for us at 6Y2A, the long-path direction was completely blocked by a huge volcanic cliff behind the station. We did get multipliers for most of those Zones later in the day during the short-path direct opening, so not all was lost to the cliff. Besides, we were way too busy running Europeans at 100+/hour rates to worry about such exotic paths!

10 Meters

On 10 meters, the W1 in Boston will have a shorter, but stronger, opening to Europe, as shown in **Fig 14**. His signal will peak at S9 + 10 dB for 14 and 15 UTC, even though the signal from 6Y2A will hit S9 earlier, at 12 UTC. As soon as the East Coast stations got strong the rate for 6Y2A dropped down to an average of about 110 per hour into Europe. Both days seemed to enjoy the same conditions on 10 meters, judging by the rate curve. Again, it seems like a signal strength of S9 is necessary to attract and then hold command of a pileup on 10 meters into Europe.

Fig 15 shows the same long-path openings to the Far East that 15 meters displayed. Again, we were unable to take advantage of these predictions because of the cliff blocking that direction towards the south. However, the direct-path opening to JA was productive for us, with peak rates of almost

120 per hour at 22 UTC on Saturday afternoon, right when our predicted signal strength in Japan was S9. The rate fell off dramatically when the predicted signal strength dropped below S8 after 23 UTC.

And What About 160 Meters?

IONCAP and its derivatives don't do particularly well below 2 MHz. They will operate down that low in frequency, but I'm not convinced that the numbers produced are accurate. The problem is that *IONCAP* doesn't explicitly take into account the effects of the geomagnetic field, which can be severe at 1.8 MHz, close to the electron gyro-frequency. Instead, Tom Frenaye, K1KI, suggested a simple algorithm to extrapolate 80-meter predicted levels down to 160 meters. His methodology, which is to subtract 3 S units from the 80-meter predicted level, seems to be validated by the results on this DXpedition and in other contests as well.

Fig 16 shows the 160-meter rate into Europe, the USA and JA. The 6Y2A antenna on Top Band consisted of a pair of 57-foot-high loaded verticals with elevated radials. One vertical was set up as a reflector and the other as a driver and the array was pointed due North. Mounted close to the salt water as it was, the 160-meter array played extremely well.

To me, the rate into Europe was truly incredible, especially when you consider that USA stations were being worked at the same time! Two JA stations were worked on 160 meters too, when the predictions said this should be possible.

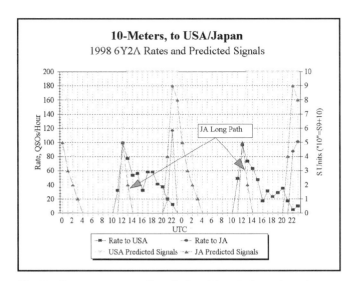

10-Meters, to USA/Japan
1998 6Y2A Rates and Predicted Signals

Rate, QSOs/Hour

S Units ("10"=S9+10)

JA Long Path

UTC

— Rate to USA   — Rate to JA
— USA Predicted Signals   — JA Predicted Signals

160-Meters, QSO Rates per Area
1998 6Y2A Europe & USA & Japan

Rate, QSOs/Hour

UTC

— Europe   — USA   — JA

Fig 15—Rate versus predicted signal levels from Jamaica to the USA and Japan on 10 meters. Again, we couldn't capitalize on the long-path openings to Japan because of the cliffs behind us.

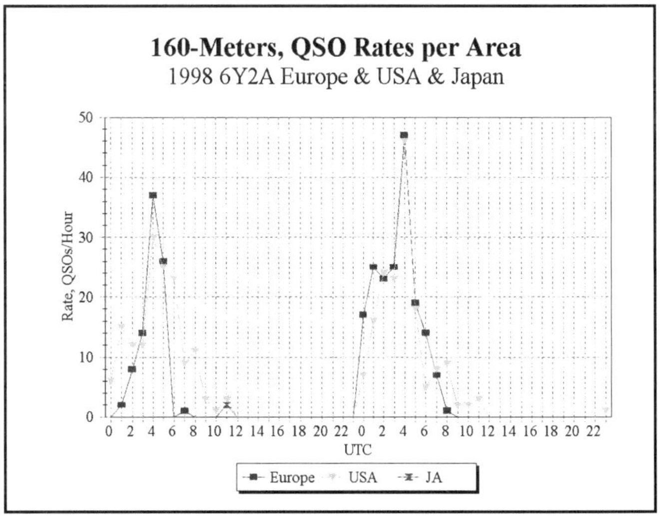

Fig 16—The 6Y2A rate in QSOs per hour from Jamaica on 160 meters. The two-element vertical array aimed North put out a very potent signal into Europe and the USA.

Conclusion

In this article I have suggested that you can derive much value from planning an operation using both long-term and short-term propagation predictions. I have demonstrated that long-term elevation-angle statistics can be used to help plan an antenna installation, whether your antennas are horizontal Yagis on towers or verticals down on the beach.

I have given some tips on how to use short-term, monthly predictions to plan strategy and to anticipate band openings for needed multipliers, whether in a contest or in making day-to-day DX QSOs. At 6Y2A, we found that passing multipliers between bands was facilitated by detailed predic- tions showing when each band could be expected to be open all throughout the world. I'm sure that there must be other tid- bits of information that can be gleaned from such propagation predictions too.

See you in the pileups—perhaps from some exotic location on the beach some- where. May your signals be loud.

Quad Antennas

Monster Quads

By Rudy Severns, N6LF
PO Box 589
Cottage Grove, OR 97424

So you're dreaming about a really big antenna for 40 meters? N6LF tells us about his monster two-element 40-meter quad, with bonus three elements on 20 and 15 meters.

Quads are fascinating antennas. I've been afflicted with the desire to build them for over 40 years. The first one was a two-element job I built while serving with the Army in Germany (DL4ND/DL4SFG) in the 1950s. To this day I'm not sure how I managed to shinny up a 70-foot pole to install the quad, but I was determined to get it working! And work it did!

True madness did not come upon me until I read Lindsay's 1968 article on quads.[1] I promptly built a six-element 20-meter monster (on a 60-foot boom) using the dimensions in the article. While I was at it, I added six elements on 15 meters and 11 elements on 10 meters. During initial testing using a small exciter (about 10 W) the first contact was the Russian Antarctic station, long path. After that I was hooked—and it's been all downhill from there!

If you live in an area where heavy icing is a regular occurrence, this article should be saved for April 1st. At my present QTH in western Oregon we seldom have ice storms. The most severe in the past ten years put about $1/2$ inch of ice on my quad. The distortion was alarming but no permanent damage occurred. More ice than that, however, would start to break things. Perhaps it is possible to build quads to stand up to heavy icing, but I doubt it is worth the trouble for antennas of the monster size discussed in this article.

The antennas I describe are large and require significant time, effort and money to implement. The point of this article is to give you some useful ideas and perhaps some inspiration. I have included the dimensions, performance predictions, many mechanical details and some of the mistakes I made along the way. You can, of course, replicate any of these antennas directly but you will get better results if you consider them a starting point and then design an antenna to meet your own particular needs and preferences.

Modeling

Good *NEC-2* and *NEC-4*-based software is now available and is a worthwhile investment for a project of this size. Quads are generally lower-Q antennas than comparable Yagis and therefore somewhat less sensitive to dimensional variations, supporting structures and interlaced multi-band elements. But you will still find the best results can be had only by modeling the complete structure and designing for your particular needs.

I did all my modeling for this article using *GNEC-4*, which is *NEC 4.1*-based.[2] I modeled the WØHTH six-element quad in free space, while my 40/20/15-meter multiband quad is centered at 100 feet, over average ground ($\varepsilon = 13$, $\sigma = 0.005$ S/m) using the Sommerfeld ground model.

While there is remarkably little interaction between elements of different bands, you must take some care to prevent unexpected resonances due to the matching sections and the open-circuited feed lines on those driven elements not in use. I fed each driven element separately and led the feedline to a multi-pole coax relay mounted at the center of the boom. I used the modeling program to select lengths of feedline that did not result in any spurious resonances that would upset the performance on another band. This was not very difficult, but required some attention.

WØHTH Quad

Just for old time's sake. I went back and took a look at the multi-element quad I built in 1968 to Lindsay's dimensions (see **Table 1**). In those days I didn't have a computer on my desk to do antenna modeling, so I just relied on his information. The results had been great, but I was curious to see how modern modeling would compare with Lindsay's experimental work. Based on his

---

Table 1

Dimensions of 20-Meter WØHTH Six-Element Quad

Element	Location (ft)	$1/4$ Length (ft)
Reflector	0	18.04
Driven	12	17.60
Director 1	24	17.28
Director 2	36	17.28
Director 3	48	17.28
Director 4	60	17.32

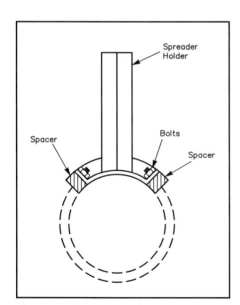

Fig 1—WØHTH 6 element 20-meter quad, free-space radiation patterns. At A, E-plane pattern and at B, H-plane pattern.

(A) E-Plane Plot

Freq = 14.2 MHz
Max. Gain = 11.60 dBi

(B) H-Plane Plot

Fig 2—A method for accommodating a larger boom diameter for a spreader hub.

experimental work at 440 MHz, scaled down to 14.2 MHz, Lindsay predicted a forward gain of 13.4 dBi. It is hard to tell exactly what the F/B ratio is from Figure III-3A in his article but it looks to be roughly 15 to 20 dB.

With *NEC-4.1* software the predicted pattern is shown in **Fig 1**. I computed a forward gain of 12.1 dBi and a F/B of 14 dB. This was not too bad, but I suspect that these numbers could be improved with a bit of fiddling with the model. I remember that I adjusted the reflector length slightly for maximum F/B when I built the antenna, and the F/B was quite good.

For 15 meters I scaled the 20-meter element dimensions (retaining the same element spacing) and then adjusted the reflector for maximum F/B and the driven element for resonance. On 10 meters I again scaled the dimensions and adjusted the reflector, but in the true ham spirit of "If a little is good, more should be lots better," I added five more directors. I spaced each 10-meter element by 6 feet.

I made my boom from two 30-foot lengths of 4-inch-OD irrigation pipe. Most commercial spreader hubs are designed for 3-inch, not 4-inch, diameter booms, so to accommodate the larger boom, I placed spacer blocks between the hub sections. See **Fig 2**. This worked well for hubs made from four separate pieces. However, some commercial hubs have one-piece castings and can't be expanded like this. To match to 50-Ω feedline I used λ/4 75-Ω transmission line sections on each band.

With an 11-element quad on a 60-foot boom, I noticed some interesting propagation effects on 10 meters. On several occasions the band dropped out during a transcontinental QSO, with signal strengths dropping from S9+ to just above the noise level. Nonetheless, we were able to continue the QSO for an extended period of time, when for all intents and purposes the band was dead. There is nothing like a big antenna!

A Two-Element 40-Meter, Three-Element 20 and 15-Meter Quad

In 1989 I built another quad based on Lindsay's article. It had five elements on 20 and 15 meters—and nine elements on 10 meters—on a 50-foot boom. I did not yet have antenna modeling software so again I just used Lindsay's dimensions. The antenna worked very well but it also provided me with a lesson on wind loading and wind strengths on mountaintops in Oregon. The antenna itself stood up very well, but my

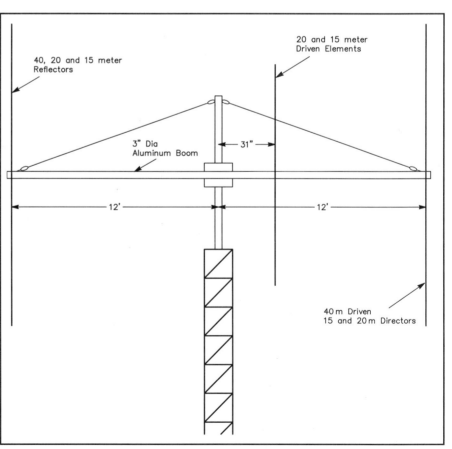

Fig 3—N6LF three-band quad dimensions: two elements on 40 meters; three on 20 and 15 meters.

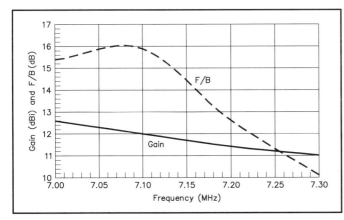

Fig 4—Gain and F/B characteristics on 40 meters.

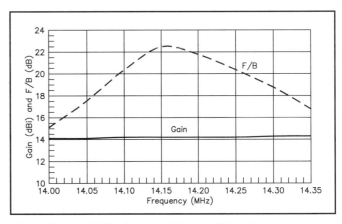

Fig 5—Gain and F/B characteristics on 20 meters.

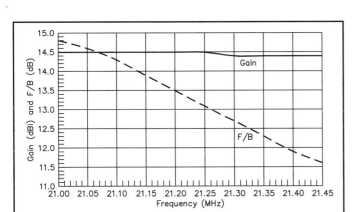

Fig 6—Gain and F/B characteristics on 15 meters.

Table 2

40, 20 and 15-Meter Quad Dimensions

Element	Location on Boom (ft)	$^{1}/_{4}$ Length (ft)	Spreader Length (ft)
40-meter Reflector	0	36.8	26.02
20-meter Reflector	0	18.4	13.01
15-meter Reflector	0	12.5	8.84
20-meter Driven	14.58	17.96	12.70
15-meter Driven	14.58	11.84	8.37
40-meter Driven	24	35	24.75
20-meter Director	24	17	12.02
15-meter Director	24	11.58	8.19

72-foot unguyed tower collapsed in the first real storm that year. The antenna did not take kindly to this!

I replaced this system with a new tower and a monoband six-element 20-meter Yagi. The Yagi worked great but was only good for 20 meters. At that time the sunspot cycle was headed down the tube and it was clear that 40 meters was going to be a big-time DX band for the next several years. However, 20 meters was not going to go away, and there would be some openings on 15 meters even at a sunspot low. So I began to think about a new multi-band quad with full-size 40-meter elements and good performance on 20 meters.

Of course 40-meter elements are twice as long as the 20-meter elements I was accustomed to, so it was pretty intimidating. The wingspan is over 50 feet! I found a source for the spreaders and the hub hardware,[3] and I now had good modeling software to design the antenna, so I went ahead with the project. The antenna has been up since 1993 with no real problems. It has proven to be durable, practical and a very good performer. It is a real killer on 40 meters. **Fig 3**, along with **Table 2**, gives the dimensions and element arrangement of the antenna.

The predicted gains and front-to-back (F/B) ratios for the three bands are given in **Figs 4** to **6**. The 40-meter band is wide enough that it is very difficult to obtain high gain and high F/B over the entire band with a simple two-element array. I chose to emphasize the CW end of the band, and this can be seen in Fig 4. I could have moved everything up in frequency and improved the phone-band performance but that would have meant a poorer F/B in the CW band. In my design, the F/B peaks at 16 dB and is above 15 dB over the entire CW part of the band. The gain peaks just outside the lower band edge and I could have traded a bit of F/B for a little more gain. The old rule that you can't have peak gain and peak F/B at the same frequency definitely applies.

The 20-meter performance is very good. In this case I chose to optimize at roughly midband; Fig 5 shows a minimum F/B of 15 dB over the entire band, with a peak F/B of greater than 22 dB. The gain is also very flat over the entire band. Overall, this is a very nice compromise for a three-element array.

This is a good point to go back to Fig 3 and discuss the choice of boom length and element placement. Normally a two-element array has a boom length of 0.12 to 0.15 λ for best performance. That would have resulted in a 16 to 20-foot boom for 40 meters. However, even at a sunspot low 20 meters is still a workhorse DX band and I wanted to have a really good three-element array on that band. Thus I made the boom a few feet longer to improve the 20-meter performance. The result on 40 meters was to slightly reduce the gain and F/B, but the longer boom had the advantage of presenting an approximately 112-Ω feed-point impedance. This could be easily matched with a 75-Ω (RG-11) λ/4-matching section. The greater spacing also broadbanded the antenna somewhat on 40 meters, which in the end more than compensated for the lower peak gain and F/B.

If you look closely at Fig 3 you will see something unusual. Because the elements in a three-element quad extend well below the boom, the middle element must be moved off center to stay well clear of the tower. In most designs the driven element is moved closer to the reflector. In my case, however, I went the other way because I felt it gave me a better set of compromises. The 20 and 15-meter driven elements are closer to the director. This gave me very nice perfor-

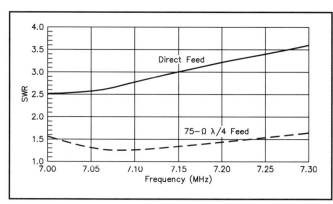

Fig 7—Solid line shows 40-meter 50-Ω SWR with direct feed. The dashed line shows the 40-meter 50-Ω SWR using a quarter-wave 75-Ω matching section.

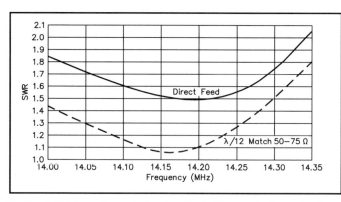

Fig 8—Solid line shows 20-meter 50-Ω SWR with direct feed. Dashed line shows 20-meter 50-Ω SWR with a 50 + 75-Ω series transformer.

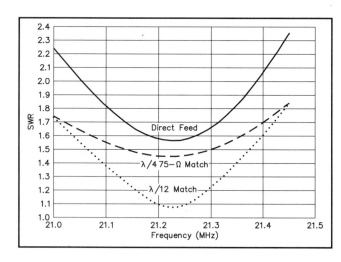

Fig 9—Solid line shows 15-meter 50-Ω SWR with direct feed. Dashed line shows 15-meter 50-Ω SWR with quarter-wave 75-Ω matching section. Dotted line shows 15-meter 50-Ω SWR with a series transformer match.

mance on 20 meters but compromised the F/B on 15 meters. Since I did not expect 15 meters to be a primary DX band during the sunspot minimum I accepted this. This reduced 15-meter performance is shown in Fig 6. The gain is good and very stable over the entire band but the peak F/B is low. I have again deliberately emphasized the CW end of the band just from personal preference.

Figs 7, 8 and **9** show the SWR performance for several matching choices. On 40 meters, if you do no matching, the SWR will be unacceptable (solid line in Fig 7). By adding a λ/4-matching section of 75-Ω line the match is very good over the entire band, as is shown by the dashed line in Fig 7.

On 20 meters you do not have to use a matching section, since the SWR is less than 2:1 over all but the uppermost portion of the band (solid line in Fig 8). However, because I have a nearly 200-foot run of cable, every little bit of loss hurts. I used a twelfth-wave or series-section transformer using 50-Ω (RG-213) and 75-Ω (RG-11) sections.[4,5] The result is shown in Fig 8 as the dashed line.

On 15 meters there are several possible choices. The solid line in Fig 9 shows the SWR for no matching. It is acceptable over most of the band but not at the band edges,

especially considering my long feed line. The dashed line in Fig 9 illustrates the effect of a λ/4 75-Ω matching section and the dotted line in Fig 9C shows the effect of a λ/12 matching section. The λ/12 match is better near midband but about the same as the λ/4 section at the band edges. I chose to go with the slightly simpler λ/4 section.

The forgoing discussion illustrates some of the design trade-offs that you must make. It is for this reason I suggested earlier that these designs are more for inspiration than exact replication. You must decide for yourself what the trade-offs should be.

Just for the curious, because of the harmonic relationship between 15 and 40 meters, the 40-meter antenna has a low SWR on 15 meters and can even be operated on that band. There is some gain but the F/B is essentially 0 dB.

Some Mechanical Details

The support hub for the 20/15-meter driven elements was a standard commercial cast-aluminum piece made for 20-meter quads. These hubs are, however, totally inadequate for a 40-meter quad. **Fig 10** is a sketch of the welded hub assemblies (two each) I used for the 40-meter spreaders.

These hubs are made from 3/8-inch aluminum plate. I obtained these from the same source as the long spreaders but you could fabricate them yourself.[3]

Wire! A big quad uses a lot of wire. Over the years I have used many different kinds of wire for the elements, ranging from copper house wire, solid Copperweld and stranded Copperweld. In an antenna this large the wire is a key structural element and it must have considerable strength in order to give years of service. Solid or even stranded pure copper wire is unsatisfactory, mainly due to rapid work-hardening from the constant motion of the spreaders as the wind blows. For this antenna I used #13 AWG stranded copperclad steel wire with high-density polyethylene insulation.[6] For some time I used an uninsulated version of this wire but even though I live in a rural area with no pollution, acid rain or salt atmosphere, I found that the wire still corroded. This potentially could weaken the wire and might increase losses. The insulated wire is more than strong enough and shows very little sign of corrosion even after several years. The wire size is also large enough to keep the losses acceptable (≈ 0.2 dB, according to the model).

When I first built this antenna I made some basic errors in the boom diameter and wall thickness, and in the guying (or the lack thereof). When I took down the 20-meter Yagi, I used two sections of that boom for the new quad. The boom tubing was 3 inches in diameter with quite thin walls (≈ 0.060 inch) and I used only a single support guy to each end, as shown in Fig 3. That was not good enough—after a couple of windstorms the boom started to bend sideways. No doubt some better engineering up-front would have told me that!

If you want to use 3-inch thin-wall tubing you must use side guys. There is simply too much mass and wind loading, even though the lever arm is only 12 feet long. Besides side guying, another approach would be to use larger-diameter tubing with a heavier

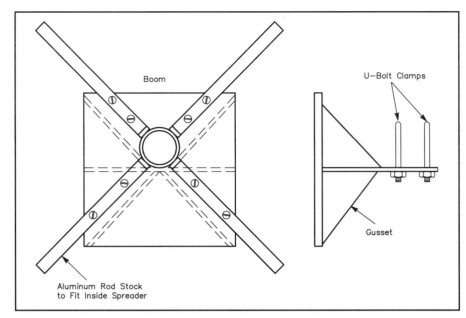

Fig 10—40-meter spreader hub design.

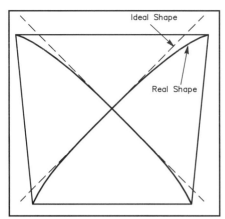

Fig 11—Distortion due to the weight of the spreaders when not anchored at the corners.

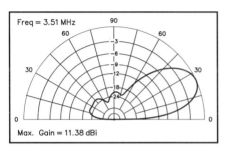

Fig A—80-meter quad elevation pattern at 3.510 MHz, at 100 feet above flat, average ground, including losses in the copper wire elements and Q = 250 inductor loading.

wall. For antennas larger than this example you will certainly have to do both. Since designing this antenna I have obtained copies of Leeson's book[7] as well as articles by Weber[8] and Bonney[9] on the mechanical design of large arrays. These have shown me the error of my ways and I strongly recommend you read them for any new design.

The spreaders for a 40-meter quad are twice as long as the 20-meter ones. They are also much heavier—3 to 5 times heavier. In my past experience with 20-meter quads the droop in the spreaders was very small and I used only a light wire jumper across the corners to keep the wire from sliding through the corner holder. In this antenna the stress on this wire was much higher and one jumper promptly broke, allowing the wire to slide through the corner mounting devices. This in turn allowed the spreaders to droop. The result was distortion in the shape of the loop like that shown in **Fig 11**. The shape is more like a trapezoid than a square. At first I though this was no big deal but a quick check showed the F/B had practically disappeared at the low end of the band.

Modeling the "new" shape showed that in fact the peak F/B had moved up to the high end of the band and the gain was degraded. The lesson is: Solidly anchor the corners of the elements to the spreaders. Realize that there will be a substantial load on this anchor due to the dead weight of the spreaders and the wind loading.

A commercial spreader hub for 20-meter and higher frequency quads usually resembles the one shown in Fig 2. While they are generally pretty reliable, I wanted something more rugged. What I did was to use two hubs, facing each other, trapping the

spreader ends between the two faces of the hubs. The result is a much stronger anchor at the base of the spreaders.

Any large array requires a first class rotator. I have been using an Orion OR-2300 rotator. It has given me more than a little heartburn, but then again I did have practically the first one sold. The manufacturers have been very responsive to problems and I believe the latest version (OR-2800) is a first-class rotator. The average ham rotator won't cut it in this league. With the large mass of the 40-meter spreaders and the heavy-duty hubs at the ends of the array, the moment of inertia is large.

Once you get the array rotating, the rotator has to bring it to a halt again. This can result in high stress on the rotator and also on the top of the tower itself. I can see the whole top of my tower twisting a bit as the rotator applies the brakes. To protect everything I have adopted the policy of using a low rotator speed for small angular changes. For a large change in direction I use a faster speed initially but then slow it down with the speed control as I approach the desired heading.

After the collapse of my old tower I installed an 89-foot motor-driven telescoping model. You can believe I am now a fanatic about keeping the tower down except while actually using it. I don't think the insurance company would be nearly so nice a second time. If a particularly severe storm is expected I will often throw a line over the boom and lash it down to ease the strain on the rotator.

More Madness

Because the present antenna has survived

many years of hard use, it's obviously too small. I am in the processes of designing a new antenna, now that the sunspots are back. (By the way do you know how you can tell that Shakespeare was a 160-meter man? Who else would say, "Out, out, damned spot"?)

The new antenna will have three elements on 40 meters, five elements on 15 meters and nine elements on 10 meters. Four of the 10-meter elements will be Yagi-style dipoles, because for single-band elements they are simpler mechanically (not to mention the fact that I have a 10-meter Yagi I can cannibalize). The tentative boom length is 50 feet, which is reasonable in the light of my earlier work. I may also include elements for the 30, 17 and 12-meter bands but that is still to be determined. Perhaps this will be a topic for *The ARRL Antenna Compendium, Vol 7*.

The ultimate madness is on the drawing boards also. A full-size two-element 75/80-meter quad. I intend to tune this behemoth to cover the entire band with a simple relay scheme. See the sidebar for a brief description. Stay tuned for the next installment—coming to you as soon as I can get leave from the asylum!

The Ultimate Insanity

As shown in Ref 11, it is possible to build a full-size, rotary, two-element quad for 75/80 meters. There are two problems to be solved: First, how to tune it remotely so that I can have good performance in at least the two DX windows (3.510 and 3.790 MHz) or better yet, over larger sections of the band. Second, how to solve the mechanical problems imposed by the need for spreaders nearly 50 feet long and boom more than 50 feet long.

Bandspreading the antenna is not just a matter of an acceptable SWR. You also need to keep the gain and F/B as near peak values as possible. If you are going to all the trouble to build this monster there is no reason to compromise! I expect that I'll design the basic quad for the higher end of the band, say 3.850 or 3.790 MHz and then use relays to add in a small amount of inductive loading in both the reflector and the driven elements. If the elements are already near full size then the amount of loading will be small and will introduce very little loss. Of course, the inductors must still be designed for high Q. I will try to optimize the antenna at 3.790 MHz with the loading inductances shorted out with relays and then open the relays for 3.510 MHz operation.

Table A shows the typical dimensions for such an antenna, on a 44-foot boom at 100 feet above average ground. The elevation radiation pattern at 3.510 MHz is given in **Fig A**. Note that the effect of wire and inductor losses are included in this model. In the right location this would be a dominating antenna. By adjusting the loading inductances, this kind of performance could be available at any point in the band.

Because it is not necessary that the entire length of the spreader be insulated, 40-meter fiberglass spreaders could be extended with 2-inch-OD aluminum tubing. In effect, the hub would have a 44+ foot diameter. Modeling work indicates that this large a mass of metal inside the perimeter of the antenna would have little effect on the performance, so long as the longer support guys are broken up with insulators. I'd probably make the support guys from Kevlar or other insulating material.

The hub is designed along the lines of a bicycle wheel and shown conceptually in **Fig B**. Note that Fig B is only for the hub, the fiberglass spreaders are mounted on the ends of the hub arms. Two of these hubs, one on each end of the boom, would be needed. Obviously the boom will have to be guyed to support the weight.

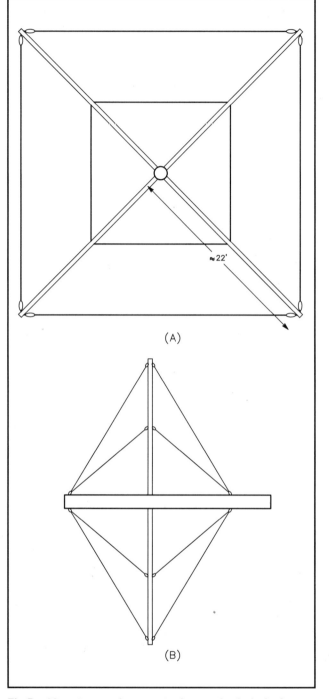

(A)

(B)

Fig B—80-meter quad conceptual spreader-hub design.

Table A
75/80-Meter Quad Dimensions

Element	1/4 Length (ft)	1/2 Diagonal (ft)
Driven Element	65.4	47
Reflector	68.2	49

References
[1]J. Lindsay, Jr, WØHTH, "Quads and Yagis," QST, May 1968, pp 11-19, 150.
[2]GNEC-4, Nittany Scientific, Inc, Hollister, CA 95023, 408-634-0573.
[3]Lightning Bolt Antennas, RD 2 Rte 19, Volant, PA 16156, 724-530-7396.
[4]The ARRL Antenna Book, 18th Edition (Newington: ARRL, 1997), pp 26-4, 26-5.
[5]D. Emerson, AA7FV, "Try a Twelfth-Wave Transformer," QST, Jun 1997, pp 43-44.
[6]The Wireman, Inc, 261 Pittman Road, Landrum, SC 29356, 803-895-4195.
[7]D. Leeson, W6NL (ex-W6QHS) Physical Design of Yagi Antennas (Newington: ARRL, 1992).
[8]D. Weber, K5IU, "Determination of Yagi Wind Loads Using the Cross-Flow Principle," Communications Quarterly, Spring 1993.
[9]S. Bonney, K5PB, "Practical Application of Wind-Load Standards to Yagi Antennas: Part 1," QEX, Jan/Feb 1999, pp 46-50.
[10]Another source for quad parts: The Antenna Mart, PO Box 699, Loganville, GA 30249, 770-466-4353.
[11]J. Devoldere, Antennas and Techniques for Low-Band DXing, 2nd Edition (Newington: 1994), Chap 13, Sec. 4.

Improving the Cubex Three-Element, Five-Band Quad

By Danny Mees, ON7NQ
Van De Reydtlaan, 86
B-2960 Brecht
Belgium

The Cubex three-element quad is a mechanically sound antenna with good basic performance. However, through the judicious use of antenna models and experimentation, improvements are possible that make the antenna a consistently good performer on all of its five bands. My aim in this article is to describe the adjustments I made to this quad to make two significant improvements. First, I achieved an independent 50-Ω feed on all bands without using 75-Ω, $^1/_4$-λ coaxial matching sections. Second, I improved the gain, front-to-back ratio and operating bandwidth on some of the bands—especially 10 meters.

Background

I used a Yagi for about three years, but decided to take it down and sell it because I wanted more gain on the higher bands. It is not easy to compare antenna specifications that many manufacturers advertise. I spent several weeks collecting data from different reflectors and Web pages. I also used *NEC-2*, *NEC/Wires* and *YO* (Yagi Optimizer) to get a better look at things by modeling various antenna types. Although good multiband Yagis have reached the market lately, my modest tower cannot support a 30+ foot boom or a 90+ pound antenna.

Here is where the quad comes into play. I went with a three-element, five-band model by Cubex. When I modeled it using *NEC/Wires* by K6STI, the gain figures came close to the gain of standard three-element Yagi monobanders. This antenna weighs 50 pounds.

The quad's weight caused me some anxiety at first, as I was afraid the tower would get more beating in the wind with the quad

on top compared to having a Yagi there. Since I have a home-brew tram system on the face of the tower, I decided to go ahead with the quad plan. My idea was to take down the antenna any time there was too much wind. We are fortunate at my location—this is not a windy area.

Why Cubex?

My choice to go with Cubex was purely based on the references I received from different Cubex hardware users. I opted for the pretuned and ready-to-assemble antenna because I did not have an accurate device to measure the loop wires, and did not want to spend weeks sorting it out. (With the kit form of this antenna, the builder measures the loop wires.) Many US amateurs recommended Cubex hardware to me because of the rugged spiders and good fiberglass spreaders.

I received the quad about a month after ordering it. It was shipped in two boxes. One contained the boom and spreaders, and a second held the wires, spiders, and other hardware. It took me about three weeks to construct the antenna by myself. I took my time to ensure that I did not mix up the wires.

The tram system was very helpful in the assembly and erection process. The antenna was assembled with the boom about 12 feet above ground. I chose the box, or square-shape, configuration because this makes the antenna look smaller than the diamond-shape version, and it leaves some room for low-band wire antennas.

Although Cubex had drilled holes in the spreaders, I constructed my own wire connectors. They consist of a hose clamp, wire tie, and flexible PVC tubing. The holes may have also been effective, but I did not want

to take the risk of breaking a spreader. I had heard rumors about wires snapping in heavy winds with the standard method.

I use an Ameritron RCS-8V five-position remote coax switch in combination with separate feed lines to the driven elements, providing separate feeds for each band. Amidon beads are used for feed-line decoupling.

For 20 and 17 meters, direct 50-Ω feeds were recommended to me by Cubex quad owners. The other bands were reported to need $^1/_4$-λ, 75-Ω matching sections. When I modeled the whole design using *NEC-2*, I found that the 15 and 12-meter driven elements could also be fed directly with 50-Ω coax, and did not require matching sections. However, the feed-point impedance on the 10-meter band was above 90 Ω.

The Cubex design uses three sets of spreaders. The 3-inch boom is 18 feet long. The element spacing is as follows: reflector to driven element, 10 feet; driven element to director, 8 feet. These dimensions are, obviously, constant for all bands.

Computer Model Checks—and Rechecks

I used computer modeling software (*NEC/Wires* by K6STI) to evaluate the antenna. The SWR curve was measured with an MFJ 259 at the base of the tower and confirmed the model in *NEC/Wires*. The results using the factory recommended loop dimensions are give in **Table 1**.

According to the computer model, the antenna's 10-meter gain was poor compared to the other bands. Also, the front-to-back ratio varied considerably from band to band. The diverse feed-point impedances could also stand improvement. The bands with

Table 1
Performance of the Stock Antenna

Frequency (MHz)	Gain (dBi)	F/B (dB)	SWR	Impedance (Ω)
14.2	8.16	11.1	1.82	$33.2 - j\,18.2$
18.1	8.08	13.9	1.19	$42.7 - j\,3.1$
21.2	8.39	15.2	1.24	$35.5 + j\,17.7$
24.9	8.18	25.2	1.22	$61 + j\,0.8$
28.4	6.95	5.1	1.82	$90.5 - j\,5.6$

Note: Gain and F/B are from the free-space model. SWR and feed-point impedance are given as modeled and confirmed by measurement.

Table 3
Antenna Performance After Modification

Frequency (MHz)	Gain (dBi)	F/B (dB)	SWR	Impedance
14.2	8.04	11.6	1.31	$41.7 + j\,9.3$
18.1	8.29	17.6	1.23	$40.7 + j\,0$
21.2	8.39	30.4	1.09	$47.2 + j\,3.2$
24.9	8.30	21.8	1.01	$50.2 - j\,0.4$
28.4	9.06	11.5	1.06	$51.7 + j\,2.3$

Note: Gain and F/B are from the free-space model. SWR and feed-point impedance are given as modeled and confirmed by measurement.

Table 2
Dimension Comparison, Before and After Modification

Band/Element	Original	Modified
20-m Reflector	217.25	218
20-m DE	211.25	213.74
20-m Director	207.25	206
17-m Reflector	170.5	169.61
17-m DE	166.5	166.5
17-m Director	161.5	161.5
15-m Reflector	146	144.8
15-m DE	142	142
15-m Director	139	138
12-m Reflector	124	124
12-m DE	120.75	120.75
12-m Director	117.25	118
10-m Reflector	107.125	109.2
10-m DE	104.125	105.6
10-m Director	100.8	104.2

Note: Dimensions are given in inches per side.

higher SWRs at the target frequencies had relatively narrow 2:1 SWR bandwidths.

While tweaking the loop dimensions, it occurred to me that the 12-meter director was interfering with the 10-meter reflector, which resulted in a poor front-to-back ratio on 10 meters. Indeed, some of the revisions I made are the direct result of making improvements to performance on adjoining bands. The wires of a five-band quad interact quite a bit, so arriving at dimensions for any one band requires that the entire quad be modeled at one time. Although this procedure is time-consuming, it produces reliable models whose dimensions can be transferred directly to the antenna.

Dimension Revisions

After considerable modeling and testing, I arrived at dimensions that suit my operating needs. The original and final dimensions are listed in **Table 2**. Loop wire dimensions are in inches per side. For a better sense of the amount of each change, multiply the difference between the new and old dimensions by four to arrive at the total change in loop length.

Modeled and Measured Performance after Revision

Table 3 shows post-tweaking performance as modeled and confirmed by measurement, where possible. My emphasis was increasing gain and bringing feed-point impedance close to 50 Ω, with front-to-back ratio a secondary aim. The modifications result in more equal gain from band to band. All bands show a feed-point impedance that eliminates the need for 75-Ω matching sections. This permits me to place decoupling beads at the driven element feed points to maximize isolation.

On-the-Air Tests

On-the-air tests, while not equal to range tests, do tend to confirm the improvements predicted by the models. The additional gain on 10 meters is noticeable, as is the im-

provement in SWR bandwidth on all bands. One thing I know for sure: The gap between the guys who used to beat me in the pile ups is closed on all bands. This was my primary goal. This antenna, as revised, is a vast improvement over the stock one! I do not mean to criticize the original quad, which offers good performance. Also, further improvements beyond those noted here might be obtained by those who want improved front-to-back ratio on 20 and 10 meters. I offer these notes as a starting point for those who, perhaps, need ideas for optimizing their own three-element, five-band quads.

Acknowledgments

This article is based on personal experience, but others helped along the way. I thank W4RNL, ON4AJW, K2US, W1RZF, N5HV (SK) and W7ZQ for additional information and great support. W4RNL checked the modified dimensions using the more professional *NEC-4* and found minor differences compared to the *NW* results.

A Vertically Polarized Inverted Soffit Monopole Antenna

By Grant Bingeman, KM5KG
1908 Paris Ave
Plano, TX 75025

I operate QRP SSB on 20 meters, and subscribe to the diversity theory of antenna operation. In other words, I like to be able to switch between several different antennas when I am about to answer a CQ in order to determine which aerial produces the best combination of received signal strength and reduced interference. In order to operate QRP successfully, it really helps to have a variety of good antennas. As an antenna engineer it bothers me to see an operator compensate for a bad antenna by increasing his transmitter power.

After I begin a QSO, sometimes it turns out that a different antenna will produce better reception at the other end of the RF propagation path, in which case I end up switching between two antennas whenever the conversation passes from one party to the other. According to the theory of reciprocity, the antenna that produces the highest received signal strength is also the best antenna for transmit effectiveness. However, the ionosphere can be tricky, and I have often had better results when using different transmitting and receiving antennas, particularly when there is a noise problem.

The ability to quickly switch among antennas is particularly useful when more than two stations are sharing the same QSO, or when propagation conditions are changing (which is often the case).[1,2] And flipping a switch is quicker than turning a rotator. You may also be aware that the polarization of an incoming signal can vary wildly and rapidly, and this change in polarization can contribute more to QSB than an actual change in signal amplitude. In other words, sometimes it is your receiving antenna's inability to track a signal's changing polarization that causes a change in *perceived* signal strength. If you can follow the changing polarization your QSO will be more successful.

What I would like to convey in this ar-

KM5KG describes his soffit-mounted broadband inverted monopole antenna. He also tells how to add a second inverted monopole for improved performance.

ticle, besides the details of a specific vertical antenna, which I call an *inverted soffit monopole*, is a sense of how the practical mechanical compromises in simple antenna designs affect electrical performance. We will look at polarization, pattern and impedance bandwidths. We will do this by comparing the far-field performance of the inverted soffit monopole to common dipole designs. You may be surprised by the real-world performance of the simple dipole antennas presented in this article. For example, not everybody understands that horizontal wires radiate vertically polarized signals. So dipole radiation behavior is a bit more complex than ordinarily perceived.

I wanted to add a low-take-off-angle vertically polarized (v-pol) antenna to my 14-MHz attic QRP antenna *garden* in order to discriminate against QRM that arrives from high elevation angles, and to improve the strength of signals arriving from low elevation angles. I was also interested in comparing the relative received strength of vertically polarized signals with horizontally polarized signals. If a signal leaves an antenna exclusively horizontally polarized (h-pol), how much of that signal gets twisted to v-pol during its ride through the iono-

sphere? Will a v-pol antenna be able to hear what originates as an h-pol signal, and vice versa? My existing horizontal dipole and inverted V antennas emphasize the high-angle signals, and do not have much gain at low elevation angles such as 10°, where I would be looking for long-range (DX) communications. My dipoles have a v-pol component, but it is directional and weak as we shall see later.

All my analysis is done over *average* ground having a conductivity of 5 mS/m and a dielectric constant of 13. I use *EZNEC 2.0* software, and the current element, or segment length, is typically 1 foot. All wires are copper, and all antenna input impedances are close to 50 Ω at resonance. The azimuth angles correspond to the compass bearings, where 0° is North, 90° is East, etc. Elevation angles range from 0° on the horizon to 90° straight up towards the zenith. All the horizontal elements of the antennas are aligned along an East-West axis, and "broadside" is North-South. According to their bearings, I refer to elevation plots as: broadside (North), diagonal (Northeast) and endfire (East). The azimuth plot is taken at the average take off angle of the elevation lobes.

I print an azimuth and three elevation patterns for each of my antennas. I then glue them on the top and three sides of an octagonal box (one box for each of my antennas—See **Fig 1**). I mark the boxes with the compass points associated with the actual orientation of my attic antennas and use them for handy reference in my ham shack. These three-dimensional models of my antenna patterns help me to quickly grasp what is happening when I switch antennas, and how best to take advantage of antenna diversity and shifting propagation conditions.

It only takes about an hour to model an antenna, print the patterns and glue them to a box. I highly recommend that you build three-dimensional models of your radiation patterns. You might be able to simply cut the patterns from your antenna manufacturer's literature. You may also want to try mounting the patterns on both the inside and outside of the box to see which works best for you.

A Plan Develops

Because the neighborhood homeowners association does not permit obvious antenna structures, I can't easily erect antennas outside. I needed a design for a compact and inconspicuous antenna. Fortunately, I have a large attic with up to 12 feet of headroom, and this is where I have built my air-conditioned ham shack. The highest point on the roof is about 32 feet above the ground, and the soffits (underside of the eaves) are exactly 20 feet above ground. There is lots of room inside my attic on three sides of the shack partition for antennas.

I rejected the idea of a conventional vertical monopole (ground plane antenna) that would poke through my roof and have a set of horizontal radials in the attic. I decided instead to create an inverted monopole by dropping a vertical wire from the soffit. The wire drops about a foot from the exterior wall of the house.

The counterpoise is located inside the attic, where it is easier to install and maintain. That's better than hanging it outside, where it would be exposed to wind, weather and the view of my neighbors. I especially wanted to minimize the amount of time I spent on a 20-foot ladder. By drilling a small hole in the soffit from the interior attic side, I was able to avoid using a ladder completely! The location of this inverted monopole at the edge of the attic prevented me from running the usual four-radial counterpoise wires, so I decided on a pair of collinear horizontal wires run along the soffit. The configuration is shown in **Fig 2**.

There are two advantages that I found attractive in the inverted monopole concept. The first advantage is that the earth losses are reduced by the relatively high location of the counterpoise wires. The second is that

Table 1

Impedance Bandwidth of Bow-Tie Inverted Monopole

Freq (MHz)	Input Impedance (Ω)	SWR
14.00	46.1 − j 9.4 Ω	1.24
14.05	46.5 − j 6.0 Ω	1.16
14.10	47.0 − j 2.6 Ω	1.09
14.15	47.5 + j 0.7 Ω	1.06
14.20	47.9 + j 4.1 Ω	1.10
14.25	48.4 + j 7.5 Ω	1.17
14.30	48.9 + j 10.9 Ω	1.25
14.35	49.4 + j 14.3 Ω	1.33

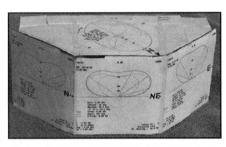

Fig 1—Photo of the KM5KG pattern box for his bow-tie dipole antenna. Patterns show horizontally polarized, vertically polarized and total fields. See text.

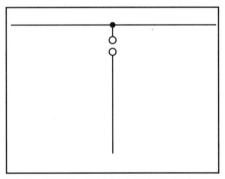

Fig 2—Configuration of an inverted monopole antenna.

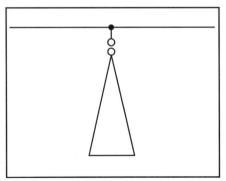

Fig 3—Configuration of a bow-tie inverted monopole.

the feed point is much closer to the attic transmitter than with a conventional base-fed, ground-mounted vertical. Thus the soffit antenna allows a shorter transmission line that is protected from the weather. In fact, my balun, counterpoise wires and connectors are all installed inside the attic.

The bottom of the #20 AWG vertical wire used in my soffit antenna is 1 foot above earth. About 0.2 dB of gain is lost in the copper wires, and this can be improved upon by using larger diameter wire.

Bow-Tie Inverted Monopole

A bow-tie arrangement reduces copper losses and improves bandwidth without having to increase wire diameter. Of course, a bow-tie does require twice as much wire, but this is still more economical than using a single very large wire having the equivalent bandwidth.

My bow-tie vertical element consists of two drop wires fanned out two feet at their lower ends, which stop three feet from the ground (see **Fig 3**). The wires are connected to each other at both ends. **Table 1** shows the bandwidth of the bow-tie configuration, which you can see is quite good. Gain is flat over the entire 20-meter band and is, therefore, not shown in the table.

I adjusted the antenna for an impedance of 50 Ω at resonance. I did this by trimming the vertical wires for 50 Ω of resistance, and trimming the horizontal wires for 0 Ω of reactance.

I always use a current balun with my antennas, and the balun usually has some inductive reactance, so I adjust the antenna input impedance to be a bit capacitive in order to compensate for the balun inductance (about 15 Ω at 14 MHz). Your 1:1 balun may be advertised as having no inductance, but I recommend you terminate it in a reliable 50-Ω dummy load and measure the balun input impedance just to be sure.

If your local ground conductivity is high like mine (about 30 mS/m), you may have to shorten your vertical wires to achieve an input resistance near 50 Ω. For that reason, the lower end of my inverted monopole is a bit higher than three feet above ground.

If you are using a solenoidal coil choke made by coiling your coaxial cable at the antenna input instead of using a transformer balun to isolate the transmission line from the antenna, I suggest you use the 10:1 rule. That is, in a 50-Ω system the choke should produce at least 500 Ω of inductive reactance, which at 14.25 MHz is about 6 µH or nine turns of RG-58 (about eight linear feet) wound on a three-inch-diameter form. Ferrite beads slipped over the coax cost more, but are perhaps a bit more elegant and convenient.

Since I operate QRP, I use #20 AWG copper stranded, insulated wire for all the antenna elements. In this application with bow-tie elements this does not cause any significant reduction in radiated power. If you want to operate at higher power levels, you will have to use larger wire to accommodate the higher currents.

The insulation makes the wires look slightly longer electrically, perhaps 3%. In other words, compared to bare wire, resonance occurs on a shorter length of insulated wire. Larger diameter wire will also tend to shorten the resonant length, and has the additional property of slightly improved bandwidth. But in all cases you will want to start with wires about 10% longer than the theoretical design values, and trim for the desired performance.

My Installation

Because of limited space inside the attic, I folded the counterpoise wires. For the same reason, I also placed the counterpoise a couple of feet behind and above the exterior vertical wire (see **Fig 4**).

The counterpoise, located slightly behind the monopole, tends to create a slight reflector effect. The result is that the North field intensity is about 1 dB greater than the South field (see **Fig 5**). There is no h-pol component on North and South bearings, and a

small h-pol signal bearing East and West, so the pattern is still essentially omnidirectional and vertically polarized. The high-elevation-angle v-pol null is not as sharp when comparing the diagonal bearing patterns, or the broadside bearing patterns. Thus the desired pattern shape is not exactly attained, and my overall goal is diluted by the installation compromises. I decided to try the bent configuration anyway, because I could always get the ladder out and hang an external counterpoise directly above the vertical drop wires at some future date.

The average gain of the bent bow-tie monopole is about 1 dB greater than that of the single-wire monopole. Also, the bent bow-tie monopole's take-off angle is slightly lower, which is an additional advantage for DX. This is partly caused by the fact that moving the counterpoise inside the attic increased the height a couple of feet, and partly by the bottom-loading effect at the horizontal end of the bow tie, close to

ground. This bottom-loading changes the current distribution on the monopole and tends to make it look a bit longer than its physical dimensions would imply. However, if we extend the bottom-loading concept too far by making the bow tie even wider, the earth losses also increase and there is no significant improvement in gain, unless we also increase the antenna height.

Horizontal Bow-Tie Dipole

My other attic antennas include a half-wave horizontal bow-tie dipole and a bow-tie inverted V. I like the high gain at high take-off angles afforded by horizontal wire antennas. Since the radiation off the ends is weak, I installed the two antennas oriented at right angles to each other. This allows me to cover all compass bearings by switching between them as the need arises.

The arms of my horizontal dipole are about 14-feet long, and 2-feet wide at the ends (see **Fig 6**). All wire is #20 gauge insu-

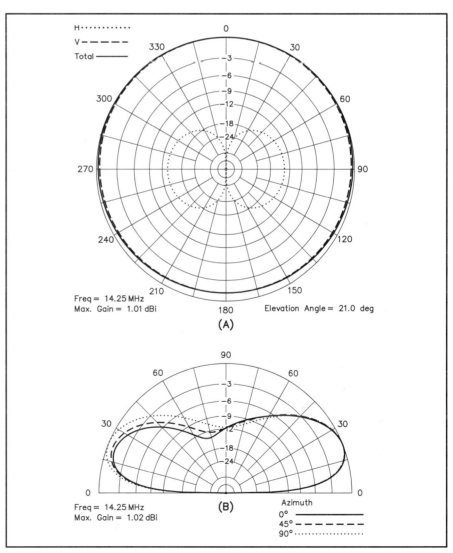

Fig 4—The KM5KG inverted soffit monopole antenna.

Fig 5—At A, azimuth pattern of the bow-tie inverted monopole of Fig 4. At B, elevation patterns at 0°, 45° and 90° azimuth.

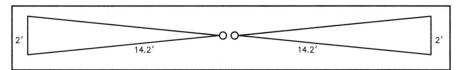

Fig 6—Configuration of the bow-tie dipole.

lated copper. It is instructive to look at the radiation patterns in **Fig 7**, and compare them to our inverted monopole's patterns (Fig 5). The elevation pattern off the sides of this dipole looks pretty conventional. However, endfire radiation is vertically polarized and its maximum intensity is only about 4.6 dB (less than one S unit) below that of the horizontally polarized major lobe.

The take-off angle of the v-pol endfire lobe is substantially higher compared to the h-pol lobe (52° vs 32°). Visualizing these patterns in three dimensions is much easier when you use the octagon box paste-up shown in Fig 1. Being able to hold such a model in your hands while you look at the world map can be helpful.

The azimuth pattern of the bow-tie horizontal dipole shows that a vertically polarized component of radiation exists on all bearings except broadside. Similarly the horizontally polarized component exists everywhere except along the dipole axis. But the average h-pol field intensity is the stronger of the two polarizations when averaged around the full horizon. My point is that the performance of a simple dipole is really pretty complicated. Note that Fig 7A is the azimuth pattern for an elevation angle of 40° above the horizon, which is midway between the take-off angle of the broadside lobe (32°) and that of the endfire lobe (52°). So when you think "horizontal dipole" you should *not* be thinking "horizontal polarization only."

Bow-Tie Inverted V

The arms of my attic inverted-V antenna are skewed to one side (see **Fig 8**). This changes the radiation pattern slightly compared to an inverted V aligned entirely in one vertical plane. The apex of the inverted V is 30 feet above ground. The ends of the arms are 23 feet above ground, and displaced horizontally 7 feet behind the apex. The horizontal distance between the ends of the arms is 22 feet. The maximum width of the bow-tie is 2 feet. The performance of the bow-tie inverted V (either slanted or vertical) is similar to that of the horizontal bow-tie dipole.

The bow-tie slanted inverted V broadside elevation pattern (**Fig 9**) compares favorably with the bow-tie dipole. Since there is physical symmetry about one plane of the slanted V, but not about the other, we might expect the slanted V's pattern to be asymmetrical about the zenith. But the major-to-secondary lobe ratio of 0.09 dB is as close to bilateral symmetry as you can get in the real world. The radiation take-off angles of the slanted inverted V are a few degrees higher than those of the horizontal dipole, but the maximum gains are similar.

Summary

The vertically polarized DX performance of the inverted monopole antenna is significantly superior to that of the horizontal dipole and the inverted V, when you consider the combination of transmission gain and high-angle interference attenuation. The ideal soffit vertical antenna receives no signal from the zenith, and my soffit antenna reduces this signal by one or two S units compared to the horizontal antennas. The soffit antenna v-pol gains at low elevation angles are clearly superior to those of the horizontal antennas. Of course the higher maximum h-pol gains obtained from the horizontal antennas at higher elevation angles makes them superior for medium-range communication.

The omnidirectional characteristic of the soffit antenna means that only one such aerial is required. By contrast, the directional nature of the horizontal antennas requires that I install two of them at right angles to each other to cover all possibilities. Thus, a minimum set of three fixed attic antennas allows me fairly good all-around coverage of the compass at high and low take-off angles, and both polarizations.

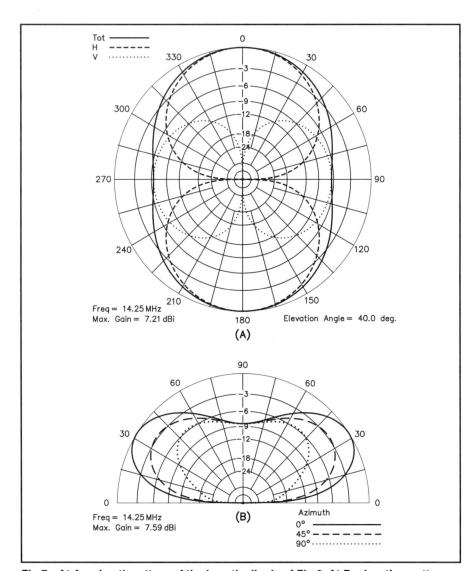

Fig 7—At A, azimuth pattern of the bow-tie dipole of Fig 6. At B, elevation patterns at 0°, 45° and 90° azimuth.

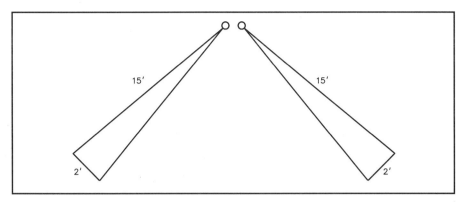

Fig 8—Configuration of the bow-tie inverted V.

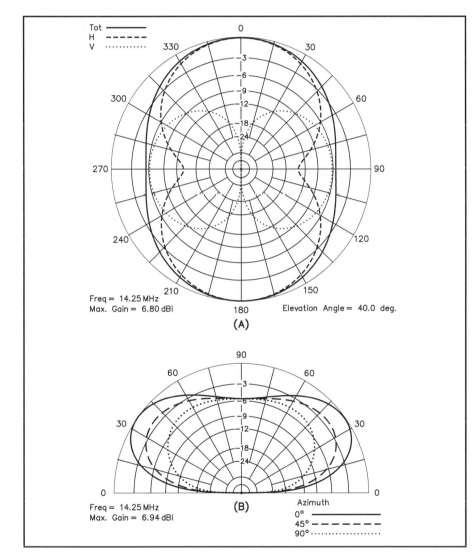

Freq = 14.25 MHz
Max. Gain = 6.80 dBi

Elevation Angle = 40.0 deg.

(A)

Freq = 14.25 MHz
Max. Gain = 6.94 dBi

(B)

Azimuth
0° ———
45° ———
90° ··········

Fig 9—At A, azimuth pattern of the bow-tie inverted V of Fig 8. At B, elevation patterns at 0°, 45° and 90° azimuth.

One of the practical advantages of having low-angle and high-angle antennas is the fact that, by switching between the two types, I can quickly determine if a signal is DX before I hear the call sign. What I have found in practice is that generally a DX signal is stronger on my vertical than on the other antennas. Now that the sunspot cycle is allowing incredible propagation, the DX signals are so strong that you can no longer assume that a weak signal is more likely to be DX.

I have also found that odd noise sources that can be heard on the soffit vertical can't be heard on the horizontal antennas, and vice versa. In particular I have noticed some occasional man-made noise that is decidedly v-pol in nature, but I have not yet determined if it is local in origin. Lightning noise may also have a stronger v-pol than h-pol component, but I have not been able to verify this empirically. However, it appears that QRN in the 20-meter band can be several S units stronger on the vertical soffit antenna than on the horizontal dipole antennas when an electrical storm is within a couple hundred miles. This may be related to polarization or it may be related to take-off angle, or both. I have also noticed that QRN is a bit stronger from my dipole that is aligned broadside towards the Gulf of Mexico, as opposed to the dipole that is orthogonal to that bearing. This is another hint that electrical storms are the culprit, at least during the daytime when they are more prevalent.

A Directional Soffit Array

After a few weeks of listening to chronically higher noise on the soffit vertical, I decided to add a second soffit antenna spaced a quarter wavelength (17 feet) from the first. I tuned the new element as a reflector (**Fig 10**). I had to change the dimensions of the original soffit antenna a bit to keep a reasonable impedance match when the second element was added. The folded counterpoise is now closed at the top. I also made the bow-tie considerably fatter to broaden bandwidth, which usually narrows with increased gain.

I kept the dimensions of the second soffit antenna the same as the modified original, so I could easily switch driven and parasitic elements to shift my directional pattern 180° in azimuth. The patterns in **Fig 11** show a substantial increase in gain, and a front-to-back ratio of about 13 dB. I made no particular attempt to optimize the theoretical forward gain, front-to-back ratio, impedance and pattern bandwidths, etc. I decided that with the relatively primitive test equipment I had on hand, I would not be able to verify a few tenths of a decibel in performance anyway.

At an elevation angle of 10° above the horizon, the directional soffit array has a gain of about 1.6 dBi, which compares very favorably with the −1.3 dBi of my single soffit antenna. This is an improvement of almost 3 dB, which is equivalent to doubling my transmitter power. In the world of QRP, this extra half an S unit can mean the difference between a QSL card and a negative copy. Plus being able to switch among beaming East, West and omnidirectional adds great versatility to my QRP operation.

If you install relays, avoid the temptation to simply switch the parasitic tuning reactance from an inductor to a capacitor in

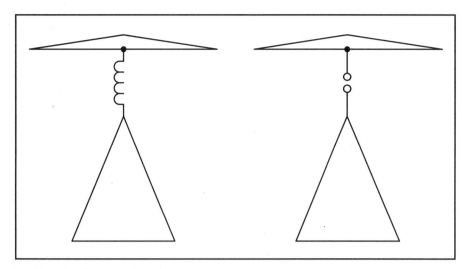

Fig 10—The directional soffit array.

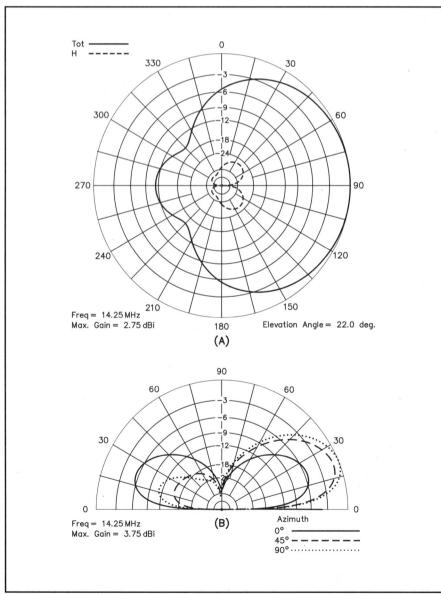

Fig 11—At A, azimuth pattern of the directional soffit array of Fig 10. At B, elevation patterns at 0°, 45° and 90° azimuth.

order to shift from reflector to director operation. Such an arrangement requires less parts, but the lesser performance of the director configuration is not worth it. Instead install two baluns, two lengths of coax and two tuning coils with appropriate relays for the task.

I used a $+j\,20\,\Omega$ tuning coil between the parasitic inverted bow tie and its soffit counterpoise (on the left in Fig 10). If you want to switch easily to omnidirectional operation, just install a relay that opens the tuning coil connection in the reflector. However, when you do this, your input resistance and reactance will each fall about 14 Ω. That's right; the higher-gain directional soffit array actually has an input resistance greater than that of the lower-gain omnidirectional single soffit antenna configuration. The amount of resistance change will vary according to the ground conductivity. If you had perfect ground, your input resistance would not increase as noticeably when you switch from omnidirectional to directional operation, and in fact it might even be lower than the self resistance of the antenna, depending on how much gain you tune for. In other words, your input impedance depends on where your reflector tuning coil is ultimately tapped, and this is going to vary from one site to the next. Don't assume that 50-Ω resistance is going to give you the best gain!

Well, you don't get something for nothing, as you can see in **Table 2**. The pattern and impedance bandwidths are not as good as they were for the omnidirectional soffit antenna described in Table 1. However knowing what to expect is half the battle, isn't it? As you can see, the performance of the directional soffit antenna favors the SSB side of the 20-meter ham band. For a directional antenna, the bandwidth is not that bad actually.

When tuning this directional array, you will need to monitor the relative current magnitudes at the top of each of the two vertical elements. If you adjust the value of the reflector tuning coil for a reflector current about 75% of the driven element's input current, your pattern will be reasonably close to Fig 11. The relative phase of the two currents will be about 110°, but you don't have to worry about measuring that. However, a word of warning: if your parasitic soffit antenna is smaller than the driven soffit antenna, or you tune the parasitic element with less than the optimal reactance, you could end up with a director instead of a reflector. You want to avoid this since a director will provide less gain and bandwidth. You especially want to avoid the point of maximum current and minimum input resistance, as this creates a peanut shaped azimuth pattern, higher losses, and poor bandwidth. This peanut-shaped pattern theoretically occurs when the two elements are identical, and the parasitic element is tuned close to zero reactance or a short-circuit.

Here is another tuning strategy for the

Table 2

Bandwidth of Dual Bow-Tie Inverted Monopole (reflector tuned with 20-Ω coil)

Freq (MHz)	Input Impedance (Ω)	SWR	Max Gain (dBi)	F/B (dB)
14.000	38.5 − j 10.3	1.42	3.7	6.4
14.050	40.6 − j 7.1	1.30	3.8	7.3
14.100	42.8 − j 4.2	1.20	3.8	8.3
14.150	45.0 − j 1.6	1.12	3.8	9.2
14.200	47.0 + j 0.7	1.07	3.8	10.2
14.250	49.0 + j 2.8	1.06	3.8	11.1
14.300	50.8 + j 4.7	1.10	3.7	11.9
14.350	52.4 + j 6.5	1.15	3.6	12.6

dual soffit antenna: measure the input resistance of the driven element with an open circuit in place of the tuning coil (this is the self resistance). Adjust the tuning coil until you see the input resistance increase and then begin to decrease again, but not far enough to bring it back to the self resistance value. This will put you in the ballpark.

Conclusion

The compact, easily installed soffit antenna provides a vertically polarized signal at low elevation angles that allows some advantages over conventional ground-mounted monopoles. These advantages include a shorter transmission line for attic or second-story ham shacks, no ground system, and no guy wires. However, it appears that at times QRN may be two S units stronger on the soffit antenna compared to the dipoles, and the signal-to-noise ratio may actually degrade when the soffit antenna is switched into use. This can be alleviated by adding a second soffit antenna tuned as a reflector to increase gain in the desired direction and reduce gain at the back. Noise is a strong reason for having a diverse collection of antennas from which to choose.

Notes
[1]Nichols, Eric P., "An HF Polarimeter," Jun 1998 *QST*, p 61.
[2]Nichols, Eric P., "How the Ionosphere Really Works," Mar/Apr 1998 *QEX*, pp 37-40.

Plastic Antennas, Part Two

By Patrick E. Hamel, W5THT
1157 E Old Pass Road
Long Beach, MS 39560
phamel@datasync.com

W5THT updates us on some very practical issues he's faced since his last article in The ARRL Antenna Compendium, Vol 5.

In Vol 5 of *The ARRL Antenna Compendium* I described the construction of an HF log-periodic antenna based on PVC plastic pipe. In the time since then, this antenna has served me well, but I've also learned a lot. I want to pass along the results of these lessons, hopefully to make things easier for other hams on a budget.

I still think that an uncut boom is the strongest way to construct the antenna. I have, however, continued experimenting with regular Home Center 10-foot lengths of PVC and fittings (Schedule 40). My original method had involved using an uncut 20-foot length of PVC tubing to make the boom. I had created the boom-to-mast joint by laboriously carving and sanding out the inside of a T-fitting to allow it to slide over the uncut length of PVC pipe. My new technique to make the boom-to-mast junction is to pin each end of a properly glued PVC Tee with a cotter pin placed through a hole drilled in the Tee. This produces a joint that is just as strong, perhaps even stronger, than my previous method. As an added bonus, the new method also allows boom lengths longer than 20 feet (the standard length of PVC pipe), since lengths may be joined without losing strength.

I also gave up on the use of various types of rope as a truss to support the weight of the boom and elements. At a Home Center store I found $1/8$-inch steel cable with a heavy plastic coating. This cable has lasted more than two years without needing to be replaced or tightened (as the rope did) and no rust is evident—here in coastal Mississippi that is unusual!

I also wanted to have a good 2-meter antenna, so I put a smaller-diameter, 30-foot-long PVC boom 60 inches above the HF boom and tied them both together with diagonal cables for rigidity. I thus now have a 14-element 2-meter Quagi above the HF log-periodic. I can't tell any difference in performance compared to the quad 8-element Quagis I ran a few years back, and the total weight of this VHF/HF antenna is about that of the quad Quagis alone.

By using one continuous plastic-covered cable and turnbuckles, the booms become a rigid structure against gravity. Side-to-side they are still somewhat flexible, but I think this is why they have survived the windstorms here on the coast.

Things to Avoid

If you are on a budget, don't make the same mistakes I did. I went for a drive and bought some aluminum tubing from a supplier 100 miles away. It turns out that what I bought was too soft for what I was intending to use it for. If you look carefully in the photo in **Fig 1**, none of the longer aluminum-tubing elements are straight—they "wander" even though I have attempted to bend them back as straight as I could manage to get them.

If you want an economical antenna, use the wire-element "Telerana" construction technique using PVC tubing and guy the PVC arms back to the upper boom.[1] If beauty is more important than cost, the aluminum tubing idea works, but I don't see any real difference in performance compared to an all-wire antennas.

Originally, I had taped my transmission line onto the HF LPDA boom to keep the spacing constant. This attempt failed because flexing of the boom caused the wires to move together, changing the characteristic impedance of the transmission line. This affected pretty dramatically the SWR performance of the log periodic array. It took several disappointments for me to learn that even $1/4$ inch of movement in the spacing of the wires was enough to make the SWR unacceptable.

The simple way to cure this is shown in **Fig 2**, where black vinyl tape is used to hold back the two wires on opposite sides of the boom, backed up by additional hold-down tape over the initial tapes. [Tie wraps covered with black tape for UV protection should work well also for the outer wrap. —Ed.] Since I used this taping method, the SWR has remained constant. This method will not work with a metal boom, but the PVC boom will not affect the spacing, which will be the calculated value derived from the formulas in *The ARRL Antenna Book*.

Multiple Resonances

LPDA antennas covering wide frequency ranges have multiple resonances in the radiating elements. Further, the transmission line feeder connecting the elements can also exhibit additional resonances. It is well documented that a termination-end loop can be used to provide an additional resonance

Fig 1—Photo of PVC-boom LPDA with long-boom 2-meter Quagi mounted above it at W5THT. Note how soft aluminum elements are difficult to keep in straight lines!

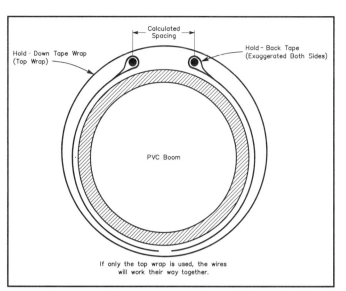

Fig 2—Method to keep the feed line wires that connect the LPDA elements together spaced properly and held in place on the PVC boom. Separate vinyl tapes are used to hold back the two wires, with hold-down vinyl tape wrapped over the top of the hold-back tape to make sure the wires don't wander.

by acting as a "hairpin" on a frequency lower than that of the longest element. My first LPDA was designed for 15 meters and up but a long shorted portion of feedline made it a good performer on 17 meters too.

There are other possible multiple-resonance situations that could be either frustrating or beneficial. When your antenna just won't work, even though the connections are good and the balun is OK, look at changing the terminating loop. A problem may show up in any portion of the frequency range, not just at the low end of the frequency range.

The idea of taping the terminating loop to the bottom of the boom back toward the mast seemed like a good one at one time, but in my case this did not result in better SWR or a usable 30 meter resonance, probably because of coupling between the main feed line and the stub.

Summing Up

PVC pipe allows the average family man to build a useful and practical beam antenna a few dollars at a time. The idea of using aluminum tape over PVC can produce a usable temporary antenna, but weathering and corrosion will require frequent attention. I recommend sticking with wire elements.

Using the vinyl covered steel cable with the proper connectors can eliminate the sag and rot problems of the rope I originally used for the boom truss. The truss wire is perpendicular to the radiators, so no undesirable interactions come about due to it.

Painting the PVC black makes it less noticeable and should also help withstand UV deterioration. Don't forget, however, to make sure that the pipe can drain rainwater!

Reference
[1]M. Hansen, "The Improved Telerana, with Bonus 30/40-Meter Coverage," *The ARRL Antenna Compendium, Vol 4* (Newington: ARRL, 1995), pp 112-117. A. Eckols, "The Telerana—A Broadband 13- to 30-MHz Directional Antenna," *QST*, Jul 1981, pp 24-28.

The Diamondback Antenna

By Floyd Koontz, WA2WVL
8430 W Park Spring Place
Homosassa, FL 34448-2717

The Diamondback is a bidirectional wire array designed to hang off the side of an existing tower. It is a continuous piece of wire running from the top to the bottom of the tower as shown in **Fig 1**. One or more diamonds can be used, depending on the frequency of design and the height of the tower. The characteristics of this antenna are:

- Simple construction
- High gain
- Horizontal polarization
- Low takeoff angle
- Wide horizontal beamwidth (typically 80°)
- Bidirectional pattern

Like its namesake, the Diamondback can bite the DX!

- Feed point close to the ground
- Radiates as vertically stacked dipoles, broadside to the diamonds

Each side of a diamond is approximately ¹/₂ wavelength long, as can be seen in Fig 1. All of the horizontal current vectors add while the vertical components cancel to yield horizontal polarization. The vertical stacking of dipoles suppresses most of the higher angle lobes, as shown in **Fig 2**, where the Diamondback is compared to a single dipole at the same top height.

Where Did It Come From?

The Diamondback antenna evolved as follows. For several years I have been using Bisquare antennas on 20 meters with excellent results. I got to thinking about stacking two Bisquares and it became apparent that one half of this antenna would also work and

would give a wider beamwidth (but less gain). **Fig 3** shows this progression, resulting in the Diamondback. The Bruce antenna shown in Fig 3D has a similar current distribution and is a close cousin to the Diamondback.

For both the Bisquare and the Diamondback, the height of the supporting structure determines the takeoff angle. I expect that the Diamondback antenna will mostly be used between 14 and 50 MHz and with structures of 50 to 100 feet high.

A Design for 21 MHz

Having only a dipole for 15 meters, I decided to design a Diamondback for this band. Using Brian Beezley's *AO* (Antenna Optimizer) program, I determined that the vertical height of each diamond should be 32.6 feet at 21.3 MHz. Since I intended to support this antenna from a 100-foot tower,

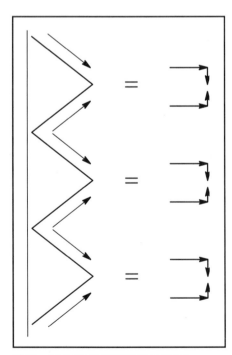

Fig 1—Layout of WA2WVL's three-dipole Diamond array for 21.3 MHz, with current-vector arrows. The net result is that the vertical polarized components cancel while the horizontal components add in phase.

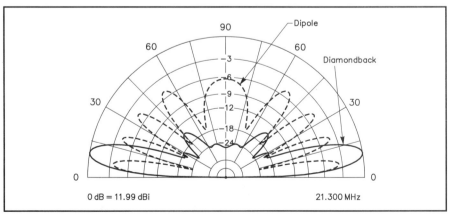

Fig 2—Comparison of six-dipole WA2WVL Diamondback and a single flat-top dipole at the same top height.

0 dB = 11.99 dBi   21.300 MHz

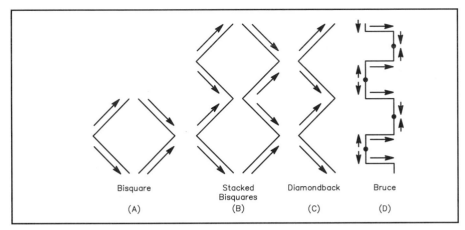

Fig 3—Evolution of the Diamondback. At A, the Bisquare; at B, two stacked Bisquares; at C, the Diamondback and at D, the Bruce array.

Table 1
Computed Characteristics of Diamondback vs Frequency

Freq (MHz)	21.000	21.100	21.200	21.250	21.350	21.450
Gain (dBi)	12.18	12.20	12.20	12.19	12.17	12.14
Z_r (Ω)	73.1	62.3	53.6	50.0	44.2	39.9
Z_i (Ω)	−12.66	−8.28	−2.55	0.61	7.26	13.96
SWR	1.54	1.30	1.09	1.01	1.22	1.47

Table 2
Characteristics of Diamondback Antennas for Various Amateur Bands

Freq (MHz)	Number Dipoles	Gain (dBi)	Height (Feet)	Takeoff Angle°	Dipole Leg Lengths (Feet)	L-Net (pF/µH)
14.2	2	7.06	49	29	38.9	26.6/2.4
14.2	4	10.50	97	14	38.5/38.5	52.4/1.2
21.3	2	7.12	33	28	26.4	20.4/1.2
	4	10.50	65	15	25.7/25.7	44.1/0.9
	6	12.10	97	10	24.7/24.7/24.7	38.3/1.0
	6 (opt)	12.29	97	10	20.3/25.2/23.1	45.4/1.3
28.5	4	10.51	49	14	19.26/19.26	34.4/0.5
	6	11.89	73	10	18.1/18.1/18.1	29.4/0.8
	8	13.12	97	7	18.3/18.3/18.3/18.3	36.4/0.6
	8 (opt)	13.84	97	7	12.3/17.4/19.6/17.1	55.1/0.5
50.4	6	12.07	42	10	10.35/10.35/10.35	19.1/0.4
	8	13.06	55	7	10.32/10.32/10.32/10.32	23.4/0.4
	8 (opt)	13.73	55	7	6.76/9.64/11.15/9.73	30.0/0.35
	10	13.85	69	6	10.29/10.29/10.29/10.29/10.29	25.4/0.4
	10 (opt)	14.60	69	6	6.76/8.69/9.79/10.83/9.91	21.6/0.4
	12	14.49	82	5	10.18/10.18/10.18/10.18/10.18/10.18	25.8/0.3
	12 (opt)	15.26	82	5	6.76/8.29/10.00/10.5/10.47/9.84	23.6/0.4
	14	14.71	94	4	10.11/10.11/10.11/10.11/10.11/10.11/10.11	27.1/0.3
	14 (opt)	15.45	94	4	6.76/8.30/10.30/10.57/10.02/10.5/9.8	25.5/0.4

Note: the (opt) optimum numbers were generated by letting *AO* vary the wires lengths of each diamond independently.

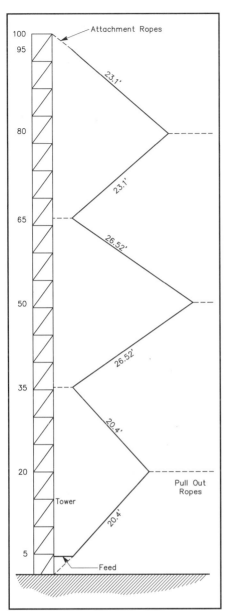

Fig 4—Physical layout of WA2WVL's three-dipole Diamondback, suspended from a 100-foot tall tower.

I used a vertical height of 30 feet for each diamond. An optimum design is where the wires slope down at 45° from horizontal, but this is not very critical. Three diamonds would fit on a 100-foot tower, so I chose the feet point to be 5 feet off the ground.

Fig 4 shows the layout of my antenna. The stranded #12 copper wire is held near the tower in four places (95, 65, 35, 5 feet) with ³/₃₂-inch Dacron rope[1] such that the antenna is 2 feet from the tower. The centers of the diamonds are pulled out with long Dacron ropes to a post about 150 feet away. The antenna was erected on the west side of my tower so that the pattern would be north/south. By the way, when I tie knots in Dacron I usually tape the knots with black vinyl tape to keep them from coming loose.

This three-diamond array had a calculated feed impedance of about 750 Ω, so I decided to use a simple L network to match it. I mounted the matching network in a small box on the tower leg just below the bottom rope. A large stainless-steel hose clamp was placed around the box and the tower leg.

I designed the L network using the ARRL program *TL*, written by Dean Straw, N6BV.[2]

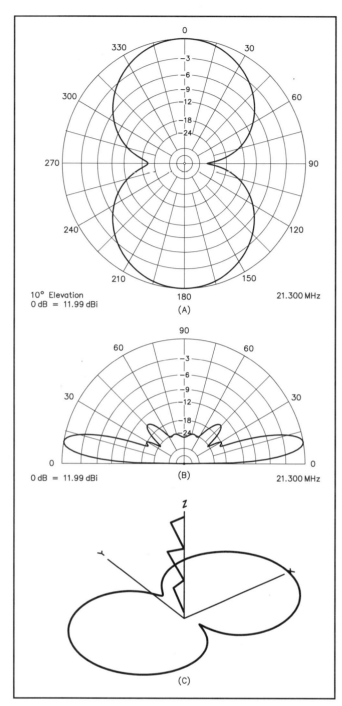

Fig 5—At A, azimuthal response of WA2WVL's three-dipole Diamondback. At B, elevation response for the antenna, showing its excellent low-angle response.

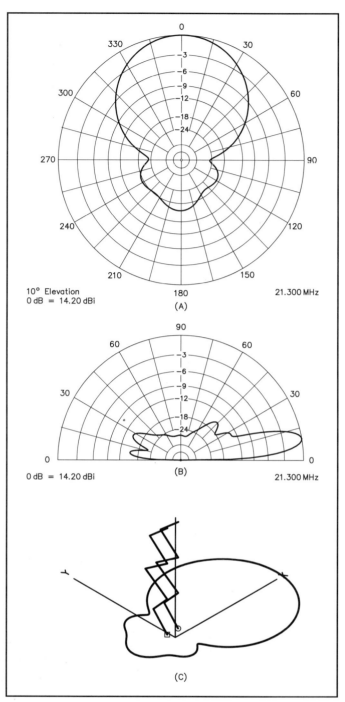

Fig 6—At A, azimuth response of a Diamondback beam, using a coil-tuned reflector. At B, the elevation response. At C, the layout of this antenna with azimuth pattern overlaid for comparison.

The result was a shunt capacitor of 38 pF from the wire to the ground (tower) and a series coil of 1.4 µH to the 50-Ω input connector. I used a large feed-through insulator to attach the wire since the feed voltage is about 1000 V at a power level of 1.5 kW. If children or others could possibly touch this antenna while you are transmitting, you need to take this into consideration when you do your installation. The capacitor must handle 5 A of RF current at 1.5 kW.

I used a porcelain capacitor made by American Technical Ceramics, but you may want to consider a transmitting air variable of 50 to 100 pF max. The coil was wound with #14 copper bus wire and measured with an MFJ 259B antenna analyzer. After assembly in the box, a 750-Ω carbon resistor was connected from the insulator to the ground and the coil was adjusted for a 50-Ω input using the MFJ-259B. **Fig 5** shows the calculated azimuth and elevation patterns for this antenna.

What about the bandwidth of this system?

The L network was added to the *AO* model and re-computed over the entire 15-meter band. The results are shown in **Table 1**.

Designs for 14 through 50 MHz

Table 2 lists designs for 20, 15, 10 and 6 meters. The designs are for heights from 24 feet to nearly 100 feet. Although I put it in Table 2, I don't recommend a two-dipole design (half of a Bisquare), since a full Bisquare could be used for more gain at the same height. I also omitted the 30, 17 and

12-meter bands but you could scale the dimensions from Table 2.

The numbers in Table 2 assume the bottom of the antenna is 1 foot from the tower and the feed is 1 foot above the ground. I found that this gave better performance than the initial 21 MHz design.

I obtained the optimum numbers in Table 2 by letting the computer vary the wire lengths of each diamond independently. I highly recommend that anyone attempting to maximize the gain of a Diamondback antenna run their final design on an optimizing program such as *AO*.

Feeding and Matching the Diamondback

The Diamondback can be fed at the bottom or in the center of any of the dipoles. The bottom end is very convenient since it is close to ground level and is an unbalanced feed point. The slight increase in gain you get by feeding the antenna in the center is more than offset by the added coax loss running up the tower. Matching can be done with a ferrite step-up transformer, but to keep things simple I prefer to use an L network.

A word about grounds—feeding with respect to the tower means that there is some excitation of the tower by the current flowing to ground. This results in some vertically polarized radiation from the tower at angles above 60° (in my 21-MHz example). This is of no concern so long as the feed point is well under $1/4$ wavelength from ground. The Diamondback could also be fed against a ground rod since it is a high-impedance feed. This would reduce the tower excitation.

Some Other Ideas Involving Diamondback Configurations

Two at Right Angles

I modeled two Diamondbacks at right angles, and they gave full 360° coverage as anticipated. The use of the single Diamondback in the October 1998 CQWW contest convinced me, however, that I didn't need the second antenna.

30, 17 and 12-Meter Bands

Someone who has a tower with a tribander might wish to use the tower for one or more Diamondback antennas to cover the 30, 17 and 12 meter bands.

Hanging the Diamondback from a Tall Tree

I can imagine mounting a Diamondback from a tall tree. You might use a bow and arrow to shoot a 30-pound-test nylon line over a 90-foot pine tree and then pull up a heavier support line. Of course, the Diamondback would have to be pulled out with ropes from both sides. Good luck if you try this—it would be interesting to see!

Hanging the Diamondback from a Tall Building

It should also be possible to drop this antenna over the side of a tall building (assuming you had permission) and feed it in the center of the first dipole. It might cause lots of TVI, however.

A Triband Diamondback?

I also modeled three Diamondbacks on a common tower for 20, 15 and 10 meters. The best design appeared to be one in which the 20- and 15-meter antennas were nested together and the 10-meter one was on the opposite side of the tower. It might be possible to connect the three matching networks in parallel at the 50-Ω connector but I haven't tried to design this.

Two-Wire Diamondback Beam

I investigated a two-wire Diamondback beam with good results. For a two-element parasitic design, you could attach aluminum tubes to the tower at the appropriate places to make a supporting boom. Short ropes would be attached to the ends of this boom. I found that a 15-meter design (with 3×2 diamonds) was optimum, with a reflector spaced 8 feet behind the driven element. Since both Diamondbacks were identical in size, the reflector was tuned with a 1.66-μH coil to ground. With everything at ground level this antenna could be easily reversed with two relays. **Fig 6** shows the azimuth and elevation patterns I obtained with *AO*. (All *AO* computations have been confirmed using *NEC-4.1.—Ed.*)

Three-Wire Diamondback Beam

By using a parasitic director and reflector, you can increase the gain. The azimuth beamwidth drops to about 57°, as you'd expect. In a reversible design, the front and back elements should be the same length and the back one tuned as a reflector with a coil to ground. The driven element's length is not critical.

Two Elements in Broadside

Two Diamondbacks in broadside gave impressive gain but reduced the 3-dB azimuth beamwidth to a narrow 35°. At 21 MHz, when mounted 8 feet from each side of the tower, the patterns in **Fig 7** were obtained. You should note that since the feed points of the dipoles go in opposite directions you must feed one of the two with a $1/2$-wavelength longer coax to excite both Diamondbacks properly in phase. The two coax cables could then be paralleled (to yield 25 Ω) and matched back up to 50 Ω with either a $7/5$ transformer or another L network. At 21 MHz the L network requires a coil of 0.2 μH from the 25 Ω point and a capacitor of 150 pF to ground at the 50-Ω point (the coil is in series from the 25-Ω junction point to the 50-Ω connector).

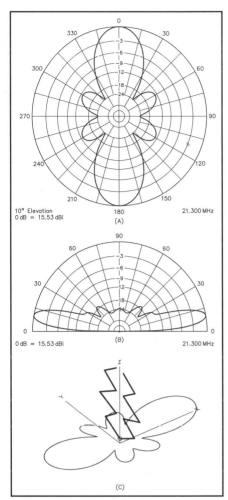

Fig 7—At A, azimuth response of a pair of broadside Diamondback antennas. Note that the narrow, bidirectional nose beamwidth. At B, the elevation response. At C, the layout of this antenna with azimuth pattern overlay.

Two Beams in Broadside

By using a pair of the two-element Diamondback beams at 21.3 MHz (as in the 21 MHz example) a gain of more than 18 dBi resulted. The patterns are shown in **Fig 8**. With a beam as narrow as 35° it would be advantageous to use beam steering to get more coverage. Feeding the left and right beams at 90° or 180° showed that headings up to ±45° degrees could be covered (with somewhat reduced gain, and strange-looking patterns!). These patterns are shown in **Fig 9**.

Summary

I think the Diamondback antenna has a lot of potential as a DX antenna, especially for those who don't already have stacked 6 over 6 Yagis! You can easily add a Diamondback to an existing tower, with minimal coax loss because you don't even have to run coax up the tower.

Even though the Diamondback exhibits very little high-angle radiation I have been

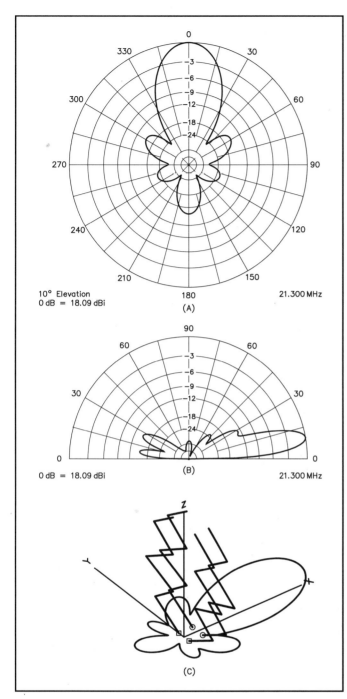

Fig 8— At A, azimuth response of a pair of Diamondback beam antennas surrounding a tower and fed in phase. **At B,** the elevation response. **At C,** the layout of this antenna with azimuth pattern overlay.

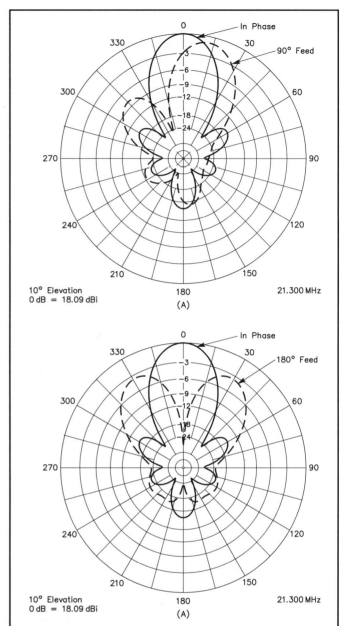

Fig 9—At A, azimuth response of the same pair of Diamondback beams, but with one fed 90° out of phase with the other. **At B,** azimuth response with feed to one Diamondback beam 180° out of phase with the other. The beams can thus be steered electrically somewhat to make up for the narrow nose beamwidth of the arrays when fed in phase.

surprised by its ability to work stations on 15 meters at all distances. And as bonus features, the Diamondback costs little, has low wind resistance and requires no rotator!

Notes
[1]Synthetic Textiles, Inc, 1145 North Grove St, Anaheim, CA 92806.
[2]The *TL* (Transmission Line) program is bundled with the software for *The ARRL Handbook*. A more sophisticated version called *TLA* (Transmission Line, Advanced) is available on the diskette bundled with the 18th Edition of *The ARRL Antenna Book*.

The Bumbershooter

By John Sherrick, W3HVQ
3127 Harness Creek Road
Annapolis, MD 21403-1613

This antenna is made like an umbrella, or "bumbershoot." The six hinged arms shown in **Fig 1** form a non-conducting support framework, collapsing much like the ribs of an umbrella. Such a mechanical design means the antenna can be large but can still survive winter icing—in just a few minutes it can be collapsed into a vertical "protective" mode. The antenna is large enough that wire arrays for 40, 30, 20, 17, 15, 12, and 10 meters can all be supported by it.

In 1993 I completed a four-band version of the antenna and it was very effective for both routine QSOs and contests on 40, 20, 15 and 10 meters. I added 30-meter coverage in 1996, and then modified it in 1997 to include not only 17 and 12 meters but also to handle the legal power limit. I modeled the antenna on my PC. It has good efficiency and forward gain, together with high front-to-back ratios. In short, it is a good beam antenna on all bands from 7 MHz to 29.6 MHz!

The Bumbershooter can be built at moderate cost and it can be rotated using a mid-sized rotator. It works well on my unguyed Rohn HDBX 48-foot tower. Using the Bumbershooter feature, I can place the antenna in a protective vertical mode that puts the weight of heavy snow and ice directly on the mast shown in **Fig 2**. I have used this feature to protect the antenna from dozens of ice and sticky snow storms over the years. This same feature also allows me to climb up inside the antenna to repaint it or make fine-tuning adjustments of the element lengths. See **Fig 3**.

This antenna has remained undamaged by wind gusts of as much as 65 mph. Although it's not been tested (thank goodness), I believe that even marginal hurricane force winds can be tolerated, provided that the antenna is collapsed and secured tightly to the tower. So far I've collapsed the antenna only to protect it from heavy wet snow or ice, not from wind.

Here is a truly amazing piece of mechanical and electrical work! W3HVQ's unique multi-band antenna features three-element Yagis on 40 and 30 meters, together with a log-periodic design for 20 through 10-meter coverage—and it even folds down for protection against nasty weather.

Fig 1—The Bumbershooter antenna at the author's QTH.

Fig 2—Bumbershooter, collapsed for icy/snowy weather!

Fig 3—Bumbershooter, collapsed for maintenance.

Mechanical Features

I made this antenna really big so it would not be just another "ho-hum" multi-band antenna! It encloses a whopping 2187 square feet of horizontal area, equivalent to three tribanders side by side. The antenna stands up well in high winds because of the tough welded-steel construction of the mast, the hexagonal shape and the many sturdy triangles in the structural geometry. Unlike an umbrella, which is deployed with push rods,

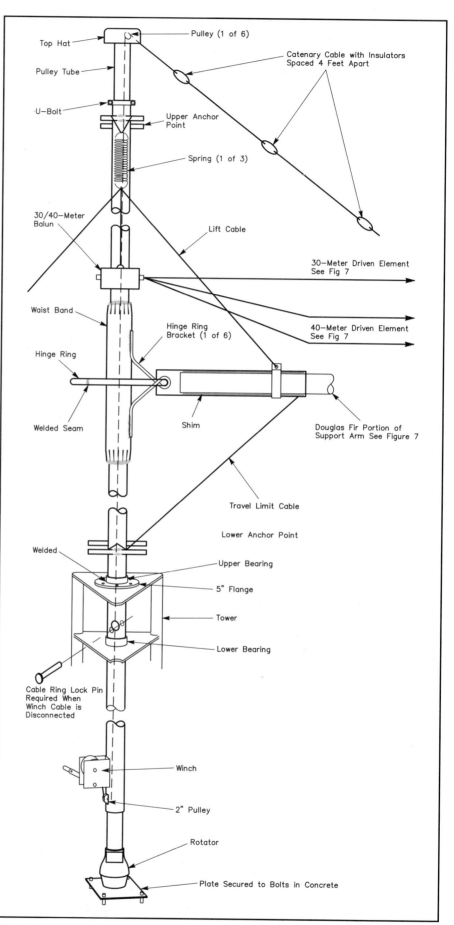

Fig 4—Antenna hinging and rotating configuration details.

the Bumbershooter is pulled up by cables from above. The hinging, cabling and rotating configurations are shown in **Fig 4**.

The antenna rotator is mounted on a steel plate just above the concrete base of the tower. It is connected to the antenna mast by a long torque tube. A winch is welded to the side of this torque tube near the rotator at waist-height above ground. The winch revolves on the torque tube when the antenna is turned and therefore must have a removable handle so everything is free to turn inside the tower. A woven steel cable from the winch goes into the torque tube by way of a pulley mounted just below it.

The winch cable travels upward about 40 feet through the center of the torque tube. When it reaches the antenna mast just above the lower bearing in the tower, the winch cable is secured to a heavy steel ring inside the mast called the *cable ring*. Six smaller woven steel cables secured to the upper side of this ring travel parallel to each other upward in the antenna mast to six solid-brass wheel pulleys. Above these pulleys is a stainless-steel top hat that keeps the pulleys free of snow or ice. These pulleys feed the six cables out radially at a slightly downward angle toward the support arm midpoints. The catenaries provide sufficient lift to the antenna's six support arms to keep them horizontal in the normal configuration (springs also supply part of the needed lift).

The winch, torque tube, winch cable, cable ring, catenary cables, pulley tube, six pulleys, and top hat can be conveniently built as a group, except for the welding of the winch mounting hardware (two rebars and two bolts) and two couplers at the bottom of the torque-tube section.

Construction of the Rotator Plate, Torque Tube and Internal Cabling

The rotator mounting plate shown in **Fig 5** is a $1/8$-inch thick galvanized steel plate held four inches above the concrete base of the tower. The plate is secured by $1/2$-inch diameter threaded rods that were suspended in the concrete when the tower base was poured. If the base is already in place, outriggers to secure anchors in the ground will serve as well. Plate height must be sufficient that the bolts securing the rotator can be inserted from underneath and tightened with a wrench.

You will probably devise your own system of tubing between the rotator and the mast. The rotator applies considerable torque to the torque tube when rotating the antenna, but even more torque is applied in braking the antenna in high winds. Slight twisting due to torsional loading and unloading of the long torque tube in high winds helps absorb the rotational forces applied to the rotator. This helps prevent damage to the rotator gears, bearings, and brake. The mid-

size CDR Ham III rotator used with my Bumbershooter has never given me any problems. If you wish to install the Bumbershooter on a tower taller than 48 feet, I recommend that you use a motorized winch and that the rotator be elevated up the tower so that the torque tube does not exceed approximately 40 feet in total length (use on a taller tower has not been tried to date).

Fig 5 shows the three sections of torque tube and the couplers between them. I used twenty-foot lengths of ($1^{1}/_{2}$-inch OD, $^{3}/_{16}$-inch wall thickness) aluminum pipe for

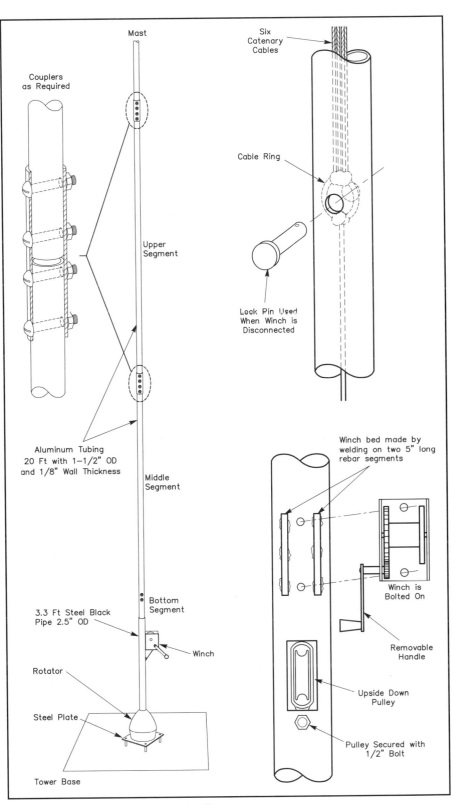

Fig 5—Torque-tube construction details.

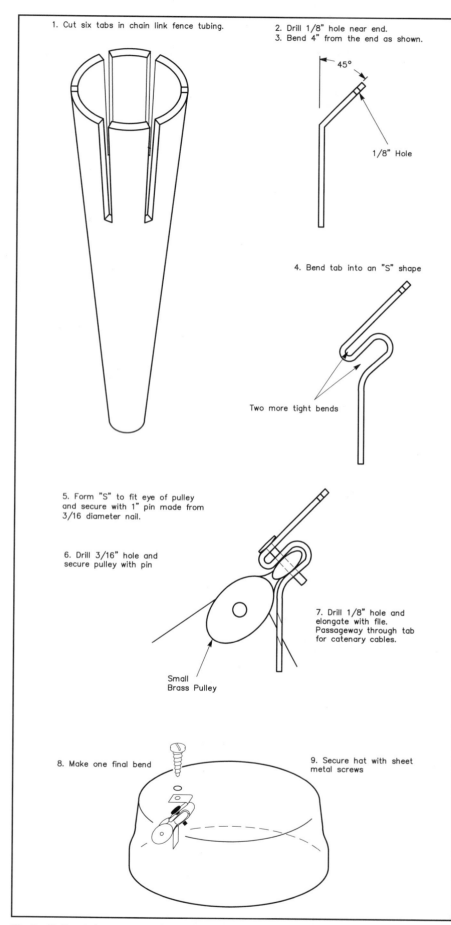

1. Cut six tabs in chain link fence tubing.

2. Drill 1/8" hole near end.
3. Bend 4" from the end as shown.

45°

1/8" Hole

4. Bend tab into an "S" shape

Two more tight bends

5. Form "S" to fit eye of pulley and secure with 1" pin made from 3/16 diameter nail.

6. Drill 3/16" hole and secure pulley with pin

7. Drill 1/8" hole and elongate with file. Passageway through tab for catenary cables.

Small Brass Pulley

8. Make one final bend

9. Secure hat with sheet metal screws

Fig 6—Pulley-tube construction details.

the two top torque tube sections. A 36-inch long (2½-inch OD) black iron pipe was chosen for the bottom section. Two 6-inch long intermediate diameter (2 inch OD) black steel pipes were telescoped into the top and bottom ends of the lower section and welded in place to served as couplers to the rotator and the torque tube.

I used a ½-inch threaded rod as a pin through the torque tube to secure the winch cable pulley so that it is aligned with a 1¼-inch by 2¾-inch window cut 12 inches below the spool of the winch. A pulley with a solid wheel should be used in this application. The great tension on the cable would crack the single-sided (hollow) wheel of a typical inexpensive galvanized pulley. The cable below the cable ring is ¼-inch aircraft cable. The catenaries above this ring are the same, except they are ³/₃₂ inch in diameter.

Pulley Tube

Look at Fig 4 again. You will see that the pulley tube plugs securely into the top end of the mast. The penetration distance into the mast is determined by the position of a U-bolt (muffler) clamp mounted on the tube. The pulley tube is held in place only by gravity so that it can be easily removed should a problem ever develop with the cables or pulleys. Since this tube is well above the tower, it must be lifted out of the mast using a pole held from the highest climbable position. An assistant unwinds winch cable as the pole hook lifts up on the top hat. The pulley tube then telescopes up and out of the mast. As the winch is unwound further, the pulley tube will lower down to a level that is well within reach. While this maintenance feature may seem unnecessary, it can actually save a lot of time if a cable ever gets caught in a pulley. The alternative is to raise the whole antenna up and out of the tower (using a gin pole), lower it to the ground, and install it on a test stand low enough that this part of the antenna it can be conveniently worked on, although this is not a very attractive alternative!

Pulley Tube Construction

Construction of the pulley tube will require careful attention to the illustrations and instructions provided in **Fig 6**. I made my pulley tube from a 2-foot length of 1½ inch diameter chain-link fence post. This does not require welding. You will need some tools, including a vise, drill, pliers and metal-cutting saw. Pins to secure the pulleys are made from heavy spike-sized nails cut to a length of 1½ inches. I created the top hat by using a small flat-bottomed stainless steel bowl.

Support Arms

You will need six 16-foot Douglas fir poles to construct the inner halves of the six

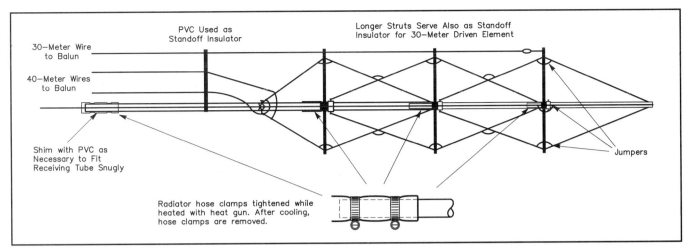

Fig 7—Support-arm construction details.

support arms. I made the outer halves of these arms using three progressively smaller-diameter 5-foot lengths of thin-wall PVC tubing (1.75, 1.25, and 0.75 inch ID, with $^{3}/_{32}$-inch wall thickness). The wooden inner halves have no struts, but the outer halves have three sets of vertical and horizontal struts each. One set is located at the intersection of the Douglas fir pole and the largest PVC tube. The other two sets are further out where the PVC tubes change to smaller diameters.

I stretched copper clad steel wire tightly between the strut tips and anchor pins located on the support arm. These lines keep the arms straight by compensating for the forces of gravity, wind, and weight of the antenna elements. These conductive lines must be kept short to keep them from being any significant part of a wavelength at the highest frequency. Since the strut material is nonconductive, you needn't provide insulators at every connection. Drill separate attachment holes at least one inch apart near the strut tips for the wires so that they are well insulated from each other even at high RF potentials. There are six places along the support arm where wires do contact each other, where they wrap around the anchor pins. Only four wires are joined at these locations, however, and these travel in the same direction for only the distance to the next strut (4 feet).

Copper jumper wires bridge the strut insulation at every opportunity on two of the support arms to form the 40-meter biconical element, shown in **Fig 7**. The remaining four support arms have none of these jumpers.

Support Arm Construction

Fig 7 shows construction details for the support arms. I couldn't manage to telescope the PVC tubes used to construct the outer half of the arms without modification.

At each junction of these tubes, the larger tube is first heated with a heat gun and then, while still hot, a radiator clamp is tightened around the heated area to compress it to the correct size of the smaller (cold) tube. The clamp is removed after the tubing has cooled. The process is repeated at one other point along the same junction where the tubes overlap.

A heat gun is also used to advantage making the vertical and horizontal struts from PVC tubing. Heat the middle several inches of each tube and then cut on opposite sides of the hot area with a sharp knife. The slits are then pried open while the material is still very pliable. The holes are sized while cooling using a deep socket of desired size from a socket wrench set (or equivalent forming device).

When you do this correctly, the strut will slide over the small end of the support arm and fit tightly at the arm location where it is to be installed. Finally, drill a hole through the strut and arm and insert a 4-inch long pin made from a nail to keep the strut from sliding or twisting on the arm. These pins are made plenty long so that they can also serve as the anchor points needed for the strut wires. I used caulking to keep the pins from falling out.

Four or more temporary stanchions should be provided to keep the support arms perfectly straight when you install the strut wires. The wires I used to support the arms are steel-cored copper electric-fence wire (#17). Make loop connections at the ends of the struts by drilling a hole, inserting the wire end through it, and then wrapping the wire back on itself (with pliers to make good wraps and to preserve your fingers). Solder all wire twists immediately to prevent any slippage. At the inner end of each support arm, install a shim of PVC tubing so that this end of the arm has sufficient diameter to fit

snugly inside the receiving tube on the mast (see mast construction details below).

Repeat the clamp-tightening-with-heat method used before to make the PVC shim fit the Douglas fir pole or use an expandable filler such as a spray-foam insulation to secure the shim on the arm. Once completed, the arms should be sprayed with several coats of paint. A light gray color blends well with a hazy sky. Whatever color is selected, you will want to paint the arms to protect the wood from the rain and the PVC materials from the sun.

Mast

In the earliest version of this antenna I used steel TV masting for the mast material and made the support arms of bamboo. The mast bent about 2° further each time there was a wind storm. Because the arms were not collapsible in my first attempt, an ice storm eventually turned the antenna into a shape resembling a weeping willow tree.

So, the antenna was redesigned to be collapsible in nasty weather. Also, at this time the mast was made larger in diameter, of thicker material, and in the area of the mast where welds were required, I gave it a double wall. The Bumbershooter mast is shown in **Fig 8**.

The support-arm receiving tubes constitute hinges for, and provide a place to plug in, the six support arms. These tubes also provide convenient attachment points for the lift-spring and travel-limit cables. The lift-spring cables are in the shape of an upside down V. At the apex I connected a 2-foot long, 1½ inch diameter spring suspended from the upper cable anchor on the mast. The bottom ends of the lift-spring cable connect to clamps on support-arm receiving tubes on opposite sides of the mast. When the antenna is fully deployed, the springs should be stretched only 1 inch.

When the system is collapsed into its protective position, the springs will stretch to at least twice their normal length.

Mast Construction

You will need to have a welder assist you with the construction steps in this section. Please wear appropriate eye protection, a protective apron, boots and gloves if you assist in this effort. Heat the middle 4 inches of a 2-foot rebar until it is bright yellow (this rebar, or iron rod, is $1/2$ inch in diameter). With a short length of scrap $1/2$-inch rebar clamped in the vise, wrap the heated rebar all the way around it until the cold ends form a 70° angle with each other, as shown in Fig 8. Repeat this procedure until six such looped rebars have been made. Trim the ends to a length of 7 inches, as measured from the center of the loop.

Clamp a 1-foot length of $3/4$ inch diameter scrap steel pipe into the vise for use as a bending aid. Heat one end of a looped rebar to the same bright yellow temperature as before, and insert this end 2 inches into the bending aid. Apply a lateral force on the cold end of the rebar to bend it. Bend it in the plane that includes the loop and bend it toward the loop. If the bar is inserted the proper distance into the bending fixture, a tight bend 5 inches from the loop and 2 inches from the end will result. Continue bending the rebar until you have an angle of approximately 125°. Allow this to cool briefly and then dash it into cold water. Now bend the other end of this rebar. When finished, hold the newly formed bracket against the work bench. Verify that the two bent ends lay flat against the table top and that the loop is $3^1/2$ inches above the table. A scrap $3/8$-inch rebar should pass easily through the loop, as shown in Fig 8. Repeat to make a total of six such brackets.

Form a 3-foot length of $3/8$-inch rebar into an $8^1/2$ inch diameter circle. This will also require the vise and rebar bending aid. Heat and bend the rod every $1/2$ inch as you slowly pull it out of the bending fixture. When you've formed it into a circle cut the ends so that they overlap approximately 1 inch (at this point we don't yet know the exact size needed).

Make the six support arm receiving tubes by cutting 2 inch ID, $5/16$-inch, thick-walled, aluminum pipe (or equivalent) into 3-foot lengths. A $9/16$ inch diameter hole is drilled straight through both walls of the pipe at a distance 1 inch from the end. Orient these holes horizontally and drill a hole through one wall of the pipe vertically (for connection of the raise-limit-cable). See Fig 8.

Clamps for connecting the lift-spring cables can be hand made from metal strapping. Install these on the receiving tubes 21 inches from the hinge. The hinge brackets and support arm receiving tubes are

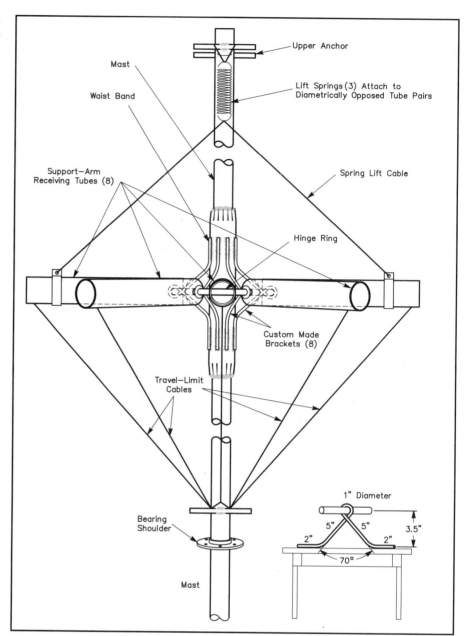

Fig 8—Mast construction details.

"threaded" alternately onto the open circular hinge ring just made (bracket-arm-bracket-arm and such.). The waist-band tube (an 18 inch long, 2.5 inch ID black-iron pipe with tabs cut into the ends) is inserted in the center of the ring so that all twelve bracket ends contact it. Then weld the bracket ends to the waist band such that they support the hinge ring. Trim the hinge ring of excess circumference and make it continuous by welding its ends together.

The waist band is then slipped down over the top end of the mast and positioned so that the ring is 5 feet 3 inches down from the top. Bend the tabs at both ends of the waist band equal amounts down against the mast surface, using light taps with a hammer. Once

the tabs are all in contact with the mast and bent uniformly the tabs are welded to it. Finally the seams between the tabs are closed to the weather by welding them shut.

Weld short lengths of rebar on either side of the mast two inches from the top and 2 feet below the hinge ring. Screw a $2^1/2$-inch pipe nipple into a 5-inch pipe flange and cut tabs into the other end of it. Slide the nipple onto the mast from the bottom end and bend the tabs equally to contact the mast surface, using a hammer as before. The tabs are welded to the mast pipe at a location immediately below the lower cable anchor. The plane of the pipe flange must be perfectly normal to the axis of the mast (this flange applies the weight of the antenna to the top tower bearing).

Install the raise-limit cables between the lower cable anchor and the holes in the ends of the receiving tubes. Be sure to use a non-conductive cable material. Install the lift springs between the upper mast anchor and the apexes of the v'd lift-spring cables. The lift spring cable ends are attached to two diametrically opposed receiving tubes (located on opposite sides of the mast) using the clamps already installed on them. (See Fig 8.) Drill two ¹/₂-inch holes at the bottom end of the mast for attachment of the torque-tube coupler. Two inches above the upper hole just drilled, drill a ³/₈-inch hole all the way through the mast to accommodate the cable lock pin.

Antenna Mechanical Assembly

The winch cable, lock ring and six catenary cables are now stuffed through the mast from the top end. Keep the catenary cables parallel while pulling them into the top of the mast. Look into one of the lock pin holes using a flashlight. When the cable ring comes into view and is centered on this hole insert the lock pin through the mast to capture it.

Temporarily remove the top hat from the pulley tube and stuff the six parallel catenaries into the other end of this tube until you can reach the cable ends with long-nose pliers. Push each catenary cable end through a center passageway in one of the tabs (see Fig 6) and over the wheel of the pulley connected to the tab. Reinstall the top hat, being careful not to rotate the pulley tube (keep the catenaries parallel and untwisted). Plug the pulley tube into the top of the mast. Continually take up slack in the six catenary cables while it is being telescoped. Install a U-bolt clamp on the pulley tube and adjust it so that half of the tube is inside the mast.

Tens of feet of loose winch cable entering the bottom of the mast will not be needed for a while and it could become damaged. I folded them in zigzag fashion and stuffed them into the bottom of the mast. I then taped the end of the mast to keep the cable from falling out. Insert the mast into a ground-mounted test stand pipe (a 5-foot length of 3 inch diameter steel pipe half-buried in the ground). With the help of an assistant, insert the support arms into the receiving tubes and hold them horizontal while the catenary cables are secured to the support arms. A stepladder will be required because this connection is made to the top end of the innermost vertical strut. Before twisting this connection tight, the length of the catenary is carefully adjusted to set the support arm exactly horizontal.

With all support arms installed and supported by the catenaries, set the vertical struts perfectly vertical and then drill a ³/₈-inch hole all the way through each receiving tube (through the shim and support arm that

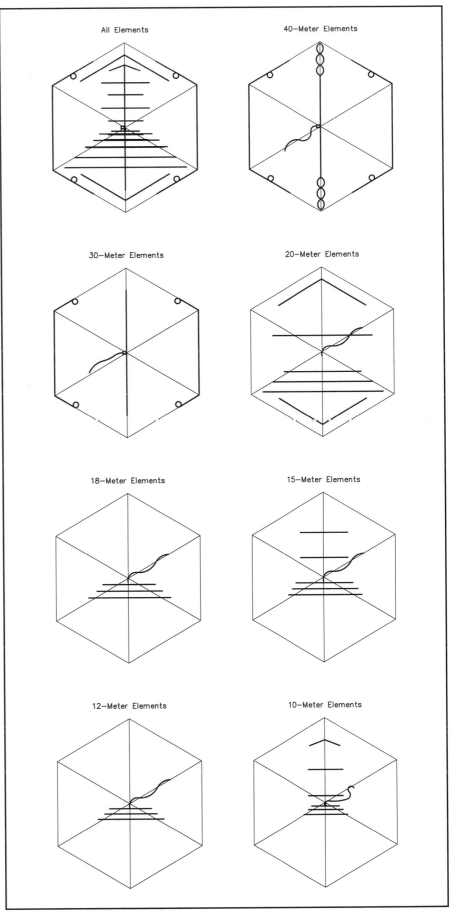

Fig 9—Active wires for each band.

141

are inside the tube as well). Install a $^3/_8$ inch, OD 5 inch long spike nail through this hole as a pin to secure the arm in the receiving tube. Bend excess nail down against the receiving tube to secure the pin permanently in the hole (this pin will bear one-sixth of the icing load).

At this stage you should set the support arms exactly 60° apart. I suggest that you use inexpensive lines, such as nylon cord, between the support arms to initially set the angle between them. Connect equal length lines between the arm ends and midpoints. The difficult mechanical work is done.

Electrical Design

I use *NEC-2* antenna modeling software that can handle more than 4000 wire segments. I have done extensive modeling of the entire antenna using this model, including the traps and the log-periodic feed line. The results show good performance relating to all parameters that matter to the average ham operator (gain, front-to-back, efficiency, and SWR). You can always improve on a design as complex as this one, however, especially if a particular band or a subset of bands are of special interest.

You might want to insert additional traps in the Yagi elements of the log-Yagi portion of the antenna, for example, to enhance performance on the WARC bands (although this might adversely impact power-handling capability). Data files are available for those wishing to model my antenna (or a portion of my antenna) themselves.

You can best understand the electrical characteristics by considering that only certain wires in the antenna will be resonant, or nearly resonant, when a particular band is used. Wires with no current on them can be ignored. The operator must select either the low-band coaxial feed cable (30/40 meters) or the high-band feed cable (20 through 10 meters). I used a coaxial relay at the base of the tower to do the actual switching between feed cables. Keep in mind that the main lobe changes direction 90° when the low-band cable is selected.

The 40-meter portion of the antenna is an almost full-sized, wide-spaced 3-element 40-meter Yagi. I used two diametrically opposed support arms to construct a 55 foot long biconical driven element for 40 meters. Biconical elements (capacitively loaded) are shorter than the standard half-wave length. To create the needed capacitive loading, I simply soldered jumper wires across all of the homemade strut insulators in these two arms. This is shown in Fig 7.

This formed 14 foot long, cylindrical wire cages varying from 4 to 2 feet in diameter at both ends of the element. Pairs of #14 steel-core copper wires spaced 4 inches apart stretch between the balun and the cages to make the middle portion of the element. Due

to the high capacitance at the ends of this element, the resonant frequency can be trimmed by inserting or deleting parallel wires in this middle section. The resonant frequency decreases with additional parallel wires. I used a commercial 1:1 balun at the center feed point.

A 40-meter Yagi director and reflector are placed at the periphery of the hexagonal-shaped support frame, as shown in **Fig 9**. These and all remaining elements are made of twisted pairs of #17 aluminum electric-fence wire. The alloy used in aluminum wire of this kind is amazingly tough and the wire has not broken even after years of use on the Bumbershooter. The twisted pair style I wanted is not available commercially, so I made it by hand. I had originally paired these wires to decrease wire resistance and thereby accommodate the legal limit power level, but later I found that the twisted pair wire also seemed to hang better, without coiling or snagging, while the support arms were being raised up from the collapsed position.

I installed traps in the 40-meter parasitic elements to provide a director and reflector for the 30-meter band. These traps had an insignificant effect on the 40-meter beam. (See trap construction details below.) I connected a 30-meter half-wave driven element to the balun in parallel with the 40-meter biconical driven element. After installing the 30-meter beam, I discovered that the antenna patterns of the higher frequency band antennas (20 through 10 meters) were improved. Apparently, the traps had broken up some unwanted harmonic resonances occurring in these wires in my original configuration. I had originally thought that adding the 30-meter traps might reduce the power-handling capability of the Bumbershooter, but then I realized that the legal power limit on 30 meters is only 200 W. No other traps are used in the antenna.

I added a standard log-periodic dipole array (LPDA) covering 20, 17, 15, 12, and 10 meters inside the 30/40 meter antenna by installing it at right angles to the 30/40-meter Yagi. (See Fig 9.) These LP elements had to be at right angles for electrical isolation. This was important to obtain good antenna patterns and SWRs below 2 to 1.

I made a very lightweight feed line for the LPDA from a roll of aluminum flashing material and a single shortened element from an old 10-meter beam. See the section on LP feed-line construction below. The target characteristic impedance for this feed line was 100 Ω. On the third attempt at building it, I measured 95 Ω (off by only 5%) and so I stopped experimenting. The feed line resembles an upside-down eaves trough with a pipe running the length of it and centered in it.

To optimize the performance of the bands

I used in contesting (20, 15, and 10 meters), I added as many Yagi parasitic directors for these bands as possible ahead of the LP section. Thus this portion of the Bumbershooter became a log-Yagi antenna. Also, I added a Yagi reflector for 20 meters behind the LP section to enhance the front-to-back ratio on that band.

Construction of Elements, Traps and LP Feed Line

Construction of the antenna elements requires plenty of #17 aluminum electric-fence wire. Ironically, the smallest size spool of this kind of wire you'll find at a farm/garden store will contain a half of a mile of it so this won't be a problem! (The steel-core copper wire required for the support arm struts comes in big spools also.) Make a twisted pair of bare wire using individual wires off the spool. Stretch one wire between two points and temporarily coil up the second wire in your hand. Wrap the second wire, coil and all, around the first—playing out wire from the coil as you go. Pull the wire tight often as you do this. Three or four tight twists per foot and you've got it.

Fig 10 shows the lengths and locations of the elements you will be installing, using the test-stand framework. Suspend the wires with 400 pound test, deep-sea fishing line and terminate the support lines with ferrule loops. The smaller numbers shown in parentheses in Fig 10 indicate where the wire bend points or traps are located. These numbers also show the element half-lengths in feet connected to the LP feed line. The numbers above the LP feed line indicate the element separations. The larger numbers indicate overall element lengths.

Fig 11 shows details of the LP feed line, as well as the four 30-meter traps used in the director and reflector of the 40-meter Yagi. These traps are made using waterproofed Christmas-wreath styrofoam forms sold at craft stores. I applied a water-based weatherproof coating to the wreath forms and allowed them to dry. The trap coils are most conveniently made outdoors because they are actually an integral part of the 40-meter parasitic element wires. That is, these elements are stretched out in a straight line and the wire ends are then used to wind the toroidal coils. Start the coil-winding process at the correct distance from the center of a 40-meter wire, or the traps will not be the correct distance apart when completed.

The wreath forms I used were $6^1/_2$ inches in loop diameter and the Styrofoam material itself was $1^1/_2$ inches in diameter. What is required is to continually "put the thread through the eye of the needle" until the wreath has 43 toroidal turns, spaced about $^3/_8$ inch apart. This is done most easily with the assistance of another person—the "thread" in this case is a twisted-pair wire

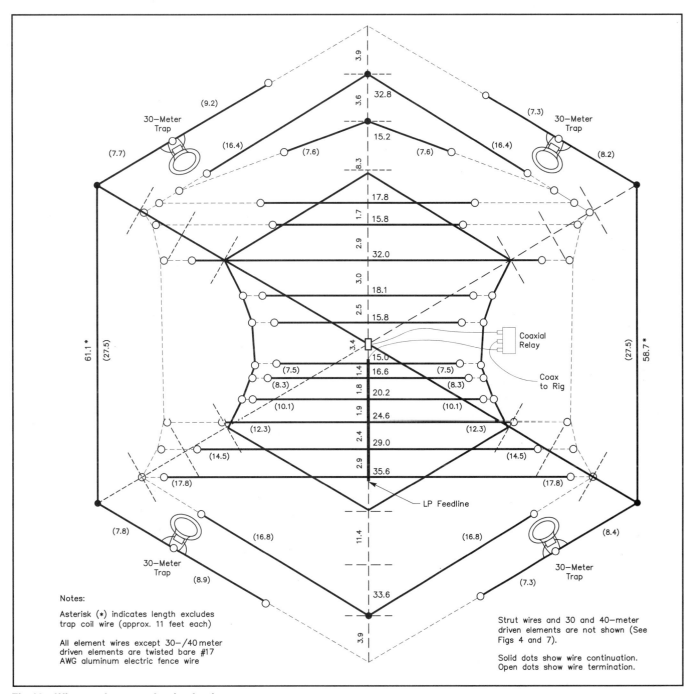

Fig 10—Wires and nonconductive leaders.

with a beginning length of 18.5 feet (director) or 20.1 feet (reflector). The object is to avoid cutting the wire if possible, since it is aluminum and hard to splice. The process must include installing a strain insulator at the trap terminals. Compress each turn of wire you add down against the toroidal form before starting the next turn.

A 10,000-V doorknob capacitor is connected in parallel with the toroid coil using two short lengths of twisted element wire to connect it. Refer to Fig 10. A 50-pF capacitor should resonate the coil at 10.1 MHz. If

a grid dip meter or impedance meter shows otherwise, the number of turns in the toroid should be adjusted to obtain this frequency.

One-inch ferrules made from $1/4$-inch aluminum tubing should be crimped over these wire twists as insurance that the joint will maintain good electrical continuity. It is essential that any aluminum joints that you must make have a constant pressure applied to them by a crimped ferrule, screw or other means.

The log-periodic feed line was made from a roll of aluminum flashing material. This

material is very thin and would not be suitable were it not for the sturdy $3/4$ inch diameter aluminum tubing running through the center of it, forming one half of the feed line. The shape and dimensions of this feed line can be seen in Fig 11. An insulating bracket between the outer end of the center tube and the upper side of the support arm mounts one end of the LP feed line on the antenna. A similar bracket between the other end of the center tube and the associated receiving tube mounts the other end of the transmission line. See Fig 10.

At this end, the feed line is allowed to pass along side of (and contact) the nonconductive spring lift cable. An insulator at each point where elements connect to the feed line keeps the aluminum tubing and the aluminum flashing separated. When connecting the elements to the feed line, be sure to connect them so that the left and right connections alternate, as shown in Fig 11. A 9-inch shorted stub connected across the rear element reduces the SWR at the bottom end of 40 meters.

Remember that you can do maintenance of this sort in a manner of minutes using the antenna collapsing feature, but please always use your climbing belt. I wound RG-8/U coax into a 5-turn choke balun on a 5 inch diameter form and installed it at the LP feed point.

Antenna Installation

The antenna without the torque tube will weigh about 175 pounds; keep this in mind in the following steps. Remove the antenna from the test stand and bring it within a foot of the tower by temporarily disconnecting some of the element support lines on one side. Reconnect these lines on the other side of the tower and hoist the antenna up above the tower using a gin pole (attach the lift rope to the top anchor point on the mast, where the springs connect). Insert the mast into the thrust bearing at the top of the tower.

The HDBX 48 tower has a mast-sized hole through the rotator mounting plate where the lower mast bearing will be installed. With the antenna properly seated in the two bearings, the winch cable is now untaped and allowed to hang freely from the bottom end of the mast, ready for insertion through the torque tube sections as these are installed.

The torque-tube sections are installed top to bottom. See Fig 5. You may need to trim the bottom torque tube for it to fit perfectly into the antenna rotator clamp. The rotator clamp is tightened with the rotator set to north and the log-Yagi pointed north. With long-nose pliers the winch cable is pulled through the pulley mounted inside the wall of the torque tube. It is connected to the winch spool and trimmed in length if necessary so that 10 feet is wrapped around the spool. The winch is now cranked until there is evidence that the weight of the antenna is totally on the winch and completely removed from the cable ring lock pin. Then remove the lock pin. Crank the Bumbershooter down into the protective position and then back into the normal position to verify that it functions normally. Make sure you then remove the handle from the winch when you are finished!

Operating

A hinged heading placard for the antenna

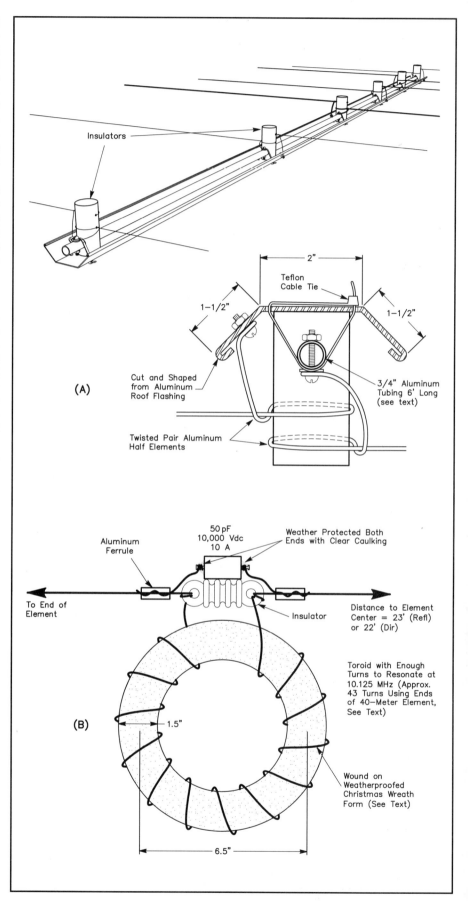

Fig 11—Construction of log-periodic feed and 30-meter trap. At A, the LP feed line, made of aluminum tubing and aluminum roof flashing material. At B, details of the 30-meter trap.

rotator control box is an operating aid that I consider to be indispensable. See **Fig 12**. When you change to 30 or 40 meters, you will want to flip this placard up across the face of the bearing indicator so that you won't have to mentally add 90° to the beam headings indicated.

In the six years I've used the Bumbershooter, I've found it to be great during contests, where you need a little extra signal to bag multipliers, to hold a CQ frequency or to work that rare Yukon Territory station in a deep Sweepstakes pileup. I've also enjoyed using the Bumbershooter on 40 meter SSB at night, turning the beam away from all of the European broadcast interference and chatting with stateside hams to the west. Often hams found in this part of the band say they've never had such a successful QSO on 40-meter SSB at night.

Being able to use any of the WARC bands allows me to avoid the congestion present on the older frequency bands and take best advantage of the WWV propagation infor-

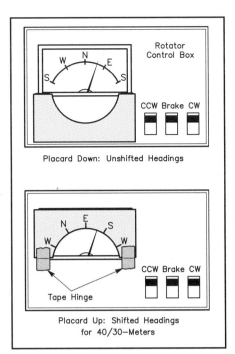

Placard Down: Unshifted Headings

Placard Up: Shifted Headings for 40/30—Meters

Fig 12—An indispensable operating aid for the Bumbershooter—this helps tell you which way it's pointing depending on the frequency band in use.

mation. All this makes the Bumbershooter really fun to use.

I received a BSEE degree from Valparaiso Technical Institute in 1972. My sincere thanks go to daughters Annie (N3EBR) and Jennifer (N3TRP) and wife Margaret for their valuable assistance and support during the development of the Bumbershooter. Thanks also go to W3LPL, KE3Q, K1HTV and W3AZ, who encouraged and assisted me with this documentation. Finally, I must acknowledge my tutors in the art of home brewing ham antennas: W8HKH (now W5RSK), W8AKR (SK) and W3KS (SK).

Through-the-Roof Antenna Mounting System

By H. Kaz Soong, K8KS
3902 North Michael Rd
Ann Arbor, MI 48103
hksoong@umich.edu

A t one time or another, many of us have been thwarted in our efforts to erect antennas of our liking. This often results from local restrictive covenants, shortage of space, sympathy for our neighbors or simply aesthetic reasons. Most of us, myself included, perceive beauty (albeit somewhat perversely) as an 80-foot-high, tower-mounted, multielement beam antenna. Our opinions, of course, are skewed by our vested interest in owning a high-performance antenna system, whether it be due to smoking our competitors in a contest, being the king of the mountain in a DX pileup or merely being able to ragchew without being adversely affected by the ethereal elements. But when I detach myself for a moment from my preconceptions and somewhat wayward biases, I can see that, according to universal aesthetic standards and common sense, all that hardware on and around an otherwise beautiful home *is* ugly.

I live in a suburban development that has a clearly spelled-out antenna restrictive covenant, specifically including towers, either ground-mounted or roof-mounted. Being an avid DXer, I noted that a multiband vertical antenna was fine for the working the first 275 countries, but for the last remaining countries (the real gems and rare ones), the pileups were going to be intense and impossible to break. I no longer was satisfied with being the hyena in the feeding frenzy. I have a wife and three children and thus could not afford to waste hours in a mega-pileup. I wanted an antenna with gain. I needed a beam antenna, a tribander, that could be mounted high enough off the ground to work well, yet not require a tower.

After picking the minds of several of my ham buddies (NU8Z, WB8DKX, and WB8VDC), I decided to place the tower *inside* the attic (**Fig 1**) and extend the mast

Ever thought about putting your antenna through your roof but were worried about trying it? Read how K8KS accomplished the task.

Fig 1—Four-legged roof-mount tower bolted to attic floor at K8KS. Two parallel, 6-foot lengths of 2×8-inch boards support the tower. These boards are, in turn, bolted to all the floor joists they contact. See text for details of the noise-reduction methods in use in this installation.

through a single hole in the roof. The basic concept is not new. The setup is relatively low-profile, with only the mast and Yagi visible from outdoors (**Fig 2A** and **2B**), and most of the "ugly" stuff (tower and rotator) tucked away in the attic. If need be, the coaxial feedline could be hidden inside the mast—an option that I elected not to take. Aside from an aesthetic standpoint, the setup has a comparatively low wind profile. Moreover, the attachments of the mast and the tower to various structural points inside the attic really secures the system well.

Tower Assembly

My attic has a 16-foot clearance between the floor and roof peak. Although this is a higher clearance than most attics, this scheme would also work in attics with vertical clearances as low as 6 feet. In attics with even lower clearances, one might forego the tower altogether and instead mount the rotator assembly directly to the floor or to adjacent structural supports inside the attic.

I used a 4$\frac{1}{2}$-foot-tall roof-mount tower (Glen Martin Engineering RT-424) and bolted all four of its legs to two parallel six-foot lengths of 2×8-inch wooden slats, which were in turn bolted crosswise to at least three consecutive floor joists. The slats

 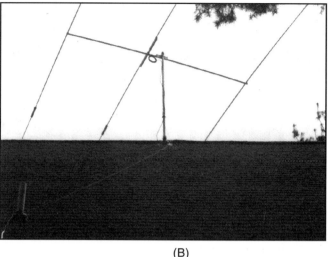

(A)   (B)

Fig 2—At A, a front view of the house reveals only the antenna and mast. At B, the waterproof rubber boot, Fernco coupler, and mast grounding wire are visible from the rear.

are cushioned from the underlying floor boards by an inexpensive bathroom rug sandwiched between them. The metal tower legs are cushioned from the 2×8-inch wood boards by rubber grommets at each of the bolts (cut up squares of old tires, mouse pads or rubber porch mats can be used here). The cushioning minimizes rotator noise and wind vibration transmitted through the attic floor to the rooms below.

The rotator plate fits on a shelf mounted at the tower's midsection. A thrust bearing at the tower apex is highly recommended to assure minimum vibration and wobbling of the mast during rotation.

Mast Assembly

The mast may exit the house exactly at the roof peak or slightly to one side. I chose the latter, since my house has a peak vent along the entire length of the roof. Therefore, I positioned the mast exit point 6 inches lateral to the peak, on the slope of the roof facing the rear of the house and away from the street. This reduces the visible profile (Fig 2) from the front of the house. Many tall pine trees on my lot also help conceal the assembly. A 2-inch-OD galvanized steel mast passes through a $1^1/_2$-foot section of a $2^1/_4$-inch-ID steel pipe welded at 45° (the roof pitch) to a $^1/_4$-inch-thick steel plate (see **Fig 3**). This short pipe section then passes through a $2^1/_4$-inch hole cut in the roof. Emotionally, this was by far the most difficult part of the entire process—putting a hole this size in my roof! To make matters worse, during installation of my antenna, one of the helping hams glibly quipped that I "had reduced the value of my home by several thousand dollars the moment the hole was made." I was wrought with angst and guilt, but only for a few minutes.

The steel plate is bolted to two roof rafters

straddling each side of the hole. The mast rotates concentrically inside the slightly wider $2^1/_4$-inch outer pipe. The $1^1/_2$-foot length of outer pipe seems optimum in that it provides adequate restriction of sideward mast movement during antenna rotation and in high winds, yet it is not so long as to create excessive friction against the mast. The steel plate assembly, the mast and the tower are grounded for safety.

Weather Sealing

To prevent precipitation from entering the attic, I spread Mastic brand sealant in

and around the hole. In addition, the $2^1/_4$-inch pipe is passed through a constrictive rubber boot made for fitting around roof ventilator pipes. The upper part of the rubber boot base plate is then tucked *under* the shingles immediately above, and the lower part of the plate is placed on *top* of the shingles below. The rubber boot plate essentially functions as a shingle, enhancing waterproofing.

A cylindrical rubber skirt is clamped around the mast slightly above the upper end of the $2^1/_4$-inch pipe section. The hem of this rubber skirt should drape over and cover the wider pipe, thus sealing the gap between the two concentric pipes. I used a rubber plumbing coupler (**Fig 4**) designed for joining two disparate-diameter pipes (a Fernco coupler). These are available at most hardware and plumbing supply stores. I used a coupler of 2-inch ID on the mast end and $2^1/_4$-inch ID on the other end. The Fernco coupler is clamped only on the mast end; the hem end rotates freely around the $2^1/_4$-inch pipe. These couplers come in many sizes and combinations, readily fitting other pipe diameters. I recommend that these rubber couplers be checked at least every 3 years for signs of mechanical fatigue or photochemical breakdown from the sun's ultraviolet rays.

As an alternative to a Fernco coupler, a cone-shaped, sheet-metal skirt could be fashioned and attached around the mast. Another *udderly* ingenious alternative would be to befriend a dairy farmer and ask for a large rubber suction cup from his milking machine.

After the mast assembly is complete, it's time to mount and secure the antenna to it. A gin pole may make the job easier and safer. The top of my mast extends about

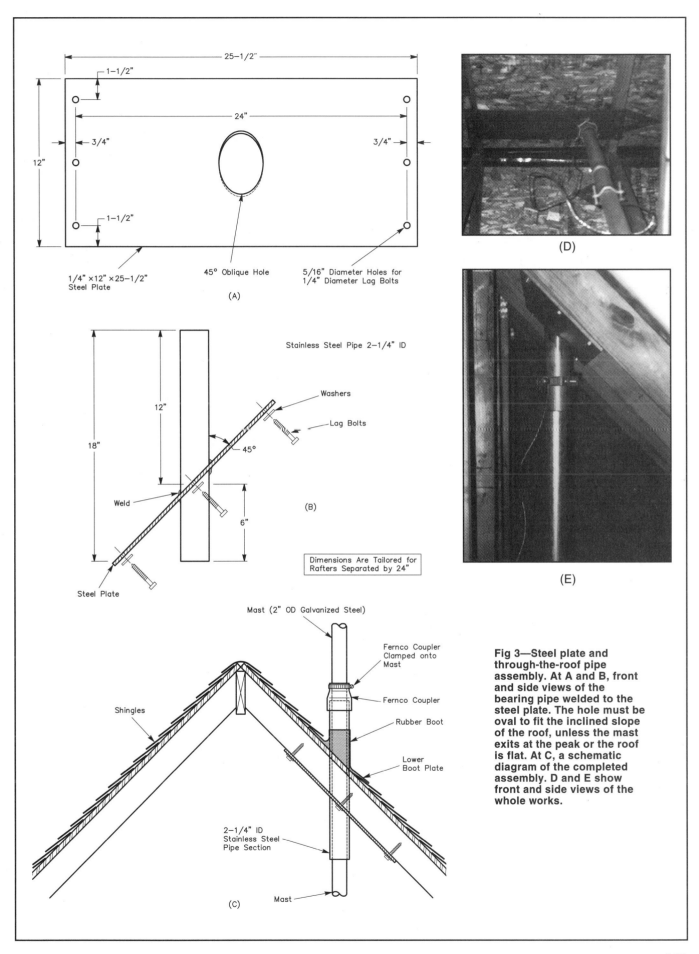

25-1/2"

1-1/2"

24"

3/4" **3/4"**

12"

1-1/2"

1/4" ×12" ×25-1/2"
Steel Plate

45° Oblique Hole

5/16" Diameter Holes for
1/4" Diameter Lag Bolts

(A)

Stainless Steel Pipe 2–1/4" ID

Washers

Lag Bolts

12"

18"

45°

Weld

6"

(B)

Steel Plate

Dimensions Are Tailored for
Rafters Separated by 24"

(D)

(E)

Mast (2" OD Galvanized Steel)

Fernco Coupler
Clamped onto
Mast

Fernco Coupler

Rubber Boot

Shingles

Lower
Boot Plate

2-1/4" ID
Stainless Steel
Pipe Section

Mast

(C)

**Fig 3—Steel plate and
through-the-roof pipe
assembly. At A and B, front
and side views of the
bearing pipe welded to the
steel plate. The hole must be
oval to fit the inclined slope
of the roof, unless the mast
exits at the peak or the roof
is flat. At C, a schematic
diagram of the completed
assembly. D and E show
front and side views of the
whole works.**

Fig 4—The Fernco coupler tightly adapts the bearing pipe to the mast.

7 feet above the peak of the roof (45 feet above the ground). This amount of ground clearance appears to be sufficient to isolate the antenna adequately from my house; I notice no bad effects such as high SWR and poor directivity. For a roof of less than 45° slope, ie, a flatter one, I recommend using a longer mast to obtain better electrical isolation and clearance from the structure.

Once the antenna is mounted to the mast, cap the mast with a screw-on cover to keep water from entering the pipe. Hardware stores carry these galvanized-steel endcaps for various pipe sizes.

Epilogue

It has been more than four years since I installed the through-the-roof assembly and I have had absolutely no problems. Being very concerned about leaks, I initially inspected the attic roof from the inside daily (twice daily after a rain) during the first month. After gradually gaining confidence, my forays to the attic dropped to once every two months. There have been no leaks or damage so far.

It is sure nice to be able to perform maintenance work on the tower and rotator within the well-lit convenience, comfort and safety *inside* the house, and not outdoors on a tower at the mercy of the heights and the elements. The rotator, being indoors, never ices in the winter. The attic heat also seems to keep ice from forming at the Fernco joint—an unexpected benefit. This is only time I actually have appreciated the poor heat insulation in my attic!

About the author: Kaz is an eye (cornea) surgeon at the University of Michigan Medical Center and has been a ham for 6 years. Two of his children are hams: Michael, AA8MN, and Brian, KB8PWX. His wife and daughter are not, but are nevertheless understanding and tolerant of our hobby.

Motorizing Your Crank-up Tower Isn't Difficult

By Allan H. Fusler, KI7NF
2943 W Topeka Drive
Phoenix, AZ 85027-4927
trekkie-hamcat@juno.com

Allan Fusler, KI7NF, describes how he motorized his crank-up tower.

A crank-up tower can help soothe relations between amateurs and neighbors. It also provides an easier solution to working on antennas, especially if you have a tower that offers the tilt-over option. Extending and retracting the tower manually is not a problem when you have a healthy 14 to 18 year old son at home who likes to exercise his biceps and pectoral muscles, or if you are physically strong. But what happens when that son leaves for college or for "greener pastures," or you are otherwise unable to provide the necessary muscle power?

The easiest way to motorize the tower is to purchase a complete electric winch setup from the tower manufacturer, if it is available. Being one that likes a challenge, I decided to investigate the possibility of motorizing the tower and by doing the work myself, save some money. The July 1994 issue of *World Radio* featured an article from an amateur in California who had motorized his crank-up tubular tower, and that gave me some ideas to expand upon.

I own a US Tower model TX-455 triangular tower, which I understand is their most popular model. My tower has the TRX-80 tilt-over fixture. I did not want to modify the Fulton model K1550 winch, which is part of the basic tower package. That way, if the gear motor or the 120 V ac power ever failed, I would still be able to use the hand winch to extend or retract the tower. Further, the gear motor and mounting bracket had to be detachable from the tower without having to remove any part of the tilt-over option, or without having to tilt the tower part of the way downward.

Since I don't use the tilt-over fixture very often, I did not motorize its K1550 winch. However, I wanted the hand crank on that tilt-over feature to be completely usable after I had motorized the crank-up winch.

Since I normally keep my tower retracted unless I'm using the radio, I did not feel a need to be able to remove the gear motor and bracket when the tower is extended. The appendix explains how you can do that.

To use the hand crank, the bottom part of the bracket, with the gear motor attached, has to be removed. The coupling on the K1550 winch shaft is removed next, and then the hand crank can be used. If the tower is retracted, the job is relatively easy. If the tower is extended, it's a little more difficult, but it can still be lowered by removing the gear motor from the bracket and the coupling from the shaft of the K1550 winch. Then the hand crank can be used to lower the tower by turning the winch a half turn at a time, similar to the way that you use a box-end wrench in a limited space. This is a very slow process, but at least the tower can be retracted manually.

Photo of the completed assembly.

Close-up of the gear-motor mounting bracket.

Side view showing the gear motor, its bracket and couplings, all attached to the K1550 winch.

The remainder of this article is devoted to a step-by-step solution to motorizing my tower, and others like it. I've given you complete directions, part numbers and sizes. I'm sure there are many substitutions that can be made. I did no analysis of the stresses on the mounting bracket, because the gear motor weighs only 30 pounds. Also, I used miscellaneous steel that I had at hand, so the exact sizes are not critical.

I determined the gear-motor power requirement by measuring the torque (force × lever arm) with a scale. When the tower is almost fully extended, it requires about 450 in-lbs of torque to raise the tower.

I need a 120 V ac single-phase gear motor at my QTH, and since it's exposed to weather, it needs to be of the TEFC (totally enclosed, fan-cooled) type. The motor has to be reversible, and a split-phase motor is. The gear motor shouldn't operate above 30 RPM. The friction brake of the K1550 winch would heat up too much during tower retraction if the speed is much higher.

I selected a 22 RPM, 1/2 hp Dayton brand gear motor that has 1105 in-lbs of full load torque. The motor pulls a maximum of 7.9 A at 120 V ac. It has quite a bit more than the necessary full-load torque, but a split-phase motor has only a *medium* amount of

starting torque when compared to its full-load torque. Therefore, I selected the gear motor size so that it would be able to raise the stopped tower from a less-than-fully extended position.

Grainger's stock number for this gear motor is 6Z403 in their 1996 catalogue. After installation, the gear motor raised the tower from the fully retracted position of 22 feet to the fully extended position of 55 feet in approximately 3 minutes. I measured the current with an induction type ammeter, at 5 A while running. The instantaneous start-up current is 20 A. I made both measurements with the tower mostly extended. In the interest of safety, I put this gear motor on a 20-A GFI (ground fault interrupted) circuit using 12-gauge 2-wire with ground cable. If you run underground power lines to the tower, be sure to use UF (underground feeder) wire. Electrical codes call for different burial depths for wires that are GFI protected and ones that aren't. Check and follow your local electrical code—it exists for your safety!

The connection between the gear motor and the K1550 winch has to permit some misalignment. For this, I selected a pair of Boston Gear couplings and a spider insert to connect between them. The coupling that attaches to the motor shaft is a 3/4-inch bore Boston Gear size FC20, Grainger part number 2L039. This coupling has a 0.188-inch keyway, and that matches the keyway on the gear motor.

The coupling that attaches to the K1550 winch shaft is a 1/2-inch bore Boston Gear FC20, Grainger part number 2L036. The winch shaft has two "flats" on opposite sides. The 0.125-inch key, which is purchased separately, slips into the keyway in the 1/2-inch bore coupling and against the flat on one side of the winch shaft. To obtain a longer bearing surface between the key and the flat surface of the K1550 winch shaft, I removed one of the two crimped hex head nuts. It served as a spacer and as *insurance* that the first crimped nut would not back off and loosen the brake and ratchet assembly of the K1550 winch.

To accommodate more *clamping* power on the opposite flat, I replaced the setscrew supplied with the 1/2-inch bore coupling with a 1/4 NC × 1 1/4-inch long nickel-plated, hex-head bolt. When tightened down onto the flat, it provides a tight fit that functions properly.

After checking for proper fit, I primed and painted the outside of both couplings. During final installation, I applied Locktite thread sealant to both the setscrew in the gear motor shaft coupling and the bolt in the winch-shaft coupling. I also installed and snugly tightened the winch coupling against the remaining crimped hex nut on the shaft, so that the internal mechanism of the K1550 winch continues to function properly.

Close-up showing the hand crank on the tilt-over fixture clearing the mounting bracket.

Table 1
Switch Connections

Wire	Number on Switch
120 V ac white wire	L1
120 V ac black wire	L2
Blue (gear motor)	T1
Yellow (gear motor)	T2
Red (gear motor)	8
Black (gear motor)	12

The spider insert, which serves as a link between the couplings, is an FC20 Bost-Bronze insert, Grainger number 2L070. The catalogue lists that insert as having a maximum torque rating of 1000 in-lbs, which is quite close to the 1105 in-lb capacity of the gear motor. The two other types of available inserts have torque ratings much lower than this, and they are not acceptable!

A special switch, known as a drum switch, is required to operate the gear motor in either forward or reverse without having to change the wires manually. For safety reasons, I believe that only a momentary-contact switch should be used in this type of setup. That means a person must physically turn the switch to one position or the other and hold it there. The instant the switch is released, the spring loading returns the switch to the NORMALLY OFF position and the circuit is broken.

Use of a maintained-contact type of switch can lead to disaster if a person turns the switch on and forgets about it or is distracted for a few minutes by something else. The tower can be damaged if the gear motor is strong enough to extend the tower past the *stops* that are installed to prevent the tower from going past its designed travel limits.

One way to prevent this type of potential damage is to use limit switches to terminate operation when the tower has reached the end of its travel in either direction. Limit switches are mandatory if the tower is controlled by remote operation. With limit switches, a maintained type of contact switch may be used. However, that level of

sophistication is not necessary and so I chose the momentary-contact drum switch.

I painted a red stripe on the outermost vertical legs of the tower that face the winch as well as near the bottom of the next interior assembly leg that align when that interior leg is 2 inches below maximum height. This serves as a visual indication of when to release the switch.

I mounted the drum switch directly on the connection box of the gear motor. I did this using the screws on the cover plate to attach the back of the switch to the junction box on the gear motor. Since it is exposed to the elements, a weatherproof switch is necessary. The only available switch that seems to meet all of the above requirements is a plastic-cased unit made by Advanced Controls, Inc. This switch will handle up to 16 A at either 120 V ac or 240 V ac. The Grainger part number is 6C014 and the Advanced Controls, Inc part number is A1734/SRC/S35.

I wired the switch so that extending the tower requires turning the handle counterclockwise and retracting the tower necessitates turning the handle clockwise. Small forked connectors are installed on the four wires coming from the motor and on the white and black wires of the 120 V ac power chord. Even though the connectors are crimped on the wires, I soldered these six wires to their connectors to prevent a poor connection from developing. I used the provided connector to connect a jumper wire between the ground on the motor housing and the green colored ground wire in the power cord. **Table 1** lists the connections I

made to the rotary switch.

I placed the UP OFF DOWN decal on the top of the switch box so that the arrow on the handle points to the position that the tower moves. If you wish to reverse the operation of the handle, simply interchange the red and the black wires at the rotary switch.

I used silicone sealant between the motor and the back of the switch box. I sealed the opening of the unused cable guard with a small piece of neoprene rubber sheet that I cut to fit the opening.

I built the gear-motor mounting bracket from $1^1/2 \times 1^1/2 \times {}^3/_{16}$-inch angle iron. The horizontal arm, which supports the motor, is $1^1/2 \times 1^1/2 \times {}^1/_8$-inch angle iron. The brace is a ${}^5/_8$-inch diameter rod.

Since the vertical leg of the gear motor bracket has to fit through the winch bracket, the part of the gear motor bracket that bolts to the tower cannot be made as a one piece "I" shape. I welded a ${}^3/_8$-inch hex-head nut to the inside of a tab on the top angle so a ${}^3/_8 \times 1^1/2$-inch long bolt can be used to attach the bottom part of the inverted "T" shaped portion of the bracket.

I installed the gear motor mounting bracket, and after checking alignment of the motor and couplings, marked the holes in the gear motor "feet." Next I drilled ${}^7/_{16}$-inch diameter holes in the ${}^1/_8$-inch thick bracket plate for the ${}^3/_8 \times 1^1/2$-inch long bolts, which with flat washers and friction nuts mount the gear motor to the bracket plate. **Fig 1** shows the dimensions I used for this particular application. If yours is the same model number of tower and the same gear motor and couplings, the bracket dimensions and configuration should work for you. Please be sure to check dimensions before you begin—just to be sure.

The photos show the finished assembly. With some additional thought, it may be improved, but it is a good basic design that should be quite serviceable for many years to come.

I spent about 24 hours investigating, purchasing, building and fitting this one-of-a-kind motorized winch. Much of my time went into establishing the exact centerline of the winch shaft with respect to the winch bracket bolts, since no plans were available for

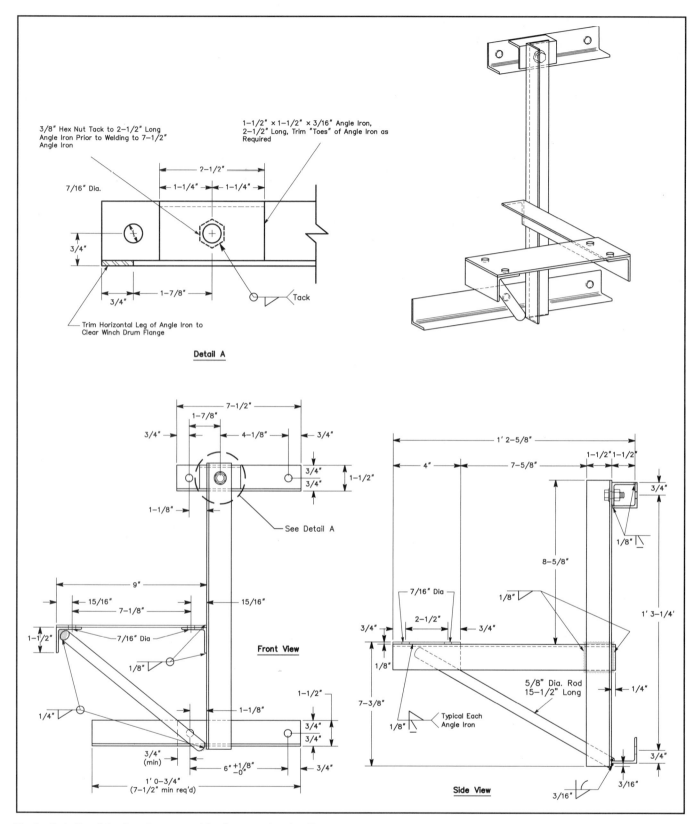

Fig 1—Details of the bracket assembly. See text for details.

the winch and its bracket. I had a drawing that shows the pertinent information required for the gear motor, but most of the bracket had to be fit by clamping everything in place. I then made final adjustments, removed the bracket and then took it to be welded at a different location. I would have saved time if I had had a portable welding outfit.

The total cost of the gear motor, couplings, insert, drum switch and miscellaneous hardware came to less than $500, including tax. You must determine if your time is worth the difference between that amount of money and the cost of a motorized winch purchased from the tower manufacturer. I trust that much of what is discussed in this article could help greatly in eliminating costly errors and wasted time in pursuit of unsatisfactory solutions.

If you have any comments or further questions, you may e-mail me at **trekkiehamcat@juno.com** or telephone me at: (602) 262-1279 (weekdays, 6:30 AM to 3:30 PM MT) or (602) 582-1044, evenings and weekends. You can write to me at the address given at the beginning of this article. If you wish a reply, please send an SASE. Good luck on your tower motorizing project!

APPENDIX

How to make the gear motor and bracket removable at any time

Four bolts attach the K1550 winch to the tower. You'll need to replace the two $^3/_8$ inch × 2-inch long flat head machine screws, as well as the two $^3/_8$ inch × 2-inch long hex head bolts with four $2^1/_2$-inch long bolts.

Since neither pair of bolts can be replaced with the tower fully retracted, the tower must be raised until the adjacent inner section is above the winch bracket. Next, insert knot-free lengths of quality 2 × 4 lumber through the cross bracing of the outermost section and underneath the bottom of that next inner section. Now lower the tower until the weight of the inner sections is resting on the wood. With the load removed from the winch, the bolts may be replaced.

After the winch bracket has been replaced and the nuts fully tightened, the tower may be raised until the wood can be removed. The gear-motor mounting bracket mounts onto the four replacement bolts and is secured by a second set of four friction nuts. Now the gear motor and mounting bracket can be removed without having to loosen the winch bracket. Remember, you can't remove the winch bracket when the tower is extended and the winch is under load.

Allan H. Fusler, KI7NF, is a Registered Professional Engineer in Arizona and Ohio.

Weatherproofing Coaxial Cable

By Jack Warren, WB4MDC
4 Tomahawk Dr
Merrimack, NH 03054-2335

WB4MDC shares a couple of his tricks for keeping the moisture out of the ends of his coaxial cable feed lines.

Ever since the invention of coaxial cable, moisture has been wicking into the braid at the exposed end of the cable. I call it wicking because the metallic braid that is used for the shield acts just like the wick in Grandma's old time coal-oil lamp. If there's moisture nearby, the capillary action of the woven metal shield strands will pull the moisture into the cable. Once the moisture gets in there, it's only a matter of time until the cable's electrical and physical properties deteriorate and the cable will no longer be usable.

What Makes a Coaxial Cable

Coaxial cables commonly available to the radio amateur are made from a center conductor, an insulator that surrounds this conductor, a woven metal shield that surrounds the center insulator, and finally an outer jacket that surrounds everything else. Coaxial cable gets its name from the relationship of the parts used to make the cable. Each of these items shares the same axis. That is, the center of each part is the center of every other part. When you look at the end of a piece of coaxial cable, you see all parts of the cable creating circles around the center of the center conductor.

The center conductor of the coaxial cable, or coax, can be a single piece of wire or many smaller strands of wire twisted together. This varies from one type of coax to another and each type has specific applications.

The center-conductor insulation can be made from solid plastic, plastic foam (plastic with tiny bubbles) or a combination of small ribs of plastic that support the center conductor in a virtual air space inside the cable. The latter insulating method makes very low loss cables, but is more expensive to manufacture and not as common as the other insulating methods.

The shield is a woven metallic mesh placed over the center insulator. It is usually made of fine strands of copper wire and in less expensive cable is not plated. Better-quality coaxial cables have their shields and center conductors plated with tin or silver. Plain copper tends to corrode very quickly when subject to moisture. Tin-plated copper fares a little better, but silver-plated copper lasts the longest. You get what you pay for, however. Coaxial cable with silver-plated conductors is more expensive than other types of coax the amateur is likely to use.

The physical properties of the cable change over time, due to exposure to sunlight and to any moisture that enters the cable. The most noticeable change is that the outside insulating jacket becomes hard and brittle. Age cracks appear, and eventually moisture enters through these cracks and renders the cable useless. Long before this happens, however, if moisture is allowed to enter the end of the cable at the braid, the chemical reactions that take place cause the center insulator to become brittle and its insulating properties to degrade. When this happens, the cable's loss increases, causing more of your precious transmitter power to end up as heat in the cable instead of being delivered to the antenna and radiated.

If Moisture Is the Enemy, How Can We Fight Back?

The major cause of coaxial cable deterioration is moisture entering the cable, especially at the ends of the cable where connectors are either not required or not suitable for one reason or another. Over the last several years I've been using an idea I developed to weatherproof the ends of the coaxial cables that I use on my wire dipoles for 80, 40 and 10 meters.

The following paragraphs describe a weatherproofing method for small diameter coaxial cable like RG-58 and RG-59. This method is also applicable to larger diameter cables such as RG-8, RG-213 and RG-214.

The Step by Step Instructions

As you can see in the photos, the assembly is rather straightforward. The following items are required for weatherproofing a piece of coaxial cable: the coax (a piece of RG-59 in this example), a length of #16 stranded wire (possibly as large as #10 stranded for larger diameter coax), some hot-melt glue and a piece of heat-shrink tubing large enough to be slipped over the cable. The size of the heat-shrink tubing, after shrinking, should be no larger than the diameter of the coaxial cable.

As **Fig 1** shows, start by removing the outside jacket from the coaxial cable. Remove enough to allow the cable to hang nicely from the center insulator. A good rule of thumb is to remove a piece of the outside jacket at least as long as the insulator. Next, prepare the #16 stranded wire by removing enough insulation from it so the bare wire can be wrapped around the shield at least once. Solder this connection using a medium sized soldering iron. The trick to soldering coax is to do it quickly. Use a rather large-tipped soldering iron that can hold the heat instead of a small tip that cools off too quickly when trying to solder the connection. I use a 45-W iron with a $^3/_8$-inch chisel tip. When compared with a 120-W soldering gun, a 45-W iron may not sound like much, but when you compare the thermal mass of the two tips, the $^3/_8$-inch tip wins every time. Don't move the cable while it's still hot because any movement could cause the softened center insulator to deform and allow the center conductor to migrate inside the insulation. This might allow the center conductor to short to the shield.

After the soldered connection has cooled, trim off the shield that extends from the connection to the end of the cable. This exposes the center insulator with the center conductor inside. Adding the stranded wire to the assembly provides substantially more support for the coax than the shield would provide under the same circumstances. The wire is also easier to work with than the loose strands of the shield. With the shield gone, the wicking action is gone, too. The stranded wire has a certain amount of wicking associated with it, but soldering the wire to the dipole will bond the strands,

eliminating the wicking. Slide a 2-inch-long piece of heat-shrink tubing over the coax, beyond the wire, onto the outside jacket, but don't shrink it yet. See **Fig 2**.

The next operation uses hot-melt glue. For the purposes outlined here, almost any type of hobby or home craft quality hot-melt glue can be used. There are special glues that are made specifically for their RF dielectric properties. The glue used here does not need to be of this type, since it is not used as insulation. The glue remains on the outside of the coax and is used to close off any spaces that might allow moisture to enter. In addition, the temperature at which the glue becomes molten is much lower than would cause damage to the coaxial cable. Liberally coat the intersection of the shield, the wire, and the outside jacket with hot-melt glue. While the glue is still hot, quickly slide the heat-shrink tubing toward the end of the cable, over the glue until the tubing straddles the glue.

Now comes the fun part. I use an old paint-stripper heat gun to shrink the tubing. Before I found the heat gun at a yard sale, I used matches, candles, cigarette lighters, even a propane torch; in short, just about anything that would get hot enough to shrink the tubing. I've found that the heat gun does the best job, however, and is much safer than most of the other heat sources. So use an appropriate heat source, and start shrinking the tubing in the middle, at the glue bump, working outward toward the ends of the tubing. By rolling the coax between your fingers and moving the heat from the center of the tubing to each end in turn, you can get the excess hot-melt glue to flow again and to ooze out of the shrinking tubing, gluing everything together and making a waterproof bundle. As **Fig 3** shows, you end up with the coax coming out

one end of the heat-shrink tubing and the center conductor and shield pigtail coming out the other. Depending on the amount of excess glue you put under the tubing, you may have glue droplets form at the ends of the tubing. You can let the glue droplets remain or remove them.

Install the coax as you would in any other situation by soldering the center conductor to one side of the center insulator of the dipole antenna and the shield pigtail to the other. Now you can stop worrying about moisture damaging your dipole's coax for a long time.

When I first developed this idea, I made two lengths of coax with ends like this. I put one on my 80 meter dipole and hung the other over a tree limb for a life test. After a year, I cut the life test one open to see if any moisture got in. It didn't. The shield inside the coax was as shiny as it was when I put it together, a year earlier. I'm very pleased with the performance of this simple coax weatherproofing scheme and use it on every antenna I install.

Weatherproofing Connectors on Coax

The coax weatherproofing scheme described above is fine for cables that don't need connectors to attach them to an antenna. What do you do when you have to attach a cable to an antenna that has a connector, and wrapping the connection with electrical tape or any one of several modeling-clay-like sealing compounds doesn't provide an adequate solution?

While planning the ground rod installation for my 160 meter vertical antenna, I realized

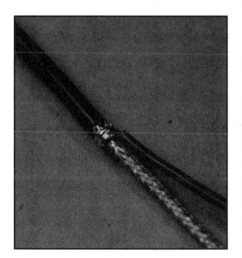

Fig 1—Remove a length of the outside jacket from the end of the coaxial cable. Strip enough insulation off a length of stranded copper wire to allow one or two wraps around the braid, then solder this wire to the braid. Do not move the coax while the wires are hot.

Fig 2—Slide a piece of heat-shrinkable tubing over the end and beyond the joint. Now cover the connection with hot-melt glue.

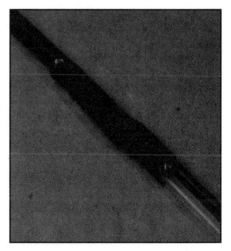

Fig 3—While the hot-melt glue is still warm, slide the heat-shrinkable tubing over the joint and apply heat from a heat gun or other source to shrink the tubing. Roll the coax and joint in your fingers to squeeze some of the glue out of the ends of the tubing. Be careful though, because the hot glue can stick to your skin and cause a painful burn.

I needed to come up with a way to weatherproof the connections between the coax and the antenna. The following idea describes the electrical connections and weatherproofing method I used for the assembly of the ground rod, coax feed line, 300-Ω twin lead (used for the driven element of the folded monopole) and radial wires.

I wanted to have a connection method that would be easy to assemble in the field with little more than a screwdriver. All of the component parts had to be easily constructed using ordinary hand tools and materials readily available from the local hardware store or electronics supply warehouse. I also wanted to be able to temporarily use the coaxial cable that ran from the house to the vertical on other antennas that I might want to install in the woods for testing. This last item could be accommodated by putting a connector on the coax. This also meant that I had to mount a mating connector on or near the vertical antenna ground rod.

The Ground Rod Connection Details

I purchased an 8-foot long, ⁵/₈-inch diameter copper plated ground rod from the local electrical supply warehouse. While I still had it in my workshop I cleaned the top end of the ground rod and wrapped and soldered a 1¹/₄-inch wide copper strap around it. The copper strap is made from a piece of roof flashing, and is long enough to fold back on itself. The soldered connection between the copper strap and the copper ground rod is mechanically rugged and electrically superior to using only a mechanical clamping arrangement. After soldering, I cut to size the copper tab that sticks out from the side of the ground rod, and drilled it to hold an SO-239 UHF connector using four machine screws. Up to this point I had what looked to be a very rugged assembly. The antenna driven element is made using 300-Ω twin lead, so I had to devise some sort of strain relief for it because the wind would be blowing it around, causing considerable strain on the fragile wires.

The Twin-Lead Strain Relief

My junk box provided the answer. I used a 3-inch square piece of ¹/₁₆-inch-thick unclad glass-epoxy circuit board. At one end of the board, I drilled five holes to pass the mounting hardware and threaded body of the SO-239. I made two ¹/₂-inch-long slots, oriented horizontally across the board, and slightly offset from the connector. These were just wide enough to pass the twin lead. The offset allows one conductor of the twin lead to be soldered to the center pin of the connector and the other to be soldered to the connector's mounting flange. The first slot is about an inch above the SO-239 and the second slot is spaced about ³/₄ inch away from the first slot. Aligning the connector

and the slots in this way allows the twin lead to be passed through the board (twice) and soldered to the connector. The insulation on the twin lead supplies all of the required strain relief without using cable ties, clamps, or other mechanical fasteners. I stripped the insulation off the twin lead wires and tinned them with solder. I temporarily mounted the UHF connector to the glass-epoxy board so that the connector's mounting flange was on one side of the board and the threaded body sticks through to the other side. Starting from the flange side of the board, I threaded the twin lead through the slot farthest from the connector, then through the slot in the center of the board until the twin lead wires rested on the connector's center pin and flange, where they were soldered.

Most vertical antennas need radial wires, and this antenna is no exception. If I wanted to stay with the *screwdriver only* assembly scheme, I'd have to find a way to attach them to the assembly at the top of the ground rod. I decided to use the SO-239 connector's mounting hardware for that purpose. I used stainless steel machine screws long enough to pass through the copper mounting strap, glass-epoxy circuit board material and the connector body and still have enough length to hold a few solder lugs. I soldered a ring-terminal lug to one end of each radial wire for connection to the machine screws.

The Last Piece of the Puzzle

The electrical parts for the antenna were ready for installation. Without some sort of cover, however, I'd only have a fair-weather antenna. What I needed was an inexpensive cover with a snap-on lid.

Inexpensive to me means I should start looking in the household recycle bin. I didn't have to search very long. I found a white plastic one-quart whipped-topping container with a snap-on lid. Imagine the plastic container setting up on its edge, with its snap-on lid facing you. This orientation allows the lid to be removed and provide access to the connections. It also allows any moisture that accumulates to drip from the lowest point; the edge of the container. Two holes have to be cut into the container before it can be mounted on the ground rod.

I cut a ³/₄-inch hole about ¹/₄ inch from the lip of the container using an auger bit. This hole passes the ground rod, radial wires, and the twin lead. I brought the twin lead out this hole because I didn't want holes in any location other than on the bottom of the container after it was mounted. The other hole is ¹/₄ inch in diameter and allows access for the coax feed line. I cut it into the container using a sharpened piece of brass tubing. The spacing between the centers of the two holes is equal to the center-to-center spacing of the ground rod and the

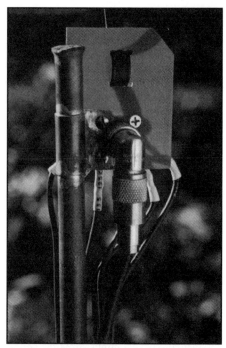

Fig 4—This photo shows the connector side of the vertical antenna assembly. See text for construction details.

Fig 5—This photo shows the back side of the assembly, with the radial wires attached to the mounting screws.

SO-239. To allow installation and removal of the container, I used tin snips to make a cut from the lip of the container to the ³/₄-inch hole and another between the two holes. Since there is only one cut across the lip of the container, the lid holds the container firmly in place on the ground rod. Moisture drains out of the container at the lowest point through the holes and the cut.

The Field Trip

The antenna installation was rather easy even though I ended up using a sledge hammer along with a screwdriver. Being careful that I didn't deform the copper strap with the sledge hammer, I drove the first 6 feet of the rod into the ground. This is not an easy thing to do here in New Hampshire. After all, there is a reason why it is known as *The Granite State*.

I placed the threaded portion of the SO-239 UHF connector next to the copper tab on the ground rod. With my trusty screwdriver, I bolted the copper tab, the unclad glass-epoxy board, the UHF connector, and the ring terminals from the radial wires together to form a single unit. **Figs 4** and **5** show the front and the back of the completed assembly. Notice that the ground radials are bolted directly to the UHF connector flange. This places dissimilar metals against each other. This could present a corrosion problem and should be inspected periodically. I used stainless steel hardware and tinned the copper flange at the mounting holes so the stainless steel screws would be against solder instead of the copper. This assembly order decreases the chance of corrosion and increases its life expectancy. I could have soldered all of the connections for longer life, but that would have meant soldering the connections in the woods.

The plastic bowl was installed by bending the lip of the bowl so I could slide the coax into the 1/4-inch hole and then slide the bowl onto the ground rod. The twin lead comes out of the 3/4-inch hole and I loosely tied it with nylon cord to the ground rod about 6 inches below the bowl. This keeps the bowl from deforming from the strain

Fig 6—Here are the plastic-container mounting details. Notice that the only cuts in the container are at the bottom, where any moisture can easily drain out.

Fig 7—This is the complete weatherproof assembly for the coaxial cable connection at the antenna feed point.

placed on the twin lead as it goes into the air.

I installed a PL-259 UHF connector on the end of the coax and used a UG-646/U UHF right-angle adapter to attach it to the SO-239. **Fig 6** shows the placement of the bowl before the lid has been snapped into place. Cutting the extra hole in the plastic bowl allows me to remove the coax without disturbing the other wires. This provides a piece of coax that runs from the woods into the house, which I can use for temporary antenna testing.

I stretched the radials out on top of the leaves in the woods and since then they have

been covered by additional leaves. I randomly sprayed the bowl with flat black spray paint to decrease its visibility. A bright white color is very easy to see in the woods and I wanted to make it blend in with the surroundings.

This installation, shown in **Fig 7**, has been in use for three years. During two of the winters the feed point has been completely covered with snow with no ill effects—electrical or mechanical. Every once in a while I take the cover off of the plastic bowl and remove the spiders and their nests. It looks like it needs another paint job soon.

A Remote Tunable Center-Loaded Mobile Antenna

By Jack Kuecken, KE2QJ
2 Round Trail Drive
Pittsford, NY 14534

KE2QJ describes a unique and very intriguing mobile antenna.

A typical ham HF mobile antenna uses a center-loading coil to cancel the reactance of the shortened whip and to permit a reasonable approximation of an impedance match. This has been written about at great length by John Belrose, VE2CV[1,2,3] in the context of ham radio and by R. C. Hansen[4] in the commercial venue. Several companies manufacture ham antennas, with names such as the *Texas Bug Catcher* and the *Hustler* antennas.

In my own professional work I have developed military antenna couplers for land, air and maritime-mobile applications. For my own ham radio mobile antennas, I have typically used a simple straight whip and a remotely tunable (or automatic) antenna coupler at the base.[5,6,7]

There are good elements in each approach. A fixed, center-loaded antenna is simple to construct and radiates effectively. On the other hand, it is not well suited to all-weather operation and rough terrain operation, where the antenna may strike all manners of obstacles, such as branches. The center-loading coil also requires considerably more inductance than a base-matched antenna. The center-loader has relatively larger radiating currents below the coil but this effect may be offset by the higher losses in the much larger inductive reactance required to tune the antenna to resonance.

Mobile Antenna Requirements

A military or commercial land-mobile HF antenna coupler/antenna system should be capable of:

Tuning the entire HF band 2 to 30 MHz without leaving the vehicle

Capable of operation in virtually any weather

Rugged enough to withstand at least some contact with branches and fixed obstacles

It should be capable of operation at highway speeds without guying or special preparation.

Be quickly and easily stowed for low-clearance situations

Operable in the stowed position.

I was able to accomplish all of these goals with the base-tuned antenna coupler arrangement. The stainless-steel whip operated well at highway speeds supported only by the base spring. The occasional clipping of leaves or branches near the top didn't bother it a bit. The coupler case mounted on the rear bumper was easy to make weatherproof and the overall operation proved quite satisfactory.

With the purchase of a new automobile, a few difficulties reared their heads. With most of the new cars taking on the shape of a jellybean (that is, very rounded), the old coupler box, which rested very well above the rear bumper, no longer wanted to fit. If I hid the box in the trunk I would have had the capacitance of a length of wire operating at very high impedance to run out to the antenna base. This would have had incurred more loss and RF would be a nuisance inside the car. It was time to consider something new. Maybe I could come up with a center-loaded arrangement that met all of the six criteria above.

Evolution—the Mechanical Considerations

To begin with, it seemed that a big center-loading coil was one of the most vulnerable points for damage from collisions. I figured that if the coil were kept below the roof line on the car, the chance of a direct collision would be minimized. I contemplated locating the coil spring on top of the coil. That way, when the antenna is stowed, the peak height where the spring bent over would be about 7 feet above the pavement.

The antenna is mounted on a plate that picks up one of the bolts on the "5-mph bumper" compression member. See **Fig 1**. The plate is made of $^3/_{16}$-inch aluminum alloy and the back end of the plate is supported by two standoff posts attached to the unibody. In the event that the bumper is bashed the posts will shear off and the compression member will not be defeated. The plate is 12 inches off the pavement.

In the initial experimental design (Model #1) I wound the coil on a 12-inch length of 2-inch ID PVC pressure water pipe. The pipe itself served as a structural member, carrying the loads from the spring and whip

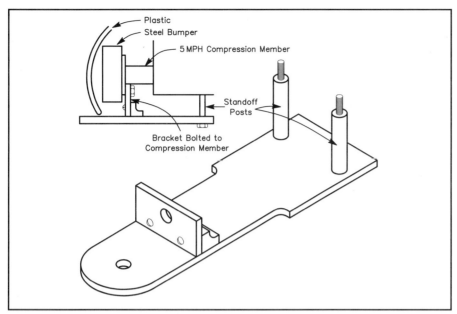

Fig 1—Drawing of the antenna base mounting plate. It is attached to the steel frame of the rear bumper, which on modern cars is part of the "5-mph compression member." The standoff posts on this base are designed to shear off in the event of a collision.

on top down to the 1-inch diameter aluminum tubing on the bottom. Maple plugs were turned to join the PVC pipe to the aluminum fittings. These joined the coil to the lower tube and the $^3/_8×24$ thread fitting for the spring. The PVC pipe was first turned down to 2.3-inch OD and a 10-inch length was grooved at 10 turns per inch (tpi). The coil was wound with #16 tinned bus wire, giving a turn spacing of two wire diameters. **Fig 2** shows the mechanics of my experimental coil, with the coil's fairing in the background.

Since the coil was a structural member I couldn't very easily rotate it. Instead a slider was fitted on a slider rod, which was connected electrically to the lower end of the coil. The slider carried a set of spring fingers that moved along the coil, varying the inductance. A windlass mechanism moved the slider. The windlass was operated by bevel gears from the center of the lower end of the coil by a shaft extending up the center of the lower radiator from the box at the base of the antenna. [The whole slider mechanism resembled a dial-cord driven slide-rule

dial mechanism in an old radio.—*Ed*.]

Fig 3 shows the complete assembly on the car with the whip in the stowed position. The coil fairing serves as a weather cover and an air drag reducer for the coil. Note also the insulated strut bracing the bottom end of the antenna. The bottom radiator tubing was clamped to the end of the strut with a hose clamp.

The unit measured 50 inches from the pavement to the top of the coil. The spring was 4 inches high and the whip was 84 inches tall, bringing the top of the whip to 11.5 feet off the pavement. This was low enough for all of the Interstates; on old small roads, however, it was sometimes necessary to stow the antenna.

The coil measured 83.9 µH with the slider all the way at the bottom. The whip and spring plus strays worked out to be 27 pF. The antenna would tune 80, 40, 30, 20 and 15 meters and most of the frequencies in-between. Tuning tended to be a bit jumpy because of the turn-at-a-time action of the slider. Once tuned, however, the coil would stay tuned while driving and transmitting. I worked nets up and down the east coast on 40 meters and from Pittsford in central NY to St Louis with 50 W. I will discuss the drive box in more detail later.

Model #2 Coil and Antenna

From experience gained with the first antenna, I decided to move on to Model #2. For one thing, the coil and fairing on Model #1 were pretty big and the inductor had more inductance than required. I found that the aerodynamic fairing on the antenna was

Fig 2—Photo of experimental coil, with fairing in the background. This coil used a sliding contact moved by a windlass mechanism similar to the "slide-rule dial" found on old radios.

Fig 3—Photo of experimental coil and fairing mounted on author's rear bumper. The fairing is substantial in this design!

strong enough to make it a structural part of the antenna. It is an example of a monocoque or "stressed skin" fairing, resembling an airplane fuselage. This type of fairing should be able to let me use a roller coil, which would make the tuning much less "steppy" since this is infinitely variable.

The roller coil was threaded at 13 tpi, with a total of 54 turns in just over 4 inches. A $^1/_2$-inch allowance at each end for the support spokes gave a total length of 5 inches. The maximum inductance was 72.8 µH. The new coil is less than half the length of the original coil and the faired construction is only 8 inches tall. **Fig 4** shows the new roller-coil design in its aerodynamic fairing.

At each end of the coil I turned down a 1-inch diameter brass shaft to a $^1/_2$-inch diameter section. I drilled two holes at right angles in this $^1/_2$-inch section to take the brazing-rod spokes used to support the coil. The shafts at both ends of the coil run in Babbit bearings. At the lower end of the coil, the bearing is fitted into a brass plate that carries the spring-load mechanism and the shorting rod on which the roller runs.

The airfoil-shaped end plates were sawed out of $^1/_2$-inch-thick rock maple. A second, smaller airfoil-shaped piece was laminated on. The turned fitting at the bottom was hollow to accept the propeller shaft from the bottom. The top fitting carries the top bearing and the $^3/_8 \times 24$ thread for the spring. The airfoil fairing is attached to the maple end plates by #6 × $^1/_2$-inch sheet-metal screws.

The shorting-rod mechanism is a bit novel since it had to fit into the rear "teardrop" of the airfoil. The shorting rod is suspended on a rod at each end that is pushed in toward the coil by a coil spring around the rod. Inward travel is limited by a collar on the rod. At the lower end the guide for the rod is attached to a brass strip that also carries the bottom bearing. At the upper end a dielectric guide insulates the shorting rod. **Fig 5** shows the antenna mounted on the car in the stowed position.

The Fairing

The fairing is obviously a significant part of the construction. A proper aerodynamic shape can reduce the air drag by factors as large as 4:1. The shape used is one developed by NACA (National Advisory Committee for Aeronautics, a predecessor to NASA) for low-speed airplane struts. I have not had the opportunity to test this in a wind tunnel myself.

I made the fairing out of Plexiglas sold at building supply stores for glazing storm doors. It is about 1/16-inch thick with a protective paper or film on each side. I cut out a rectangular piece using a 24 tpi blade and stripped the protective coating off. I then made a mold from plywood, shown in **Fig 6**. Next, I put the Plexiglas on the top of the mold in our oven and set the temperature to 300°F. As the oven temperature rose above 200° the Plexiglas began to droop and became very pliable.

When the sheet had drooped into a "U," I removed the entire assembly from the oven and then molded the tail on the mold, wearing heavy work gloves. After cooling, I molded a pair of $^1/_2$-inch strips of Plexiglas to shape and cemented them to the top and bottom edges for reinforcement. The cement I used is available at model and hobby shops and is the type where the pieces are clamped together and the liquid is brushed sparingly on the joint. It wicks in by capillary action and partially dissolves the Plexiglas.

As shown in Fig 6, I used a series of three Plexiglas spacers to support the end plates during assembly and to hold the entire assembly together with the proper spacing. I then slipped the fairing over the coil and drilled holes for the screws, starting at the rounded side of the fairing. I inserted screws alternately on the right and left sides. When the assembly was complete, I put a piece of clear vinyl packing tape to seal the back (pointy) edge, leaving a small gap on the bottom for drainage.

Since it is difficult to make this assembly

Fig 5—Photo of author's car, showing the Model #2 antenna in stowed position. The fairing is much smaller in this design, compared to the one in Fig 3.

Fig 4—Photo of "Model #2" roller-inductor in its streamlined clear plastic fairing. The roller moves on a shorting bar designed to fit in the sharp end of the teardrop-shaped fairing. The rotating coil is turned by a shaft extending through the bottom aluminum support tubing at the left-hand side of the coil in this photograph. Note also the Plexiglas spacers (mounted with L-brackets) used to space things properly before the monocoque plastic fairing is screwed to the wooden end frames.

Fig 6—Photo of the mold used for bending the Plexiglas into the proper shape.

Fig 7—Photo of the inside of the bottom box, showing the leadscrew mech-anism and gearing used to spin the roller inductor. Note the limit switches actuated by the runner block moving along the lead-screw. The neoprene O-ring used to turn the pulley on the 10-turn potentiometer is driven from the leadscrew shaft. The top of the metal box is open, with a top made of a thick plastic insulator strong enough to support the bottom of the antenna.

precise enough to be watertight on top, I fitted an extra piece of Plexiglas to overlap the top and added a $^1/_2$-inch drip strip around the rounded edge.

The Box on the Bottom

The box on the bottom contains the drive mechanism for remotely tuning the whole mechanism. Here I had to make a choice. At the minimum, I needed a motor to turn the coil, with limit switches to protect from overrunning the ends. The tuning servo also requires a multi-turn potentiometer[7] to signal the position of the coil roller for the operator. If I placed the motor and the potentiometer inside the coil housing, I'd have to provide RF choking for at least 5 leads—two for the motor and three for the potentiometer. These choke(s) would shunt the antenna feed point.

Conversely, if I placed the motor, potentiometer and limit switches in the base and operated at RF ground potential, it would only be necessary to isolate the propeller shaft. This was the option I selected for this design. **Fig 7** shows the bottom box with the cover open. The top insulator is a $^1/_4$-inch-thick Lexan plate, to which I screwed a turned fitting for the bottom radiator. The Oldham coupling serves to insulate the propeller shaft and to make up for any misalignment. The motor gear drives the leadscrew gear, and the propeller shaft is coupled to the leadscrew through the Oldham coupling.

The leadscrew also serves as a counting device for the limit switches. As shown in Fig 7, the leadscrew is suspended between two bearing blocks and fitted with a plastic runner block. As the leadscrew turns, the runner travels along it and eventually encounters a limit switch, preventing further travel in that direction. Each switch is shunted with a diode so that a reversal of polarity will let the motor back out of the stop. The leadscrew is a $^1/_4$-inch brass rod threaded at 28 tpi. I chose the plastic bearings and runner for lubricating properties rather than for insulation.

The coil and leadscrew require 54 revolutions to send the roller from one end to the other. However, the position sensing potentiometer is a 10-turn device, so a reduction of

slightly more than 5.4:1 is required for the potentiometer drive. I accomplished this with a small pulley on the leadscrew and a larger one on the potentiometer. The belt is actually a neoprene O ring. When an arrangement like this is well-tensioned and lightly loaded, slippage does not seem to be a problem. The motor is a permanent-magnet dc type equipped with a gearhead that turns about 180 rpm. It takes a little over 20 seconds for the coil to run from one end to the other.

Operation

The roller coil moves smoothly into an SWR minimum, following the potentiometer on the control panel. The minimum SWR is below 1.5:1, with the exception of small areas around 5 and 21 MHz. There seem to be resonances in the car body at these frequencies. As far as the efficiency is concerned, the antenna seems to be comparable to my older antenna system using a full antenna coupler.

References
[1]J. Belrose, "Short Antennas for Mobile Operation," *QST*, Sep 1953, pp 30-35, 108.
[2]J. Belrose, "VLF, LF and MF Antennas," *The Handbook of Antenna Designers*, Rudge, Milne, Oliver and Knight (London: Peter Peregrinus, 1983), pp 627, 630, 633.
[3]J. Belrose, "Short Coil-Loaded HF Mobile Antennas: An Update and Calculated Radiation Patterns," *The ARRL Antenna Compendium Vol 4* (Newington: ARRL, 1995), pp 83-91.
[4]R. Hansen, "Optimum Inductive Loading of Short Whip Antennas," *IEEE Trans. Veh Tech*, VT24, 1975, p 21.
[5]J. Kuecken. "Performance Comparison Between the Use of Coil-Loaded Mobile Whips and Antenna Couplers," *The ARRL Antenna Compendium Vol 4* (Newington: ARRL, 1995), pp 97-102.
[6]J. Kuecken, "A High-Efficiency Mobile Antenna Coupler," *The ARRL Antenna Compendium, Vol 5* (Newington: ARRL, 1996), pp 182-188.
[7]J. Kuecken, "Easy Homebrew Remote Controls," *The ARRL Antenna Compendium Vol 5* (Newington: ARRL, 1996), pp 189-193.

Use Low-Loss "Window" Ladder Line for Your 2-Meter Antenna

By Hal Rosser, W4PMJ
4781 Orchard Hill Drive
Grovetown, GA 30813

Take advantage of the low-loss, low-cost, lightweight characteristics of window-line and twin lead to feed your 2-meter antenna.

Ladder line? What good would it do me to use ladder line? My radio has a 50-Ω output. How would I go about using ladder line, even if I wanted to? Sound familiar? Well I was in the same boat until I heard that ladder line had very low losses, and it costs a lot less than "low-loss" coaxial cable.

[True ladder line is an open-wire feed-line constructed from two parallel conductors held evenly spaced apart using some form of insulating rods or bars. The rods form the "rungs" of the ladder, giving this line its name. The characteristic impedance of such a feed line is determined mainly by the spacing between the wires. Parallel-conductor feed lines are much easier to manufacture using a solid plastic ribbon with the wires formed into the edges. One common form of such a feed line is 300-Ω TV-type twin lead, in which the conductors are spaced about ¹/₂ inch apart. Another type of commercial line uses a similar construction, but with about a 1-inch conductor spacing. Blocks of the plastic ribbon are cut out to form windows in this line, producing a 450-Ω feed line. This type of feed line is often referred to as "window line." **Fig 1** shows examples of these types of feed line.—*Ed.*]

Let me say here at the start I do not profess to be any form of expert on this subject of antennas and transmission lines. I'm only reporting on how I brought together different articles written by experts in the field, and used them to make it work for me. And yes, even a "newbie" can make use of it.

Here are the main reasons to use window line or twin lead:
1. It has very low loss.
2. It has low cost.
3. It is very light in weight. (I use ropes

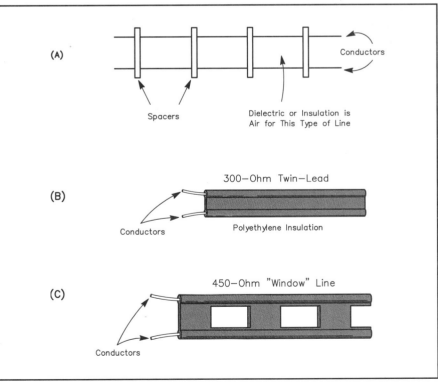

Fig 1—Parallel conductor feed lines. At A, ladder line, with insulating spacers every few inches. At B, common 300-Ω TV twin lead. At C, the construction of 450-Ω window line.

to pull up my antennas—but that's another article.)

On long runs to your antenna, using RG-58 could cost you $1/2$ to $2/3$ of your signal, both on transmit and receive. So if you now have a 100 foot or so run of RG-58, mini-8, or even some brands of RG-8, you would notice a big improvement in reception, and be able to hit that repeater on lower power. You may even hear repeaters you couldn't hear before if you switch to window line. Yes, the magic of radio is in the antennas and transmission lines you use.

Here's a quick and easy way to use 450-Ω window line for that run to your antenna. *The ARRL Handbook* and *The ARRL Antenna Book* are full of very good information. The ideas for this article came from material in those books.

First, I saw an interesting section in *The ARRL Antenna Book*, 18th edition, on page 24-12 in the Transmission Lines chapter: The paragraph labeled "Impedance Transformation with Quarter-Wave Lines," in effect says you can use a $1/4$-λ section of line to transform one impedance to another. WOW! The easy part is that all you need to do is multiply 50 Ω times the other impedance you want to match, then take the square root of the product to see what impedance the $1/4$-λ section needs to be. Hmm, interesting . . . so to match 50 Ω to 450 Ω, I multiply them then hit the square root button. That calculates to be 150 Ω, but I don't have 150-Ω coax.

That brings me to another part of the book—page 24-18. Here it says you can use a combination of lines to make lines of different impedances. (Two 75-Ω coaxial lines in parallel make a 150-Ω balanced line, for instance.) That section also says "balanced in, balanced out." See **Fig 2**.

This leads us to still another article. We need to go from 50-Ω unbalanced coax to 450-Ω balanced line, so somewhere in this conversion we need to get balanced so we won't tip over. Now on page 26-22 of *The ARRL Antenna Book* there's a nice sketch of a 4:1 balun made from a $1/2$-λ section of coax and bent into a U-shape. See **Fig 3**. Now there's the way to get us balanced. But that's a 4:1 balun. If we start with 50-Ω coax (unbalanced), this gadget will get us up to 200 Ω balanced. Here's an opportunity to use 300-Ω TV twin lead if you can live with 1.5:1 SWR. As a matter of fact, I've used this setup with good success. When I told folks I was using TV twin lead, it always incited an interesting conversation. But here we are going for the 450-Ω match. Well, we have all the tools, so with a calculator and an inventory of available coaxial cable, we can start.

In our sample inventory we have some 50-Ω coax, some 75-Ω coax, some 300-Ω twin lead, and of course some 450-Ω window line. A few calculations will let us know what we can do.

Remember, to calculate the impedance of the $1/4$-λ section we needed, we multiplied the two end impedances and took the square root. To do this in reverse (starting with the $1/4$-λ section of known impedance and finding out what we can match), we just need to square 50 or 75 or 300 or 450 or some combination of $1/4$-λ section impedance we can make, then divide that by 50 to find out what impedance we can match.

Starting with 75-Ω cable, we have $75^2 = 5625$. Now divide 5625 by 50 = 112.5. That means if we use a 75-Ω $1/4$-λ section on the end of our 50-Ω coax, we can step up the

impedance to 112.5 Ω.

Now, with 112.5 in your calculator, multiply by 4 (the 4:1 balun stuff) and there we have it—450 Ω exactly. What did we just do? A $1/4$-λ section of 75-Ω cable steps up to 112.5 Ω, then we can use that $1/2$-λ U-bent section to make a 4:1 balun. Not only are we now at 450 Ω, but we are balanced. That is, voltage to ground from both conductors is equal. **Fig 4** shows the construction.

What about loss? Practically none, assuming you solder all the connections well. When I changed from coax to window line, I realized an improvement of 2 S-units!

What else can we do? Make a matching section to match 50-Ω coax to 75-Ω coax by using two pieces each of 50-Ω and 75-Ω coax in a series-parallel combination, then make that 4:1 balun so we can use 300-Ω twin lead, or without the balun so you can use that piece of free 75-Ω Hardline someone gave you. See **Fig 5**.

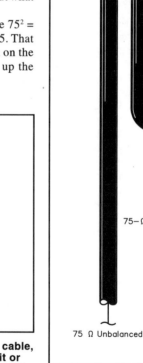

Fig 3—A balun that provides an impedance step-up ratio of 4:1. The electrical length of the U-shaped section of line is $1/2 \lambda$.

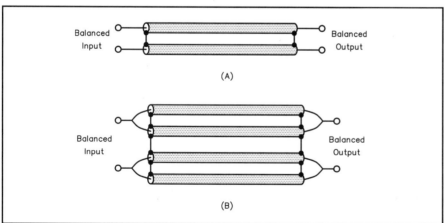

Fig 2—Shielded balanced transmission lines use standard small-size coaxial cable, such as RG-58 or RG-59. These balanced lines may be routed inside a conduit or near large metal objects without adverse effects. The characteristic impedance of the two parallel cables shown at A is equal to the sum of the coaxial cable characteristic impedances. The characteristic impedance of the four-cable line shown at B is equal to half the sum of the characteristic impedances of the cables used for either side of the parallel transmission line.

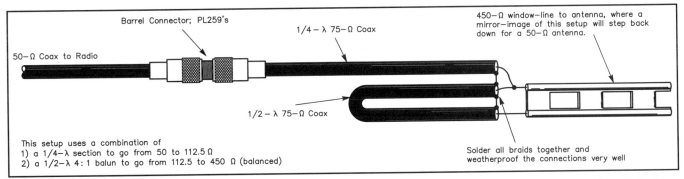

Fig 4—This diagram shows the ¼-λ matching section and ½-λ balun used to match 50-Ω coax to 450-Ω window line. A similar arrangement can be used at the antenna to transform back to a 50-Ω antenna impedance. If the antenna input impedance is not 50 Ω, then a different matching arrangement should be used. It is important to note that the lengths for the matching section and balun are frequency dependent. If you set it up for 2 meters, it will not work for 6 meters, 70 cm or other bands. Different lengths will be required for each band.

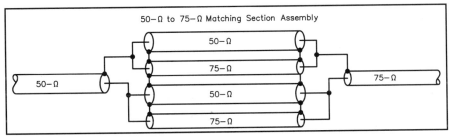

Fig 5—This setup will closely match 50-Ω coax to 75-Ω coax. A 4:1 ½-λ balun can be used to match closely to 300-Ω twin lead. Solder all braids of the matching section together and waterproof them well. No other connection is made to the coaxial braids of the matching section. By the way, the matching section measurements are made from the end of the braid on one end to the end of the braid on the other end.

I've found that the published velocity factors of most coax and twin lead are pretty accurate. To calculate the physical lengths of those ¼-λ and ½-λ sections, calculate the free-space wavelength and divide that result by 4 or 2, then multiply by the velocity factor. For a ¼-λ section of 75-Ω coax, we first find the free-space wavelength and divide by 4. Here is an example for 2 meters:

$$\text{Length (in feet)} = \frac{984}{\text{f (in MHz)}}$$

$$= \frac{984}{146} = 6.74 \text{ feet}$$

Then divide this length by 4 to find a quarter wavelength:

$$\frac{6.74 \text{ feet}}{4} = 1.685 \text{ feet} \times \frac{12 \text{ inches}}{\text{foot}}$$

$$= 20.22 \text{ inches}$$

Now multiply by the Velocity Factor (VF), which is always less than 1—mine was 0.75—so the ¼-λ section for 146 MHz of my coax is:

0.75×20.22 inches $= 15.16$ inches

Feed Line Lengths At 146 MHz for Various Velocity Factors

Velocity Factor	¼-λ (Inches)	½-λ (Inches)
0.60	12.13	24.26
0.65	13.14	26.29
0.66	13.35	26.69
0.68	13.75	27.50
0.70	14.15	28.31
0.72	14.56	29.12
0.74	14.96	29.93
0.76	15.37	30.73
0.78	15.77	31.54
0.80	16.18	32.35
0.85	17.19	34.37
0.90	18.20	36.40

The length of the ½-λ line for the 4:1 balun is just twice the length of the ¼-λ section, so it will be 30.32 inches.

Here is a hint for measuring the lengths. Many measuring tapes have the inches marked off in 16ths of an inch. So in this example you want the closest number of 16ths to make 0.16 inches. Just multiply 0.16 times 16 = 2.56. So on your measuring tape, to find 15.16 inches, go past the 15-inch point 3 marks (16ths).

They say "Give a man a fish and you feed him for a day, but teach him to fish . . . etc." I hope I've not only shown a few of you a beginning lesson of how to fish, but maybe even raised an interest in experimenting with transmission lines while you do the same with antennas.

By the way, I hope most have figured out that you can convert impedances the same way up at the antenna to get the impedance back to 50 Ω (if that's the impedance of your antenna), and if you decide to use an antenna of something other than 50 Ω, you have a tool to use for matching.

Construction Hints for Your Impedance Conversion Assemblies

You can mount the assembly inside a piece of 1¼ inch PVC pipe. Drill a hole to pass the barrel connector through on one end, and terminate the 450-Ω end with some stainless-steel screws. Be sure to provide strain relief for your connections. A piece of Plexiglas with slots for the window line can be screwed on to one end of the PVC pipe for strain relief, or make the pipe long enough so you can tape it or tie-wrap the line to a section of the pipe.

FilTuners–a New (Old) Approach to Antenna Matching

By John Stanley, K4ERO
ARRL Technical Advisor
8495 Hwy 157
Rising Fawn, GA 30738

To be thoroughly modern in antenna tuners, you sometimes have to look back to see how and why the "old timers" did things the way they did them.

Today most hams have some kind of a black box between their transceiver and their antenna. We may call it a *Transmatch*, a *Matchbox* or an *Antenna Tuner*. This black box may be a big help putting a signal on the air—or it may be a pretty good dummy load. Recently the possibility of modern tuners being very lossy in some situations has received some attention.[1,2]

It is ironic that the transmitters of the 1950s did not need a black box, because the networks designed into the transmitter made it possible to match a wide variety of impedances. Thus the *No-Tune* rigs that we use today are in many cases not what they are represented to be. Tuning is still required—it has just been moved outside the transceiver cabinet!

In the process of essentially dividing the transmitter into two parts, we have made it possible that the networks matching our active output devices (transistors) to the antenna are not optimal. Many of the tuners commonly used today are more suitable for use with a Pi-network tube-type transmitter than for a modern broadband transmitter. And our receiving ability may have been compromised as well, without our realizing it.

Some of us can still remember when every (tube) transmitter or transceiver had a Pi network in the output and we could match just about anything by adjusting the PLATE TUNE and LOAD knobs. We can also remember when almost every receiver or transceiver had a knob labeled ANTENNA, or perhaps TRIM or PRESELECTOR. This knob has in effect been moved to the antenna tuner. And it may do rather poorly what the old knob did on the tube rigs.

Admittedly, the typical modern antenna tuner does some of the same things the old Pi network and the antenna trim knob did.

That is, it helps match the output power stage of the transmitter and the input stage of the receiver to the antenna. But many modern tuners fail to do something the old methods did, and that is to *filter* the receiver input and the transmitter output.

Some attention may have been paid to the filtering aspect of modern antenna tuners, but they are tuners first and filters second. By contrast, in the old days we had tuned input circuits on our receivers and tuned output circuits on our transmitters that did every bit as much filtering as matching. The strong filtering of a properly designed Pi network is only partly replaced by the low-pass filters on the outputs of our modern solid-state rigs. And the tuned RF input circuits in our receivers have been replaced by a set of wide band-pass filters. Now that our ham rigs sport general-coverage receivers, even the once fairly narrow, ham-bands-only front-end filters of the early transceivers have been broadened for coverage from 150 kHz to 30 MHz, using a small number of switched filters. Where antenna tuners have been used for additional filtering, usually the goal is some additional harmonic attenuation, not band-pass filtering. This adds more low-pass filtering, which is prob-

ably already adequate, but does nothing in the way of narrow bandpass filtering, which is woefully inadequate.

The result is that for both transmitting and receiving, our modern radios (even including any external matching circuits) are broader than the equipment used in the 1950s. And for this we pay a price. The most obvious price is in the receiver. The ability of modern receivers in terms of dynamic range and the resultant resistance to cross modulation and desensing by *reasonably* strong close-in signals is very good. This is due to sophisticated mixer design and the careful distribution of gain throughout the front end.

For *unreasonably* strong, but not quite so close-in signals, our radios are less capable. Most of us don't realize that by having no narrow filter (less than 1 MHz bandwidth) in the front ends of our receivers, we are opening ourselves up to a host of problems. It is not by accident that modern rigs have up to 30 dB of attenuation (counting the 10 dB removable preamplifier) that can be switched into the front of the receiver. It is evident that this attenuation is often needed to prevent problems from the huge unwanted signals we often find in our front ends.

If you have ever tuned across the international short-wave broadcast bands, you know that there are some really strong signals there. A look at the HF spectrum with a spectrum analyzer shows huge peaks in the international broadcast bands. And some of these bands lie close to our ham bands. In the last few years, the 41-meter broadcast band, (7.3 to 7.6 MHz in the western hemisphere) has filled up with domestic short-wave stations with as much as 500 kW transmitting power, not to mention 20 dB gain antennas. The 16-meter band is very close to our 17-meter band; the 13-meter band is next to our 15-meter band. The 19-meter band is close to our 20-meter band and the 31-meter band is next to our 30-meter band. Thus, there will be cases where a signal 60 to 80 dB over S9 will be within the front-end passband of your modern rig. This is as much as 0.2 V, even if you don't live within the ground wave range of the stations.[3]

This level of undesired signal not only can make reception difficult, even with your attenuator switched in, but it can even produce spurious products from your transmitter. For example, if you are on 7.25 MHz, a strong signal on 7.45 MHz can get into the output stage of your transmitter and produce a strong spur on 7.05 MHz—and this spur will be radiated very efficiently. You are legally responsible for this spur. It may not be strong enough to be heard by sky wave, but your ham neighbor will surely hear it! Of course, he may also be hearing a spur produced in his own receiver by the mixing of your signal and the strong one on 7.450 MHz.

Another transmitter-related problem in modern no-tune rigs is the wide-band phase noise they often produce. This noise often shows up when a number of transmitters are located in close proximity, such as during Field Day. The best solution in all these cases is to use a narrow filter between the rig and the antenna.

In the old days, the design of networks between the transmitter tubes and the antenna (and between the antenna and the receiver tubes) used well-developed approaches that gave fully as much attention to filtering as to matching. That is, the antenna tuner network had to fulfill both functions well to be considered a success. Modern tuner design has not followed this old, tried-and-true example.

I am, therefore, suggesting that we revise our thinking when it comes to that box we connect between our transceiver and antenna. Instead of thinking of it as a matching network with a bit of selectivity, let's think of it as both a filter and a matching network. That way, we can look for an optimal design providing both, just as the old Pi network/receiver preselector did. I have built many such filter/tuner combinations over the years, and I would suggest that the name *FilTuner* seems appropriate. The differences between traditional design goals and the goals for FilTuner design are listed in **Table 1**.

Since it is unlikely in the real world that all design goals will be perfectly met, you should realize that for some applications the FilTuner design goals may not be the most suitable. For example, if all-band operation using a single tuner is an absolute necessity, the FilTuner may not be the best choice. In addition, before the simpler designs for FilTuners can be "sold" to the general ham population, the obsession with a 1.0:1 SWR may have to be overcome. Actually, there are relatively simple ways to make a perfect 1:1 match possible with a FilTuner, but I consider most of them a nuisance and unnecessary. Therefore, designs I will present aim at a good but not a perfect match in every case.

The FilTuner consists of a tuned circuit whose operating Q (also commonly called the *loaded Q*) is chosen to give an optimum trade off between bandpass filtering (high Q) and low loss (low Q). In ordinary tuners the loaded Q is allowed to vary, and thus there is no guarantee either of good filtering or of low loss. On the other hand, in a FilTuner design the loaded Q is controlled and predetermined by the design. The secret to achieving controlled Q is to couple the source (transceiver) into the tuned circuit in a controlled manner. Adjustments must *not* be provided that will allow this relationship to be changed. This is what is essentially accomplished in the pi network used with tube circuits, where a fixed coil was used for each band. Once the loaded Q is selected, typically about 10, and designed into the circuit, it cannot be changed (assuming normal power/loading). A loaded Q of 10 gives a typical loss of a few percent, along with good filtering.

Since modern rigs omit the pi network, the antenna tuner can take over its function. For it to do so, however, a similar design philosophy is called for. This means a constant-Q design.

I will present a few design examples I've built and tested many times, with consistent results. I look forward to others applying the FilTuner (constant-Q) concept and coming up with other, even better designs than these. There is also room for clever mechanical designs using the basic circuits. It is my sincere hope that once the logic of the FilTuner concept is accepted, typical ham ingenuity will step forward to provide a constant improvement in the state of the art.

Example 1

The simplest FilTuner that I have come up with consists of nothing more than a single LC tuned circuit with an input and an output link. See **Fig 1** and see the Appendix for more detailed design information. This type of tuner is something that the average ham could put together from junk box parts in a matter of minutes. Yet the results, both in terms of receive filtering and transmitter matching, should be pleasing to you.

Let's say you are using coax to feed a beam or some other type of coax-fed antennas. If you already have an SWR of under 3 or 4:1, this FilTuner should be sufficient to reduce your SWR to under 1.5:1 so that your solid state rig can put out full power.

If your SWR is more that about 4:1, you should consider fixing or tuning your antenna. Except for very short feed lines or very low frequencies, it is not very wise to operate an antenna system with high SWR

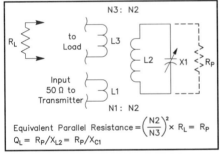

$$\text{Equivalent Parallel Resistance} = \left(\frac{N2}{N3}\right)^2 \times R_L = R_P$$
$$Q_L = R_P/X_{L2} = R_P/X_{C1}$$

Fig 1—A fundamental form of the FilTuner network, using separate input and output link coils for flexibility in matching. Once the turns ratio N3:N2 for the output link is fixed, the loaded Q of the network is determined by the load resistance transformed across the parallel tank circuit. Once the N2:N1 turns ratio is set up properly, the proper SWR measured at the input of the FilTuner will indicate that the tuner's loaded Q is proper.

Table 1
Design Goals for Antenna Tuners

Traditional Design Goals	*FilTuner Design Goals*
1. All-band operation	1. Band-pass filtering
2. 1:1 SWR at input	2. Low losses
3. Matching wide range of loads	3. Match anticipated loads to ≤ 1.5:1 SWR
4. Low-pass filtering	4. Ability to match ≤ 1.5:1
5. Low losses for all matches	5. Multi-band operation
(These are all listed in order of importance)	

on a coaxial feeder. [Since the SWR on a 80-meter dipole typically is close to 6:1 at the edges of this very wide band, you may have to extend K4ERO's definition of what is "high" SWR to about 6:1 for common antennas on the lower HF bands.—*Ed.*]

In addition to the losses, the power rating of the line will be compromised to the point where arcing and heating can occur. This is not to say that you can't make contacts with a 5:1 SWR on a coaxial feed line. But since the whole idea of the *FilTuner* concept is to keep *total* losses to a fraction of a dB, I would be remiss if I did not point out the inadvisability of running a high-loss feed line. This is so, even if your present tuner (perhaps with a few dB of additional loss) can give you a perfect match at the transmitter.

Example 2

This circuit will allow you to match virtually any high-impedance load, including most so-called "long-wire" antennas and a variety of other types, while maintaining a constant loaded Q. See **Fig 2**. It may be advantageous to place this *FilTuner* away from the rig, for example at the base of a tower, or at the window where your long-wire antenna enters the shack. This will avoid radiation in the shack that might occur if the single wire ran around the room before it connected to the antenna tuner.

This *FilTuner* works very well for portable QRP operations, where the simplest antenna is a wire tossed over a nearby tree. Such operations are frequently single band, where this type of tuner is most at home, although several adjacent bands are quite feasible. If by chance the wire will not

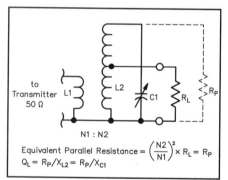

Fig 2—Another common form of the *FilTuner* network. The loaded Q (also known as operating Q) is determined by two things: (1) the transformed equivalent load resistance R_P across the tuning coil, and (2) the reactance of the tuning coil. The load resistance R_L is transformed by the tap on the main tuning coil to the desired R_P across the whole coil. For a design $Q_L = 10$, the maximum value of the load resistance is $10 \times X_L$, where X_L is the reactance of the loading coil at the frequency of operation. The input link is designed to provide the desired resistive load (usually 50 Ω) for the transmitter.

match, a slight change in length will make a match possible.

The resistor R_L represents the load, which can be either purely resistive or a complex impedance that includes reactance as well as resistance. The primary link couples power from the transmitter to the parallel-tuned main tank at a constant ratio—if the load seen by transmitter is correct (that is, 50 Ω for modern transmitters), the loaded Q is proper. The load can be coupled to the tank at any point needed for such a match using the variable tap. The tuning capacitor will be adjusted as needed to cancel out any reactance in the load impedance. (See the Sidebar "Is the Q Really Constant?")

With this circuit, and in fact in all *FilTuner* circuits, the loaded Q is determined by the choice of components and the effective turns ratios between the input (and output) link and the main inductor. Once these values are chosen (and they are purposely *not* made variable), nothing that you do to find a match will upset the optimum loaded Q. Note that the load in Fig 2 is shown connecting to a given turn on the tank. The appropriate connection will be determined as part of the matching process. I often use an alligator clip here, since each and every turn can be selected. If you want to select the tap with a switch, the turns can be selected in a geometric ratio and the SWR can usually be reduced to an acceptable value. Typically a 5 or 6-position switch will be adequate, but more positions could be used to give a finer selection and thus a lower achievable SWR.

Example 3

The circuit shown in **Fig 3** shows a *FilTuner* for balanced, open-wire feeders. This circuit should be very familiar to many hams, since it has been around for a long time. However, the *FilTuner* philosophy requires several modifications. Old timers will remember that an adjustable input coupling, either in the form of a swinging link or a series variable capacitor was usually used in this type of antenna tuner. This has been removed from the *FilTuner*. In order to maintain a constant loaded Q, the coupling between source and tank *must not* be allowed to change.

This means that the matching must all be done between the tank and the load. This is accomplished by adjusting the two taps, in a symmetrical fashion to retain balance. Again, the tuning capacitor compensates for any reactive part in the load impedance. Like the single-ended version in Example 2, this circuit is best at matching high-impedance loads, which are most typical for balanced lines.

There are only a finite number of turns available, especially on the higher-frequency bands, where only a small total number of turns may be needed for the coil. Thus

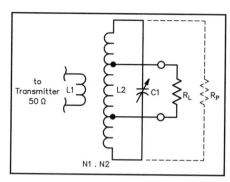

Fig 3—A FilTuner designed for balanced transmission lines. The taps at the secondary are adjusted symmetrically to provide the desired parallel resistance R_P across the total reactance of the tuning coil. Again, the system is designed so that the loaded Q is kept constant (by changing the output taps), with a fixed link coil at the input so that the resistive load for the transmitter is 50 Ω.

the ability to achieve a 1.5:1 or lower SWR may be compromised. This may be improved by adding a pair of variable inductors or capacitors in series with the *output* leads without affecting the operating Q value. If some compromise in the *FilTuner* philosophy is acceptable, a very slight variation in the input coupling may be allowed, just to provide a fine tune control on SWR. In actual practice, I have never found this necessary. It will certainly not be needed on the lower bands, where many turns in the coil provide ample fine steps in the matching.

Example 4

The *FilTuner* shown in **Fig 4** is an example of what can be done where extra filtering is needed, such as during a Field Day operation or when operating from other "hostile" environments with lots of RF around. This double-tuned circuit provides much better skirt selectivity. There is provision for adjustable coupling between the

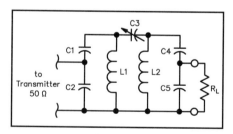

Fig 4—A more complicated FilTuner network designed to provide sharper band-pass characteristics to provide sharper selectivity, particularly for receiving. The variable coupling capacitor C3 at the top of each tank circuit is adjusted as needed for overcoupled (wider bandwidth) or undercoupled (narrower bandwidth) performance.

Is the Q Really Constant?

The key to a constant loaded Q is that the source see the most lossy element in a consistent manner. In the circuit in Fig 2, the load resistance is transformed by the square of the effective turns ratio between the two closely coupled coils into the resistance seen by the transmitter at the input of the network. Note that the effective turns ratio is only equal to the physical turns ratio when the coupling coefficient is perfect—that is, 1.0. In a practical circuit, the coupling coefficient will be less than 1.0; usually it is less than 0.2. What this means in practice is that you vary the number of turns in the link to achieve the turns ratio you would like to have. In the case of a tap on the output side of the antenna tuner, the tap is chosen by trial and error so that the SWR at the input of the tuner is what you want.

For an effective turns ratio of 10:1 and a 5000-Ω resistance in parallel with the parallel-resonant circuit, the input resistance will be $5000/10^2 = 50\ \Omega$. If the coil has an inductive reactance of 500 Ω, the loaded Q will be $5000/500 = 10$, the design value.

A 5000-Ω load would be connected directly across the entire coil, but if the load were only 500 Ω, it would be connected at a tap effectively 33% from the bottom of the coil. This would again transform to 5000 Ω across the entire coil and the loaded Q would be the same. For every value of resistance less than 5000 Ω, there is (at least in theory) a tap that would provide the proper transformation. In every case the match would be correct, and the Q would remain at the value chosen.

If a complex load is connected, the analysis is a bit more complicated. To see what happens, we convert the load to its parallel equivalent. For example, a load of $500 - j\,100\ \Omega$ in series converts to an equivalent parallel load of a 520 Ω resistor and a capacitive reactance of $-2600\ \Omega$ at the same frequency. We pick a tap on the coil such that the 520 Ω resistance is transformed to 5000 Ω across the

whole coil. The perfect-coupling turns ratio needed is $\sqrt{5000/520} = 3.10{:}1$ and this transforms the capacitive reactance across the coil to $-2600\ \Omega \times 3.10^2 = -25000\ \Omega$. The effect of the load's reactance (after transformation by the effective turns ratio) is to put a small capacitance across the coil and we must retune the main tuning capacitor to reestablish resonance. Clearly, the Q is the same as before when the load was purely resistive.

If the transformed parallel reactance is inductive, some additional capacity will have to be added to compensate for it. In this case the determination of Q is somewhat more subtle. The losses in the main coil will not change, since after resonance is reestablished the power, voltage and current it will be unchanged. There will be additional current in the capacitor, due to its increased value, but the voltage across it will be unchanged. Thus the losses in the capacitor will increase so far as they are related to currents, but not as related to dielectric losses. Thus, the losses in the tuner will be only slightly more, since the inherent Q of a typical capacitor is far greater than a typical inductor. Assuming that the tuning capacitor is set to the center of its range for resistive loads, the extra loss cannot be more that four times the normal loss, which should limit it to a small fraction of a dB for any reasonable type of capacitor.

Thus we can see that the FilTuner provides essentially constant Q, with none of the undesirable effects of variable-Q circuits, which can exhibit either drastically increased losses where the loaded Q is too high or a sharp loss of filtering where the loaded Q is too low. The bottom line is that the constant relationship between the source and the main tuning coil of the tuner forces all matches to be done such that the coil losses are constant. Once the input coupling is done correctly, it is not possible to tune up with the wrong loaded Q value!

two tuned circuits, allowing for a real-time tradeoff between bandwidth and insertion loss. The coupling capacitor can be varied to allow anything from a considerably under-coupled situation to a slightly over-coupled setting.

This flexibility allows you to exclude unwanted signals, while still allowing signals through on the desired frequency. This circuit will match about a 3 or 4:1 SWR, which would typically be the range that might be encountered on a coaxial-fed antenna. The circuit shown is a simplified version of a three-band FilTuner that I operate from the site of HCJB in Ecuador. It covers 160, 80 and 40 meters, with band switching.[3]

In spite of the very strong filtering action, the loss in this FilTuner is typically under 1 dB. This slight loss of transmit power is insignificant compared to the benefits on both receive and transmit of using the circuit. The benefits on transmit, by the way, also include

not having my rig shut down due to incoming RF signals that are interpreted as a high SWR!

One caution: a good FilTuner will require tweaking for relatively small frequency excursions. There is simply no way to avoid this since the whole idea is to provide a narrow front-end filter for your rig. Broadband tuners and wide bandpass filters are wonderfully convenient provided you can hear what you want through what you don't want to hear. Antenna tuners that you *don't* have to be touched up after a major QSY are probably "broad as a barn door."

Those of you who are using small transmitting loops have learned to accept the aggravation of having to retune after a 30 kHz QSY. You folks may also have noticed how well the loops receive. The main reason is that they are very narrow. Adding a narrow FilTuner to a small loop is unnecessary since you already have one. Instead, if you live where you can do this, try a

FilTuner with a full-sized antenna and see what a narrow filter *plus* an efficient antenna will do for your reception.

References
[1] R. Lindquist, N1RL, Ed. "*QST* Compares: Four High-Power Antenna Tuners," *QST* Mar 1997, p 73. Also see the computer program *TL*, for more examples of how tuners can cause loss. *TL* is available for the 1999 Edition of *The ARRL Handbook* at the ARRL Web site: **http://www.arrl.org/notes**. Also see J. Belrose, "Automatic Antenna Tuners for Wire Antennas," Technical Correspondence, *QST*, Apr 1994, p 84.

[2] S. Ford, WB8IMY, "The SWR Obsession," *QST*, Apr 1994, p 70.

[3] J. Stanley, "Front End Overload, A Worst Case Example," *The ARRL Antenna Compendium, Vol 3*, p 214.

[4] *The ARRL Radio Designer* Reference manual, on the use of voltage probe technique.

[5] L. Aurick, W1SE, "Do I Need a Linear Amplifier," *QST*, Apr 1994, p 73.

Appendix: Tips on Designing FilTuners

The ARRL Radio Designer software (*ARD*) is a very useful tool for designing and optimizing circuits, especially for the more complex forms of FilTuners (such as that in Example 4 in the text).[4] I usually allow between 0.2 to 1 dB of loss in the tuner as a design goal, depending on the particular situation.

One advantage of the FilTuner approach over other types of tuners is that with a FilTuner the insertion loss is part of the design. In normal usage, the loss will be close to the design value. This avoids the problem found in some other types of tuners where loss can be nearly nil on some antenna/frequency combinations, but can shoot up to 10 dB or more in other cases. When that happens, you may be happy with the 1:1 SWR and not even realize that you are putting 90% of your power into what amounts to a desktop dummy load and only 10% into the antenna. You may end up attributing your difficulties making QSOs to poor band conditions!

You might end up buying a linear amplifier when what you really need is a better antenna tuner. A linear is sometimes needed is certain types of operation, but I think you should buy one only after improving your signal with simple and cheap methods.[5]

The FilTuner concept means taking a design for a bandpass filter and optimizing it for loss, bandwidth and tuning range. So far, I have not attempted to cover more than three bands with a single FilTuner and often design for a single band. This is because the loaded Q—and therefore the tradeoff between narrowband response and loss—will change if you simply tune the capacitor(s) and nothing else. The more complex the FilTuner, the more it will need optimization for each band. Band switching is one answer, but one must remember that the parts of the circuit that are supposedly switched out are really still there and may be coupling signals from input to output. You may not have explicitly modeled such strays in your modeling software and unless you enter every stray capacity, inductance and loss resistance, no computer program can model the response properly. And every component in a tuner has strays.

Quick Design for a Simple, Practical FilTuner

It's easy to get bogged down modeling things on a computer and never actually building anything useful. Some call this *design paralysis!* So here's a simple procedure on how to go about making a practical FilTuner using the schematic in Fig 1. First, select a variable capacitor with a reasonable spacing. A split-stator broadcast-band tuning capacitor will be fine for the lower bands. A 50 pF capacitor will work for the higher bands (21-29 MHz) or a split stator with 100 pF per section can be used. Use about double that for 20 or 30 meters. If a single-section capacitor is used, you will need to float it on insulators and use an insulated knob or a nonconductive shaft. Don't forget that RF can travel through the setscrew on the knob and reach your unsuspecting fingers. I speak here with the voice of experience!

Select or wind a coil about 1 inch in diameter, with enough turns to resonate with the above capacitor at about the center of its tuning range. Count the turns on the coil. Tightly wind about 10% that many turns on each end of the coil using insulated wire. Make the turns on one end as close to the end as possible and on the other end, move the turns away just a little bit. They can be held in place with tape for tests but later you can fasten them with glue or tie them in place with string (even dental floss). Connect the input and output links to a pair of coax connectors.

Now set up your tuner as a receiving FilTuner and tune for maximum signals. Then go to transmit into a dummy load and tune for best SWR into the tuner and its load. Try reversing the input and output coax connectors for best SWR if you want. That's all there is to it! If you think you are losing too much power in the FilTuner, use a few more turns on each of the small coupling coils. If the power loss is very small and the filtering action insufficient, use fewer turns at the input link for a higher loaded Q. For 50 Ω into the tuner, with a load of 50 Ω, use the same number of turns on each link coil. If you want to transform to a different load impedance, use a turns ratio between the two links that is the square root of the impedance ratios.

A large toroid can be used for the coil also. In this case, wind the coupling coils at 180° to each other on the periphery of toroid. The idea of using the ends of the main coils for the links is to reduce the direct capacitive coupling from one link to the other, since this would result in a poor rejection floor.

Try different coils and capacitors and turns ratios on the bench until you get what you want. Then mount it all inside a nice metal box, or for lower transmitter power use an open breadboard. Use some Plexiglas shields to help you keep your fingers away from RF. If you make it look nice it will be a thing of pride as well as a useful tool, and it will also give your shack an "old time look" that will impress visitors.

Ultimate Rejection

The more-complicated two-resonator FilTuner shown in Example 4 promises 100 dB rejection to some out-of-band frequencies when modeled on *ARD*. Don't you believe it! The actual device has a rejection floor of just over 30 dB on the higher HF frequencies when tuned on 160 meters. This is good enough for most applications, since at frequencies higher than 160 meters the bandpass filters in your rig are providing good rejection. In a demanding situation, the floor could no doubt be improved with more careful parts layout, elimination of band switching or addition of some simple low-pass networks. The same FilTuner has about 60 dB ultimate rejection both above and below the selected frequency when switched to the 40-meter position.

For example, a top capacitively coupled double-tuned circuit tends to have a worse floor at high frequencies compared with one using inductive coupling. For most applications, however, the close-in filter shape is more critical than the ultimate rejection because close-in is where our present equipment is most lacking.

Handling the Power

A major part of the design will be the selection of components with suitable power ratings. The higher the Q and the narrower the passband of your FilTuner, the higher will be the voltages and currents that the components must withstand. This does not mean, however, that exotic parts are needed, especially at the 100-W level. *ARD* has convenient features for calculating the voltages on complex networks and the currents are easily calculated once the voltages are known.

You may be tempted to make a tuner for receive-only applications, and this can be quite worthwhile. However, parts that are large enough to have high Q and low losses are also big enough to allow at least 100 W of transmitter power to pass. For QRO beyond the 100-W level, one approach is to put the FilTuner between the linear amplifier and the transceiver. In this case, the benefits on receive can be realized, the match between the rig and the linear can be optimized and any broadband transmitter noise will be eliminated. This could be a reasonable compromise approach since the components for a narrow FilTuner rated at 1.5 kW could be rather formidable. In addition, if your amplifier uses tubes, it already has a normal Pi or Pi-

L output network and may not need additional filtering on transmit.

A simple approach to empirical design is that if your capacitors arc you need more spacing. Similarly, if your coils get hot you need bigger wire! Permanent damage is not usually found in either case. However, if you try to bridge your variable caps with low-voltage dipped mica capacitors, for example, you might damage one permanently (the mica, that is).

One approach with marginal components is to lower the loaded Q by heavier loading and by settling for less filtering, less loss and less voltage. This, however, will not work as well as a more robust design. And remember that any high-Q circuit will step up the voltage enough to give you RF burns, even with 100 W, so don't touch the coil or the capacitor while transmitting. All final designs should include a full enclosure. When doing experimental work be very careful where you put your fingers.

How Low is a Low SWR?

The circuits in Examples 2 and 3, may not always achieve a 1:1 match, depending on the flexibility you build into them in terms of the tap positions. However, it is always good to remember that the difference between 1.5:1 and 1.0:1 will never be heard on either end of the QSO. In addition, anything below 1.2:1 is a fiction anyway, unless you are using a laboratory grade directional coupler. Otherwise you are just matching the small imperfections of your antenna to the imperfections of your directional coupler!

Therefore, I do not consider it a disadvantage that some implementations of the FilTuner will not be able to reduce the SWR seen by the rig right down to an exact 1.0:1 SWR. This philosophy is reflected in my reluctance to use either a swinging link or a series capacitor in series with the input link. Either system allows adjustment of your SWR *meter* down to 1.0:1, but at the expense of allowing the Q to stray from the optimum value.

Some Parting Thoughts

Detailed parts lists are not included here since this is not intended to be a construction article but rather an attempt to get hams thinking about antenna tuners in a different way. I'd like to get us trying different methods for matching our rigs to our transmission lines, hopefully using stuff you have on hand.

If you want to get into the really nitty-gritty design aspects of link-coupled tuner design, I suggest you read the remarkable material on antenna tuner design by L. B. Cebik, W4RNL, on his web page (**http://web.utk.edu/~cebik/link.htm**) describing "Link-Coupled Antenna Tuners." Note that W4RNL describes all variations of the basic link-coupled type of tuner, whereas I've been emphasizing ones that have an essentially constant Q.

Balanced Transmission Lines in Current Amateur Practice

By Wes Stewart, N7WS
9550 W Rudasill Road
Tucson, AZ 85743

Introduction

The increased number of HF ham bands, along with the decreased size of the average ham's backyard, has made multiband operation of random-length wire dipoles an attractive option. This has brought about renewed interest in the use of balanced parallel-wire transmission lines, commonly called *ladder line*, to feed these antennas.[1] There is historical precedence for the use of these antennas; however, there are differences between earlier practice and today's methods. Judging by on-the-air conversations and Internet group discussions, "conventional wisdom" seems to be that ladder line has such low loss that it can be used in almost any situation without suffering any significant additional loss. Operating on the principle that if it sounds too good to be true it probably is, I decided to take a closer look at the subject.

This paper presents some of the results of my investigation. In it, I will attempt to correct some of the myths that surround the use of balanced transmission lines by contemporary radio amateurs. I will also present some data, both calculated and measured, on the losses associated with 450-Ω ladder lines as they are used today. I will discuss mainly the transmission line itself. It cannot be overemphasized, however, that other components necessary to use ladder line, namely the antenna tuner and the balun, are equally important parts of the antenna system.

"Old Time" Practice

Balanced two-wire transmission lines are not new—they were common in early ham stations. These early lines were truly *open-wire lines* and were usually constructed of relatively large wires separated by widely spaced insulators. Wire spacing was on the order of 2 to 6 inches. A well-heeled ham used Steatite spacers; everybody else used

wooden dowels waterproofed with paraffin or something similar. The lines were typically under tension and dressed carefully away from other objects.

The lines directly fed the antenna, which may or may not have been resonant. Because the antenna impedance almost never matched the transmission line impedance, the lines were resonanated as "tuned feeders" and often operated with very high standing wave ratios (SWR). At the station end, the line was connected to the transmitter by link coupling to the final stage. Tune-up consisted of adjusting the output coupling and plate tuning to maximize the antenna current using an RF ammeter[2] or a light bulb for an output indicator. No baluns, antenna tuning units or SWR meters were to be found in these early shacks.

Later the advantages of non-resonant (or "flat") lines were recognized. Antennas themselves were made resonant and were designed to match the transmission line. A procedure for graphically determining SWR and matching the line to the antenna was described in *QST* as early as 1942.[3]

The line construction, care in installation and the inherently balanced systems all contributed to high efficiency in these early applications.

Contemporary Practice Versus Old Time Practice

Speaking generally, there are significant differences between modern usage of bal-

anced lines and earlier practice. First, and the focus of the majority of this paper, is the line itself. As stated previously, early amateurs constructed their open-wire lines using a minimum of spacers, so the dielectric between the wires was predominately air. Wire size might be #12 AWG or larger. This combination made for an extremely low-loss line.

While this kind of line is still used today, we usually see lines made with a ribbon of polyethylene dielectric separating the wires. TV-type 300-Ω *twin-lead* is sometimes used, but most hams who use open-wire line nowadays use 450-Ω ladder line.

This line is basically the same as the TV-type line, except for some holes (*windows*) punched in the dielectric and somewhat wider spacing between the wires. There is much more dielectric between the wires and the wire sizes are considerably smaller than in older open-wire lines. These factors combine to increase the losses over a true open-wire line.

The second difference between old and new practice is in the antenna tuners used. Yesterday's tuners, when used, were typically constructed using large, air-wound or ceramic-supported inductors and air or vacuum dielectric variable capacitors. Usually, the tuner was an inherently balanced tuned circuit with link or balanced tap coupling. The enclosure, if there was one, was large and the inductors were spaced well away from the box to maintain their high Q.

Today's tuners, with rare exceptions,[4] are unbalanced devices. They are likely to have either roller or tapped toroidal inductors and smaller variable capacitors, often with switched fixed values in parallel. Because of their smaller sizes, these components tend to have lower unloaded Qs than their larger counterparts. These lower values of Q can be a source of significant loss in the tuner. Roller inductors can be particularly troublesome in this regard.

The third difference is in the use of baluns in today's systems. Baluns have been well described in the amateur literature[5] and their function will not be discussed in detail here. Baluns operated in severely mismatched systems can be a significant contributor to overall system loss, however.

Why Ladder Line?

The usual rationale for using ladder line is the fact that its attenuation is lower than commonly available coaxial cable. Secondary advantages are its lower cost and weight compared to coaxial cable. Unfortunately, one popular myth is that the line attenuation is insignificant and isn't even a consideration in an antenna system.

While a line with low matched loss is always desirable, it is particularly so when operating at the elevated SWRs encountered with off-resonant or harmonic antennas. To see why this is true, and to debunk the myth, we will examine the sources of line attenuation and its effects.

Line Attenuation—The Matched Case

When a transmission line is terminated with load impedance that matches the line impedance, the line is said to be *matched*. When the line is matched, all of the power reaching the load is absorbed; there are no reflections on the line; the SWR is 1:1 and line attenuation is at its minimum value.

Attenuation in this context describes the ratio of power applied to the input end of a line to the power at the load end. Attenuation is usually expressed either in decibels or in nepers where:

$$\text{Attenuation} = 10 \log\left(\frac{P_{in}}{P_{out}}\right)(dB) \quad \text{(Eq 1A)}$$

$$\text{Attenuation} = \frac{1}{2}\ln\left(\frac{P_{in}}{P_{out}}\right)(\text{nepers})$$
$$\text{(Eq 1B)}$$

There are two primary sources of loss in a transmission line: 1) loss due to the finite conductivity of the conductors and 2) loss in the dielectric that separates the conductors. In the case of unshielded balanced lines, there can also be loss due to radiation[6] or coupling into other structures. This third loss is difficult to quantify, as it will be highly dependent on installation. However, with proper installation and operation at HF to VHF, it should be negligible.

Descriptions of conductor and dielectric losses can be found elsewhere,[7] so they will not be discussed in detail here except to note that conductor loss depends both on the metal from which the conductor is made and the frequency, because of the frequency-dependent skin depth effect.

In a two-wire (copper) transmission line with a well-developed skin effect, the matched loss is given by:

$$A = 4.34\left(\frac{0.2\sqrt{F}}{\frac{d}{Z_0}}\right) + 2.78\,F\sqrt{\varepsilon_r}\,Fp \quad \text{(Eq 2)}$$

$$(dB/100\,ft)$$

Where d is the conductor diameter in inches, F is the frequency in MHz, ε_r is the effective dielectric constant, Fp is the power factor of the dielectric and Z_0 is the line impedance. The first term in Eq 2 describes the conductor loss, while the second term describes the dielectric loss.

There is another misconception that is common in the amateur community—the idea that the dielectric is a major source of loss. For polyethylene, the most commonly used transmission line dielectric, the power factor is 0.0002 and the dielectric constant is 2.26 throughout the HF and VHF range.[8] Using these values in Eq 2 demonstrates that the dielectric loss *per se* is negligible. For constant line impedance and constant wire spacing, an increase in the effective dielectric constant requires that the conductor diameter must be decreased. This can be seen in the following equation for the impedance of a two-wire transmission line:

$$Z_0 = \frac{120}{\sqrt{\varepsilon_r}}\cosh^{-1}\frac{D}{d} \quad \text{(Eq 3)}$$

where D is the center-to-center spacing between wires in the same units as d. The decreased wire diameter and attendant increased skin-effect loss is the cause of the increased line attenuation.

Line Attenuation—The Mismatched Case

For a linear source, maximum power is transferred to a load when the load impedance is the complex conjugate of the source impedance. When a conjugate match does not exist, there is a *mismatch loss*. Mismatch loss describes the ratio by which the power transferred from the source falls short of what would be delivered if the source and load were conjugately matched.

It is entirely possible to have a situation where a matched (properly terminated) transmission line presents a mismatched load to the source. For example, a 100-Ω line terminated in 100 Ω could be the load for a source with 50-Ω output impedance. In this case, the generator will not deliver all of the available power into the line, although the line will be operating with a 1:1 SWR and line attenuation will be minimal. Introduction of a lossless conjugate matching network between the source and line can correct this situation and restore full power transfer into the line. [In the old days, the operator would adjust the plate output tank until the loading was correct, no matter whether the impedance at the end of the transmission line was 50 Ω or not!—*Ed.*]

When the load impedance, Z_l, does not match the line impedance, a portion of the power delivered to the load is reflected back to the source. One of two things can happen to this reflected power. It is either dissipated by the source or it is re-reflected back into the line. The first case is typical in laboratory signal generators, where either a lossy pad or an isolator dissipates the reflected power.

The second case is typical of our transmitting situation, where the load does not match the line and the resulting line input impedance does not match the load impedance for which the transmitter was designed. Here either the transmitter tank circuit or antenna tuner can be used to create a conjugate mismatch that causes the re-reflection. Walter Maxwell in his book, *Reflections,*[9] offers an excellent description of conjugate matching.

In this second situation, absent any voltage breakdown, the line attenuation is increased because of increased circulating current in the line due to the SWR. It is important to note that increased current flows through all parts of the feed system on the antenna side of the match point, including the tuner and any balun. The loss in the tuner can be evaluated separately.[10] The effect of balun loss is less easy to analyze. As an approximation, the loss can be treated as an increase in the line loss. Remember—a 1 dB loss in the balun can be just as detrimental as a 1 dB loss in the transmission line.

To determine system loss, it is imperative that accurate values for line impedance, line loss and load impedance be known. If you require precise electrical lengths of line for matching transformers or stubs, you must know the velocity factor or phase constant as well. Because published data are not readily available for typical ladder line, you must either calculate or actually measure the line's electrical parameters.

It is tempting to use the previous equations to calculate these parameters. Unfortunately, for the polyethylene-insulated types ε_r is not known, so Z_0 cannot be determined. If you trust the published Z_0 (I don't) and you need to cut a line to some particular electrical length, you can "back into" ε_r by measuring the physical properties of the line and rearranging Eq 3.

The Measurements

Without trustworthy calculated data, we are usually left with making electrical measurements. Skilled amateurs, with rather simple instruments, are sometimes capable of making astonishingly accurate measurements. More often, however, the operator is less aware of measuring equipment limitations and/or is misled by the instrument maker's advertising. Simplified antenna analyzers, especially those with digital readouts, can lull the user into unjustified confidence in the accuracy of his/her measurements.

A major problem with simple equipment is the fact that the better the thing is that we're trying to measure, the harder it is to get accurate data! This is especially true when trying to measure small attenuation values. Popular methods of determining line loss such as shorting the far end and measuring SWR and calculating the loss are particularly suspect—especially when the line loss (and hence the return loss) is very low.

Because I'm blessed with access to high quality instrumentation, I decided to obtain some samples of readily available ladder line and gather data on them under laboratory conditions. I procured samples of four different types of 450-Ω ladder line from *The WireMan*.[11] These were WireMan types 551, 552, 553 and 554. The samples are all window lines, with two conductors held approximately 0.8 inches apart by a polyethylene ribbon with rectangular holes punched in it. The primary difference between types is in the conductor size and wire type.

The equipment I used for the measurements was a Hewlett-Packard vector automatic network analyzer (VANA). This instrument is capable of making error-corrected one- or two-port measurements over the frequency range of 45 MHz to 26.5 GHz. (See Appendix A.) For the measurements presented here, the frequency range was limited to 50 to 150 MHz, and the two-port (through) configuration was used.

One problem in the use of ladder line with such a network analyzer is that you must perform unbalanced-to-balanced transformations. For these measurements, the problem is more complicated. Both measurement ports on the analyzer are coaxial and the line is balanced, so a balun is required at each end. I used baluns consisting of four 1-inch-long Type 47 ferrite sleeves slipped over the lengths of RG-142 coax I used to extend the measurement ports of the VANA.

The effects of the coax and balun interconnects were removed by performing an open-short-load-through calibration at the balanced output terminals of the baluns.

During the through calibration, the balun outputs were connected center-to-center and shield-to-shield, respectively. As a test of balance, after performing the through calibration, the balun connections were reversed. The change in the indicated insertion loss was less than 0.1 dB.

Because of space limitations in the laboratory, each sample was cut to a length of exactly 12 feet. During each measurement, the sample was stretched horizontally without any twists and at least 2 feet of clearance from any objects. A 201-point stepped-frequency sweep was made on each sample and the data were stored on magnetic disk for later analysis.

A second measurement was then made after wetting the line with water to simulate what might happen in a typical outdoor application. Initially, the water tended to bead up and run off, making it difficult to make meaningful measurements. I believe that a typical line used outdoors would quickly lose its water-shedding ability as it degrades from sunlight and as it accumulates dust and other pollutants. To simulate this, I added a wetting agent to the water to create a water film on the surface. The results of this are probably worst-case and not something that would necessarily be encountered in a typical installation.

Fig 1 shows the results of the measurement of a typical sample. At first glance, Fig 1 may be disconcerting, so a few words of explanation are in order. The network analyzer test ports are well-matched 50-Ω terminations and the analyzer measures the *s-parameters* of the device under test.[12] Consequently, when the impedance of the line under test is other than 50 Ω, there is a mismatch loss, as was discussed earlier. This situation is different from the way that we normally operate our lines in antenna feeder applications, but it is the easiest way to characterize the line over a broad frequency range.

The figure displays "s_{21}" (the forward transmission coefficient) expressed in decibels. Both the so-called gain of the line, which of course is negative, and the effects of mismatch are expressed in the data. As presented, there isn't too much to be gleaned from Fig 1 except that the velocity factor, and hence the effective dielectric constant, can be determined by computing the electrical length of the line and comparing it to the known physical length. The frequency where the line is a half wavelength long is easily determined by determining the frequency spacing between the ripple peaks. You can determine other line parameters by mathematical means. However, I used another powerful tool, *ARRL Radio Designer* software,[13] to determine the line impedance, velocity factor and insertion loss per unit length.

ARD features a circuit optimizer that can be used to adjust various circuit parameters to closely approximate given target values. A circuit block using the *ARD* two-wire transmission line model was created with the physical line length fixed at 144 inches and the line impedance, dielectric constant and loss coefficients set as optimizable values. The measured s-parameter data sets were used as circuit modeling goals and the optimizer was turned loose to make the model's response look like the measured data. In addition to the polyethylene-insulated lines, an air-insulated line made from #16 AWG enameled wire, spaced 0.75

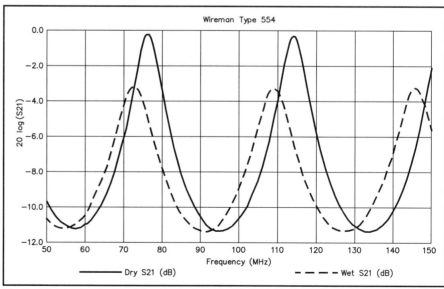

Fig 1—Plot of the forward transmission coefficient (s_{21}) of 12 feet of WireMan type 554 line in a 50-Ω system. Shown is the response with the line both wet and dry. Note the large change when the line is wet.

inches apart, was also measured as a "sanity check." The measured parameters of this open-wire line correlate well to the values calculated using Eq 2 and Eq 3. The results of the computations are shown in **Table 1**.

A couple of things are immediately obvious from the table. First, the impedance values are considerably below the nominal 450-Ω value commonly ascribed to ladder line. Second, notice the large increase in attenuation that the lines suffer when they are wet. While these data are less accurate

than when the lines are dry, they certainly point out a troubling trend.

The reason for lower accuracy of the wet measurements is that it was difficult to maintain uniform wetness during the several seconds it took to make the measurements. Nevertheless, this lack of control is not much different from the actual conditions a line might encounter in the field. Anecdotal evidence from users of ladder line confirms the changes in tuning required when lines are subjected to rain

and snow and the data show why this is the case.

The loss at other frequencies can be estimated using Eq 4. This equation neglects the effects of dielectric loss but is accurate enough for any practical calculations.

$$dB(f) = \sqrt{\frac{f}{50}}\, dB(50) \qquad \text{(Eq 4)}$$

where dB(f) = the loss per 100 feet at frequency, f, and dB(50) = the loss data from Table 1. The impedance of a transmission line is usually complex; that is, it has a reactive as well as a resistive component. Line reactance can be found from:

$$X_0 = -j\frac{\alpha}{\beta}R_0 \qquad \text{(Eq 5)}$$

where α = line loss in nepers per unit length, R_0 is the resistive part of the line impedance and the phase constant, β, in radians per unit length is found from:

$$\beta = 2\pi\frac{\sqrt{\varepsilon_r}}{\lambda} \qquad \text{(Eq 6)}$$

Table 1
Line Parameters at 50 MHz

		Line Dry			Line Wet			
Type	R_0	e_{eff}	V_p	dB/100/ft	R_0	e_{eff}	V_p	dB/100/ft
551	405	1.23	90.2%	0.33	387	1.34	86.4%	5.8
552	379	1.19	91.7%	0.38	362	1.28	88.4%	5.2
553	397	1.23	90.2%	0.38	381	1.33	86.8%	4.8
554	359	1.16	92.8%	0.41	343	1.27	88.7%	6.1
#16 at .75"	399	1.01	99.5%	0.30	NC	NC	NC	NC

NC = No Change

Appendix A
Error Correction and Network Analysis

Any electrical measure has a fundamental accuracy limitation, as there are always some errors involved. A simple example would be the use of a low-impedance voltmeter to measure a high-impedance source. The meter loads the source, so the reading is lower than the true open-circuit voltage. There is a measurement error caused by the less than ideal instrument. However, if both the meter and the source impedance are known, the open-circuit value can be calculated. The results can then be "corrected" for the measurement system error.

In network analysis there are several sources of measurement errors. A detailed discussion of these is well beyond the scope of this paper but simply put, by measuring one or more standard or known devices, the systematic errors can be identified. Once identified, modern microprocessor-controlled analyzers can remove these measurement errors and correct the answers.

Typically, the known devices include, but are not limited to, an open circuit, a short circuit, a precision termination (load) and for two-port (insertion) measurements, a through connection of the measurement ports. Each of these standards has an expected response, which when not realized, indicates the presence of systematic error. For instance, a perfect short-circuit should create a 100% reflection with a 180° phase shift. If anything other than this is measured, it indicates an error that can be accounted for in the measurement of the device under test. To characterize all of the systematic errors, both the *magnitude* and *phase* response of the standards must be measured, hence the terminology vector network analyzer.

Once this process, commonly called *calibration,* is complete, modern network analyzers are capable of amazing accuracy. Amplitude resolutions of hundredths of a dB and phase resolution of fractions of a degree are readily achieved. For reflection measurements, equivalent directivities of 50 dB or better are possible.

If, as in the case of the measurements presented in this paper, it is necessary to add some cable between the instrument test port(s) and the device under test, the calibration is performed at the far end of the intervening cable, thereby removing its effects. The major accuracy limitation in the measurements is the result of uncertainties in the reference standards. For instance, the open circuit has some residual capacitance that is normally taken into account with precision calibration standards but was not done for these measurements. Nevertheless, it is believed that the data presented herein are sufficiently accurate for amateur applications.

Once Through—With Numbers

A popular multiband wire antenna is the so-called *G5RV*.[14] This antenna is rarely used as was intended by its originator Louis Varney, but for some reason the 102-foot length has taken on mystical properties, so I used it for an example. I assumed that the wire was at a height of 40 feet and was fed with 100 feet of WireMan type 554 line.

Using *EZNEC*[15] I calculated the feed-point impedance of the wire at the middle of each of the HF ham bands. Then using a *Mathcad*[16] worksheet and equations from a paper by Macalpine,[17] I calculated the SWR at both ends of the line, the input impedance at the station end of the line and the total line attenuation. (See file N7WS.MCD.) For those without *Mathcad,* later versions of Dean Straw's *TL* program[18] will compute the line reactance in addition to a number of other useful parameters, including the total mismatched line loss.

Space doesn't allow the presentation of data for each band but the worst case occurs on the 160-meter band, where the antenna is considerably shorter than one half wavelength long. The 1.9 MHz matched-line attenuation of 0.08 dB/100 feet increases greater than 10 dB due to the mismatch. When the wet attenuation value is used, the total line attenuation is greater than 22 dB!

Another item of note is the effect that changing the length of the line has on the total line attenuation. One might expect that a change in line length from say 100 feet to 50 feet would reduce the loss by one half (3 dB), but in the previous example, it actually decreases 5 dB. In other words, it pays to do the calculations.

Closing Thoughts

Contrary to conventional wisdom, ladder line is not a panacea for every transmission line problem. As stated in the introduction, when planning an antenna installation, it is important to look at the transmission line and antenna as an *antenna system*. This paper has attempted to provide useful data on one piece of the system—the electrical characteristics of solid-dielectric ladder line. I hope that the material presented serves to inspire the reader to take a critical look at all of the factors included in a system analysis—performance, cost, ease of installation and maintenance—before committing to a particular antenna design.

Acknowledgments

I am indebted to my friends John Munger, N7WB, and Chris Wassenberg, MSEE, for their review of the manuscript and their thoughtful suggestions for improvements. Any errors or omissions, however, remain the responsibility of the author.

Notes

[1] S. Ford, "The Lure of the Ladder Line," *QST*, Dec 1993, pp 70-71.

[2] J. Stanley, "Revisiting the RF Ammeter," *QST*, Feb 1994, pp 35-37.

[3] T. A. Gadwa, "Standing Waves on Transmission Lines." *QST*, Dec 1942, pp 17-21.

[4] R. Measures, "A *Balanced* Balanced Antenna Tuner," *QST*, Feb 1990, pp 28-32.

[5] R. Lewellen, "Baluns, What They Do and How They Do It," *The ARRL Antenna Compendium, Vol 1* (Newington: ARRL, 1985), pp 157-164.

[6] E. J. Sterba and C. B. Feldman, "Transmission Lines for Short Wave Radio Systems," *Proc IRE*, Vol 20, pp 1163-1202, Jul 1932.

[7] *Handbook of Coaxial Microwave Measurements*, GenRad, Inc, West Concord, MA, 1968, reprinted by Gilbert Engineering, Phoenix, AZ.

[8] *Reference Data for Radio Engineers*, Fourth Edition (New York: ITT, 1956), p 66.

[9] M. Walter Maxwell, *Reflections—Transmission Lines and Antennas*, Chapter 4 (Newington: ARRL, 1990). Out of print.

[10] F. Witt, "How to Evaluate Your Antenna Tuner," *Part 1, QST*, Apr 1995, pp 30-34; *Part 2, QST*, May 1995, pp 33-37.

[11] The WireMan, Inc, 261 Pittman Road, Landrum, SC 29356.

[12] *S-Parameter Techniques for Faster, More Accurate Network Design*, Application Note 95-1, Hewlett-Packard, 1501 Page Mill Rd, Palo Alto, CA 94304, Apr 1972. Available on the H-P Web site: **http://www.tmo.hp.com**.

[13] *ARRL Radio Designer*, Version 1.5, available from the ARRL, 225 Main Street, Newington, CT 06111-1494

[14] L. Varney, "An Effective Multi-band Aerial of Simple Construction," *RSGB Bulletin*, Jul 1958.

[15] *EZNEC*, available from Roy Lewallen, PO Box 6658, Beaverton, OR 97007.

[16] *Mathcad*, available from MathSoft, Inc. 2525 N Elston Avenue, Chicago, IL 60647.

[17] W. W. Macalpine, "Computation of Impedance and Efficiency of Transmission Line with High Standing-Wave Ratio," *Trans AIEE*, Vol 72, Jul 1953, pp 334-339.

[18] R. D. Straw, N6BV, has written several programs to compute transmission-line parameters. The *TL* program is available for free on the ARRL Web site **http://www.arrl.org/notes** in the section for *The ARRL Handbook*. A more advanced version, *TLA*, is available bundled with the 18th Edition of *The ARRL Antenna Book*.

Transmission Line Properties from Manufacturer's Data

By Frank Witt, AI1H
41 Glenwood Road
Andover, MA 01810-6250
fjw@world.std.com; ai1h@arrl.net

How to derive comprehensive information from the limited data provided by cable manufacturers.

Introduction

The information provided by cable manufacturers is, of necessity, limited. Fortunately, for many applications it is sufficient. However, when the specific cable loss is important, or when the transmission line is used as a resonator or a network element, the information provided is only a starting point. Further, when measurements are made at one end of the line and the impedance of the load at the other end of the line and the cable loss are sought, more detailed cable information is required.

Mathcad has proven to be an excellent addition to the arsenal of the technically oriented radio amateur.[1] In this article I will describe a worksheet that I developed for Versions 6.0 and 8.0 of *Mathcad*. This worksheet greatly expands the information about a particular cable. The basic frequency-dependent cable parameters are determined, and from these the electrical behavior of the transmission line at any frequency and for any length is found.

Part of the value of the *Mathcad* worksheet is that it contains a collection of transmission line formulas from a variety of sources. I avoid approximations, since they are not necessary when using a tool with the computational power of *Mathcad*.

Mathcad worksheets *TLMANV6.MCD* and *TLMANV8.MCD* are located on the accompanying CD-ROM. They should not be confused with *TLA.EXE*, the very capable transmission line and antenna tuner program written by Dean Straw, N6BV, and which is bundled with *The ARRL Antenna Book*. *TLA.EXE* provides a useful analysis of an antenna feed system (feed line plus antenna tuner) using practical components.

Companion worksheets *TLMANDATAV6. MCD* and *TLMANDATAV8.MCD* include other sets of manufacturers' and suppliers'

data for a variety of cables. These can be substituted for the data in *TLMANDATAV6. MCD* or *TLMANDATAV8.MCD* using a copy and paste procedure. Data for other cables may be pulled from catalogs and substituted for the worksheet data.

If you do not yet have a copy of *Mathcad* Version 6.0 or later, see the rich-text format (*.RTF) and PDF (*.PDF) files on the CD-ROM for the mathematical details and the accompanying documenting comments. Also, to learn more about *Mathcad* itself, visit the MathSoft Web site at **www. mathsoft.com**.

Because of the inherent accuracy of *Mathcad*, I like to use currently accepted values for the speed of light in free space (299.792458 megameters/sec) and length conversion factor (0.3048 meters/foot). Also, where conversion factors may be calculated by *Mathcad*, those values are used. An example of this is conversion from nepers to decibels. A useful fallout from using reliable values is that results using alternative derivations may be compared. Such accuracy is not normally required in practice, and it is inconsistent with the manufacturing variability encountered in real-life cables.

It is important to not lose sight of the forest for the trees in this exercise. *Mathcad* is capable of making very accurate calcula-

tions based on the input data furnished. The input data can be flawed for several reasons, however. The first is the manufacturing tolerances associated with making cable. We will use the catalog information which is only claimed to be "representative" of the actual product. So if you buy some cable of a type analyzed by this *Mathcad* worksheet, do not expect its behavior to exactly match the calculated values. Use the *Mathcad* analysis only as a guide as you use the cable in your specific application.

The second reason you should use the results with caution is that a manufacturer's data could be in error. It takes professional grade laboratory test equipment with current calibration in the hands of competent personnel to provide accurate data. Anyone who has taken meaningful measurements on transmission lines recognizes that there are many pitfalls and subtle causes for inaccuracy. So beware.

In any event, the *Mathcad* worksheet should prove to be a useful tool in helping you to intelligently use transmission lines and as a way of learning more about them. The effort is well worthwhile, since transmission lines play such an important role in amateur radio applications. Also, the self-documenting style of *Mathcad* provides a handy compilation of transmission line formulas.

Available Data

Cable suppliers furnish both electrical and physical information on their products.[2] The kind of data supplied by cable manufacturers is typified by the information supplied by the Belden Company in their product catalog. Much of the data is physical dimensions. However, with few exceptions, we will be concerned with the electrical data. Specifically, we want to know the characteristic impedance, the velocity factor, the capacitance per foot, the maximum voltage and the matched loss at several frequencies. The maximum voltage is important, since we will be able to see if it is exceeded in our applications. I also include in *TLMANDATAV6.MCD* the maximum allowable temperature and diameter of the cable. They are not used in this version of *TLMANV6.MCD*, but will be useful in a future version that will calculate the temperature of the cable for a given power stress. The information for a specific cable is listed in **Table 1**.

Some of the specifications listed above are redundant. It turns out that the product of the characteristic impedance (ohms), the velocity factor and the capacitance per foot (pF/foot) is a constant from cable to cable. The value of the constant is

$$\frac{10^6}{c_{English}} = 1016.703 \frac{\mu \sec}{ft} \quad (Eq\ 1)$$

where $c_{English}$ is the velocity of light in free space in Megafeet/sec

So it is possible to perform a consistency check by calculating that product. I define a term in the worksheet called "consistency" which is derived from the ratio of the product and the constant value or its inverse. The ratio selected is the one less than one and is expressed in percent by multiplying by 100. For the example of Table 1, the consistency is very good—99.97%.

Before proceeding with the determination of the cable properties, the velocity factor is adjusted to achieve 100% consistency of the characteristic impedance, the velocity factor and the capacitance per foot. In the case of Table 1, the velocity factor was changed from 0.66 to 0.660197. In most cases, this step does not have any practical impact, but I have run across some cases where low consistency has caused me to question the validity of the supplier's data.

Derivation of Cable Parameters

Matched Loss

The data provided by the manufacturer is sufficient to derive a very good estimate of the properties of the cable over a very wide frequency range. All that is required is a transmission-line model that provides a

Table 1
Belden 8259—RG-58A/U Type Manufacturer's Data

Frequency (MHz)	Matched Loss (dB)
1	0.44
10	1.4
50	3.3
100	4.9
200	7.3
400	11.5
700	17.0
900	20.0
1000	21.5

Solid polyethylene insulation
Characteristic Impedance = 50 Ω
Velocity Factor = 0.66
Capacitance = 30.8 pF/foot
Maximum Voltage = 1400 V RMS
Maximum Temperature = 75°C
Diameter = 0.193 inch

good match to the furnished data. We start with the matched-loss data. It can be broken into two components, the loss due to the conductors and the loss due to the insulation.

Fortunately, the loss due to the conductors follows a predictable behavior, increasing in proportion to the square root of the frequency because of "skin effect." The loss due to the insulation, which is usually negligible at lower frequencies, is not as predictable. A reasonable assumption is that it increases in proportion to frequency raised to some power. We can find the exponent in this relationship, g, from the loss data.

The equations for the frequency dependence of matched loss are thus:

$$A_{0TOT}(f) = A_{0COND}(f) + A_{0INS}(f) \quad (Eq\ 2)$$

$$A_{0COND}(f) = A_{0COND}(F_{REF}) \sqrt{\frac{f}{F_{REF}}} \quad (Eq\ 3)$$

$$A_{0INS}(f) = A_{0INS}(F_{REF}) \left(\frac{f}{F_{REF}}\right)^g \quad (Eq\ 4)$$

where F_{REF} is one of the frequencies where data has been provided by the manufacturer, $A_{0TOT}(f)$ is the total loss in dB/100 feet, $A_{0COND}(f)$ is the loss due to the conductors, and $A_{0INS}(f)$ is the loss due to the insulation.

The *Mathcad* worksheet forces the total matched loss to exactly agree with the loss figures provided at two frequencies. I manually adjust the insulation exponent, g, to minimize the RMS error for the entire set of loss data. The net result is shown in **Table 2**. The third and next-to-last data points were chosen to be exact matches. Two different data points could have been selected. For the data points selected for an exact match, g = 1.1 yields the best RMS error of 0.032 dB.

The significance of the above procedure is that we have separated the two loss-producing elements of the transmission line. Further, it has been done in a way that these elements may be evaluated at any frequency, not only the specific frequencies for which data were supplied by the manufacturer. See **Fig 1** for a plot of the matched loss from 1 MHz to 1 GHz.

Since the loss due to the non-ideal conductors dominates at low frequencies, and the loss due to the insulation becomes more important at higher frequencies, it is interesting to calculate at what frequency the two loss contributions are equal. I call this frequency the *loss crossover frequency*, F_X. For the Belden 8259 cable the worksheet calculates F_X to be 2277 MHz.

At F_X and only at F_X the characteristic impedance is real. Below F_X the imaginary part of Z_0 is negative, and above F_X it is positive. The value of the characteristic impedance at F_X is the same as the characteristic impedance supplied by the manufacturer.

Propagation Constant

We want to know the *propagation constant*, γ, of the transmission line. The value

Table 2
Belden 8259—RG-58A/U Type Manufacturer Versus *Mathcad* data

Frequency (MHz)	Belden Matched Loss (dB)	Mathcad Matched Loss (dB)	Error (dB)
1	0.44	0.43	−0.01
10	1.4	1.39	−0.01
50	3.3	3.3	0.00
100	4.9	4.89	−0.01
200	7.3	7.39	+0.09
400	11.5	11.46	−0.04
700	17.0	16.74	−0.26
900	20.0	20.0	0.00
1000	21.5	21.58	+0.08

g = 1.1
RMS error = 0.032 dB

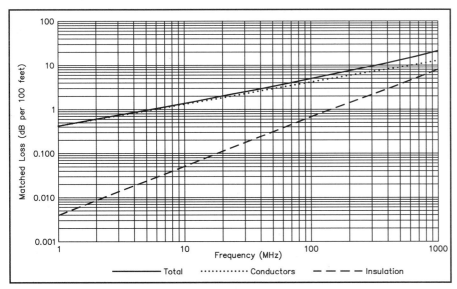

Fig 1—Matched loss versus frequency for Belden 8259 cable.

$\gamma = \alpha + j\beta$ is a complex number that describes the propagation properties of the line. The real part, α, the *attenuation constant*, is a measure of the dissipative loss of energy along the line. Its units are nepers per foot. The imaginary part, β, the *phase constant*, describes how the phase of voltage or current change along the line. Its units are radians per foot.

$$\alpha(f) = \frac{\ln(10)}{2000} A_{0TOT}(f) \qquad \text{(Eq 5)}$$

$$\beta(f) = \frac{2\pi f}{c_{English} \times VF} \qquad \text{(Eq 6)}$$

where f is the frequency in MHz, and VF is the velocity factor.

Complex Characteristic Impedance

In order to make detailed transmission line calculations, we need the complex characteristic impedance as a function of frequency. We use the classical transmission line model which contains series inductance and resistance per unit length and shunt capacitance and conductance per unit length. For convenience the unit length is 1 foot. In general, all of these elements vary with frequency. Over the 1 MHz to 1 GHz frequency range we can assume that the inductance and capacitance per unit length are independent of frequency.[3] One of these parameters, the capacitance per foot, C in pF/ft, is usually supplied by the manufacturer. The inductance per foot, L in µH/ft, may be calculated from the other provided parameters as follows:

$$L = \frac{C Z_{0LC}^2}{10^6} \qquad \text{(Eq 7)}$$

where Z_{0LC} = real part of the characteristic impedance in ohms—the resistive value

supplied in typical data sheets. Here, I use the term Z_{0LC} to denote the value of the characteristic impedance provided by the manufacturer. As noted above, the characteristic impedance is complex at all but one frequency, F_Y.

The resistance per foot, R, is due entirely to the cable's conductors and may be assumed to vary in proportion to $\sqrt{\text{frequency}}$ because of skin effect. The conductance per foot, G, is due to the insulation and varies nearly in proportion to the same power g discussed above. The formulas for R and G in Ω and siemens, respectively, are:

$$R(f) = \frac{\ln(10) R_0(f) A_{0COND}(f)}{1000} \qquad \text{(Eq 8)}$$

$$G(f) = \frac{\ln(10) R_0(f) A_{0INS}(f)}{1000 |Z_0(f)|^2} \qquad \text{(Eq 9)}$$

where $R_0(f)$ is the real part of the complex characteristic impedance, $Z_0(f)$.

The complex characteristic impedance is given by:

$$Z_0(f) = \sqrt{\frac{R(f) + j2\pi f L(f)}{G(f) + j2\pi f C(f) \times 10^{-6}}} \qquad \text{(Eq 10)}$$

Examination of Eqs 8 and 9 reveals that Z_0 must be known before R and G can be calculated. Also, from Eq 10, Z_0 depends on knowledge of R and G. Further, R_0 is frequency dependent. This dilemma is readily handled by the *Mathcad* worksheet by using an iterative process.

First, Eqs 8 and 9 are applied by using the "real" characteristic impedance supplied by the manufacturer as estimates for R_0 and $|Z_0|$. Then an estimate of Z_0 is calculated using Eq 10. Then those values of Z_0 and R_0 are used in Eqs 8 and 9. Z_0 is recalculated. The new value of Z_0 is used to calculate R and G, and Z_0 is recalculated again. This process provides a very good formula for the frequency-dependent complex characteristic impedance.

Properties for Any Length of Cable at Any Frequency

Now we are armed with everything we need to make detailed calculations of a given cable segment at any frequency in the 1 MHz to 1 GHz range. To demonstrate this capability, we will look at the properties of a 50-foot length of Belden 8259 cable at 28.8 MHz. See Table 3 for a summary of the results from the *Mathcad* worksheet.

Transmission Line Calculations for Any Termination, Frequency, Length and Input Power

All of the properties determined thus far are independent of the load impedance.

Table 3
Belden 8259—RG-58A/U Type
Properties for 50 feet at 28.8 MHz

Electrical length	798.34°	
Wavelengths	2.218 λ	
Interesting	Half Wavelength	11.27 feet
Lengths	Quarter Wavelength	5.64 feet
at 28.8 MHz	Eighth Wavelength	2.82 feet
Interesting	Half Wavelength	6.494 MHz
Frequencies	Quarter Wavelength	3.247 MHz
for 50 feet	Eighth Wavelength	1.623 MHz
Characteristic Impedance	50.002 − j 0.436 Ω	
Attenuation Constant	2.809×10⁻³ nepers/foot	
Phase Constant	0.279 radians/foot	
Resistance/foot	0.2619 Ω	
Inductance/foot	0.077 µH	
Conductance/foot	7.611×10⁻⁶ siemens	
Capacitance/foot	30.8 pF	
Matched Loss	1.22 dB	

Table 4

Belden 8259—RG-58A/U Type
100 Feet at 14 MHz with 1500 W Applied

Load Impedance = 50 − j 500 Ω

Matched Loss	1.66 dB
Total Loss	13.15 dB
$\lvert \rho \rvert$ at Load	0.978
SWR at Load	90.37
$\lvert \rho \rvert$ at Input	0.667
SWR at Input	5.01
Input Impedance	12.3719 − j 25.6079 Ω
Maximum Voltage Stress	619.4 V RMS
Maximum Voltage Rating	1400 V RMS
Maximum Power Stress	27.7 W per foot

Table 5

Belden 8259—RG58A/U Type
100 Feet at 14 MHz with 1500 W Applied

Input impedance = 12.3719 − j 25.6079 Ω

Matched Loss	1.66 dB
Total Loss	13.15 dB
$\lvert \rho \rvert$ at Load	0.978
SWR at Load	90.37
$\lvert \rho \rvert$ at Input	0.667
SWR at Input	5.01
Load Impedance	50 − j 500 Ω
Maximum Voltage Stress	619.4 V RMS
Maximum Voltage Rating	1400 V RMS
Maximum Power Stress	27.7 W per foot

Since a frequent application involves the influence of various terminations on the loss and SWR of the line, I placed these calculations on separate *Mathcad* pages. One set of pages covers the case when the load impedance is known and the input impedance is to be found. The other set of pages is for the opposite situation.

You must specify the frequency, length, input power and cable's load impedance (or input impedance). This gives us enough data to find the loss, reflection coefficient, SWR and input impedance (or load impedance) for any length cable at any frequency with any load impedance (or input impedance). The frequency, length, input power and load impedance (or output impedance) may be changed in the *Mathcad* worksheet so that other examples may be solved. The worksheet also calculates the maximum voltage and power stress along the cable.

Continuing with our example using Belden 8259 cable, **Tables 4** and **5** show the *Mathcad* calculations for 100 feet of cable at 14 MHz, when the input power is 1500 W. In Table 4 the load impedance is specified as 50 − j 500 Ω. In Table 5 the input impedance used is 12.3719 − j 25.6079 Ω, the result shown in Table 4. Note that four decimal digits were used. This precision for the input impedance specification was required to get the same numerical results for both tables.

Notice that even for this high SWR load

on a low-power cable with 1500 W applied, the voltage limit is not exceeded. On the other hand, the power stress of 27.7 W per foot would probably lead to cable damage through overheating. The source of most of the heating is along the surface of the center conductor of the cable. It would be nice to be able to determine whether this power stress at a given ambient temperature would lead to excessive cable internal temperature. I hope to include this calculation in future versions of the worksheet.

Designing Transmission Line Resonators

A transmission line segment can be used as a resonant circuit.[4] This behavior occurs at frequencies that are multiples of a quarter wavelength. For example, a shorted quarter-wavelength cable behaves like a parallel-resonant circuit and an open-circuited quarter-wavelength cable simulates a series-resonant circuit.

When the resonant frequency is given, the properties of interest are the required length, the Q of the resonator and the reactance (or susceptance) level at resonance. The reactance (or susceptance) level, X (or B), is the reactance (or susceptance) at resonance of the inductor or capacitor of the equivalent lumped element resonant circuit that would have the same properties.

The resonator calculations are made for four cases: All combinations of quarter- and

half-wavelength cables with either a short or an open at the far end. In the worksheet I take advantage of the knowledge of the frequency dependence of Z_0 and γ to find "exact" values for X (or B) and Q. The frequency dependence is required because a derivative with respect to frequency must be taken. The Q of all the resonators are almost the same, however the reactance and susceptance level can be changed by using different length resonators.

Examples of the use of the worksheet for resonator design at 21 MHz are shown in **Tables 6** and **7**, for series and parallel resonators, respectively. The length, impedance magnitude at resonance, reactance (or susceptance) level and resonator Qs are given.

Designing Inductive and Capacitive Reactances from Transmission-Line Segments

A transmission-line segment shorter than a quarter wavelength is a convenient way to realize an inductive or capacitive reactance. The segment is shorted at the far end to yield an inductive reactance and open circuited to yield a capacitive reactance.

When the frequency and desired reactance are given, the properties of interest are the required length, the complex impedance, the equivalent inductance or capacitance and the Q of the equivalent inductor or capacitor. The component Qs realized in this manner are often low, so they are worth knowing. I arranged the worksheet so that both of these cases are calculated.

As an example, 100-Ω inductive and capacitive reactances at 21 MHz are realized using short segments of Belden 8259 cable. See **Table 8**. Notice that the sum of the cable lengths for the inductive reactance and the capacitive reactance equals a quarter wavelength.

Summary

You can see how *Mathcad* can be used not only to make accurate calculations on transmission lines, but that it is also a useful

Table 6

Belden 8259—RG-58A/U Type
Series Resonator at 21 MHz

	Open circuited Quarter-Wave	Short Circuited Half-Wave
Length	7.73 feet	15.461 feet
$\lvert Z_{IN} \rvert$	0.916 Ω	1.832 Ω
X Level	39.26 Ω	78.44 Ω
Q	42.85	42.82

Table 7

Belden 8259—RG-58A/U Type
Parallel Resonator at 21 MHz

	Open circuited Half-Wave	Capacitive Quarter-Wave
Length	15.461 feet	7.73 feet
$\lvert Z_{IN} \rvert$	1365 Ω	2729 Ω
B Level	0.03137 siemens	0.0157 siemens
Q	42.82	42.85

Table 8

**Belden 8259—RG-58A/U Type
100 Ω Reactance at 21 MHz**

	Inductive Short-Circuited	Capacitive Open-Circuited
Length	5.45 feet	2.28 feet
Z_L	$4.3 + j\,99.9\ \Omega$	$0.3 - j\,100\ \Omega$
Effective L or C	0.757 μH	75.79 pF
Q	23.4	314.5

learning tool. Starting with the limited data supplied by the cable manufacturer, you can find many useful properties of the line. Extreme applications, such as resonators, where the SWR on the line is very high, are readily handled. These properties are available for any frequency for which the transmission line model is valid. Of course, the value of the calculated results depends on how well the input data represents the cable of interest.

A companion paper uses the same techniques to find the properties of a transmission line when the starting point is short and open circuit measurements of impedance.[5]

Notes and References

[1]W. E. Sabin, "*Mathcad* 6.0: A Tool for the Amateur Experimenter," *QST*, Apr 1996, pp 44-47.

[2]Some suppliers of transmission lines for Amateur Radio applications are:

Belden Wire and Cable Co
PO Box 1980
Richmond, IN 47375
800-BELDEN-1
www.belden.com
(Catalog available on line)

The Wireman, Inc.
261 Pittman Road
Landrum, SC 29356
800-727-WIRE
www.thewireman.com
n8ug@thewireman.com

Radio Works
Box 6159
Portsmouth, VA 23703
800-280-8327
www.radioworks.com
jim@RadioWorks.com

[3]R. A. Chipman, *Theory and Problems of Transmission Lines*, Schaum's Outline Series (New York: McGraw-Hill, 1968), pp 134-135.

[4]Frank Witt, "Broadband Matching with the Transmission Line Resonator," *The ARRL Antenna Compendium, Vol 4* (Newington: ARRL, 1996), pp 30-37.

[5]Frank Witt, "Transmission Line Properties from Measured Data," elsewhere in this volume.

Transmission Line Properties from Measured Data

By Frank Witt, AI1H
41 Glenwood Road
Andover, MA 01810-6250
ai1h@arrl.net; fjw@world.std.com

With very few measurements you can learn an enormous amount about your transmission lines.

Introduction

With two simple measurements at a single frequency, you can calculate the important properties of a transmission line. From these properties, prediction of the behavior of the line for other lengths and frequencies is possible. These calculations are made using *Mathcad* worksheets,[1] which takes advantage of the ease with which *Mathcad* handles complex numbers. I created these worksheets using *Mathcad*, and it may not work with earlier versions. Each worksheet uses techniques that are extensions of some BASIC programs written by Walt Maxwell, W2DU,[2] and it complements some other useful transmission line programs.[3,4]

I will address some interesting issues regarding transmission lines, such as the importance of using complex characteristic impedance and alternative methods for determining cable loss. Some of the references used for the transmission-line calculations are listed at the end under Notes and References.

The *Mathcad* worksheet contains many exact formulas, without any approximations. The literature available to most radio amateurs has often lost sight of the exact formulas. Along with the exact values, I will show some useful approximations, so that you can make comparisons.

The worksheet also shows how closely one can estimate certain cable characteristics with some easy measurements. And along the way, I will demonstrate that the matched loss is *not* the minimum loss of a cable.

Copies of *Mathcad* worksheets are located on the CD-ROM in the back of this book. The workhorse is *TLMEASV6.MCD*. Its input data are measurement results for a 22-foot 3 1/2-inch segment of RG-58C 50-Ω coaxial cable measured at 3.6 MHz. With other input data, the same worksheet may be used for other trans-

mission lines. A PDF and an RTF-format printout of the *Mathcad* worksheet are also on the CD-ROM. The second worksheet, *TLMEASDATAV6.MCD*, provides additional data that can be substituted for the data in *TLMEASV6.MCD* using a copy and paste procedure. (Worksheets for *Mathcad* Version 8 are also on the CD-ROM).

The transmission-line model assumes that the line does not radiate any of the energy it carries. For coaxial cable, this means that the shield is essentially perfect (hence no leakage of radiated energy) and that no current flows on the outside of the shield.[6] For balanced lines, the assumption means that the spacing is very small compared to a wavelength, and the currents in the two wires are equal and opposite at all points along the line.

One application of the worksheet is to calculate the properties of cable from the same batch at other frequencies and for different lengths. Also, you may determine the properties of transmission line resonators and reactances made from the same cable batch. I have also found the worksheet useful for comparing the manufacturer's published data with the cable's calculated properties. If you have an old piece of cable whose quality is in question, you can measure it and then compare with

calculated values to see if its properties have deteriorated.

I do caution you to keep the results reported by the worksheet in perspective. The kind of accuracy achieved on the computer screen is usually not required in real-world, practical applications. Further, manufacturing tolerances for the cable properties are limited, and the accuracy of the equipment used for measuring the input data is another limitation. You should always remember that the results provided by the worksheet are only as good as the accuracy of the measured data and, of course, the validity of the transmission line model.

The axiom "garbage in, garbage out" definitely applies here! The quality of the RF impedance measuring equipment that have been brought to market lately has been rapidly improving. The transmission-line model based on quantities per unit-length, has stood the test of time. If need be, assumptions regarding frequency dependence of the per-unit-length quantities can be refined and modified in the worksheet.

The tutorial and reference value of the *Mathcad* worksheet lies in having in one location a host of transmission-line formulas that came from many sources. The worksheet is self-documenting and shows the formulas used to solve each particular problem.

Physical Constants and Conversion Factors

Because of the inherent accuracy of *Mathcad*, I like to use currently accepted values for the speed of light and conversion factors. Also, where conversion factors may be calculated by *Mathcad*, those values are used. An example of this is conversion from nepers to decibels. **Table 1** shows the values used in the *Mathcad* worksheet. One good thing about using reliable values is that you can easily compare results using alternative derivations.

Input Data

In order to demonstrate the use of the worksheet with real data, Pete Schuch, WB2AUQ, measured a 22-foot $3^1/_2$-inch segment of RG-58C 50-Ω coaxial cable (Wireman 127) at 3.6 MHz. He measured the impedance with the far end both open and short-circuited, using a Hewlett Packard Model 8753B Network Analyzer. He chose a frequency at which the cable is near an odd multiple of $^1/_8$ wavelength. This maximizes the accuracy of the measurement.[7] The results were:

$$Z_{OC} = 0.80 - j\,50.20\ \Omega$$
$$Z_{SC} = 3.53 + j\,51.78\ \Omega$$

You must enter an estimate of the velocity factor in order to resolve an ambiguity arising from the calculation of the phase constant. The estimate for the velocity factor is the published value of 0.66. The choice of this value is not critical for the example at hand because the length of the cable is less than a quarter wavelength. For cables longer than a quarter wavelength a rough estimate is required for the worksheet to resolve the ambiguity.

I assume that the conductance per unit length increases exponentially with frequency. This means that the loss due to the insulation will increase at the same rate. This is analogous to the loss due to the conductors increasing as $\sqrt{\text{frequency}}$ due to the skin effect.

To account for the different rates at which the insulation loss increases, I define the insulation exponent, g. For the cables I have

studied, g is near unity. If g is unknown, unity is a good choice. The insulation exponent may be found by using manufacturer's published data. The insulation exponent chosen is the one which gives the best fit to the matched-loss data over the published frequency range, usually 1 MHz to 1 GHz, but sometimes as high as 4 GHz. See my other article "Transmission Line Properties from Manufacturer's Data" elsewhere in this volume. For the RG-58C cable used in the example, g = 1.0.

Basic Cable Properties at the Test Frequency

In the spreadsheet, a large number of decimal digits are often shown. This is done to demonstrate the degree of equivalence between two quantities. The approach involves deriving the cable parameters that are valid over the entire length of the cable at the measurement frequency. Then, with assumptions of how these parameters vary with frequency, a set of frequency and length-dependent cable parameter functions are derived. Using these functions, you may determine a wide range of cable properties for arbitrary frequencies and lengths.

Characteristic Impedance

Note that the formula for characteristic impedance, Z_0, yields a complex number. The real part of this number is much greater than the imaginary part, so the imaginary part is often assumed to be zero. Except for lossless lines and for a very special case, called the distortionless line case, which occurs at a single frequency, the imaginary part of Z_0 for any line with loss will not be zero. We will see later instances when the full complex value is required in order to get the correct answers.

One way of describing the characteristic impedance is that it is the impedance that yields no standing waves when the line is terminated in it. There would be no reflected voltage or current wave for this case. It is often referred to as a *matched line*. However, as will be demonstrated later, it is not the termination that yields the minimum loss on the line.

Propagation Constant

At the measurement frequency, we want to know the *propagation constant* of the

transmission line, γ. Here, $\gamma = \alpha + j\,\beta$ is a complex number that describes the propagation properties of the line. The real part, α, the *attenuation constant*, is a measure of the dissipative loss of energy along the line. Its units are nepers per unit length. The imaginary part, β, the *phase constant*, describes how the phase of voltage or current change along the line. Its units are radians per unit length.

We can derive the propagation constant from the open and short-circuit impedance data, but there is an ambiguity in the phase constant because of the cyclic nature of the arctangent function. There is no problem if we know the line is less than a quarter wavelength long. By using an estimate of the velocity factor, however, we can find out the nearest number of half wavelengths that make up the cable length and thereby resolve the ambiguity.

Velocity Factor and Effective Dielectric Constant

Earlier, we made an approximation in the input data for the velocity factor. Once β is known, we can calculate the actual velocity factor. One implication of the assumption that the capacitance per unit length is independent of frequency is that the velocity factor is also independent of frequency. This is equivalent to an assumption that the *effective dielectric constant* of the insulation is independent of frequency, which for most practical cables is a fairly good assumption. The effective dielectric constant is also calculated in the worksheet.

Resistance, Inductance, Conductance and Capacitance per Foot

The usual model assumed for a transmission line supports a single mode of propagation and may be thought of as having distributed resistance, inductance, conductance and capacitance per unit length. You may calculate these distributed elements from the complex characteristic impedance and propagation constant. The reactive elements, L and C, are almost independent of frequency, and the contributors to cable loss, R and G, increase with frequency. R is due to ohmic losses in the cable conductors and G accounts for the imperfect insulation.

Frequency Dependence

Characteristic Impedance and Propagation Constant as a Function of Frequency

By taking advantage of knowledge of the way in which the per-unit-length properties vary with frequency, we can derive Z_0 and γ for other frequencies. The capacitance per unit length may be regarded as constant to the extent that the effective dielectric constant of the insulation does not change with fre-

---

Table 1
Values Used in the *Mathcad* Worksheet

Parameter	Value	Source
Speed of light c in Megameters/s	299.792458	*Mathcad*
Feet per meter	0.3048 (exactly)	*Mathcad*
Nepers per dB	ln(10)/20	*Mathcad* calculation

quency. I assume no variation with frequency.

The inductance per unit length varies because skin effect influences the current distribution in the conductors (and hence the magnetic field). However, over the frequency range of interest, 1 MHz to 1 GHz, we can assume that the inductance per unit length is independent of frequency. The resistance per unit length is assumed to be due to skin effect and proportional to $\sqrt{frequency}$. The conductance per unit length is assumed to increase exponentially with frequency, as discussed earlier.

The frequency-dependent characteristic impedance and the propagation constant will be used to find the cable properties at other frequencies and lengths. If the original input data is error-free, the only sources of error are the transmission line model and the per-unit-length frequency dependence assumptions.

If the measured data is in error, the amount of the error can be magnified for frequencies away from the test frequency. For example, if the measurement is made at lower frequencies, where the loss is primarily due to the conductors, the calculated value of G, the conductance per unit length, will be very small, and the error in its calculated value could be large. The impact of the error will be very small at HF, but at VHF and beyond, the error in G and the loss due to the insulation may be large. A more accurate determination of G will come from a test frequency in the VHF region. For this case, since the impact of G is small at HF for common cables, the calculation of cable properties at HF will usually be valid.

Matched Loss versus Frequency

Matched loss occurs when the cable is terminated in its characteristic impedance. Under this condition, the reflection coefficient is zero along the line and the line is considered *flat*; ie, the magnitude of the voltage and current along the line always decreases as we move away from the generator. There are no standing waves along the line. The attenuation constant, α, is the matched loss per unit length expressed in nepers per foot. We usually express matched loss in units of decibels per 100 feet.

The matched loss may be broken down into two elements, that due to losses in the conductors and that due to the insulation. To a first order, the loss due to the conductors is proportional to $\sqrt{frequency}$, and the loss due to the insulation increases with frequency raised to the gth power. When these two components of loss are separated, it is seen in the matched loss versus frequency graph that conductor losses dominate at HF, and that it is only at VHF and above where insulation losses begin to show up.

The *Mathcad* worksheet shows the matched loss over a wide frequency range.

Note that the total matched loss versus frequency graph in the *Mathcad* worksheet resembles those published in *The ARRL Handbook* and *The ARRL Antenna Book*.

Loss Crossover Frequency

Since the loss due to the non-ideal conductors dominates at low frequencies and the loss due to the insulation becomes more important at higher frequencies, it is interesting to calculate the frequency where the two loss contributions are equal. I call this frequency the *loss crossover frequency*, F_X.

At F_X the characteristic impedance is real. The *Mathcad* spreadsheet takes advantage of this fact by calculating F_X in two steps, first at the measurement frequency and then at F_X. Below F_X the imaginary part of Z_0 is negative and above it is positive. The value of the characteristic impedance at F_X is the same as the "Physical Characteristic Impedance" that I will describe later.

The value of F_X of 65 GHz for the example given in the appendix is unrealistically high. Here is an example where the measurement frequency is too low (3.6 MHz) to yield valid cable characterization beyond the HF region.

Solutions for Arbitrary Frequency and Length

For each of the following calculations, the same frequency and/or length are used. I define the new frequency to be F_{NEW} and the new length to be $Length_{NEW}$. The following quantities are calculated at the new frequency and length, which were arbitrarily selected to be 28.8 MHz and 50 feet, respectively.
• Electrical angle
• Length in wavelengths
• Half, quarter and one-eighth wavelength cable lengths for the new frequency
• Frequencies at which the cable is a half, quarter and one-eighth wavelength for the new length
• Characteristic impedance at the new frequency.

Evaluation of Approximations

In the remaining sections of the *Mathcad* worksheet, I evaluate the accuracy of some approximations for various transmission line parameters. These methods are useful because they allow you to use simple test equipment and data furnished by the cable manufacturer to ascertain other useful cable information and to validate the furnished data.

The procedure I use is to assume that the cable properties derived from the open and short-circuit impedance measurements are the actual properties. Then I compare the estimated values with those values. I have found that this technique provides much insight in dealing with alternative methods for obtaining cable properties.

"Real" Characteristic Impedance

Cable manufacturers furnish a value for the characteristic impedance of a cable. It is always a real number and is never shown to be dependent on frequency. Since we know that the actual characteristic impedance is complex, but mostly real, what is the meaning of the published "real" characteristic impedance?

Here are some candidates for the meaning:
• "Physical" characteristic impedance is defined as that established by the inductance per unit length and the capacitance per unit length. It is defined as:

$$Z_{0LC} = \sqrt{\frac{L}{C} \times 10^6}$$

The 10^6 factor is necessary because the units for inductance and capacitance are in microhenrys and picofarads, respectively.
• It is a real number and is independent of frequency to the extent the capacitance and inductance per-unit-length are independent of frequency.
• The real part of the characteristic impedance, R_0, is nearly independent of frequency. The magnitude of the characteristic impedance, $|Z_0|$, is also nearly independent of frequency.

The three quantities are not identical, but for most applications the differences are inconsequential. All three values are compared in the worksheet. Since Z_{0LC} is most nearly independent of frequency in practice, it is reasonable to interpret the published "real" characteristic impedance to be Z_{0LC}. Manufactures of cable need not really define what they mean by their Z_0 specification because the differences among the above candidates are much less then the manufacturing tolerances for that specification.

"Real" Characteristic Impedance from Capacitance per Foot and Velocity Factor

The following approximation is sometimes used to find the characteristic impedance of a transmission line:

$$Z_{0LC} = \frac{1016.703}{C \times VF}$$

Some digital multimeters measure capacitance very accurately. The measurement frequency is conveniently very low. By measuring the capacitance of a length of cable and dividing by the length in feet, C (in pF/foot) may be determined. The velocity factor may be obtained from furnished data or by a variety of measurement methods, usually involving finding the frequency where the cable length is some integer multiple of a quarter wavelength. The very close agreement seen for the examples is typical.

The equation for the "real" characteristic

impedance shown above may be rewritten as follows:

$$Z_{0LC} \times C \times VF = 1016.703$$

Z_{0LC}, C and VF are usually provided by the suppliers of cables. This equation provides a good way of checking the consistency of cable specifications.

Complex Z_0 from Propagation Constant

Suppliers of transmission lines do not provide a complex value for characteristic impedance. The reason for this is that the imaginary part of the complex impedance is frequency dependent. To find an estimate of the complex Z_0 for the case when most of the loss is due to the conductors and not the insulation, the propagation constant may be used. You can compute the propagation constant, $\gamma = \alpha + j\beta$, from the data provided. The suppliers provide the attenuation in dB per 100 feet, A_{0FR}, at some reference frequency, F_R, the velocity factor, VF, and Z_{0LC}, the "real" characteristic impedance. Calculate α_R (in nepers/foot) from:

$$\alpha_R = \frac{\ln(10)}{2000} A_{0FR}$$

To find α at the frequency of interest, F, use:

$$\alpha = \alpha_R \sqrt{\frac{F}{F_R}}$$

β (in radians/ft) may be calculated from:

$$\beta = \frac{2\pi F \times 10^6}{c \times VF}$$

An estimate of the complex characteristic impedance is given by:

$$Z_{0est} = Z_{0LC}\left(1 - j\frac{\alpha}{\beta}\right)$$

This estimate is useful at frequencies where the cable loss is dominated by conductor loss.

Inductance per Foot from Capacitance and an Estimate of the Physical Z_0

The inductance per foot may be calculated from an estimate of the physical characteristic impedance and C. This quantity is difficult to measure directly and is usually not provided by the cable manufacturer.

Magnitude of Z_0 and One-Eighth Wavelength Frequency from Impedance Measurements

One technique for finding cable characteristics capitalizes on a property of a cable whose electrical length is one-eighth wavelength. For such a cable, the magnitude of the input impedance will be close to $|Z_0|$ when the far end is terminated in a resistor of *any* value. This equivalence is exact if Z_0 is real, but we know this is never true except at F_x or if the cable is lossless. This section of the *Mathcad* application illustrates how close this equivalence is in practice. The error is expressed as a percentage of the actual magnitude of the characteristic impedance.

The measurement technique is as follows: Estimate the frequency at which the cable an eighth wavelength. Terminate the far end of the cable with the AI1H Geometric Resistance Box.[8,9] Measure the magnitude of the near-end impedance as the load resistance is changed.[10] Change the frequency until the measured quantity is approximately the same for the highest and lowest load resistances. The frequency is the eighth-wavelength frequency and the value of impedance at the highest and lowest load resistances is a good approximation to the magnitude of the characteristic impedance. This value is very close to the real part of the characteristic impedance and the physical characteristic impedance.

Matched Loss from Reflection Coefficients

An accepted method for determining the matched loss of a cable is to measure the reflection coefficient, or equivalently the SWR, at the generator end when the other end of the cable is either open or short circuited. The theory behind this method is based on the concept that a wave launched at one end, which is totally reflected at the far end, will experience twice the matched loss while traversing the cable. Twenty times the log of the reflection coefficient is called the *return loss*. Half of the value of the return loss is an estimate of the matched loss in decibels.

The accuracy of this method depends on the reference impedance used for measuring the reflection coefficient. Ideally, the reference impedance should equal the line's complex characteristic impedance. In that case, the method gives the correct result when the line is terminated in either a short or an open circuit.

However, this measurement is usually made with a resistive reference impedance, rather than the complex characteristic impedance of the cable. Note that when you use a resistive reference impedance, the results are different for a short and for an open termination, and neither value is correct. The errors are larger when the cable length is short compared with a wavelength. However, notice that the geometric mean of the two reflection coefficients (obtained with the open- and short-circuit tests) yields a very good approximation to the matched loss. I recommend that this geometric averaging be used when loss is measured this way.

Minimum Loss

It is commonly believed that the matched loss, treated in the last section, is the minimum loss that a cable will have. One impact of the fact that Z_0 is complex is that the cable loss can be lower than the matched loss. While this is an interesting scientific result, it has little practical value. The actual minimum loss occurs when the cable termination is the conjugate complex of the characteristic impedance. Through the use of the abcd matrix parameter representation of the cable, I calculate the loss in the worksheet. It is slightly less than the matched loss.

For the true matched-loss case, the standing wave ratio is 1:1. The line behaves as though it were terminated in a line of infinite length and hence no reflections occur. However, when the load is the conjugate of the characteristic impedance, the cable loss will be at its minimum value, and there will be voltage and current standing waves on the cable, albeit low in magnitude. This SWR is calculated in the worksheet. Thus there are standing waves on a cable when it is terminated in the impedance that provides minimum loss.

Transmission Line Calculations for Any Termination, Frequency and Length

All of the properties calculated thus far are actually independent of the load impedance. Since a frequent application involves the influence of various terminations on the loss and SWR of the line, these calculations are located on separate *Mathcad* pages. One page covers the case when the load impedance is known and the input impedance is to be found. The other page is for the opposite situation.

You must choose the frequency, length and cable's load impedance (or input impedance). This gives us enough data to find the loss, SWR and input impedance (or load impedance) for any length cable at any frequency with any load impedance (or input impedance). The frequency, length and load impedance (or output impedance) may be changed in the sample *Mathcad* worksheet so that other examples may be solved.

For one of the cases, the loss is calculated in two ways, using modified reflection coefficients[11] and then by using the abcd matrix representation of the transmission line. The results are identical.

Designing Transmission Line Resonators

A transmission line can be used as a resonant circuit. The behavior occurs at frequencies that are multiples of a quarter wavelength. For example, a shorted quarter-wavelength cable simulates a parallel resonant circuit, and an open-circuited quarter-wavelength cable simulates a series resonant circuit.

When the resonant frequency is given, the properties of interest are the required length, the Q of the resonator and the reactance (or susceptance) level at resonance. The reactance (or susceptance) level, X (or B), is the reactance (or susceptance) at resonance of the inductor or capacitor of the equivalent lumped element resonant circuit that would have the same properties.

The resonator calculations are made for four cases: all combinations of quarter and half-wavelength cables with either a short or an open at the far end. Note from the worksheet that we take advantage of the knowledge of the frequency dependence of Z_0 and γ to find "exact" values for X (or B) and Q. The frequency dependence is required because a derivative with respect to frequency must be taken. The Q of all the resonators are almost the same; however, the reactance and susceptance level can change by using different length resonators.

Approximate values for X (or B) and Q are also shown. Note that a derivative with respect to frequency is not required for these calculations. Also note that the calculated resonator Q is the same for all four resonators at a given frequency. Examination of the equations shows that for a given cable type, the Q will increase with the $\sqrt{\text{frequency}}$. Also, a comparison of the approximations with the exact result shows that the approximations are excellent.

Designing Inductive and Capacitive Reactances from Transmission Line Segments

A transmission line segment that is shorter than a quarter wavelength is a convenient way to realize an inductive or capacitive reactance. You short the segment at the far end for an inductive reactance and open circuit it for a capacitive reactance.

Given the frequency and desired reactance, the properties of interest are the length, the complex impedance, the equivalent inductance or capacitance and the Q of the equivalent inductance or capacitance. The components realized in this manner often exhibit low Qs, so this calculation is important. The worksheet calculates both the inductive and capacitive cases.

Summary

You can see how *Mathcad* can be used to not only make useful calculations on transmission lines but also as a useful learning tool. Starting with only two impedance measurements on a single segment of cable at a single frequency, you can compute many useful properties of the line. These properties are not only available at the measurement frequency but at other frequencies. Of course, the value of the calculated results depends on the accuracy of the input data.

I appreciate the valuable comments of Walt Maxwell, W2DU, Bill Sabin, WØIYH, Chris Kirk, NV1E, Charlie Michaels, W7XC, and Fred Griffee, N4FG. I thank Pete Schuch, WB2UAQ, for making the measurements on the line in worksheet *TLMEASV6.MCD*.

A companion paper in this book uses the same techniques to find the properties of a transmission line when the starting point is the limited data furnished by the cable manufacturer.[12] The matched loss versus frequency graphs in the *Mathcad* worksheets resemble those published in *The ARRL Handbook* and *The ARRL Antenna Book*. I recommend that the methodology presented there be used to validate and/or update the ARRL graphs.

Notes and References
[1] W. E. Sabin, "*Mathcad* 6.0: A Tool for the Amateur Experimenter," *QST*, Apr 1996, pp 44-47.

[2] M. W. Maxwell, *Reflections –Transmission Lines and Antennas*. (Newington: ARRL, 1990), Chapter 15.

[3] R. D. Straw, *TLA.EXE*. This program analyzes transmission lines and antenna tuners. *TLA.EXE* is bundled with *The ARRL Antenna Book*.

[4] W. E. Sabin, "Computer Modeling of Coax Cable Circuits," *QEX*, Aug 1996, pp 3-10. Another example of how *Mathcad* may be used to address some transmission-line problems.

[5] List of transmission line references:
R. A. Chipman, *Theory and Problems of Transmission Lines*, Schaum's Outline Series (New York: McGraw-Hill, 1968)
P. C. Magnusson, G. C. Alexander, and V. K. Tripathi, *Transmission Lines and Wave Propagation*, Third Edition (Boca Raton: CRC Press, 1992)
M. W. Maxwell, *Reflections—Transmission Lines and Antennas* (Newington: ARRL, 1990).
The ARRL Antenna Book, 18th Ed (Newington: ARRL, 1997)
Reference Data for Radio Engineers, Fifth Edition (Indianapolis: ITT, Howard W. Sams, 1969)
G. L. Matthaei, L. Young, and E. M. T. Jones, *Microwave Filters, Impedance-Matching Networks, and Coupling Structures* (New York: McGraw-Hill, 1964)
F. Witt, "Broadband Matching with the Transmission Line Resonator," *The ARRL Antenna Compendium, Vol 4* (Newington: ARRL, 1995), pp 30-37.

[6] W. E. Sabin, "Exploring the 1:1 Current Balun," *QEX*, Jul, 1997, pp 12-20.

[7] R. A. Chipman, *Theory and Problems of Transmission Lines*, Schaum's Outline Series (New York: McGraw-Hill, 1968), pp 134-135.

[8] For a description of the Al1H Geometric Resistance Box see:
Frank Witt, "How to Evaluate Your Antenna Tuner–Parts 1 and 2," *QST*, Apr and May, 1995, pp 30-34 and pp 33-37, respectively.
Frank Witt, "Baluns in the Real (and Complex) World," *The ARRL Antenna Compendium, Vol 5* (Newington, ARRL: 1996), pp 171-181.

[9] Al1H Geometric Resistance Boxes are available from the author. Send an e-mail request or SASE for details.

[10] A convenient way to measure the magnitude of impedance is to use:
Autek Research RF Analysts Models VA1 and RF1, Autek Research, PO Box 8772, Madeira Beach, FL 33738, 813-886-9515.
MFJ Antenna Analyzer Model MFJ-259B, MFJ Enterprises, PO Box 494, Miss. State, MS 39762, 601-323-5869.
AEA Complex Impedance Analyzer Model CIA-HF, AEA, 1221 Liberty Way, Vista, CA 92083, 800-258-7805.

[11] K. Kurokawa, "Power Waves and the Scattering Matrix," *IEEE Trans Microwave Theory and Tech*, vol. MTT-13, Mar 1965, pp 194-202.

[12] Frank Witt, "Transmission Line Properties from Manufacturer's Data," elsewhere in this volume.

Vertical Antennas

Elevated Vertical Antennas Over Sloping Ground

By Al Christman, K3LC
Grove City College
100 Campus Drive
Grove City, PA 16127-2104

In mid-1994, I received a letter from some hams in Sweden who were preparing to construct an elevated four-square vertical array. The ground at their site was not level, but sloping, and they wanted to know the best way to orient the antennas and the radials. I gave them an initial answer, based on some analyses that I had performed using *ELNEC*.[1] Since then, I've obtained better software, and this article presents the results of that updated study.

Computer Simulation

All of the computer modeling shown here was carried out using *EZNEC pro*.[2] This is an improved version of Roy (W7EL) Lewallen's widely used *ELNEC* software, but it incorporates *NEC-4*[3] as its computing engine rather than *MININEC*.[4] Because of this upgrade, *EZNEC pro* can model antennas that touch or even penetrate the ground, and it also handles real ground much more accurately than *ELNEC*. My 1988 *QST* article on elevated vertical antennas[5] was derived from computer analysis I had completed using *NEC-GSD*, a special version of *NEC-3* that was configured to efficiently model vertical antennas with large numbers of symmetrically disposed radials and/or top-hat wires. *NEC-4* is, itself, a descendant of *NEC-3*, and is similar to it in many ways.

Fig 1 shows a single vertical monopole antenna with four horizontal radials; each conductor has an electrical length of 0.25 λ at a frequency of 3.8 MHz. All wires are #12 AWG (radius = 1 mm) and the base of the antenna is 15 feet above the ground. The monopole and the outer ends of the radials are supported by metallic masts, which are anchored to the earth via 5-foot ground rods. The height of the radial-support masts is 15 feet, and they are separated laterally from the tips of the radials by a distance of 6 inches. The central mast supports the monopole, but

One important part of antenna analysis that's frequently neglected is ground slope. Here's a look at how to configure a single elevated vertical, a pair in a cardioid array, and a four-square array to meet your needs under sloping-ground conditions.

is only 14.5 feet high, so it is *not* electrically connected to the vertical radiator. This arrangement, which I called "isolated feed" in the earlier *QST* article, reduces the amount of

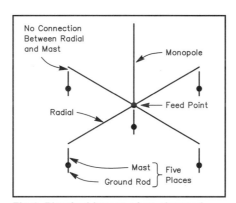

Fig 1–Physical layout of an elevated-vertical antenna with four elevated, horizontal radials. The coax shield is connected only to the four radials, and not to the central support mast (so-called isolated feed). Height=15 feet.

current that flows on the center mast.

At this point I ran into a minor problem caused by a limitation in *EZNEC*. My earlier *NEC-GSD* model had used an aluminum monopole and copper radials, plus steel masts and ground rods, while *EZNEC* requires that all metallic conductors be composed of the same material. To overcome this difficulty I used an *EZNEC pro* model in which all the conductors were made of aluminum. The conductivity of aluminum is intermediate between those of copper and steel, so I felt that selecting aluminum for the entire antenna would be a good compromise.

Finally, I decided to change the conductivity of the soil for the *EZNEC pro* computer models. Back in 1988, I had used a conductivity value of 0.003 Siemens/meter, in conjunction with a dielectric constant of 13. Since W7EL includes several standard sets of ground constants, I chose to follow his lead and assume a soil conductivity of 0.005 S/m, which allows me to keep the dielectric constant fixed at the previous value of 13.

Sloping-Ground Strategy

The next area of concern is the technique for modeling sloping ground. With *NEC* it is possible to construct a ground composed of two regions, each with its own conductivity and dielectric constant. However, the authors of the code didn't anticipate the need to model a large expanse of smooth but *sloping* ground. The easiest way to do this is simply to tilt one or more portions of the antenna so that the geometrical orientation of the tilted antenna over flat ground is identical to that of a normal upright antenna over sloping ground. This concept is illustrated in **Fig 2**; rotating the drawing at (a) by α in a clockwise direction produces the drawing at (b). Of course, *EZNEC* doesn't know that you have done this, so all of the elevation-plane radiation patterns that it produces will be correct for flat ground, and these must also be rotated clockwise by α to make them correct for sloping ground.

Throughout this article I have used a slope angle of 8°, which means that the ground is fairly steep. I chose such a large angle for two reasons. First, I am sure that some amateurs have antenna farms situated on terrain similar to this, or even worse. In the mid-1970s I worked in the coal mines of southern West Virginia, and I had almost two hours less daylight at my QTH "down in the hollow" than the fellows who lived 50 miles away in the flatlands. Second, I wanted to make sure that any slope-induced changes in the radiation patterns were big enough to be easily discernible on the plots, and the best way to accomplish this was to use a large angle.

Evaluation Approach

To appropriately answer the original question, namely, what's the best way to erect a four-square over sloping ground, it's necessary to take some intermediate steps to get to the core issues. In this article, I'll first look at a few configurations for a single vertical with elevated radials, then a pair in a cardioid array (90° spacing and phasing), and finally the four-square. Each analysis is based on four radials per element, except in certain specific situations where the antenna geometry allows combining radials; in these situations, I'll state how the models are configured.

Once this basic analysis is done, I'll draw some conclusions about the best approach to take for the single element, cardioid, and four-square array, depending on your particular location and goals. You can draw additional conclusions from this material as well—such as the trade-offs and advantages of building vertical antennas and arrays using sloping radials over flat ground.

Single Elevated Vertical Antenna

There are a number of different ways to

configure a single elevated vertical-monopole antenna over sloping ground, since either the radials and/or the monopole can be tilted with respect to the local earth surface. I decided immediately to always orient the monopole so it was perfectly vertical ("straight up and down"), because I don't think anyone would deliberately try to support a large quarter-wave radiator in an inclined position.

If we specify that all four of the elevated radials must lie in a single plane, then there are only two ways to orient this plane, as

illustrated in **Fig 3**. Antenna A in the figure shows the radial-plane located parallel to the local (sloping) ground. Here, each of the four radial wires is always at the same height above the ground along its entire length. (Notice that the plane containing the radials is *not* perpendicular to the vertical monopole.) The other option is illustrated as antenna B, where the radial plane *is* perpendicular to the vertical monopole, but no longer parallel to the local ground level. Now the radials form a plane that is perfectly horizontal, but their height above lo-

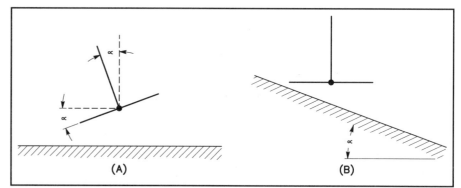

Fig 2—A tilted antenna over flat ground looks like a normal antenna over sloping ground. The tilt angle, a, is the same as the ground-slope angle.

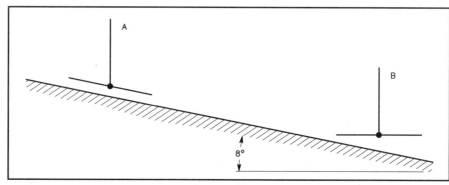

Fig 3—If all four radials must be coplanar, only two placement options exist: At A, the radial plane is parallel to local ground; at B, the radial plane is perpendicular to the vertical monopole.

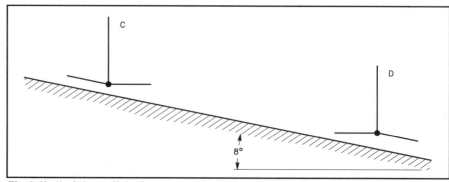

Fig 4—If all of the radials do *not* need to lie in the same plane, then two more options appear: At C, the uphill radials are parallel to local ground while the downhill radials are perpendicular to the vertical monopole; at D, the uphill radials are perpendicular to the vertical monopole and the downhill radials are parallel to the local ground.

cal ground may vary from place to place.

In contrast, if we do not force all four of the elevated radials to lie in the same plane, then two more variations in their positioning become possible, as shown in **Fig 4**. Antenna C of this figure has the uphill radial(s) drawn parallel to the local (sloping) ground, with the downhill radial(s) depicted as perpendicular to the vertical monopole. For antenna D the downhill radial(s) are parallel to the sloping ground, with the uphill radial(s) drawn perpendicular to the vertical monopole.

After the elevation-plane orientation of the radials has been selected, the next task is to determine the azimuth positioning of the four radials with respect to the sloping ground. There are many possibilities, but **Fig 5** shows the only two variations that will be discussed in this paper. In part (i), two of the radials lie parallel to the "line of steepest descent," while the remaining two radials are perpendicular to this line. For example, if the ground slopes directly downhill along a line that runs from north to south (toward 180° azimuth), then the four radials would point to the four cardinal points of the compass—north, south, east and west. Part (ii) illustrates the second alternative, wherein the radials all are turned at 45° with respect to the line of steepest descent. Thus the four radials point to the northeast, southeast, southwest and northwest, respectively.

The four elevation choices (A, B, C and D of Fig 3 and Fig 4) in combination with the two azimuth selections (i and ii in Fig 5) yield a total of eight different possible ways to construct a single elevated-radial vertical-monopole antenna. **Table 1** summarizes the computer-predicted performance of each configuration, showing the maximum gain in various directions (downhill, uphill, either side of the hill) as well as the amount of non-circularity in the azimuth-plane radiation pattern.

Table 1A

Power Gain versus Direction, Noncircularity, Front-to-Back Ratio and Front-to-Side Ratio for Eight Configurations of a Single Isolated-Feed Vertical Antenna with Four Elevated Radials with a Ground Slope Angle of 8°

Config- uration	Power gain (dBi)			Noncirc- ularity (dB)	Front/Back Ratio (dB)	Front/Side Ratio (dB)
	Downhill	Uphill	Sides			
A(i)	0.24	0.12	0.22	0.12	0.12	0.02
B(i)	0.77	−0.42	0.08	1.19	1.19	0.69
C(i)	−0.02	−0.77	0.44	1.21	0.75	−0.46
D(i)	0.78	0.07	−0.10	1.18	0.71	1.18
A(ii)	0.21	0.16	0.18	0.05	0.05	0.03
B(ii)	0.72	−0.60	0.16	1.32	1.32	0.56
C(ii)	0.47	−0.15	0.18	0.62	0.62	0.29
D(ii)	0.56	−0.21	0.21	0.77	0.77	0.35

Table 1B

Power Gain versus Direction, Noncircularity, Front-to-Back Ratio and Front-to-Side Ratio for Eight Configurations of a Single Isolated-Feed Vertical Antenna with Four Elevated Radials with a Ground Slope Angle of 4°

Config- uration	Power gain (dBi)			Noncirc- ularity (dB)	Front/Back Ratio (dB)	Front/Side Ratio (dB)
	Downhill	Uphill	Sides			
A(i)	0.25	0.19	0.23	0.06	0.06	0.02
B(i)	0.53	−0.09	0.19	0.62	0.62	0.34
C(i)	0.14	−0.22	0.39	0.61	0.36	−0.25
D(i)	0.56	0.22	−0.04	0.60	0.34	0.60
A(ii)	0.22	0.19	0.20	0.03	0.03	0.02
B(ii)	0.51	−0.16	0.20	0.67	0.67	0.31
C(ii)	0.36	0.03	0.20	0.33	0.33	0.16
D(ii)	0.39	0.02	0.21	0.37	0.37	0.18

Table 1C

Power Gain versus Direction, Noncircularity, Front-to-Back Ratio and Front-to-Side Ratio for Eight Configurations of a Single Isolated-Feed Vertical Antenna with Four Elevated Radials with a Ground Slope Angle of 12°

Config- uration	Power gain (dBi)			Noncirc- ularity (dB)	Front/Back Ratio (dB)	Front/Side Ratio (dB)
	Downhill	Uphill	Sides			
A(i)	0.20	0.02	0.21	0.19	0.18	−0.01
B(i)	0.94	−0.75	−0.15	1.69	1.69	1.09
C(i)	−0.21	−1.42	0.41	1.83	1.21	−0.62
D(i)	0.89	−0.22	−0.79	1.68	1.11	1.68
A(ii)	0.20	0.12	0.14	0.08	0.08	0.06
B(ii)	0.85	−1.11	0.10	1.96	1.96	0.75
C(ii)	0.54	−0.31	0.14	0.85	0.85	0.40
D(ii)	0.70	−0.51	0.20	1.21	1.21	0.50

This table contains several items of interest. First, if true omnidirectional coverage is desired, configuration A(ii) produces a radiation pattern that is almost perfectly circular, despite being constructed over sloping ground. This antenna has its four radials oriented at 45° to the line of steepest descent, in a plane that is parallel to the local ground.

All eight configurations have more gain in the downhill direction than uphill, so I have chosen to equate downhill with the front of the radiation pattern. Antenna D(i) has the most gain toward the front, and is especially notable for having the least amount of radiation to the sides, as well as the largest front-to-side ratio. The honors for highest front-to-back ratio belong to antenna B(ii), which also holds third place in both forward-gain and front-to-side ratio. Antenna B(i) is the runner-up in no less than three categories: front-to-back ratio, front-to-side ratio, and forward gain, where it loses to antenna D(i) by only 0.01 dB. The uphill-downhill elevation-plane radiation patterns for all three of these antennas are shown together in **Fig 6**; remember that (here) the ground slopes downhill toward the right edge of the page. **Fig 7** illustrates the side-to-side elevation-plane radiation patterns for the same three antenna configurations.

None of these antennas produces maximum gain in the uphill direction, but C(i) is very unusual because its peak gain occurs to the *sides* rather than uphill or downhill. As a result, its front-to-side ratio is actually negative, if we consider downhill to be the front. This configuration produces more signal to the sides, and less signal going uphill or downhill, than any of the others.

Rus Healy, K2UA, suggested that it would be helpful to examine what happens to the radiation pattern of a single elevated vertical antenna if the ground was sloped at some angle greater or less than 8°. Therefore, information for a slope angle of 4° is listed in **Table 1B**, and **Table 1C** includes data for a 12° slope. For both of these additional slope angles, all eight configurations *still* have the most gain in the downhill direction. Increasing the steepness of the ground causes the front-to-back and front-to-side ratios to increase proportionally, while the reverse is true when the ground becomes flatter. As before, configuration A(ii) always yields the most circular azimuth-plane pattern, while C(i) continues to produce more gain alongside the hill than it does downhill.

So, by adjusting the manner in which its four radials are positioned with respect to local ground, the enterprising ham can build a single elevated vertical-monopole antenna with either an omnidirectional radiation pattern, or a very modest beam effect. None of these antennas have any side-to-side directivity; that is, each radiates the same amount of signal on both sides of the line of steepest descent.

Two-Element Vertical Arrays

Normally, a ham constructing a two-element phased vertical array wants the antenna system to be electrically symmetrical. In other words, when building a cardioid array with 90° spacing and phasing, the operator would like the gain, front-to-back ratio and relative driving-point impedances to remain unchanged (or nearly so) as the array is switched from one direction to the other. Thus, the antenna should "look the same" and perform the same (electrically) in both directions of fire. Similarly, for bi-directional two-element arrays (such as those with 180° spacing and phasing) the goal would be to have two equal-sized lobes of radiation for a given directional setting.

However, there are two potential strategies that may be pursued by the amateur who has sloping ground at his disposal: One, construct an array designed to counteract the (undesired) directive effects of sloping ground, so that the resulting antenna system performs in a more or less symmetrical fashion, despite the sloping ground; or two, build an array that deliberately combines the normal directivity of the phased radiators with the previously undesired effects of the sloping ground to produce *enhanced* gain toward a particular compass heading. This array would, no doubt, be highly asymmetrical, and would probably be designed to beam in only *one direction* (downhill). We have already seen that an isolated vertical

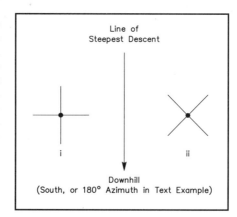

Fig 5–Top view of an elevated vertical with four elevated radials, showing two ways to position the radials (in azimuth) with respect to the sloping ground: At (i), the radials are parallel to the line of steepest descent; and at (ii), the radials are oriented at 45° to the line of steepest descent.

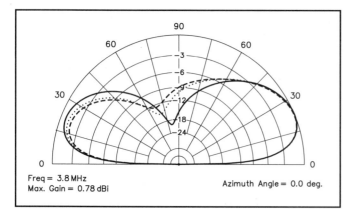

Freq = 3.8 MHz
Max. Gain = 0.78 dBi
Azimuth Angle = 0.0 deg.

Fig 6–Principal elevation-plane radiation patterns for several elevated-vertical antennas. Downhill is toward the right edge of the drawing. The outer ring of the plot represents 0.78 dBi.

Solid line = configuration D(i)
Dashed line = configuration B(ii)
Dotted line = configuration B(i)

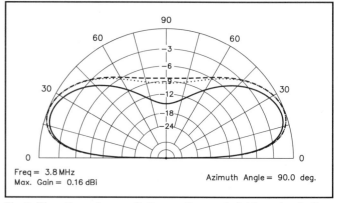

Freq = 3.8 MHz
Max. Gain = 0.16 dBi
Azimuth Angle = 90.0 deg.

Fig 7–Elevation-plane radiation patterns at right angles to the uphill/downhill line shown in Fig 6. (Downhill is perpendicular to the paper.) The outer ring of the plot represents 0.16 dBi.

Solid line = configuration D(i)
Dashed line = configuration B(ii)
Dotted line = configuration B(i)

monopole, unless carefully oriented, tends to radiate mostly downhill, so it might be possible to use this to our advantage.

Fig 8 illustrates two ways to position a two-element array over sloping ground. At (A) the antennas are placed in an uphill-downhill fashion along the line of steepest descent, while in (B) the two vertical monopoles are located side-by-side at the same elevation. These are the two limiting cases, and intermediate orientations have not been considered, for the sake of simplicity. This figure shows configuration (ii) for the radials (all are oriented at 45° to the line of steepest descent), but this was done simply for convenience, and is purely arbitrary; configuration (i) could have been drawn just as easily. Both will be modeled, and are discussed below.

First I will analyze case (A), where one antenna is higher than the other in terms of absolute elevation. As before, eight permutations will be modeled, using the four possible choices (A, B, C or D) from Figs 3 and 4 in combination with the two different radial selections (i or ii) from Fig 5. Since this is an endfire array, the main lobe of radiation will be directed either uphill or downhill, when the antennas are positioned as shown in **Fig 8A**.

The results are summarized in **Table 2**, which lists the forward gain, front-to-back ratio, and input impedances for all eight possible antenna systems, firing both uphill and downhill. Several configurations have performance characteristics that are worthy of mention.

Array C(ii) has excellent gain in *both* directions, with a variation of only 0.03 dB between uphill and downhill. This system would be the logical choice for those who want an array that performs as if it were mounted on level ground. However, there is

a noticeable change in the driving-point impedances when reversing the direction of fire, so it might be advisable to build *two* matching networks (one for each direction) to realize the full potential of this system. **Fig 9** shows both of the principal elevation-plane radiation patterns.

Array C(ii) would also be preferred if you only wanted to fire uphill, since it has the best uphill gain. On the other hand, if you were planning to just shoot downhill, array D(ii) has the highest gain in that direction, along with a decent front-to-back ratio. See **Fig 10** for the elevation-plane radiation patterns in this scenario.

Array D(i) is the optimal selection if you need an antenna that is easy to get working. Its driving-point impedances are very similar in both directions of fire, so a single matching network will do a good job, if properly designed. However, it has better gain and front-to-back ratio when aiming downhill than up, as illustrated by the radiation patterns shown in **Fig 11**.

Now let's review the case shown in Fig 8B, where the two antennas are mounted side-by-side at the same absolute elevation. Once again, eight permutations will be modeled, using the four possible choices (A, B,

C or D) from Figs 3 and 4, in combination with the two radial configurations (i or ii) from Fig 5.

The results are summarized in **Table 3**, which lists the forward gain and front-to-back ratio for all eight different antenna systems. Since the two verticals are now installed side-by-side, rather than uphill-downhill, both directions of fire are *perpendicular* to the line of steepest descent. Because of this, the array looks the same, physically and electrically, in both directions. Thus, there is no change in the gain, pattern shape, front-to-back ratio, or relative driving-point impedances within the array, when the directivity is reversed. This is in marked contrast to the situation discussed earlier (as highlighted in Table 2) wherein most of the electrical parameters were highly dependent upon the direction of fire.

What *does* occur in the side-by-side case, however, is a certain amount of skewing in the azimuth-plane radiation patterns of these arrays. Normally we would expect the peak gain to occur in the plane that contains the two verticals, but this is no longer the case. As shown in Table 3, the nose or peak of the radiation pattern is actually shifted slightly downhill in seven of the eight mounting configurations. The column la-

---

Table 2

Power Gain, Front-to-Back Ratio and Input Impedances for Eight Configurations of a Two-element Cardioid Array of Vertical Antennas with Elevated Radials (90° Spacing and Phasing)

The elements are oriented in an uphill-downhill fashion as shown in Fig 8A.

Configuration		Gain(dBi)	F/B (dB)	Input Impedances (Ω)
A(i)	Downhill	3.65	16.40	18.0 −j 12.0, 50.6 +j 15.2
	Uphill	3.26	14.40	19.8 −j 10.5, 48.8 +j 13.6
B(i)	Downhill	3.74	14.96	20.6 −j 11.2, 47.8 +j 16.1
	Uphill	3.02	12.41	18.2 −j 10.4, 50.1 +j 15.2
C(i)	Downhill	3.69	15.20	19.3 −j 11.2, 47.5 +j 15.8
	Uphill	3.27	14.71	18.4 −j 9.2, 48.3 +j 13.7
D(i)	Downhill	3.70	15.10	19.4 −j 12.0, 50.9 +j 15.5
	Uphill	3.01	12.01	19.6 −j 11.7, 50.6 +j 15.1
A(ii)	Downhill	3.70	13.06	20.8 −j 15.3, 59.6 +j 26.2
	Uphill	3.19	12.40	27.1 −j 9.7, 53.3 +j 20.8
B(ii)	Downhill	3.69	13.56	21.8 −j 15.3, 48.0 +j 19.3
	Uphill	3.11	13.45	16.5 −j 13.5, 53.1 +j 17.5
C(ii)	Downhill	3.63	11.81	20.2 −j 18.1, 49.8 +j 18.5
	Uphill	3.66	14.76	17.7 −j 15.1, 52.3 +j 15.8
D(ii)	Downhill	3.77	14.41	22.3 −j 13.6, 57.4 +j 25.1
	Uphill	3.53	15.29	18.8 −j 11.7, 60.4 +j 23.0

Notes

Since the two antennas are spaced only 0.25 λ apart, and the radials are 0.25 λ in length, all the arrays which use arrangement (i) for their radials can use a common radial between them. Thus, these systems have a total of only seven radials rather than eight; the extra radial is omitted.

Two sets of radials in arrangement A(ii) cross at right angles, and could touch each other if suspended at the same height. Insulated wires would prevent this occurrence; I solved it in my computer model by offsetting the height of each antenna by 1 inch (the uphill antenna is 15 feet, 1 inch above ground, and the downhill antenna is at 14 feet, 11 inches).

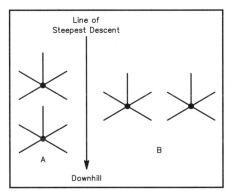

Fig 8—Two possible arrangements for a two-element cardioid phased vertical array (90° spacing and phasing) mounted over sloping ground: (A) uphill-downhill; (B) side-by-side. The orientation of the radials as shown in the figure is arbitrary; either configuration (i) or (ii) from Fig 5 may be used. Both are discussed (with their results) in the text.

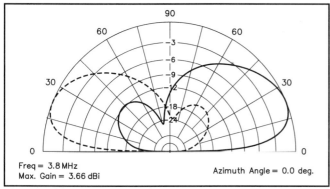

Freq = 3.8 MHz
Max. Gain = 3.66 dBi
Azimuth Angle = 0.0 deg.

Fig 9—Principal elevation-plane radiation patterns for a two-element cardioid phased vertical array (90° spacing and phasing) positioned in an uphill/downhill fashion along the line of steepest descent, using radial configuration C(ii). The outer ring of the plot represents 3.66 dBi.

Solid line = firing downhill
Dashed line = firing uphill

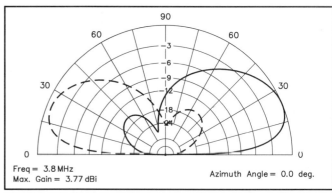

Freq = 3.8 MHz
Max. Gain = 3.77 dBi
Azimuth Angle = 0.0 deg.

Fig 10—Principal elevation-plane radiation patterns for a two-element cardioid phased vertical array (90° spacing and phasing) positioned in an uphill/downhill fashion along the line of steepest descent, using radial configuration D(ii). The outer ring of the plot represents 3.77 dBi.

Solid line = firing downhill
Dashed line = firing uphill

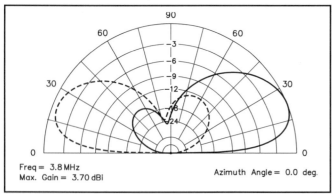

Freq = 3.8 MHz
Max. Gain = 3.70 dBi
Azimuth Angle = 0.0 deg.

Fig 11—Principal elevation-plane radiation patterns for a two-element cardioid phased vertical array (90° spacing and phasing) positioned in an uphill/downhill fashion along the line of steepest descent, using radial configuration D(i). The outer ring of the plot represents 3.70 dBi.

Solid line = firing downhill
Dashed line = firing uphill

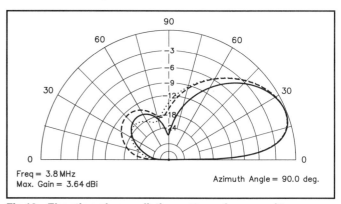

Freq = 3.8 MHz
Max. Gain = 3.64 dBi
Azimuth Angle = 90.0 deg.

Fig 12—Elevation-plane radiation patterns for several two-element cardioid arrays (90° spacing and phasing) where the antennas are mounted side-by-side, perpendicular to the line of steepest descent. Downhill is perpendicular to the paper toward the reader. The outer ring of the plot represents 3.64 dBi.

Solid line = configuration A(i)
Dashed line = configuration A(ii)
Dotted line = configuration D(ii)

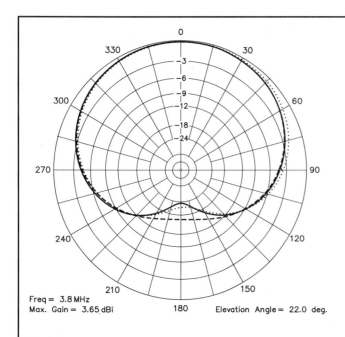

Freq = 3.8 MHz
Max. Gain = 3.65 dBi
Elevation Angle = 22.0 deg.

Fig 13—Azimuth-plane radiation patterns for several two-element cardioid arrays (90° spacing and phasing) where the antennas are mounted side-by-side, perpendicular to the line of steepest descent. Downhill is toward the right edge of the drawing. The outer ring of the plot repesents 3.65 dBi.

Solid line = configuration A(i)
Dashed line = configuration A(ii)
Dotted line = configuration D(ii)

Table 3

Power Gain, Elevation-Plane Front-to-Back Ratio and Azimuth-Plane Pattern Skewing for Eight Configurations of a Two-element Cardioid Array of Vertical Antennas with Elevated Radials (90° Spacing and Phasing)

The elements are oriented side-by-side as shown in Fig 8B.

Configuration	Gain(dBi)	F/B (dB)	Azimuth Pattern Skewing
A(i)	3.48	15.10	None
B(i)	3.41	15*	19° downhill (gain = 3.53 dBi)
C(i)	3.34	12.99	9° downhill (gain = 3.36 dBi)
D(i)	3.47	17.14	15° downhill (gain = 3.52 dBi)
A(ii)	3.46	12.88	1° downhill (gain = 3.46 dBi)
B(ii)	3.53	13.51	10° downhill (gain = 3.55 dBi)
C(ii)	3.39	11.92	5° downhill (gain = 3.40 dBi)
D(ii)	3.64	14.47	6° downhill (gain = 3.65 dBi)

Notes

Since the two antennas are spaced only 0.25 λ apart, and the radials are 0.25 λ in length, all the arrays that use arrangement (i) for their radials can share a common radial between them. Thus, these systems have a total of only seven radials rather than eight; the extra radial is omitted.

Two sets of radials in all of the arrays that use arrangement (ii) cross at right angles, and could touch each other if they were suspended at precisely the same height above the ground. In the real world, the use of insulated wires would prevent this occurrence; I solved it in my computer model by changing the height of each antenna by 1 inch (one antenna is 15 feet, 1 inch above ground, and the other is at 14 feet, 11 inches).

*The front-to-back ratio given for configuration B(i) is only an estimate, since there is no distinct rear lobe in the elevation-plane radiation pattern developed by this array.

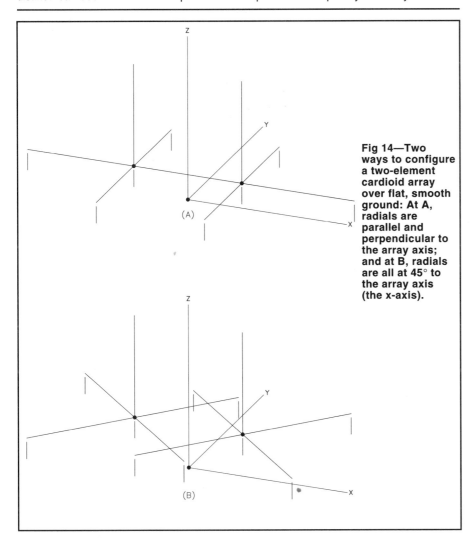

Fig 14—Two ways to configure a two-element cardioid array over flat, smooth ground: At A, radials are parallel and perpendicular to the array axis; and at B, radials are all at 45° to the array axis (the x-axis).

beled "Gain" in this table lists the maximum power gain along the theoretical direction of fire, which is perpendicular to the line of steepest descent. The right-most column shows how far the peak of the radiation pattern is skewed from the expected azimuth angle, and the maximum gain at this other compass heading.

Examining Table 3, we can see immediately that only configuration A(i) has *no* pattern skewing. The other seven versions exhibit varying amounts of pattern skewing, ranging from as much as 19° with antenna B(i) to as little as 1° for configuration A(ii). Version A(ii) has slightly less gain and front-to-back ratio than A(i). Antenna D(ii) has the highest forward gain of all eight configurations, and although it has 6° of pattern skewing, the difference in gain at the two azimuth angles is only 0.01 dB. At low takeoff angles, the front-to-back ratio of the D(ii) array is intermediate to that of configurations A(i) and A(ii). **Fig 12** illustrates the elevation-plane radiation patterns for these three antennas; the azimuth-plane patterns are shown in **Fig 13**.

By this time you may be thinking, "Fine, but what about the performance of the cardioid array when it is installed in a normal (flat-land) setting?" **Fig 14** shows two different ways to orient the radials with respect to the array axis. In Fig 14A we see that the radials are either parallel or perpendicular to the array axis. Only seven radials are needed, since one can be shared by both vertical monopoles. Eight support masts are required—two for the radiators themselves, and six more to hold up the ends of the radials.

Part B shows the alternative configuration, where each vertical has its own set of four radials, with no common connections. Now we need eight radials and ten support masts. Notice that if all the radials were actually at the same height above ground (15 feet) then there would be two places where pairs of radials would touch. To prevent this, I raised one antenna an extra inch (to 15 feet, 1 inch) and lowered the other by one inch (to 14 feet, 11 inches).

Fig 15 shows the principal elevation-plane radiation patterns for the two versions, and **Fig 16** does the same for the azimuth-plane patterns. Array (A) has slightly more forward gain (3.52 dBi versus 3.50) than antenna (B), but the take-off angle is the same (22°) in both cases. The front-to-back ratio of configuration (A) is clearly superior to that of (B), whether viewed in the elevation or azimuth planes. When combined with the lesser number of masts and radials required to build the antenna, system (A) is the clear winner.

A review of Tables 2 and 3 reveals that, as we might have suspected, several of the sloping-ground cardioid-array configurations

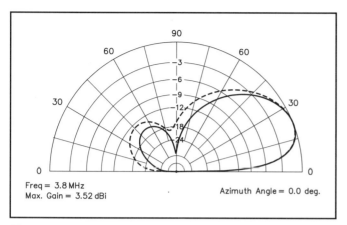

Fig 15—Principal elevation-plane radiation patterns for the two radial configurations illustrated in Fig 14. The outer ring of the plot represents 3.52 dBi.

Solid line = configuration A
Dashed line = configuration B

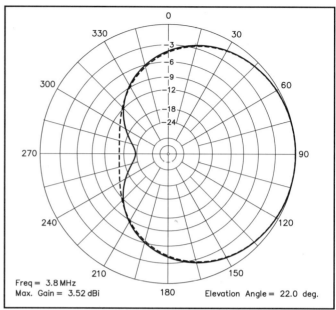

Fig 16—Principal azimuth-plane radiation patterns for the two radial configurations illustrated in Fig 14. The outer ring of the plot represents 3.52 dBi.

Solid line = configuration A
Dashed line = configuration B

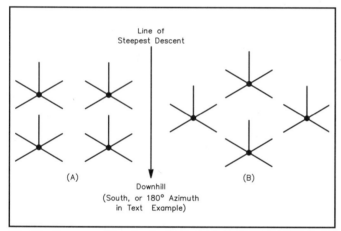

Fig 17—Two possible physical orientations for the four-square phased vertical array, when installed over sloping ground: At (A), a square; at (B), a diamond. The orientation of the radials shown in this figure is purely arbitrary; either configuration (i) or (ii) from Fig 5 may be used. Both are discussed (with their results) in the text.

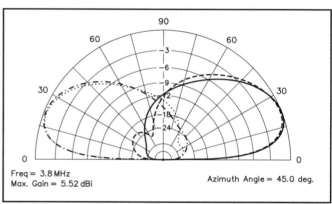

Fig 18—Elevation-plane radiation patterns for two of the four-square configurations discussed in the text. The monopoles are arranged in a square fashion. Downhill is toward the right, while uphill is toward the left edge of the drawing. The outer ring of the plot represents 5.52 dBi.

Solid & dotted lines = configuration D(i)
Dashed & dot-dashed traces = configuration D(ii)

produce more forward gain than can be achieved from the same antenna system when it is constructed over level ground.

Four-Square Vertical Arrays

The classic four-square array, using quarter-wave spacing and progressive 90° current phasing, is popular with low-band DXers. There are several ways to orient this antenna on sloping ground, and two are illustrated in **Fig 17**.

Version (A) shows a square which has two of its sides running uphill-downhill (parallel to the line of steepest descent) while the other two sides are perpendicular to this line, and extend alongside the hill.

Since the antenna system actually transmits along a diagonal line connecting opposite corners, the four directions in which this configuration radiates are *all* oriented at an angle of 45° to the line of steepest descent. For example, if the line of steepest descent pointed directly toward the south, then the array would fire to the northeast, northwest, southwest, or southeast.

The second method for siting the four monopoles, drawn as version (B), looks somewhat like a diamond, and this array fires either straight uphill, straight downhill, or in either direction alongside the hill (perpendicular to the line of steepest descent). If downhill is due south, then this

system radiates to the north, east, south, or west. I have chosen to call these two configurations *square* and *diamond,* respectively, even though both of them are actually square in their geometry, to distinguish one from the other.

Initially, I will analyze case (A), where the array resembles a square. Eight different versions will be modeled, using the four possible choices (A, B, C or D) from Figs 3 and 4, in combination with the two different radial selections (i or ii) from Fig 5. Recall that, with these eight permutations, the main lobe of radiation will be directed either partially uphill (the two lines of fire will be 45° to either side of the line of steepest ascent)

Table 4

Power Gain and Front-to-Back Ratio Data for Eight Configurations of the Four-Square Array of Vertical Monopoles with Elevated Radials

The elements are oriented in a square configuration, as shown in Fig 17A, and fire in four directions oriented either partially uphill or partially downhill.

Configuration		Forward Gain(dBi)	Change in Gain (dB)	Front/Back Ratio (dB) Elevation	Azimuth
A(i)	Downhill	5.47		30*	29.55
	Uphill	5.23	0.24	30*	33.13
B(i)	Downhill	5.45		25*	27.60
	Uphill	5.07	0.38	25.44	26.39
C(i)	Downhill	5.39		30*	29.59
	Uphill	5.13	0.26	29.82	31.60
D(i)	Downhill	5.52		30*	34.03
	Uphill	5.16	0.36	29.22	30.16
A(ii)	Downhill	5.22		23.44	24.65
	Uphill	4.86	0.36	22.56	23.60
B(ii)	Downhill	5.12		20.58	23.89
	Uphill	5.33	0.21	20*	25.30
C(ii)	Downhill	5.04		22.00	23.60
	Uphill	5.15	0.11	24.09	25.67
D(ii)	Downhill	5.29		21.54	23.98
	Uphill	5.43	0.14	23.36	25.41

Notes

Since all four sides of the Square are 0.25 λ, and the length of the radials is 0.25 λ, those arrays with arrangement (i) for their radials can share several common radials. Thus, these systems have a total of only 12 radials rather than 16, with the four redundant radials being omitted.

All of the arrays using radial arrangement (ii) have a quarter-wavelength radial extending from the base of each monopole directly toward the exact center of the array. Since these radials partially overlap each other, these four interior radials were deleted and replaced by two longer radials that span the diagonal distance across the center of the array. Thus, these systems have a total of 14 radials; 12 are 0.25 λ and the other two are 0.3535 λ.

Several sets of radials in the arrays that use configuration (ii) cross at right angles, and could touch each other if suspended at the same height. Insulated wire would prevent this occurrence; I solved it in my computer models by raising two of the radials by 1 inch (to 15 feet, 1 inch above ground) and lowering the other two to 14 feet, 11 inches.

*The actual front-to-back ratio for those configurations indicated by an asterisk is uncertain, since there is no distinct rear lobe in the radiation patterns of these arrays. The value given in the table is therefore an estimate.

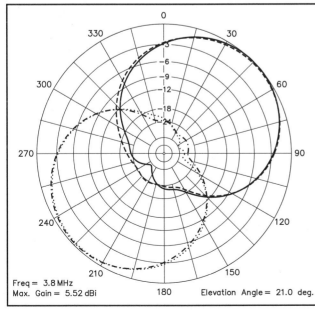

Fig 19—Azimuth-plane radiation patterns for two of the four-square configurations discussed in the text. The monopoles are arranged in a square fashion. Downhill is toward the right edge of the drawing. The outer ring of the plot represents 5.52 dBi.

Solid and dotted lines = configuration D(i) Dashed and dot-dashed traces = configuration D(ii)

or partially downhill (the two lines of fire will be 45° to either side of the line of steepest descent).

Information on the forward gain and front-to-back ratio for all eight configurations is listed in **Table 4**. Although the array has four directions of fire, the results for the two downhill quadrants were always extremely similar to each other, as was true for the two uphill azimuths. Thus, only two sets of values are shown for each arrangement of radials.

In many of the configurations that were modeled, the elevation-plane radiation pattern did not have a distinct rear lobe, so it was impossible to accurately determine a specific number for the front-to-back ratio, as noted in the table. An azimuth-plane radiation pattern was also derived for each version (at the takeoff angle where maximum forward gain occurred) and this value of front-to-back ratio was recorded from the plot.

Table 5 includes the computer-predicted driving-point impedances when the antennas are firing in different directions, along with the average variations of the input resistances and reactances, as the beam is switched from partially downhill to partially uphill. Together, these two tables contain much important data. We can see that only configuration A(ii) fails to achieve at least 5 dB of gain in all directions of fire. Version D(ii) has the highest average gain, at 5.36 dBi, followed closely by A(i) at 5.35 dBi, and D(i) at 5.34 dBi. Configuration D(ii) is very consistent as we switch the direction of fire, with no more than 0.14 dB variation in forward gain from one quadrant to another. This version also yields an average front-to-back ratio of well over 20 dB. The main disadvantage with configuration D(ii) is the relatively large change in both input resistance and reactance that occurs when switching directions. One possible solution would be to use two separate phasing/matching networks, one for downhill operation and another for uphill.

Configuration D(i) has the *smallest* overall variations in its driving-point impedances, averaging about 3 Ω for the real parts and just 0.5 Ω for the imaginary parts. It should be possible to construct a single phasing/matching network for this array, if the design calculations use median values of resistance and reactance as the input parameters. This antenna has very good gain when firing both uphill and downhill, with an average of 5.34 dBi, just 0.02 dB less than the best performer. Version D(i) also provides the highest overall front-to-back ratio in the azimuth plane, at more than 30 dB in any direction of fire, while the front-to-back ratio in the elevation plane is at least 25 dB at most take-off angles. Gain variations when switching from uphill to downhill amount to 0.36 dB, nearly the worst of any

Freq = 3.8 MHz
Max. Gain = 5.52 dBi
Elevation Angle = 21.0 deg.

197

Table 5

Input-Impedance Data for Eight Configurations of the Four-Square Array

The elements are oriented in a square configuration, as shown in Fig 17A.

Configuration	Vertical Monopole Input Impedances (Ω)	Average Variation (Ω) in Resistances	Reactances
A(i) Downhill	68.6 +j 52.3, 37.8 −j 1.7, 35.8 −j 8.9, 7.4 −j 0.7		
Uphill	66.8 +j 45.1, 36.0 −j 9.2, 37.7 −j 1.7, 9.1 +j 6.7	1.80	7.32
B(i) Downhill	61.5 +j 48.3, 34.7 −j 4.7, 43.4 −j 2.3, 11.4 +j 4.8		
Uphill	72.4 +j 52.7, 39.7 −j 2.2, 32.7 −j 6.8, 6.3 +j 2.2	7.93	3.47
C(i) Downhill	60.7 +j 46.4, 34.4 −j 5.3, 37.6 −j 5.9, 8.6 −j 0.7		
Uphill	65.6 +j 43.8, 35.6 −j 9.4, 32.8 −j 3.4, 7.2 +j 3.3	3.06	3.34
D(i) Downhill	69.6 +j 54.3, 38.2 −j 1.0, 41.5 −j 5.5, 10.3 +j 4.6		
Uphill	73.7 +j 54.0, 40.1 −j 1.9, 37.4 −j 5.3, 8.2 +j 5.4	3.05	0.52
A(ii) Downhill	73.5 +j 69.7, 47.6 +j 6.5, 44.2 −j 2.4, 9.2 −j 2.4		
Uphill	70.4 +j 58.9, 44.6 −j 1.8, 47.2 +j 8.2, 12.1 +j 6.1	3.02	9.52
B(ii) Downhill	62.8 +j 59.2, 40.4 +j 1.6, 54.6 −j 6.6, 12.7 −j 9.3		
Uphill	80.6 +j 62.6, 48.5 −j 6.9, 36.7 −j 9.7, 4.0 −j 1.1	13.12	5.75
C(ii) Downhill	60.5 +j 57.0, 39.1 +j 2.9, 45.3 −j 2.7, 11.8 −j 5.1		
Uphill	68.0 +j 58.0, 42.9 −j 1.8, 37.6 −j 4.1, 8.0 +j 0.2	5.70	3.09
D(ii) Downhill	76.5 +j 72.6, 48.1 +j 4.7, 55.8 −j 3.6, 10.0 −j 5.6		
Uphill	88.2 +j 72.5, 51.8 −j 4.0, 42.7 −j 4.7, 6.5 +j 3.4	8.01	4.78

array in the table, but not unreasonably large.

Fig 18 shows the principal elevation-plane radiation patterns for arrays D(i) and D(ii), when firing either partially downhill or partially uphill. System D(i) has a slight gain advantage when firing downhill, but D(ii) has the edge when the directivity is reversed. At low takeoff angles, D(i) has superior front-to-back ratio in all four quadrants, while the same is true for D(ii) at elevation angles above roughly 50°. Plots for the corresponding azimuth-plane radiation patterns are included as **Fig 19**.

All eight configurations yield a very slight azimuth skewing in their radiation patterns. The nose of the beam does not occur *precisely* at the expected compass angle, but is shifted by 1° or 2° because of the effects of the sloping ground. However, the impact of this azimuth offset upon the performance of the arrays is minor, and can probably be ignored.

Now let's look at the results from case (b) of **Fig 17**, where the four-square array is oriented to resemble a diamond. This arrangement produces radiation in any of four quadrants: straight uphill, straight downhill, or in either direction perpendicular to the line of steepest descent. As usual, eight different permutations must be modeled, using the four choices (A, B, C or D) from Figs 3 and 4, in combination with the two possible radial orientations (i or ii) from Fig 5.

Table 6 lists the gain and front-to-back ratio for each of the eight configurations. These arrays are capable of firing in four different quadrants, of course, but the results for the two directions which are oriented alongside the hill were always quite similar to one another. Therefore, only three sets of data are displayed for each version.

As was true before, some of the elevation-plane radiation patterns did not have a distinct rear lobe, and in these cases the front-to-back ratio had to be estimated. An azi-muth-plane radiation pattern was also plotted for each configuration, to determine the front-to-back ratio at the take-off angle where maximum forward gain occurs.

The driving-point impedances for the eight antennas, in various directions of fire, are supplied in **Table 7**. This compilation also includes the average variations in input resistance and reactance values, as the main lobe was switched around the points of the compass.

An examination of these two tables reveals that version D(ii) has the highest average gain at 5.405 dBi, followed by A(ii) with 5.355 dBi, while arrangement B(i) finishes a very close third at 5.350 dBi. These values are so similar that they would probably be indistinguishable on the air. However, the average front-to-back ratio of configuration B(i) is less than 25 dB, clearly inferior to that of both A(ii) and D(ii), which typically attain values of 30 dB or more. When switching from one quadrant

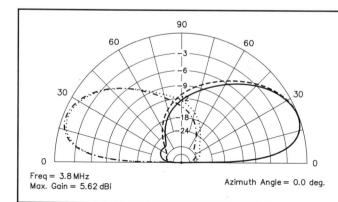

Fig 20—Elevation-plane radiation patterns for two of the four-square configurations discussed in the text. The monopoles are arranged in a diamond fashion. Downhill is toward the right edge of the drawing. The outer ring of the plot represents 5.62 dBi.

Solid and dotted lines = configuration A(ii)
Dashed and dot-dashed traces = configuration D(ii)

Freq = 3.8 MHz
Max. Gain = 5.62 dBi

Azimuth Angle = 0.0 deg.

Table 6

Power Gain and Front-to-Back Ratio Data for Eight Configurations of the Four-Square Array with Elevated Radials

The elements are oriented in a diamond configuration, as shown in Fig 17B.

Configuration		Forward Gain (dBi)	Change in Gain (dB)	Front/Back Ratio (dB) Elevation	Azimuth
A(i)	Downhill	5.27		23.95	25.15
	Uphill	4.76		22.48	23.46
	Sides	5.05	0.51	22.88	24.02
B(i)	Downhill	5.01		16.39	18.71
	Uphill	5.69		23.98	26.73
	Sides	5.35	0.68	21.80	25.84
C(i)	Downhill	4.88		20.17	20.84
	Uphill	5.10		20*	21.35
	Sides	5.18	0.30	22.03	25.19
D(i)	Downhill	5.39		18.63	21.28
	Uphill	5.34		17.64	21.99
	Sides	5.26	0.13	18.80	22.05
A(ii)	Downhill	5.52		28.82	29.48
	Uphill	5.18		33.81	36.16
	Sides	5.36	0.34	30*	30.8
B(ii)	Downhill	5.52		25*	27.08
	Uphill	4.99		27.40	28.33
	Sides	5.27	0.53	25.41	26.3
C(ii)	Downhill	5.47		30*	29.67
	Uphill	5.05		28.95	30.0
	Sides	5.28	0.42	33.37	33.71
D(ii)	Downhill	5.62		30*	33.41
	Uphill	5.16		30.17	31.12
	Sides	5.42	0.46	33.45	33.55

Notes

All of the arrays using radial arrangement (i) have a quarter-wavelength radial extending from the base of each monopole directly toward the exact center of the array. Since these radials partially overlap each other, these four interior radials were deleted and replaced by two longer radials that span the diagonal distance across the center of the array. Thus, these systems have a total of 14 radials; 12 are 0.25 λ and the other two are 0.3535 λ.

Since all four sides of the square are equal to 0.25 λ, and the length of the radials is 0.25 λ, those arrays that use arrangement (ii) for their radials can share several common radials. Thus, these systems have a total of only 12 radials rather than 16; the four redundant radials were omitted.

Several radials in the arrays using configuration (i) cross at right angles, and could touch each other if suspended at the same height. Insulated wires would prevent this occurrence; I addressed this issue in my computer models by raising two of the antennas by 1 inch (to 15 feet, 1 inch above ground) and lowering the other two to 14 feet, 11 inches.

*The actual front-to-back ratio for these configurations is uncertain, since there is no distinct rear lobe in the radiation patterns of these arrays. The value given in the table is an estimate.

to another, the gain of arrangement A(ii) is more consistent than D(ii), but only by about 0.12 dB. Comparing the variations in driving-point impedances, A(ii) does well in terms of input resistance, but rather poorly for reactance, while the reverse is true for D(ii). Overall though, version D(ii) has better performance in this area, and a single set of phasing/matching networks should suffice for driving this array.

Fig 20 shows the principal elevation-plane radiation patterns for arrays A(ii) and D(ii), when firing either downhill or uphill. System D(ii) has a very small advantage when firing downhill, but the forward gain of both systems is virtually identical when the directivity is reversed. At low takeoff angles, D(ii) has superior downhill front-to-back ratio, while A(ii) is better when beaming uphill; the reverse is true for both antennas at elevation angles above roughly 45°. Plots for the corresponding azimuth-plane radiation patterns are illustrated in **Fig 21**.

When configurations A(ii) and D(ii) are firing alongside the hill, the resulting elevation- and azimuth-plane patterns are given in **Fig 22A** and **B**, respectively. Patterns for only one side of the hill are displayed, since their size and shape are the same in both directions. We can see that version D(ii) has a bit more forward gain at most elevation angles, plus better rejection of undesired signals off the back of the beam at all takeoff angles, when the antennas are firing alongside the hill.

All of the eight diamond configurations modeled for this section of the analysis produced a slight azimuth skewing of the radiation pattern when the arrays were firing alongside the hill. Here, maximum gain does not occur precisely at the expected azimuth angle, but is shifted from 1° to 3° due to the sloping ground. As before, the repercussions seem to be negligible, and most hams probably could not detect the change.

Four Square over Flat Ground

Finally, for comparison, let's examine the performance of the four-square array when it is installed over flat, level ground. **Fig 23** is a top view showing two ways to orient the radials of the system with respect to the sides of the square. In part (A) we see that the radials are either parallel or perpendicular to the sides of the square. Only 12 radials are needed, since several are shared by each vertical monopole; similarly, just 12 support masts are required.

Part (B) shows the second configuration, where all the radials are at a 45° angle with respect to the sides of the square. One radial from each monopole normally extends directly toward the geometrical center of the array, and would partially overlap the radial coming from the diagonally-opposite corner, if allowed to do so. This is prevented by

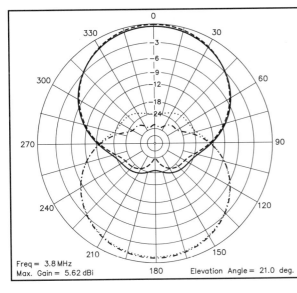

Freq = 3.8 MHz
Max. Gain = 5.62 dBi
Elevation Angle = 21.0 deg.

Fig 21—Azimuth-plane radiation patterns for two of the four-square configurations discussed in the text. The monopoles are arranged in a diamond fashion. Downhill is toward the upper edge of the drawing. The outer ring of the plot represents 5.62 dBi.

**Solid and dotted lines = configuration A(ii)
Dashed and dot-dashed traces = configuration D(ii)**

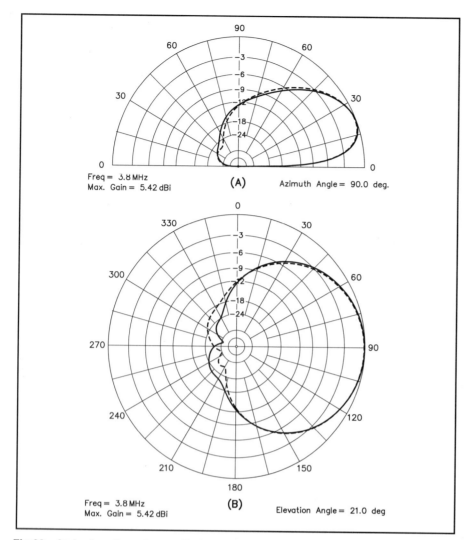

Freq = 3.8 MHz
Max. Gain = 5.42 dBi   **(A)**   Azimuth Angle = 90.0 deg.

Freq = 3.8 MHz
Max. Gain = 5.42 dBi   **(B)**   Elevation Angle = 21.0 deg

Fig 22—At A, elevation-plane radiation patterns for two of the four-square configurations discussed in the text. The monopoles are arranged in a diamond fashion and firing alongside the hill. At B, the corresponding azimuth-plane radiation patterns for A. The outer ring of the plots represents 5.42 dBi.

Solid line = configuration A(ii)
Dashed line = configuration D(ii)

replacing the four quarter-wave radials that occupy the interior of the system with two long radials that span the diagonals of the square. As a result, the total number of radials is reduced from 16 to 14. Notice however, that if all of these radials were ac-

tually at the same height above ground (15 feet), there are several places where two radials would intersect as they cross each other at right angles. To solve this problem, I raised two of the antennas by one additional inch (to 15 feet, 1 inch) while simul-

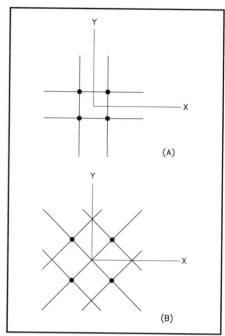

Fig 23—Two ways to configure a four-square array over flat, smooth ground: At A, the radials lie parallel and perpendicular to the sides of the square; at B, radials are all at 45° to the sides of the square.

taneously lowering the other pair by an inch (to 14 feet, 11 inches).

Fig 24 compares the elevation-plane radiation patterns for the two radial arrangements, while **Fig 25** does the same for the azimuth plots. Configuration (A) has more peak gain (5.39 versus 5.07 dBi, both at a 21° takeoff angle); in fact, (A) seems to have higher gain at all takeoff angles below about 50°. Similarly, version (A) provides about 10 dB of extra rejection off the back at low elevation angles, and is roughly equal in performance at higher angles. Since (A) also requires two less radials and four fewer masts, it is definitely the preferred choice.

As mentioned earlier, Tables 4 through 7 indicate that several of the four-square arrays constructed over sloping ground can

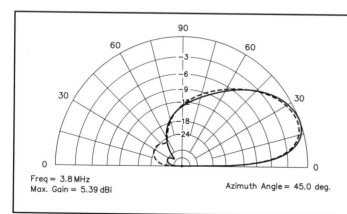

Freq = 3.8 MHz
Max. Gain = 5.39 dBi   Azimuth Angle = 45.0 deg.

Fig 24—Elevation-plane radiation patterns for the two flat-ground four-square arrays of Fig 23. The outer ring of the plots represents 5.39 dBi.

Solid line = configuration A
Dashed line = configuration B

Table 7

Input-Impedance Data for Eight Configurations of the Four-Square Array with Elevated Radials

The elements are oriented in a diamond configuration, as shown in Fig 17B.

Configuration		Vertical Monopole Input Impedances (Ω)	Average Variation (Ω) in Resistances	Reactances
A(i)	Downhill	74.1 +j 71.8, 46.0 +j 1.8, 46.0 +j 1.8, 8.6 −j 4.2		
	Uphill	69.8 +j 56.8, 46.0 +j 3.4, 46.0 +j 3.4, 12.7 +j 7.7		
	Sides	72.0 +j 64.5, 47.9 +j 9.3, 43.7 −j 4.1, 10.7 +j 2.0	3.17	10.49
B(i)	Downhill	58.6 +j 59.1, 48.3 −j 1.5, 48.3 −j 1.5, 11.2 −j 13.2		
	Uphill	82.0 +j 59.0, 39.6 −j 7.2, 39.6 −j 7.2, 4.0 −j 2.1		
	Sides	71.9 +j 62.5, 36.3 −j 5.7, 51.7 −j 11.1, 8.7 −j 4.2	13.66	7.51
C(i)	Downhill	58.1 +j 58.6, 47.8 +j 0.3, 47.7 +j 0.3, 9.9 −j 4.6		
	Uphill	69.4 +j 56.9, 43.8 +j 1.2, 43.8 +j 1.3, 5.9 −j 5.0		
	Sides	69.3 +j 61.4, 36.4 −j 3.9, 43.9 −j 4.4, 13.5 −j 1.1	8.54	4.8
D(i)	Downhill	74.8 +j 72.3, 46.4 −j 0.4, 46.4 −j 0.4, 9.9 −j 12.6		
	Uphill	83.4 +j 59.2, 40.5 −j 6.1, 40.5 −j 6.1, 12.0 +j 11.6		
	Sides	74.2 +j 65.6, 47.1 +j 7.3, 50.5 −j 11.3, 5.5 −j 0.8	8.05	15.4
A(ii)	Downhill	68.9 +j 54.1, 36.8 −j 5.6, 36.8 −j 5.6, 6.9 −j 1.9		
	Uphill	66.3 +j 44.0, 36.9 −j 5.8, 36.9 −j 5.8, 9.4 +j 8.5		
	Sides	67.8 +j 48.4, 38.1 +j 0.1, 35.5 −j 10.2, 8.3 +j 2.7	1.94	7.75
B(ii)	Downhill	59.7 +j 47.8, 39.0 −j 3.1, 39.0 −j 3.1, 13.5 +j 5.9		
	Uphill	76.0 +j 54.7, 34.6 −j 5.0, 34.6 −j 5.0, 5.9 +j 2.4		
	Sides	66.2 +j 50.0, 32.7 −j 6.4, 44.4 −j 1.2, 8.0 +j 2.9	10.02	4.39
C(ii)	Downhill	58.8 +j 45.1, 35.2 −j 5.9, 35.2 −j 5.9, 8.6 −j 1.6		
	Uphill	64.6 +j 42.2, 33.2 −j 6.9, 33.2 −j 6.9, 6.6 +j 3.1		
	Sides	61.6 +j 43.7, 32.4 −j 4.6, 36.2 −j 8.3, 7.6 +j 0.9	3.41	3.09
D(ii)	Downhill	70.4 +j 57.1, 41.5 −j 2.3, 41.5 −j 2.3, 11.0 +j 5.3		
	Uphill	78.3 +j 56.9, 39.0 −j 3.2, 39.0 −j 3.2, 8.0 +j 7.1		
	Sides	74.1 +j 56.9, 37.9 −j 2.3, 43.2 −j 3.3, 9.2 +j 6.2	4.65	0.99

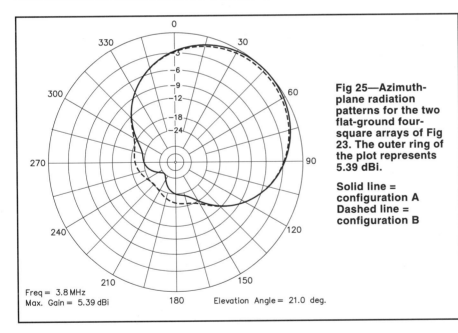

Freq = 3.8 MHz
Max. Gain = 5.39 dBi
Elevation Angle = 21.0 deg.

Fig 25—Azimuth-plane radiation patterns for the two flat-ground four-square arrays of Fig 23. The outer ring of the plot represents 5.39 dBi.

Solid line = configuration A
Dashed line = configuration B

front-to-back ratios can vary much more widely. In certain instances, the driving-point impedances change quite a bit as the directivity is switched from one azimuth to another. Some of these variations can be tolerated by the commercial boxes in use today, but other situations may require the construction of several properly designed feed networks to assure correct operation. I hope that the information presented here will help those who are planning to build an elevated vertical antenna in hilly terrain.

achieve higher peak values of forward gain than their level-ground counterparts.

Conclusion

This article has evaluated the performance of elevated vertical-monopole antennas and phased vertical arrays when they are located over sloping ground. Alternative configurations were modeled using the *EZNEC pro* software package, with the results described in both tabular and graphical form. Many of the choices that were presented have values of forward gain that are similar (within a decibel or so), although the

Notes
[1]*ELNEC* is available from Roy Lewallen, W7EL, PO Box 6658, Beaverton OR 97007.
[2]Several versions of *EZNEC* are available from Roy Lewallen. See Note 1.
[3]G. J. Burke and A. J. Poggio, "Numerical Electromagnetics Code (*NEC*)—Method of Moments" (San Diego: Naval Ocean Systems Center, January 1981).
[4]J. C. Logan and J. W. Rockway, "The New MiniNEC (Version 3): A Mini-Numerical Electromagnetic Code" (San Diego: Naval Ocean Systems Center, September 1986).
[5]A. Christman, "Elevated Vertical Antenna Systems," *QST*, Aug 1988, pp 35-42.

A Close Look at the Flattop Vertical Antenna

By Thomas Kuehl, AC7A
620 S Avenida Princesa
Tucson, AZ 85748

When it comes to a simple and effective antenna, the half-wave dipole installed a half wavelength above ground, is hard to beat. It offers good overall performance with the low radiation angle needed for DX communications. Many can accommodate the horizontal span of the dipole on their lot, but it is that half-wave above ground that is often a problem. This is especially true on 40, 80 and 160 meters. On 40, the half-wave height requirement is about 66 feet, and this doubles, and then doubles again as the frequency is moved down to 80 and 160 meter bands. Erecting, or even obtaining the appropriate supports, can prove difficult. For these reasons, or others such as aesthetics, many hams resort to a full-sized or shortened vertical to attain the much desired low-angle performance.

Almost everyone who experiments with, or builds their own, antennas is familiar with the quarter-wave (λ/4) vertical formula:

$$L \text{ (ft)} = 234/f \text{ (MHz)} \qquad \text{(Eq 1)}$$

A quarter-wave 40 meter (7 MHz) vertical, as an example, requires a length of about 33 feet—a height usually managed without too much difficulty. Aluminum tubing or TV mast can often satisfy this requirement. But when the frequency is moved down to the lower bands, 80 and 160 meters, the element lengths increase to 66 and 134 feet, respectively. Only a single tall vertical element is required, but that may still pose a problem.

An alternative is a vertical that uses capacitive top loading to reduce the overall antenna height. One such design is the flattop vertical antenna. In its simplest form it consists of a vertical element, less than a quarter wavelength long, with two opposing horizontal top wires. It looks much like

On 80 and 160 meters, quarter-wave verticals are 66 and 134 feet tall. That may pose a problem. Thomas, AC7A, describes the flattop vertical antenna, which uses capacitive top loading to reduce the overall antenna height.

the letter T and is sometimes referred to as a T-top antenna. The horizontal top wires provide capacitive loading that brings the short vertical section to resonance.

The vertical element length may be almost any convenient length; as long as sufficient horizontal space is available to accommodate the width, or span, of the top wires.

Keep in mind, as with any shortened vertical, making it progressively shorter brings along some unavoidable compromises: lower radiation resistance (R_r), and a narrower operating bandwidth. Low R_r usually isn't a problem by itself, but efficiency suffers when it is combined with high ground resistance (R_g). By using a flattop the problem is not as severe as it could be; it will always produce higher efficiency than its equally tall, inductively loaded vertical counterpart. The reasons for this will be explained later.

A variety of flattop schemes are possible but the most easily understood and built use the single-wire-T design. Multiple-wire designs are also practical and do allow for substantial reductions in the horizontal real estate requirements. Both designs will be examined.

The Single-Wire Flattop Antenna

Fig 1A shows the current distribution along a quarter-wave vertical. The vertical element is divided into 12 segments and an average current is listed for each segment. A normalized reference current of 1 A has been established at the feed point. From the figure it is evident that the current distribution is maximum at the feed point, then slowly decreases as you move upward along the element, dropping off rapidly toward the end of the antenna. If you plot these points, you'll see that the current distribution follows a cosine function along the antenna's quarter-wave (90°) length.[1]

In a similar fashion, Fig 1B shows the current distribution along the vertical and horizontal lengths for a practical flattop-antenna design. Once again the feed-point current has been normalized to 1 A. Start at the flattop's base, and compare the vertical-segment currents to those of the quarter-wave vertical and you'll see that they are nearly equal in value. At the top of the ver-

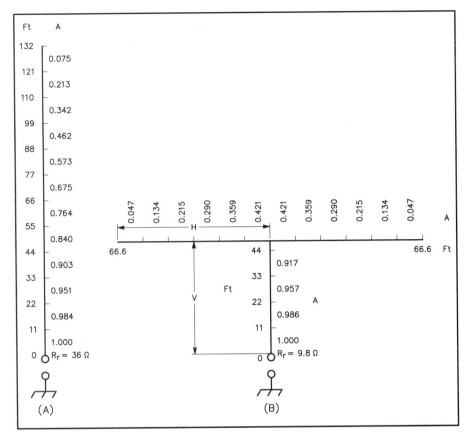

Fig 1—Comparison of current distribution in a ¼-λ vertical (A) and a typical flattop vertical (B). Both antennas are resonant at 1.825 MHz.

pattern is less than that of the full-sized vertical. While the quarter-wave vertical of Fig 1A has an R_r of 39.3 Ω, the flattop in Fig 1B has an R_r of 12 Ω. Assuming all other losses are 0.5 Ω, and R_g is 6 Ω, the efficiency (η) for the two antennas is 85.8% and 64.9%, respectively. Antenna efficiency is equal to:

$$\eta = 100 \, [\, R_r / (\, R_r + R_l) \,] \% \qquad \text{(Eq 2)}$$

where R_l is the sum of the loss resistances, which is mostly R_g for each of the two antennas.[3,4]

Establishing the vertical element length is often dictated by available end supports. Taller is better, but in restricted height applications very short heights can be tolerated if a good, low resistance ground return can be provided.

Once the vertical length is decided, it is then a matter of resolving the correct top-wire lengths. Lacking more information, it has been a common practice to start with a horizontal (H) length, plus vertical (V) length, equal to a quarter-wavelength. This may serve as a starting place, but it isn't always accurate.

To understand what is involved in determining the proper top-wire lengths, it is best to visualize each top wire and the earth below it as parts of an open-wire transmission line. The top wire is easy to visualize as one conductor, but the earth return is more complex and is not as easily visualized. It consists of the earth beneath the top wire, and any conductive ground radials. Its boundaries are much more difficult to define than that those of the top wire, but nonetheless do exist. The spacing of these two conductors, their effective diameters, and the dielectric characteristics of the materials between them—earth and air—define the transmission line properties; the surge impedance, Z_s (usually hundreds of ohms), and the velocity factor (VF), which is always less than unity.

The far end of this transmission line is an open circuit, or more correctly, the line is unterminated. With a length less than a quarter wavelength, the unterminated line will appear as a capacitance to the vertical element. Additionally, the top wires exhibit capacitance directly to the vertical element. Together, each top wire contributes to the total capacitance. If the lines are of the correct length, they will add just enough capacitance to overcome the short vertical's capacitive reactance and bring it to resonance.

Some physical transmission-line variables, like the ground-conductor diameter, are not readily determined. And that in turn makes determining the line characteristics and top-wire lengths difficult. One solution is to use a modeling program, such as *EZNEC,* that takes into account the antenna environment. The ground conductivity and

tical element, where the horizontal wires join, the current splits into two equal, but opposite, components. If these two segment currents are summed, their value is very close to that of the corresponding quarter-wave-vertical segment. Thus, the current distributions produced by the two antennas are nearly identical. Because the vertical and flattop will have unequal feed-point resistance in practice, the currents will be different in magnitude, but have proportional distributions.[2]

Fig 2 shows *EZNEC* far-field elevation patterns for the quarter wave and the flattop vertical antennas. The quarter-wave vertical produces a slightly lower takeoff angle. Thus, little pattern difference exists between the two antennas, even though the flattop is much shorter!

Because of the flattop's lower R_r, its

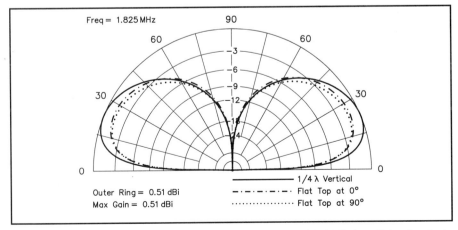

Fig 2—Elevation patterns for ¼-λ and flattop verticals with 16 ¼-λ radials elevated 0.5 feet over real ground. The flattop pattern at 0° is for the plane that contains the flattop, and the pattern at 90° for the plain that is perpendicular to the flattop.

dielectric constant can be selected, and even two different ground media can be modeled.[5] Using this approach, and starting with a vertical slightly less than a full quarter-wavelength, the horizontal top-wire lengths can be adjusted until the antenna is resonant at the desired frequency.[6]

I used this method to establish the relationship between the flattop's vertical (V) and horizontal (H) lengths. Results from the modeling are shown in **Fig 3**, where the V and H relationship is expressed as the ratio V/H. For any vertical length (V), from 0.025 λ to 0.2375 λ, the corresponding top-wire length (H) can be determined. The vertical lengths are listed and entered as a decimal fraction of a wavelength on the horizontal axis. While the vertical axis gives the V/H ratio.

As earlier stated, conductor diameter is a factor in determining the transmission line impedance (Z_s); therefore, three different length-to-diameter (l/d) curves are given in Fig 3. I used ratios of 25,000:1, 1000:1 and 100:1 in the modeling. These nonlinear curves reveal why simply using V + H = ¹/₄ λ is often inaccurate.

When relating a quarter-wavelength to a length in feet, as in Eq 1, the constant 234 provides the conversion factor that takes into account the speed at which radio waves travel in free space, and antenna end effects. Likewise, conversion constants are provided for each of the 3 flattop l/d ratios, but here they differ from Eq 1, in that they are being specified for a full wavelength:

For l/d = 25,000:1
λ (ft) = 961/f (MHz)   (Eq 3)

For l/d = 1000:1
λ (ft) = 950/f (MHz)   (Eq 4)

For l/d = 100:1
λ (ft) = 930/f (MHz)   (Eq 5)

Since the flattop's V/H ratio will be a function of the selected vertical length, it was decided to use a full quarter wavelength as the l/d reference value. Just take a full-size quarter-wave vertical's length, the element diameter, and calculate the l/d ratio. Although a 25,000:1 l/d ratio may appear a bit high at first, a 160-meter flattop made with #14 AWG wire has this ratio. On the other end, a 10-meter flattop made from 1-inch tubing would have an l/d ratio of about 100:1. Therefore, the above l/d ratios pretty well cover most designs.

Due to the wide V/H range presented in Fig 3, resolving the ratio precisely can be difficult. Most installations will tend to use short vertical lengths, so expanding the scales for these lengths helps improve resolution. In **Fig 4**, the graphs have been expanded to better show the V/H details for

vertical lengths of 0.025 λ to 0.125 λ.

Use of the V/H graphs is not difficult. Consider a flattop for 1.825 MHz. A vertical length must be decided upon: let's use the 44 foot length from Fig 1B. The antenna will be constructed of #14 AWG wire, which has a diameter of 0.064 inch. Plugging 1.825 MHz into Eq 1, and then dividing by 0.064 provides an l/d ratio of about 25,000:1. Next, using λ Eq 3, take 961 and divide by 1.825. One wavelength, for this antenna design, is then 526.6 feet. Now taking 44 feet, and dividing by 526.6 feet, yields 0.084—the vertical section's fraction of a

wavelength (0.084 λ).

Using the expanded scale of Fig 4, enter the Vertical Element–Fraction of a Wavelength scale at 0.084 λ, and follow it up to where it intersects the 25,000:1 curve. Moving straight across to the V/H scale produces a ratio of about 0.66. This means the vertical (V) element has a length 0.66 times that of each horizontal (H) top wire. The 44 foot V length divided by 0.66 indicates a top-wire length of 66.7 feet. The total flattop span is twice this; about 133.4 feet—about the same length as shown in Fig 1B.

To test the V/H information of Figs 3 and

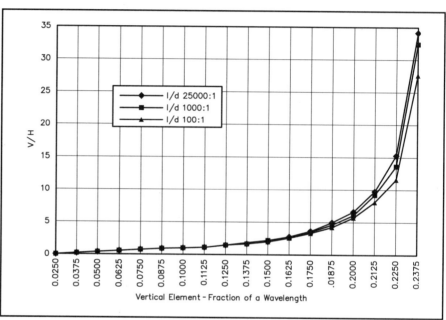

Fig 3—Ratio of vertical segment (V) to horizontal (H) for a single-wire flattop vertical.

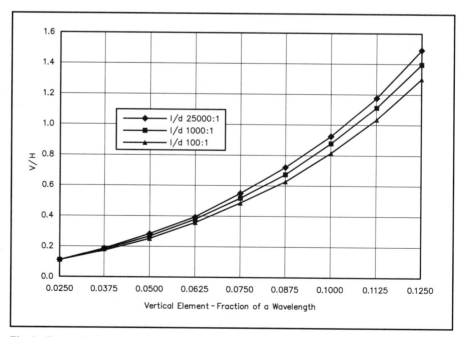

Fig 4—Expanded scale presentation of V/H ratio for the single-wire flattop vertical.

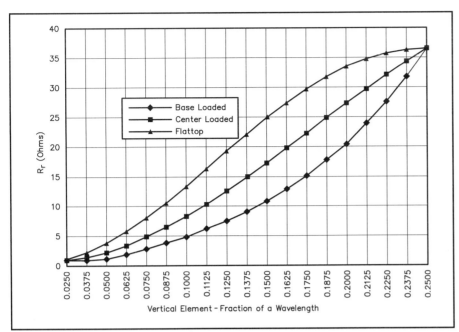

Fig 5—Comparison of radiation resistance (R_r) for the flattop and inductively loaded verticals.

4, I constructed a 6-foot tall 20-meter flattop from #12 wire. From Fig 4 the top-wire lengths (H) were derived and established at 8.5 feet per side. The test antenna was built using this length, but when all the pruning was done, the top wires were actually closer to 7.25 feet—about 15% shorter!

I was a bit concerned at first, but further analysis of the *EZNEC* model provides a clue why this happened. The V/H graphs were developed using R_g equal to 0 Ω. When a higher R_g was included in the model, the top-wire length decreased. The test antenna's ground return had been hastily constructed using four quarter-wave radials, suspended a few inches above landscaping pebbles. Certainly this is a high loss ground return at most locations. All this suggests that ground has a greater-than-expected effect on the antenna's *transmission line* characteristics.

To test the idea, 12 additional quarter-wave radials were added to the original 4. This would have the effect of substantially reducing R_g from its former value. SWR measurements made before and after the radial additions, indicated an increase in the resonant frequency by nearly 300 kHz! Additional top-wire length was required to

reestablish resonance. In most practical applications where the ground return is not ideal, the top-wire lengths will be 5 to 15% shorter than called for in the ideal case, but it is easier to start out too long and then trim the wires shorter for resonance.

If a less-than-optimum ground return is employed, one with few radials, the return currents must flow through the lossy earth. The earth then plays a larger part in the transmission line characteristics; acting not only as one conductor, but also as part of the dielectric between the two conductors. As a result, the transmission line characteristics change considerably from the ideal case; not only in impedance (Z_s), but also by reducing the velocity factor (VF). The VF reduction causes the speed at which the electromagnetic wave propagates along the antenna length to slow. Therefore, for the wave to traverse the quarter-wavelength in the same allotted time, the length must be made shorter. This effect is also at work in coaxial cable, where the dielectric causes capacitance to increase and the velocity factor to decrease.

As I stated earlier, reducing the flattop's vertical length (V) results in progressively

lower R_r, as illustrated in **Fig 5**. Following the flattop's R_r curve, it increases in a sine-like manner until it converges on 36 Ω maximum at a quarter-wavelength.

Curves for base and center-loaded verticals using lossless loading inductors are also included in Fig 5 for comparison. These produce exponential and *nearly* straight-line curves, respectively, which also converge on 36 Ω. At that point, the antenna is a quarter-wavelength vertical with no loading. Fig 5 shows that the flattop always provides a higher R_r than an equally tall base- or center-loaded antenna. For this reason, it will always operate with higher efficiency. And because the base and center-loaded antennas use loading coils, with their inherent losses, it further reduces their efficiencies.[7]

The flattop's advantage is even more dramatic when the vertical length is in the range of 0.125 λ to 0.2 λ, and a low R_g return is present. These longer lengths often use a tower as the vertical element on the low bands. An HF beam antenna atop the tower will provide capacitive loading in the same way as top wires.

Efforts must be made to minimize the ground return resistance, R_g, if maximum efficiency is to be attained with any ground-dependent antenna. This dictates that many buried ground radials, or alternately elevated radials, be employed at the base of the antenna.[8] Radio waves penetrate the earth more deeply at lower frequencies, and the earth becomes more lossy at higher frequencies.[9] An extensive ground-return system will lessen the antenna's sensitivity to the earth directly surrounding the antenna by making the antenna less dependent on the earth return.

One might assume that using large diameter conductors could provide an antenna with a substantially shorter horizontal span, but the curves of Figs 3 and 4 suggest the contrary. It is true that a top-hat with larger surface area will result in greater capacitance to ground, however, it is the current distribution along the vertical element that has a profound affect on the final dimensions. This can bring some surprising results.

Using the earlier 160-meter flattop example, **Table 1** gives the horizontal top-wire lengths required to bring a 44-foot

Table 1

Relationship of Element Diameter and Required Length for the 160-meter Flattop

Vert Element	Vert	Horiz Element	Top Wire (per side)	Feed Point R_r	2:1 SWR BW
#14 wire	44 ft	#14 wire	66.7 ft	9.8 Ω	38 kHz
1.5 in. tube	44 ft	#14 wire	78.8 ft	9.9 Ω	50 kHz
1.5 in. tube	44 ft	1.5 in. tube	68.5 ft	9.8 Ω	54 kHz
#14 wire	44 ft	1.5 in. tube	55.5 ft	9.7 Ω	40 kHz

vertical element into resonance when the vertical and horizontal sections use the same, or different, conductor diameters. Two element diameters have been selected for the example; 0.064 inch diameter wire (AWG #14) and 1.5 inch tube.

When the vertical and horizontal element diameters are the same, as in the first and third cases, the antenna dimensions are not considerably different, but note that the thinner diameter does result in a somewhat shorter top wire. Now look what happens when the element diameters are mixed; a difference of over 23 feet per side takes place between the second and fourth cases! The case of the thin vertical element, and the wide diameter horizontal element clearly provides the antenna with the most compact dimensions; while a thick vertical element and thin top-wire element produce the opposite effect—unfortunately!

A thin vertical element, while desirable from a size standpoint, may not be optimum from a bandwidth standpoint. As might be expected, the 2:1 SWR bandwidth is narrowest when the elements are made of thin wire, and broadest when the elements are made of tubing. These bandwidths will increase as greater ground loss (R_g) is introduced into a real antenna system. The bandwidth—narrow or wide—should not be of any consequence when a transmatch and low-loss feed line are employed at the station.

Multiple-Wire Flattop Antenna

The previous example shows that the horizontal top-wire length can be reduced significantly if its diameter is made large compared to the vertical element. In fact this may not be practicable. Conductors of large diameters can be heavy and difficult to support over a wide span, but the same benefit can be realized by using multiple parallel

wires of smaller diameter. The more wires used, and the wider they are spaced, the greater the span reduction will be. The parallel-wire configuration changes the transmission line impedance (Z_s) such that it provides the required loading capacitance in a shorter length.

Fig 6A shows a simple, multiple-wire flattop using three parallel wires, each spaced 1 foot apart. For direct comparison, I've used a 44-foot vertical element tuned to 1.825 MHz. In this antenna the three parallel wires are connected together at the center and at each end. Each wire carries nearly identical current and maintains the same phase relationship with its adjacent wires.

This flattop arrangement produces an antenna with a total span of 78.8 feet, an R_r of 9.7 Ω, and a bandwidth of about 38 kHz. When compared to the single-wire equivalent, with a 134.4 foot span, the width is reduced by about 40% with almost no change in R_r or bandwidth! Such a design permits a 160 meter flattop in a space not much larger than a 40 meter dipole.

Fig 6B shows another three-wire flattop with one important difference; only the center wire connects to the vertical portion. In this configuration, the required horizontal span is reduced to 132.8 feet. This is not much difference in length, but it is quite different from a current distribution standpoint as you will see.

If the antenna of Fig 6B is momentarily opened at points "a" and "b" little change in resonant frequency will be noticed. (It may move up slightly.) That is because the current at these points is nearly zero and opening them has little affect. The majority of the current flow is in the center wire, and it divides as it reaches the end of its length. It then folds back in the outer wires flowing in the opposite direction. The outer wire cur-

rents are thus out of phase with that in the center wire, but drop off rapidly so their interaction is minimal. Performance of this design is virtually identical to that of Fig 6A.

Using the same method described for the single-wire flattop, I developed a similar V/H graph for a three-wire flattop, like that of Fig 6A. Since most applications will likely use the shorter vertical lengths, the graph shown in **Fig 7** is expanded like Fig 4. This graph represents a 25,000:1 l/d ratio, and a length-to-spacing (l/s) ratio of about 132:1. Once again, for purposes presented earlier, the spacing is also referenced to a full quarter wavelength.

A nice feature of the flattop is that for a given vertical element length the feed-point R_r is essentially independent of the top-wire design. Single and multiple-wire flat-tops, of most any design, will result in nearly identical R_r—provided the wires lie in the same plane or have the same slopes to them. This is shown in Table 1 for single-wire flattops when different top-wire lengths are employed. When the three-wire designs are used, they all have nearly equal R_r—about 9.8 Ω.

If the flattop spacing, shown in Fig 6A, is stretched and the ends are pulled in, so that a square is formed, a conventional top-hat structure is created. With appropriate sizing, the top-hat and flattop produce equivalent top loading and the same R_r. Note that the multiple-wire flattop can employ as many wires as can be practically accommodated resulting in even greater span reductions.

Coaxial Line Radiator Flattop

In a previous article, I suggested using an 80-meter dipole as a top-loaded vertical (flattop) on 160 meters.[10] This is accomplished by shorting the feed line at the end nearest the transmitter, and driving the feed-line (the vertical) and dipole (the horizontal top wires) against a ground-return system. The coaxial line becomes the actual radiator. Typically, the coaxial line is whatever length happens to be in the installation and that length may not be optimum for this particular application. That may result in an inability to achieve resonance on the band, and the radiation pattern may differ from expectations. Therefore, give some thought to the antenna dimensions before attempting this approach.

Let's replace the 44-foot vertical wire with a 44 foot length of coax. The coax ends nearest to ground are shorted together, while the other ends connect across the dipole center insulator. It may not be obvious, but in operation the coax is now serving a dual role. First, the actual radiation takes place along the outside of the coax braid. Second, the inside of the outer braid and the outside of the inner conductor form a transmission line stub. This can best be visualized with the help of **Fig 8A**. Here a single wire rep-

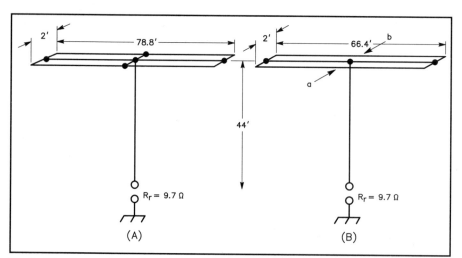

Fig 6—The three-wire flattop. At A, all horizontal wires are connected at the center and at each end. At B, only the the center wire connects to the vertical portion. All elements are constructed of #14 wire.

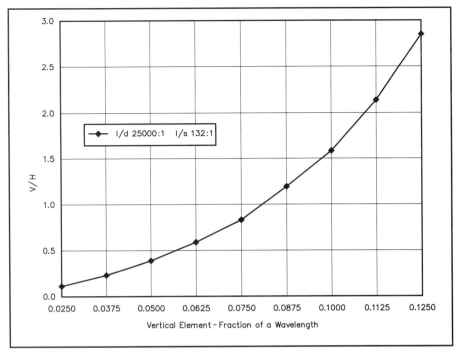

Fig 7—V/H ratio for the three-wire flattop.

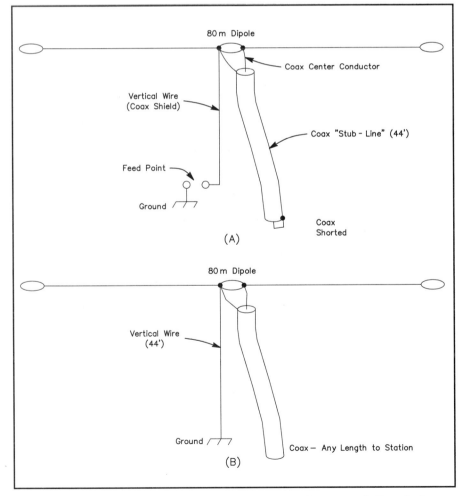

Fig 8—At A, *EZNEC* model of the 160/80-meter two-band antenna. At B, a design based on Eichenauer. See text.

resents the radiating coax braid, while a parallel coaxial line represents the stub. This is exactly the way it can be modeled in *EZNEC*.

A 44-foot coaxial stub, made from RG-8 or RG-58, will have an impedance of about 52 Ω, and have a velocity factor (VF) around 0.66. Divide 44 feet by the 0.66 VF, to find an electrical length of 66.7 feet—approximately $1/8$ wavelength on 160 meters.

A $1/8$ wavelength shorted stub will yield an inductive reactance (X_1) equal to the line's surge impedance (Z_s), or in this case; 52 Ω. Since the radiating braid connects to one side of the dipole, the stub lies in between it, and the other side of the dipole. Therefore, one side of the dipole has the equivalent of a 52 Ω inductor in series with it.

The addition of this inductor on one side unbalances the top-wire currents such that they are no longer equal and opposite. This effect results in some minor pattern distortion in the form of an increased horizontally polarized field component. Additionally, the inductor loads the antenna and causes it to resonate at a lower frequency, and reduces the antenna's bandwidth.

For this example, where the inductive reactance (X_1) is relatively low, the effects are small and the horizontal field increases by just a few decibels. Typically, it is down about 30 dB from the vertical field. But as the stub is made longer, X_1 increases and the loading and pattern distortion effects become more pronounced. To compensate for the added loading, the top-wire lengths must be reduced to reestablish resonance on 160 meters. At the same time, the top wires are becoming too short for resonance on 80 meters.

Elimination of the stub's inductive effect can be achieved by placing a capacitor between the center conductor and braid at the feed point. The coax braid is then driven against ground. For the 44 foot, eighth-wavelength example, the capacitor should have a reactance (X_c) equal to the impedance of the transmission line, eg, 52 Ω. Connected in this fashion, the 52-Ω X_c will appear as a short (0 Ω) across the dipole insulator, completing the top-wire connection. Since high voltages can develop across the capacitor in this application, one should assess the voltage and current handling requirements to make certain the component can withstand the applied levels.

Use of a balanced feed line, such as open-wire or ladder line, eliminates the stub problem altogether. Ideally, the current divides equally between each side of the balanced line and flows to the corresponding top wire. Each side sees the same loading and no stub is formed.

Probably the biggest drawback to using this approach for a two-band antenna is that the ideal feed point R_r is significantly different for each band. For the previous ex-

Antenna control box used at AC7A. The box contains relays and a broadband torroidal matching transformer.

ample R_r will be about 10 Ω on 160 meters and 40 Ω on 80 meters. Even though ground loss resistance will raise the total antenna resistance on 160 meters, this suggests the use of an impedance matching network for 160, and then the ability to switch it out when using 80 meters. A better approach is one offered by Eichenauer in his 1983 *QST* article.[11] The basic layout is shown in Fig 8B. Although similar in design to the co-axial flattop, the feed line now only serves to feed the antenna. The antenna feed-point impedance is transformed to a value closer to 50 Ω on 160 meters, and is already near that on 80 meters. No complex matching or switching required!

Matching

A few words need to be said about matching the flattop's low feed point R_r. Fig 5 clearly shows that R_r will usually be much lower than the 52-Ω coax impedance often used in Amateur Radio applications. Even when R_g is summed with R_r, the total will likely result in a SWR that exceeds the 2:1 that most transceivers will tolerate. This can be handled in a number of ways: using a broadband multi-tap, autotransformer of the kind presented in the author's previous article, or a Sevick multi-impedance unun.[12,13] Similarly, a simple LC network such as an L network can be employed. Their design is covered in *The ARRL Antenna Book*.

Probably the easiest feed method to apply is to feed the antenna directly with a low-loss coaxial cable such as Belden 9913 or International 9089, and then rely on a transmatch to provide the 1:1 SWR. This would even relieve one from having to precisely tune the antenna for lowest SWR. Yes, the SWR may be high 3, 5, or even 10:1, but the losses will almost always be tolerable if the feed line length is kept reasonably short. This is easily realized at the lower frequencies where this type of antenna is most likely to be used. Operating with high SWR and high power levels can lead to high voltage levels being developed within the transmission line. But the voltage only increases by the square root of the SWR, over that of the 1:1 SWR condition; so in most cases the cable will be able to withstand the higher peak voltage.

Conclusions

The flattop antenna offers another possibility for an efficient, reduced-size antenna that should appeal to those who can't erect full-sized dipole or vertical antennas, but still want a low-angle radiator. Even though the text concentrated on the lower bands, these principles can be applied equally to antennas for the higher HF bands and beyond. Putting this in perspective, one can imagine an 11-foot, under-the-eve flattop for 40 meters, or a 2- or 3-foot 10-meter flattop barely visible above the roofline, or even a much improved replacement for your VHF hand-held's rubber ducky!

Acknowledgments

In particular, I would like to thank Ken, KO6RK, for his on-going e-mail discussions about various subjects presented in this article. And also Charlie, W4MEC, who raised the question about the difference in shorting, or not shorting the wires at the feed-point of the three-wire flattop.

A special "thank you" to my friend Jim, W7LM. He has always been very supportive of my writing efforts, and he comes to my rescue when I am having computer-related problems.

Notes

[1]W. J. Byron, "Short Vertical Antennas for the Low Bands: Part 1," *Ham Radio*, May 1983, p 36, Fig 1A.

[2]An impedance matched condition is assumed in each case.

[3]Richard C. Johnson and Henry Jasik, editors, *Antenna Engineering Handbook*, 2nd ed., (New York, McGraw-Hill, 1984), p 26-5.

[4]Thomas Kuehl, "Build Efficient, Short Vertical Antennas," *QST*, March 1998, p 39. A few readers suggested that there is more to the radiation efficiency than this simple equation involves. They pointed out that the imperfect ground surrounding the antenna, out many wavelengths, leads to what is referred to as "suck-in," a product of the Brewster effect. It results in signal cancellation at angles below the critical Brewster angle (see Note 9). If this effect is included in the equation, it would be equivalent to multiplying by a k factor (k < 1, at low angles). But there is little one can do to change the earth characteristics out tens or hundreds of wavelengths from the antenna, so one can realistically only affect R_a (by design) and R_g (by supplying the best possible return). Therefore, the equation is accurate considering those factors that we have some control over.

[5]Roy Lewallen, *EZNEC Users Manual*, Version 2.0, 1997, p 55.

[6]Modeling was accomplished using *EZNEC*, *MININEC* and high-accuracy grounds. When using the high-accuracy ground, 16 quarter-wave radials with tapered segments were employed. This ground type is recommended when dealing with horizontal wires at a height less than 0.1 λ. The *MININEC* ground type is an ideal ground, and allows the ideal radiation resistance (R_r) to be determined. In the model, I used a frequency of 1.825 MHz, an average ground conductivity, G=0.005 S/m, and an average dilelectric constant of 13.

[7]Kuehl, p 42, Table 1. Efficiency comparisons are made for base and center-loaded verticals. Refer to p 43, Table 2, example 1, for the flattop.

[8]Ibid, p 41.

[9]Capt Paul H. Lee, USN (Ret), *The Amateur Radio Vertical Antenna Handbook*, 2nd edition (Hicksville, New York, CQ Communications, 1996), Chapters 2 and 12. *Author note–this is an excellent source of information on vertical antennas.*

[10]Ibid, p 42.

[11]Carl Eichenauer, "A Top-Fed Vertical for 1.8 MHz–Plus 3," *QST*, September 1983, pp 25-27. For more information on feeding an antenna at the top-hat, see the article in note 4, pp 40 and 41.

[12]Thomas Kuehl, "An Efficient Multiband Vertical for 160 through 20 Meters," *QST*, October 1998, p 45. Also see, "Feedback," *QST*, November 1998, p 75, for a correction.

[13]Jerry Sevick, "A Multimatch Unun," *CQ*, April 1993, pp 28-30.

Broadbanding the Elevated, Inverse-Fed Ground Plane Antenna

By Sam Leslie, W4PK
1038 Lone Pine Terrace
Goode, VA 24556-2545

N4KG's elevated ground-plane has become a popular antenna for the lower frequencies. W4PK offers some ideas on making it cover both CW and SSB portions of the 80-meter band.

Constructing an antenna that will operate with reasonable SWR in the CW DX segment at the bottom end of 80 meters *and* the SSB DX segment at 3.8 MHz has always been a challenge. I discovered the approach I'll describe here quite by accident while evaluating Tom (N4KG) Russell's inverse-fed, elevated ground-plane concept (described in June 1994 *QST*) on my tower.

To make a long story short, what I found was that two sets of radials at 90° with respect to each other could each be cut to achieve a low SWR at their respective parts of the band, producing two dips in the SWR curve. As ON4UN states in his ARRL book, *Low Band DXing,* two in-line radials provide good ground-plane performance. Thus, one pair is dedicated for the CW portion of the band and the other pair is set for the SSB portion of the band. This, of course, assumes that the radials are sufficiently elevated to avoid coupling losses with the ground.

The challenging part is to find the right spot on the tower to make this technique work. Basically, this is where the electrical length of the tower, as loaded with antennas, is equivalent to 90° (λ/4) above the feed point. N4KG's article describes a procedure you can use to estimate this, both in terms of an equation derived from ON4UN's book, and with a table describing the effective equivalent loading effect of several types of Yagi antennas.

A step-by-step approach to constructing this antenna is as follows:

1. Approximate the electrical height (in degrees) of your tower from the equation in N4KG's article as follows:

L = 0.38F[H+(2S)$^{1/2}$]

where F is in MHz, H is in feet, and S is the equivalent area of the Yagi(s) in square feet of wind area. This number must be greater than 90° ($^{1}/_{4}\lambda$) for this concept to work. An electrical length of 120° or more will assure that the radials are sufficiently elevated above ground for reasonable performance.

2. Next subtract 90° from the number obtained above to determine the electrical height (in degrees) above ground that represents the target "sweet spot."

3. Now convert degrees into feet or meters for the frequency halfway between your two target SWR minima (ie, 3.65 MHz). For feet, the relationship is simply:

$$\text{Feet} = \frac{(\text{Electrical length, degrees}) \times 492}{180° \times F_{MHz}}$$

In meters, the relationship is:

$$\text{Meters} = \frac{(\text{Electrical length, degrees}) \times 150}{180° \times F_{MHz}}$$

This will be the starting point for finding the "sweet spot" above ground level for your tower.

4. Cut one pair of $^{1}/_{4}$-wavelength radials near the bottom end of the 80-meter band. I used 69 feet each, or a total of 138 feet from radial tip to radial tip for 3.550 MHz.

5. Cut the second pair of radials for the phone portion of the band (65 feet each for 3.8 MHz)

6. Join all four radials together at an insulator temporarily hooked to the calculated "sweet spot" in step 1 above. Make sure that the CW radial pair is at right angles to the SSB radial pair. Also, pull the radials out to temporary posts such that the ends are at least 8-10 feet off the ground, and that the sag is minimum (less than 3 feet or so).

7. Connect the center lead of a short piece of coax cable (less than 2 feet) to the cross point where the radials are joined together, and temporarily connect the braid of the coax to the tower. Since the impedance of this antenna will be quite low, connecting a 50:25-ohm unun transformer at the end of this short piece of

coax may make measuring SWR easier. Connect the 25-Ω port of the unun to the short piece of coax, and connect the SWR meter to the 50-Ω port.

8. Measure the SWR, and determine whether the SWR minima are low or high with respect to the target. NOTE: *Do not attempt to adjust the length of the radials to move the SWR minima!* You will likely not be successful if you are too far from the actual "sweet spot" on the tower. The goal is to move the connection point on the tower to where a reasonable SWR match is obtained for both portions of the band.

If the SWR minima are low in frequency, then you need to raise the connection point on the tower. Likewise, if the SWR minima are higher than desired, you will need to lower the tower connection point. An easy way to do this is to climb the tower with your handy battery-powered SWR box and have a helper loosen and then retighten the radials as you work your way up or down the tower.

The hard way (my way) is to climb down each time you make an adjustment and check the SWR. If you check the SWR at the bottom of the tower, connect a length of coax from the 50-Ω port on the unun, and run this coax down *inside* the tower to the base. I made my measurements at the tower base primarily to remove any temptation to drop the SWR analyzer while I was on the tower. With either method, you will find that the final adjustment will be a matter of inches to balance the SWR minimum at each target frequency.

I used Amidon's multiple-tap unun (part number W2MFI-1.78:1-HMMUSD) since I was expecting a fairly low impedance (below 18 Ω or so). However, I found that drooping the radials at an angle of 35-45° from horizontal raised the impedance above 20 Ω. Be careful about getting the ends of the radials too close to the ground. I had observed some unpredictable effects when the ends were less than 6 feet or so from ground. Eight to 10 feet or higher should be okay, and would be preferred anyway if you have large mammals roaming the area. The 50:22.16-Ω tap on the Amidon unun proved to be the best match in my case. Any 50:25-Ω unun rated at your preferred power level should work just as well.

A quarter-wave matching network cut for 3.65 MHz and made from 75-Ω coax as described in N4KG's article may work just as well. It might be worth a try if you wish to save the cost of an unun transformer and minimize complexity.

Note that the above approach assumes that your guy wires are insulated from the tower and that the guys are either broken into nonresonant lengths or made of insulating material.

An Example

Fig 1 represents my specific application. I have a rather large multiband beam on a 24-foot boom that covers 40 through 10 meters. In addition, I have a dual-band VHF/UHF gain antenna on top of this tower (more on this later). Applying the formula in step 1 above (and ignoring the VHF/UHF gain antenna on top), I calculated an electrical height of 144°.

Subtracting 90° from this number gives a point on the tower where a quarter wavelength at 3.65 MHz remains above the target "sweet spot." This point is thus 54° above ground. The initial starting point is therefore (54° × 492)/(180° × 3.65 MHz), or 40.4 feet above ground. My initial try resulted in two SWR minima, with one at around 3.2 MHz and the other at about 3.5 MHz. This indicated that I was too low

on the tower, and that the VHF/UHF gain antenna was contributing, as expected, to the tower's electrical length.

I then raised the attachment point until I found the best compromise for operation in the desired band segments. This point was 46 feet above ground. Again, do not succumb to the temptation to trim the radial lengths to move the points where the SWR minima occur. I found that it's better to move the attachment point on the tower in increments as small as six inches, if necessary, to achieve the desired balance. The key point here is that you should try to find the point where an equivalent antenna length of 90° above the connection point is halfway between your two desired band segments. With the 50:22.16 transformer in place, the SWR curve that I ended up with for this arrangement is shown in **Fig 2**.

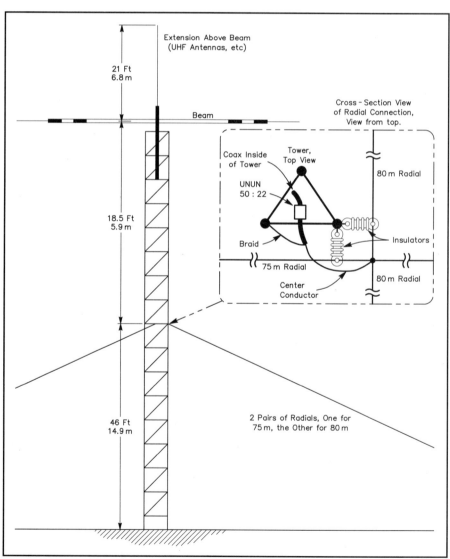

Fig 1—Details of the reverse-fed ground-plane at W4PK. The inset shows the feed-point details. Keep the two sets of radials as close to 90° from each other as possible. Don't try to resonate the antenna by adjusting radial lengths.

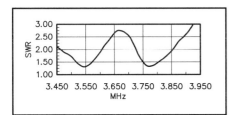

Fig 2—SWR curve of the reverse-fed ground-plane antenna installed on W4PK's tower. The antenna is placed on the tower at a height that places the SWR minima at 3.55 and 3.8 MHz. This equates to 90° above the feed point at 3.65 MHz. The antenna is fed with a 50:25-Ω unun transformer or quarter-wave coaxial matching section.

Note that the VHF/UHF antenna on my tower contributes as a part of the radiator for the elevated ground plane. If you have a similar arrangement, be sure to check the 3.5-MHz RF signal level at the input to your VHF/UHF equipment. Likewise, check the level of your VHF/UHF transmitted signal at the input to your HF transceiver. In my case, I routed the coax for the VHF/UHF antenna down the inside of the tower to reduce coupling from the 3.5 MHz signal onto the coax shield. In addition, I employ two VHF/UHF lightning protectors (one at the tower base, the other at the entry point to the house) rated for 30 MHz and above. They provide some degree of attenuation at 3.5 MHz, and the signal at the input to my VHF/UHF equipment is at a very safe –40 dBm level with a kilowatt applied to the 80-meter antenna.

You may need to employ a high-pass or band-pass filter if the level that you measure is significantly higher. I also found that the signal level from the VHF/UHF equipment at the HF transceiver input to be negligible. Note that the VHF/UHF antenna is not necessary for the successful application of this approach.

Results

I have been very pleased with this antenna's performance. I installed it as a temporary arrangement while I was constructing a full-size 4-square antenna for 75/80 meters. I had the opportunity to compare its performance with the first vertical of the 4-square, under which I had 72 buried radials of nominally 0.31 λ each. Basically, I found that the difference in signal levels with a local ham about two miles away was less than 1 dB. On-the-air listening tests on low-angle signals from Europe further confirmed that there was no discernible difference in received signal levels between the full-size, ground-based vertical and the elevated, top-loaded groundplane. For reference, I have since completed the 4-square array, and as expected, the 4-square does show a solid S-unit (4-5 dB) improvement in its favored direction over the elevated ground-plane.

Short Radials for Ground-Plane Antennas

By Rudy Severns, N6LF
PO Box 589
Cottage Grove, OR 97424
Rudys@ordata.com

Think your elevated radials always have to be full size? N6LF lets you in on some great ideas to lessen the "wingspan" of radials, especially near the beach.

Dean Straw's (N6BV) article[1] in this book describing the 6Y2A operation and beach-front verticals for DXpeditions shows how useful a vertical or vertical array can be—if you can put it over or adjacent to saltwater. For 20 meters and higher in frequency it is practical to use $\lambda/2$ verticals with little or no ground plane. For 40 meters and lower in frequency, however, a $\lambda/2$ height becomes prohibitive and a $\lambda/4$ ground-plane with elevated radials is a more practical form of vertical. Unfortunately, as you go down in frequency the length of the quarter-wave radials becomes very long (approximately 132 feet on 160 meters), and this takes up a lot of area. In addition, most DXpeditions can't place the radials very high off the ground. This results in a number of wires to trip over or strangle on. And if you have several verticals, the beach really becomes an obstacle course!

One way to reduce the problem is to shorten the radials (leaving the vertical part of the antenna as near a quarter-wave as possible) and use either a loading inductor, a top-loading hat or some combination of the two. The question is, "How much do you lose as you shorten the radials?" I took a look at this using *GNEC-4*, a *NEC-4.1*-based modeling program, and the following is what I discovered. Keep in mind of course that all this assumes *NEC* knows what it's talking about!

A 160-Meter Vertical

I have been planning on a beach-front 160-meter vertical for some property I have on Willapa Bay, WA, so I started with that model. While you probably wouldn't try to construct a full-size quarter-wave 160-meter vertical for a DXpedition, the com-

puted results are very similar no matter what band you use with a beach-front vertical. The antenna I am planning will use four elevated radials and will be made of #13 wire. I was planning to use a wooden A-frame made from three Douglas fir trees (as shown in my *QEX* article[2]) to support the antenna. For modeling, the initial lengths of the radials and the vertical were made equal and adjusted for resonance at 1.840 MHz. I then progressively shortened the radials (keeping the vertical height the same) and re-resonated the antenna with a single series inductor feeding all four radials at the feed point.

An inductor Q of 250 was assumed and with a little care this should be readily achievable. In a salt atmosphere you must put the coil in a sealed enclosure, or by morning the Q will be close to zero. I modeled the base of the antenna at 1 foot and at 10 feet, and for comparison used three types of ground: perfect, seawater ($\varepsilon = 80$, the dielectric constant, and $\sigma = 5.0$ S/m, the conductivity) and average ($\varepsilon = 13$, $\sigma = 0.005$ S/m).

The results are shown in **Figs 1** and **2**. These graphs include both the ground loss

and the loss due to the series resistance of the loading inductor. The small wire loss was not included. We can see from Fig 1 the advantage of seawater over average ground: about 4.2 dB more gain for full-length radials. In addition, the peak gain occurs at an elevation angle of 7° for seawater, as opposed to 21° for average ground. As the radial length is reduced the peak gain angle changes very little, but the peak gain goes down. The height of the radials over seawater made very little difference, and the difference between ideal ground and seawater was also very small. The primary difference over seawater is the added loss in the loading inductor.

While Fig 1 shows the peak gain, you can see the variation much better in Fig 2, where the *change* in gain is plotted. Even if you use radials only 40 feet long (0.07 λ!), over seawater the loss is less than 0.2 dB. This is very attractive for DXpeditions. The value of the loading inductor is very nearly the same for all the grounds and heights so that the loss due to the inductor's series resistance is pretty much the same at each radial length. Over average ground, however, the gain reduction is much larger due to in-

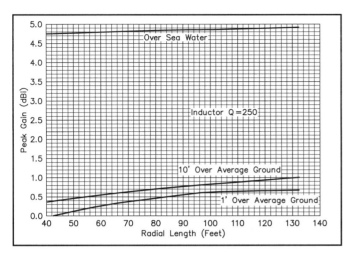

Fig 1—Peak gain for (λ/4-high vertical with four, coil-loaded short radials on 160 meters. The loading coil is assumed to have an unloaded Q of 250. Over seawater, the peak gain doesn't change much, even for quite short radials, while the gain is close to 5 dB less over ground with average conductivity and dielectric constant.

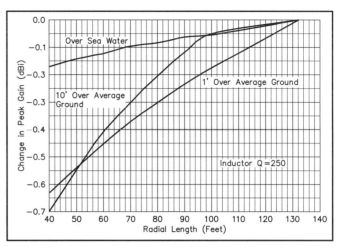

Fig 2—The same data presented in Fig 1, but magnified by showing the change in peak gain versus radial length on 160 meters.

creased ground losses as the radials are shortened.

At some sites the antenna may actually be over seawater, but it is more likely it will be up on the beach adjacent to seawater. How much effect will that have? That depends on two things: the beach's ground characteristics and the distance to the water. If the ground under the antenna is regularly flooded with seawater the conductivity is going to be pretty high. But that may not always be the case, and fairly poor ground characteristics may be encountered—especially on coral islands.

To check this out I modeled the 160-meter antenna site as though it were a circular island located in a sea of saltwater. The island was made up of ground with average conductivity and dielectric constant, and the distance to the saltwater was varied by changing the radius of the island. The results are shown in **Fig 3**. As soon as you move away from the water (that is, you have a larger-diameter island) the peak gain starts to drop and the increased ground loss due to shorter radials shows up.

The message is simple—select a nice salt marsh that is flooded twice a day, or put the antenna out on the reef with water under it! Otherwise, put the antenna as close to the water as practical.

Reducing Losses

We know that the losses due to use of a loading device such as a coil can be reduced by using a higher-Q coil, by moving a loading coil from the base of the antenna to a more optimum location up the vertical radiator, by top-loading or some combination of these.[3,4] For a ¼-λ vertical with shortened, loaded radials over seawater the

ground losses are very small, and even the losses due to base loading of a shortened vertical radiator are small. It is questionable, therefore, whether it is worth the trouble to spend much time trying to minimize the loading loss, except for the case where a vertical's electrical height is much shorter than λ/4.

Unfortunately, short verticals with loading are often used for 80 and 160 meters. On those bands all of the tricks for minimizing losses will have to be used, because shortening the radials as well as the vertical itself can seriously degrade performance, even with a seawater ground.

I looked at modifying the ground plane to see if a more complex radial structure would help. Using eight radials, the difference in ground loss was insignificant. However, the additional radials did reduce the reactance needed to resonate the antenna by almost ½. That would reduce the loading coil loss, since a smaller amount of inductance would be needed.

I then looked at tying the ends of the radials together with cross conductors to form a square wagon-wheel shape with four radials. Again, the ground losses were not reduced greatly (≈ 0.2 dB). There appears to be no substitute for long radials if you want that last fraction of a dBi in gain. We really have known this since the 1930s![5,6,7] The reactance, however, was greatly reduced and with the wagon-wheel structure the antenna is resonant—without loading—with a radius of 58 feet, less than half that for normal radials.

Given the fierce corrosion experienced over or near seawater, it would be a good idea to use insulated wire for the radials, some paint on the vertical tubing, conduc-

tive joint compound and very careful sealing of all joints and connections.

A Closer Look at Ground Losses

The increase in ground loss with shorter radials is worth a closer look. The additional loss shows up as an increase in feedpoint resistance over that for ideal ground. **Fig 4** is a graph of feedpoint resistance as a function of radial length, without the resistance of the loading inductor. Over seawater the effect of ground loss is very small. It's hard to see it on the graph. Over average ground, however, the effect is very obvious and the loss increases at lower heights.

When generating the data for Fig 3, I noticed that the feedpoint resistance was constant for different values of "island" radius. This is due to the way *NEC* computes impedance, where it takes into account only the first ground characteristic and assumes for this purpose that the ground under the antenna is infinite. For far-field calculations, however, the two ground zones (that is, the ground under the vertical and the seawater surrounding our model island) are taken into account. This means that the ground loss in the model, as reflected in the feedpoint resistance, may be higher than it actually is when close to the water.

NEC can provide a direct calculation of total ground losses using the so-called "RP" card. This card sets the parameters for radiation patterns and can provide a calculation of average gain. An example is given in the Appendix.

Conclusions

If you are lucky enough to be near or on seawater, you can drastically reduce the size of your elevated ground-plane. With a little

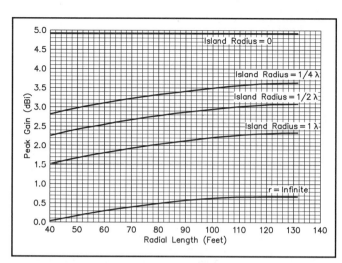

Fig 3—Peak gain for a (λ/4-high vertical with four, coil-loaded short radials on 160 meters, but this time where the antenna is located on a circular island in a saltwater ocean. Three different radial heights are shown over average ground. The radius of the circular island is equal to the length of the shortened radials in this model. Obviously, you should mount your antenna and radials over—or at least as close to—salt water, as you possibly can!

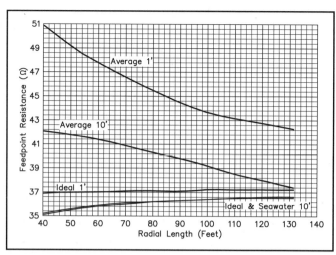

Fig 4—Feed-point resistance as a function of radial length and radial height above ground. Here, the loss resistance of the loading inductor is removed. The effect of ground loss over soil is large compared to that over salt water.

care, loss due to the loading components can be small, on the order of a few tenths of a dB. If you must place the antenna over poorer ground, such as the beach, you should try to get as close to the water as possible and keep the radius of the ground-plane radials greater than λ/8. You can, of course, use a smaller ground plane if you are willing to accept the reduced peak gain.

And here is another important consideration: Even with λ/4 radials, you should decouple the feed line from the antenna with a common-mode choke (balun). As the radials become shorter this becomes even more important, since the voltage between the base of the antenna and ground increases.

References

[1]D. Straw, N6BV, "Antennas Here Are Some Verticals on the Beach...," Elsewhere in this book.

[2]Rudy Severns, N6LF, "Another Way To Look at Vertical Antennas," QEX, Mar/Apr 1999.

[3]J. Belrose, VE3BLW, "Short Antennas for Mobile Operation," QST, Sep 1953; see also subsequent ARRL Mobile Manuals.

[4]B. Brown, W6TWW, "Optimum Design Of Short Coil-Loaded High-Frequency Mobile Antennas," The ARRL Antenna Compendium, Vol 1 (Newington: ARRL, 1985), pp 108-115.

[5]G. Brown, "The Phase and Magnitude of Earth Currents near Radio Transmitting Antennas," Proc IRE, Feb 1935, Vol 23, No. 2, pp 168-182.

[6]Brown, Lewis and Epstein, "Ground Systems as a Factor In Antenna Efficiency," Proc IRE, Jun 1937, Vol 25, No. 6, pp 753-787.

[7]J. Devoldere, ON4UN, "Antennas and Techniques for Low-Band DXing," (Newington: ARRL, second edition 1994),

Chapter 9, Fig 9-40 and supporting text.

[8]GNEC-4 Users Manual, Nittany Scientific, Airline Highway, Suite 361, Hollister, CA 95023.

[9]Gerald J. Burke, Numerical Electromagnetics Code—"NEC-4, Part I: Users Manual (NEC-4.1)," Lawrence Livermore National Laboratory, Jan 1992, UCRL-MA-109338 Pt I, pp 76-78.

Appendix

The average gain for a lossless antenna in free space is 1.0 (or 0 dBi). For a lossy antenna the average gain will be lower by the amount of the total loss. If you model using ideal conductors and lossless loads, then the reduction in average gain directly reflects the ground loss. Inserting the correct parameters for average gain can be a little tricky, however, until you get used to it. For example, when modeling an antenna over ground, instead of averaging over the surface of a sphere, the averaging is done over a hemisphere. Because the total power is radiated into only half as much space, the gain of a lossless antenna will be 2.0 (or 3.01 dBi).

You have to keep track of these things as you go along. As a check on my "card" entries (following the terminology for the FORTRAN-based NEC-4 software) when starting a new analysis, I make the ground perfect and the conductors lossless. I thus should get an average gain very near 1.0 or 2.0, depending whether I'm modeling in free space or over ground. If all is well, then I insert the real ground constants and proceed with the modeling.

The RP card has the following format:[8,9]

RP I1 I2 I3 I4 F1 F2 F3 F4 F5 F6

where:

I1 = Selects the mode of calculation; I1 = 0 for this example

I2 = Number of values of theta at which the field is to be calculated

I3 = Number of values of phi at which the field is to be calculated

I4 = An integer consisting of 4 digits (XNDA), each of which has a different function

X = Controls antenna output format; X = 1 for this example

N = Causes normalized gain to be printed; N = 0 for this example

D = Selects either power gain or directive gain; D = 0 for this example

A = requests calculation of average gain; A = 2 for this example

F1 = Initial theta angle

F2 = Initial phi angle

F3 = Increment for theta

F4 = Increment for phi

F5 and F6 are not needed for this example.

Greek letter θ (theta) is the angle measured from zenith (directly overhead) downward. For a free-space antenna, θ will vary from 0° to 180° and for an antenna over ground, the range is 0° to 90°. Greek letter φ (phi) is the angle moving counter-clockwise (viewed at the antenna from the X axis towards the Y axis) rotating around the Z axis. The range of φ is 0° to 360°. The number of values for theta (I2) and phi (I3) will be the range selected divided by the increment (F3 or F4) plus 1. The number of values must be an integer.

The number of increments of theta and phi must be large enough to cover the entire field, unless there are known symmetries that can be exploited to reduce the number of calculation points. For example, a free-space antenna will require a sphere, and an antenna over ground will require a hemisphere. For the case of an elevated-radial, ground-plane antenna with four radials, the field will repeat every 90° of phi. It is thus only necessary to compute one quadrant of the hemisphere. The accuracy of the averaging will depend on the number of points over which the gain is averaged. Fewer points mean less accuracy but much faster computation. The way you check your setup is to calculate the average gain for a lossless system, with perfect ground, no wire loss, etc. Under those perfect conditions the average gain ideally will be 1.0 or 2.0. The difference in the actual calculation is the error due to specification of overly coarse steps in the angles. The error in dB, for antennas over ground, can be expressed as error = 10 log (average gain/2). This gives the error directly in dB. Typically, I accept an error of 0.01 dB.

I usually start with 2° increments and go up or down after checking the lossless gain. The number of field points generated with $^1/_2$° increments can be quite large and noticeably slows the computation even on a workstation. This great a resolution will seldom be needed but you should always check an ideal version of the antenna model before proceeding with a real ground and lossy antenna.

In some cases where the field does not vary greatly with either θ or φ you can use larger increments in one plane to reduce the computation time. For example, with a four-radial ground-plane antenna, the field variation with φ, at a fixed θ, is quite small and usually needs only two values for φ—, that is, 0° and 90°. This greatly reduces the computation time. However, for a two-radial antenna, the pattern is asymmetrical and you must use smaller increments for φ.

A key point is to recognize that the number of points (I2 and I3) must be adjusted to give total coverage of the desired sector (sphere, hemisphere, or quadrant) when the increments (F2 and F3) are selected. Don't forget to include one extra point for the ends.

My RP card looks like this for one quadrant and 1° increments:

RP 0 91 91 1002 0 0 1 1

With four radials and only a small error this can be reduced to:

RP 0 91 2 1002 0 0 1 90

For an antenna over ground with a pattern symmetrical about the X axis:

RP 0 91 181 1002 0 0 1 1

The average gain will appear at the end of the output file in terms of absolute gain. You can convert it to dB by using 10 log (absolute gain) or 10 log (absolute gain/2).

Antennas Here are Some Verticals on the Beach...

By R. Dean Straw, N6BV
Senior Assistant Technical Editor, ARRL
5328 Fulton Street
San Francisco, CA 94121

To me it was a contest adventure of a lifetime—I was to be a member of the team operating 6Y2A on the 1998 DXpedition for the CQ World Wide DX CW Contest. My 84-year-old father came along too. Although he's not a ham, for almost 40 years he's watched me doing radio and has helped me put up lots of antennas. On this trip, he had ample opportunity to put up and take down lots and lots of antennas!

As a result of a lot of planning, hard work and dedication, the 6Y2A team set a new world's record for the multi-operator, multi-transmitter classification. The world record was particularly remarkable since we accomplished it from the continent of North America, where contacts with the USA and Canada only count for two points, rather than the three points accorded QSOs made with other continents, such as Europe or Asia.

We operated from a rented villa on the north coast of Jamaica. This location had been carefully chosen for its clear, over-the-ocean shot towards Europe, the USA and Japan. While long-path directions toward the south were blocked by a nearby steep volcanic cliff, the spectacular short path more than made up for that deficiency! As hams are fond of saying, "We could practically *see* Europe from our front porch."

Located about an hour from Montego Bay, we were well removed from the usual tourist haunts. This meant that expenses were moderate rather than tourist-level. And most importantly for our mission, we didn't suffer from the electrical noise typical in a densely populated urban environment. We had rented two villas. One was for operating the contest; one was for sleeping. Since the villas were side-by-side we had a beach front of about 800 feet on which we could place antennas. The story of the planning and execution of those antennas is the real subject of this article.

> ## A DXpedition to Jamaica for the CQ World Wide Contest, "Field Day" Style

Planning, Planning, Planning

Except for myself, the rest of the 6Y2A team had operated the CQWW CW contest as 6Y4A in 1997 from the same location. 6Y4A had come in second worldwide to 5V7A in Togo. The 5V7A team was intending to go all-out to defend their title in 1998, and the 6Y2A crew publicly announced that we were going to give them some heavy competition, even if only from a "two-point" country. Then we heard that there were going to be two other serious North American continental entries: the J6DX group was trying out the multi-multi category and so was a team headed by world-famous contester N6TJ, operating the superstation of TI2CF in Costa Rica. They were going to reactivate the TI1C call sign. I felt some irony in the situation, because the last time I had done a serious multi-multi from outside the USA was at TI1C in 1984, some fourteen years ago, together with fellow six-landers N6TJ, N6AA, N6ZZ and N6AW. I'll never forget the kindness and gracious hospitality of Carlos, TI2CF, on that trip. He had put together a really terrific station, with very big antennas.

The three teams from the North American continent were all gunning for a new North American record, but few among us hoped to seriously challenge the world's record, simply because we were operating from two-point land. The team at 5V7A was operating from the continent of Africa, where every European, USA or Japanese QSO was worth three points. Then, just before the contest we heard that there were some problems in Togo with the hotel from which 5V7A operated last year. This was really becoming an interesting horse race!

In 1997 the team at 6Y4A had engaged in what seemed then to be a daring experiment—they had used verticals near the saltwater, rather than horizontal Yagis on high towers. We intended to expand this approach in 1998.

What Elevation Angles Did We Need?

The first step planning an antenna system is to determine what elevation angles must be covered. Our operating credo could be summarized in the personal motto of Dave Patton, W9QA, the 40-meter operator at 6Y2A: "Be loud or be hosed!" We wanted to be loud in all areas around the world with large ham populations, especially on three-point continents. That meant that we needed to be loud, nay *very loud*, in Europe and Japan. Since the path to Japan from Jamaica is right through downtown Kansas City, we figured we might just as well be loud in the USA also.

Fig 1 shows an overlay of the enhanced elevation-angle statistical data from the 18th Edition of *The ARRL Antenna Book* on CD-ROM. This is for the 80-meter band from Jamaica to the continent of Europe. The bar graph shows elevation angles ranging from 1° to 27°. This statistical elevation-angle data was generated from thousands of computer runs using the *VOACAP* program. The data show the percentage of time a particular angle is open to Europe, for all months of the year and for all levels of solar activity. The biggest bargraph spike occurs at an elevation angle of 12°, representing about 11.5% of all the times the 80-meter band is open from Jamaica to Europe. A secondary peak occurs at 7°, for almost 10.5% of the time when the band is open.

That these angles are quite *low* angles is not readily apparent from a casual glance at Fig 1, at least not until the other lines on the graph are viewed carefully. The line with the small black rectangles represents the elevation pattern response of a really large 80-meter antenna—a three-element Yagi placed 200 feet above flat ground. Its peak response is at a 20° elevation, and at 7° the response is down some 5 dB from the peak.

Next, look carefully at the line with the small, lighter-shaded ovals. This represents the response of a two-element vertically polarized parasitic array on the beach right next to the saltwater. This array, a two-element Yagi turned on its side to be vertical—if you will, a *Vagi*—is just a bit stronger at an elevation of 7° than its 200-foot high three-element horizontal cousin. At 3° the two-element vertical array is some 8 dB stronger than its lofty cousin and at 17° elevation it is down only about 4 dB. Note how "flat" the response of this simple vertical parasitic array is over the

range from 1° to 30° elevation. This is actually one of its distinct advantages, since there are no *nulls* in the response, especially at higher elevation angles where signals often occur. We'll examine this important consideration some more later.

Let's examine the responses for some other types of 80-meter antennas. The line on Fig 1 with the small upward-pointing arrows represents the same kind of two-element vertical parasitic array, but this time located over "good ground," well removed from saltwater. This is typical for the kind of farmland found in parts of the US Midwest, with a conductivity of 5 mS/m and a dielectric constant of 13. This landlocked vertical array is down uniformly some 7 dB from its brother located at the edge of the ocean. The only difference between the two vertical arrays is the quality—or should I say, the *lack* of quality, so far as RF is concerned—of the ground. Sea water is hard stuff to beat when it comes to making loud signals with verticals.

Next, we have what most people would consider a darned good antenna, a dipole located 100 feet above flat ground. At 7° elevation, the dipole is down about 12 dB compared to the saltwater verticals and about 6 dB down at 12°. In other words, a darned good antenna, something most hams could only dream about, would be about 2 to 3 S-units down from the 80-meter antenna planned for 6Y2A for the range of elevation angles needed to cover Europe. (This assumes that a typical modern transceiver is

calibrated for about 4 dB per S-unit.)

Fig 2 shows the another 80-meter plot, but this time for the path from Jamaica to Japan. The prevailing angles are even lower than for the path to Europe. The elevation response of a parasitic array on the beach would be even more advantageous on this path compared to even a 200-foot high three-element Yagi. By the way, this antenna is not just a figment of our fervid imaginations. Rumor had it that one of our competitors had just such an antenna ready to play during the contest. (It turned out that the antenna was tuned for phone and wasn't actually used during the CW contest.)

Fig 3 shows the elevation angles needed on 40 meters plotted together with the responses for two types of antennas. The one with black rectangles is a common type of contest antenna on 40 meters, a two-element horizontally polarized Yagi mounted 100 feet over flat ground. Compared to this is the elevation pattern of the antenna used at 6Y2A, a pair of "ZR" vertical dipole antennas by Force 12, with one dipole tuned as a parasitic reflector. This is a very interesting antenna in that it is only 15 feet high! I'll describe it in more detail later on.

Again, theory says that a two-element vertical parasitic array on the beach should be very competitive with a much higher horizontally polarized Yagi antenna. And like the situation on 80 meters, this setup would be even more favorable for the 40-meter path from Jamaica to Japan, where the prevailing angles are very low, peaking at 2° for some 22% of the time when the band is open. Theory says that the vertical array should be loud on this band, and it was loud.

Fig 4 shows the situation on the 20-meter band from Jamaica to Europe. For angles less than about 11°, a vertical parasitic array located at the seashore would have the upper hand over a four-element Yagi located 100 feet over flat ground. At 6Y2A, we ended up using the array labeled "2×2 Verticals" in Fig 4 on 20 meters for some very practical reasons, despite the fact that the array labeled "4 Halfwave Verts" exhibits about 2 dB more gain over the range of angles needed. I'll discuss the different types of vertical arrays shown in Fig 4 in more detail later on in this article.

Fig 5 illustrates the important 15-meter situation towards Europe. We all felt during the planning stages that 15 meters was going to be a very important band in 1998, where many QSOs were going to be made. Here again, vertical arrays on the beach should be very competitive with an installation using a four-element Yagi mounted 60 feet over flat ground. This is the sort of antenna that an ambitious DXpedition might install. We intended to operate six stations from 160 to 10 meters. If we didn't put up a lot of verticals, we would have had to install no fewer

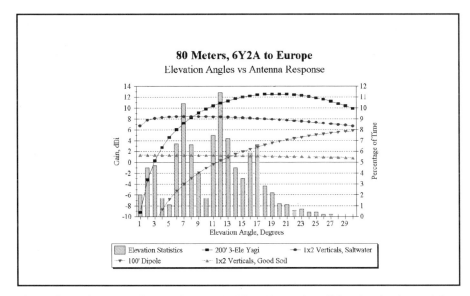

Fig 1—Statistical elevation angles needed for all months, all levels of solar activity, from Jamaica to Europe, compared with typical elevation-plane patterns for some 80-meter antennas. The array of two verticals (reflector/driver) located over salt water is superior even to a 200-foot-high three-element Yagi for angles less than 8°. Note that the same vertical array placed over soil with good conductivity is greatly inferior to the array over salt water, although the land-locked vertical would be superior to a 100-foot high flattop dipole until about 13° in elevation. Verticals do best, however, over salt water!

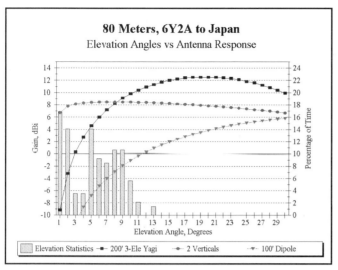

80 Meters, 6Y2A to Japan
Elevation Angles vs Antenna Response

Fig 2—Statistical elevation angles for Jamaica to Japan on 80 meters, again for all months and levels of solar activity. The needed angles are much lower on this path than they are, statistically speaking, on the Jamaica-to-Europe path. Again, the two-element reflector/driver array over salt water has a decided edge over most of the elevation-angle range.

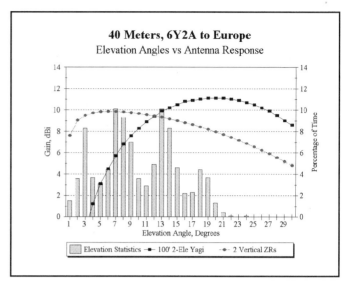

40 Meters, 6Y2A to Europe
Elevation Angles vs Antenna Response

Fig 3—Comparison of needed elevation angles and typical antenna elevation-plane responses on the 40-meter path from Jamaica to Europe. Here, the antennas are a reflector/driver pair of 15-foot-high "ZR" verticals by Force 12 over salt water compared to a 100-foot high two-element Yagi. The vertical array over salt water is stronger for most of the range of necessary angles.

than three tall towers, probably even more to be really effective.

Note that the vertical array in Fig 5 should cover nicely all the angles needed from 1° up to as high as 26°, while the single 60-foot high Yagi on 15 meters would be at a considerable disadvantage at both ends of this wide range of angles. Although not shown, the situation towards Japan would involve even lower angles, with a peak elevation angle occurring at 1°. This would be the prevailing angle almost 24% of the time the 15-meter band is open from 6Y to JA. Statistically speaking, the highest possible angle to Japan would be 11°, which would occur only 1% of the time. Antennas with very low takeoff angles are vital to be really loud into Japan from Jamaica on 15 meters.

Fig 6 shows the 15-meter situation from Jamaica to all of the USA. Here we see that the range of elevation angles is surprisingly large, varying from 2° all the way up to 30°. Actually, this shouldn't be surprising, considering that the USA is a very large target area. The distance from Jamaica to the lower 48 states varies from a minimum of 575 miles to Florida, to a maximum of 3340 miles to Washington state. The vertical array labeled "2x2 Halfwave Verticals" covers this wide range of elevation angles much better than would a single Yagi at 60 feet, which would have degraded performance because of the null in its response from about 14° to about 28°.

This aspect of vertical performance—wide elevation coverage—is often overlooked in the Amateur literature. Avoiding such nulls is the reason why vertical stacks

of horizontally polarized Yagis are becoming so prevalent among really serious contesters and DXers at their home stations. Putting up multiple stacks on a DXpedition would have required an effort beyond our enthusiasm for the sport of contesting.

Fig 7 shows the needed elevation angles and antenna patterns on 10 meters for the path to Europe. Once again, a vertical array on the seashore should be a potent performer over the whole range of angles needed—and it proved so in reality. The pileups calling us on 10 meters from Europe were truly phenomenal.

We also wanted to be loud on 160 meters into our targeted geographic areas. The elevation-angle statistics from the 18th Edition of *The ARRL Antenna Book* don't cover 160 meters, because *VOACAP* is not designed to operate reliably below 2 MHz. The team knew from experience in 1997 at 6Y4A, however, that a single 160-meter vertical on the beach could do very well. And we were prepared to up the ante for 1998!

The choice of what types of antennas to use at 6Y2A was set—it would mainly be verticals, backed up by a few rotatable horizontal Yagis at relatively low heights.

Why Verticals?—Some Other Parameters

Other than raw gain at low elevation angles, we had other important parameters to consider about the 6Y2A antennas. First, they had to be light and compact enough to qualify as regular carry-on baggage on the airplane. Remember, this operation was supposed to resemble a Field Day setup (minus generators, of course), not a typical

major multi-multi contest station with huge towers and monoband Yagis.

We also had to take our transceivers, power amplifiers, computers, coax, and other peripheral equipment in our carry-on baggage. Luckily, the weather in Jamaica does not require much heavy clothing. Shorts and tee-shirts were perfect for our operation. I wore a set of blue jeans on the plane for "formal" occasions, and because the temperature in San Francisco when we left was about 50° F, just a bit different from 85° F in Jamaica.

Second, we didn't want to pay excess baggage fees, as we would have had to do if we were hauling hundreds of feet of tower, guy wires, rotators and large Yagis! Getting large antennas and towers through Customs has always been a challenge I've tried to avoid as much as possible—both arriving in a foreign country and returning to the USA.

Tom Schiller, N6BT, of Force 12 Antennas and Systems, made all of the antennas, some of them entirely custom-manufactured specifically for 6Y2A. Tom was one of our "secret" advantages. Not only is he a superb operator, but he managed to fit all 19 of the antennas we used into six fiberglass "golf-bag carriers." Each golf-bag carrier could transport individual pieces up to four feet in length, setting the size limit for each telescoping piece of aluminum tubing. Each item was carefully inventoried and packed so that each carrier weighed 69 pounds, just under the 70-pound limit for a carry-on item. One other advantage with golf-bag carriers—Airline personnel are very familiar with them, especially when your destination is a tourist spot like Jamaica. By the way, not only antenna parts went into the golf-bag carriers. They also held about 14 pounds of 6Y2A tee-shirts, all the tools and four large containers of Gatorade (another secret weapon in the tropics).

Bigger and Better

Experience from the 1997 6Y4A operation indicated that more gain would be desirable on 20 through 10 meters. On the higher-frequency bands, it is easier for others to erect reasonably competitive antenna systems. Remember, "Be loud or be hosed" was our operating credo. Fig 5 shows that a relatively modest station with a four-element Yagi at 60 feet would have a peak gain that is just a bit more than the two-by-two vertical array at 6Y2A. While such a horizontal Yagi at 60 feet would not have the same elevation response at very low elevation angles, it would still be a very competitive station for much of a typical opening to Europe. Fig 4 shows that more heroic efforts are required on 20 meters to be really competitive with our verticals on the beach, but nonetheless, a 100-foot high Yagi on 20 meters will be much more competitive than will an antenna at that height on 40 or 80 meters. The lower bands are where the verticals really shine in terms of dB per foot of height.

With the wide expanse of beach-front real estate available to us, we chose to use three sets of "two-by-two" vertical arrays for the all-important path into Europe on 20, 15 and 10 meters. The basic building block is a parasitic reflector and driver, spaced approximately 0.25 λ, tuned mainly for gain,

with a compromise 9 dB front-to-back ratio. This first set of verticals (a "two-by-one") is fed in phase with another such set, spaced by about 0.6 λ. **Fig 8** is a bird's-eye view of the physical layout of this two-by-two array.

Each half of the phasing harness was made up of a 0.25-λ long RG-59 cable, in series with a 0.25-λ long RG-8X cable going to the feed point—enough to make up half the 0.6 λ physical spacing between the driven elements. The quarter-wave sections transformed 50 Ω at the end of the RG-8X sections to 100 Ω at the tee, where connecting two such impedances in parallel resulted in 50 Ω. From the tee to the shack we used RG-213 coaxes (or RG-8X on the lower bands). The coax run to the 160-meter vertical array (yes, we used a parasitic array of two verticals on 160 meters too) were rather long; about 500 feet long, in fact.

For 20 meters we chose to use vertical elements that were 1/4-wave high. For 15 and 10 meters half-wave long vertical dipoles were used. We did this because half-wave long dipoles compress the elevation-plane pattern down further towards the horizon than do quarter-wave elements, yielding additional gain. **Fig 9** shows elevation-plane patterns comparing four quarter-wave-long and four half-wave-long dipoles in the two-by-two array shown in Fig 8. The two curves cross over at about 25° elevation and the peak gain of the array using half-wave long elements is a significant 2 dB more than the array using quarter-wave verticals.

However, there is a physical problem associated with half-wave elements on

20 meters—they would have to be about 35 feet long, almost the same length as the shortened 80-meter vertical elements (which will be described in detail later on). For this reason, the 20-meter two-by-two arrays at 6Y2A used quarter-wave high vertical elements, with two elevated radials. Only two radials, you say? Yes, only two radials were used for each quarter-wave vertical element. Computations showed that there would be a negligible effect on the gain or the pattern. The system must have worked, because we had more than 4200 QSOs on 20 meters. You don't achieve these kinds of numbers without being really loud.

The half-wave vertical dipoles on 15 and 10 meters required no radials, a definite advantage when trying to walk through the forest of 28 verticals on the beach. **Fig 10** is a photograph looking down the beach showing some of these verticals. It was bad enough having to gingerly hop over the eight 20-meter radials, which were about 3 feet above the incredibly sharp volcanic rock and coral. It was, however, just a little weird to see that the 15-meter arrays were taller than the 20-meter arrays located nearby.

Besides compression in the vertical pattern, what else happens when a two-by-two array is used to increase the gain of a system? **Fig 11** shows the azimuth-plane response of a 15-meter half-wave dipole array at a 10° elevation angle, compared to the pattern of a single set of verticals arranged as a reflector/driver pair. The peak gain of the four-vertical array is increased by about 4 dB compared to the two-vertical array, coming at the expense of a narrower azi-

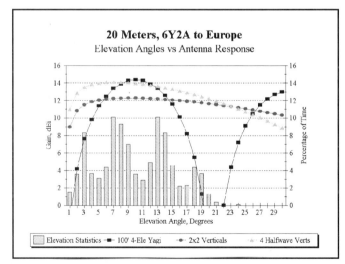

Fig 4—Comparison of needed elevation angles and typical antenna elevation-plane responses on the 20-meter path from Jamaica to Europe. Here, the antennas are a 100-foot-high four-element Yagi and two types of two-by-two vertical arrays over saltwater. The first type uses quarter-wave elements, while the second type uses half-wave long elements, compressing the elevation-plane response somewhat, but increasing the gain at lower angles.

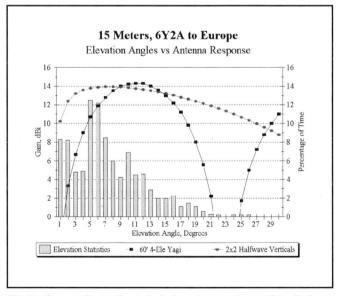

Fig 5—Comparison of needed elevation angles and typical antenna elevation-plane responses on the 15-meter path from Jamaica to Europe. At low angles the two-by-two array of half-wave verticals over salt water has the advantage, but a 60-foot-high Yagi is still quite competitive.

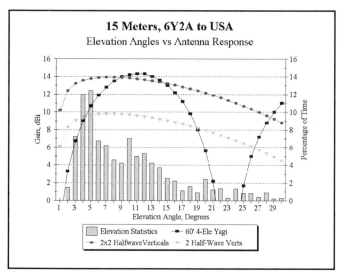

15 Meters, 6Y2A to USA
Elevation Angles vs Antenna Response

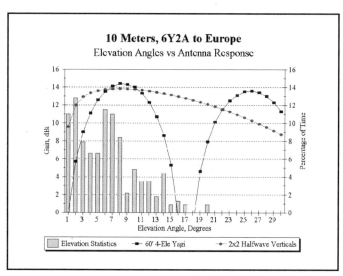

10 Meters, 6Y2A to Europe
Elevation Angles vs Antenna Response

Fig 6—Comparison of needed elevation angles and typical antenna elevation-plane responses on the 15-meter path from Jamaica to the USA. Although it would have been nice to have a two-by-two vertical array on this path, a single pair of half-wave verticals over salt water still does a very credible job, and its high-angle response is better than a single 60-foot-high Yagi above about 20° in elevation, where signals occasionally come in on this band at high levels of solar activity.

Fig 7—Comparison of needed elevation angles and typical antenna elevation-plane responses on the 10-meter path from Jamaica to Europe. While the 60-foot-high four-element Yagi is a serious competitor on this band, the two-by-two vertical array over salt water still holds its own, particularly at extremely low elevation angles.

muthal beamwidth, as you would expect. The higher-gain array also has much more distinct nulls in the azimuthal pattern.

In our case, the nulls in the higher-gain pattern were used to advantage. You will remember that we wished to improve our performance working three-point QSOs from 6Y2A. This means that not only did we need more gain into Europe but we actually needed to discriminate against North American stations, which by nature of their proximity would be much louder than the Europeans. The European antenna arrays at 6Y2A were carefully aimed to null out USA stations off the sides. That helped equalize the playing field for the Europeans. Our final percentage of Europeans (three points) versus USA stations (two points) was higher in 1998 than in 1997.

One disadvantage to narrow-beamwidth arrays aimed into Europe should be obvious. We needed separate arrays for working Japanese and USA stations. Thus we installed five separate two-element vertical arrays aimed at Japan/USA for 80 through 10 meters, in addition to the three two-by-two vertical arrays for Europe for 20, 15 and 10 meters and the two-element European vertical arrays for 160, 80 and 40 meters.

You Can Never Have Too Many Antennas

Another possible disadvantage associated with the use of narrow-beam two-by-two European arrays is that off-azimuth stations from Africa and South America would be tougher to work than in 1997, when only the wider beamwidth two-element arrays were employed. To cover these directions

we erected specially designed, very lightweight two-element horizontal Yagis for 20, 15 and 10 meters. These were placed on portable masts that were a half-wave high. Now "half-wave high" sounds pretty impressive, until you realize that this means 15 feet on 10 meters! Rotating these Yagis was by the tried-and-true Armstrong method; that is, by hand. When pointing in the same direction as the two-by-twos, the Yagis were usually down 2 to 3 S-units, sometimes more. The 20-meter two-element Yagi shows up in the background of Fig 10.

Another "secret weapon" we employed at 6Y2A in 1998 was WX0B Array Solution's *StackMatch* boxes.[3] These allowed our 20, 15 and 10 meter operators to selectively use one, two or all three of the antennas they had on those bands. Fred Cady, KE7X, one of the 15-meter operators, built special control boxes for the StackMatches tailored to our antenna configurations. (Fred and Dennis, AF7Y, also custom-built our operating tables from scratch!) For example, the 15-meter operator could simultaneously distribute his transmitter power equally among the European two-by-two verticals, the JA/USA one-by-two verticals and the rotatable 2-element Yagi. When a multiplier called in from, say, Africa, he could flip a switch to select the horizontal Yagi, which was often aimed in that direction (when it wasn't aimed into the Pacific).

We proved the old ham adage "you can never have too many antennas" many times over during the contest. We only wish we had some antennas that were high enough to peek over the 200+ foot high cliffs located about a quarter mile behind the villa. I'm sure we

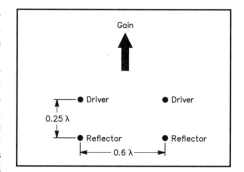

Fig 8—Bird's-eye view of two-by-two vertical array. The spacing between reflector and driver is approximately 0.25 λ, and the side-by-side spacing is 0.6 λ.

missed some multipliers because of the cliffs, but you can't have everything, can you? **Fig 12** shows the propagation prediction for 15 meters for 6Y2A for the month of November 1998, with a High level of solar activity (a Smoothed Sunspot Number of about 100, equating to a solar flux of 140). This is one of the 70,000 pages of customized predictions that are included on *The ARRL Antenna Book*, 18th Edition CD-ROM. These predictions cover a full spectrum of amateur QTHs around the world, for all months of the year and all levels of solar activity.

The 40 CQ Zones are listed in the left-hand column and the UTC hours are listed in the top row. The table is calibrated in S units, assuming that S9 is 50 µV on 50 Ω at the target receiver's input and that the receiver is calibrated at 4 dB per S unit. The transmitting and receiving antennas for this 15-meter table are assumed to be four-element Yagis

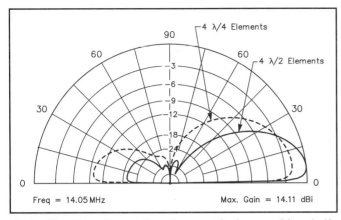

Fig 9—Elevation-plane pattern for a vertical array of four half-wave dipoles compared to four quarter-wave vertical monopoles with radial systems. The half-wave dipole system has about 2 dB more gain, at the expense of a somewhat compressed elevation lobe.

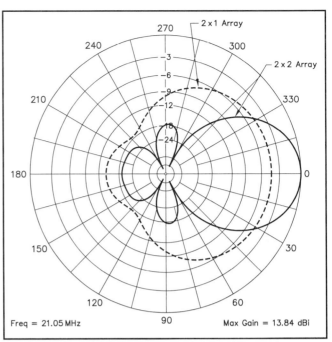

Fig 11—Azimuth-plane patterns for two-by-two (four element) 15-meter vertical array over salt water compared to an array with a single pair of verticals. Each element in this comparison is a half-wave-long vertical dipole. The two-by-two significantly compresses the pattern in the azimuthal plane, achieving about 4 dB of extra gain in the process, but making aiming of the main lobe more critical.

Fig 10—Photo looking along the beachfront of the 1998 6Y2A operation from Jamaica. In the foreground is the two-by-two vertical half-wave array for 15 meters into Europe. The 10-meter two-by-two array is behind this, and the two-element horizontal 20-meter Yagi at 30 feet shows up in the background.

that are 60 feet above flat ground, and the transmitter power is assumed to be 1500 W. Look at the table entry for 10 UTC in Zone 14, located in England. The band opens from Jamaica at 10 UTC, with a fairly weak signal of S2. By 11 UTC, the band has opened better, with an S8 signal in London from Jamaica. From 12 to 14 UTC, the signal peaks at S9+, which means that it is at least 10 dB above S9. The band closes at 20 UTC, for a total predicted opening of 11 hours at this level of solar activity in November.

Now, look at the entries for JA1, in Zone 25. Note that there are some signal predictions with asterisks (*). For example, see the entries for 03 and 04 UTC and for the times between 11 and 14 UTC. The asterisks indicate that the dominant signals are by means of the long path. Although they won't be very strong (peaking only S4 at 11 UTC), they will be there. In comparison to signals coming from Europe at S9+, however, it's unlikely that the long-path JA signals will be very useful. And besides, JA

signals are predicted to hit an S9 level in the afternoon opening starting at 21 UTC. We concluded that the long path blocked by the cliff behind us would not be a major factor to us. It would have been nice to have a good shot in all directions, but we figured that we should find the multipliers we needed on short-path beam headings over the ocean.

SOME PRACTICAL TIPS

The first practical tip for someone who goes to operate from Jamaica is "keep moving." Now why would I say *that*? We arrived at the villa a full week before the contest was scheduled to start, so that we could put up all the antennas and the six stations. As enumerated previously, we ended up with 28 vertical elements, not to mention the three horizontal Yagis and the receiving Beverages, the EWE and the low dipole! Every day out on the rocky coral beach we would be joined by a crew of very large, very ugly turkey buzzards, "John Crows" as the locals call them. These things spent all their

time gliding in lazy circles high overhead, watching us expectantly, or so it seemed. We made sure that we looked very much alive! One morning after a big storm blew by overnight, about 20 of these disagreeable-looking birds noisily congregated on the rocks overlooking the 80-meter arrays. They kept busy fighting with each other and scanning the seashore. I figured that their fondest hope must be that a dead whale would wash up on the beach.

Beware the High Voltage

The second practical tip for those who would install verticals on the beach is to have a very healthy respect for the levels of voltage that exist on the ends of radials and wherever high impedances exist. Salt spray is *guaranteed* to provide a ready path for arcing to occur when you transmit at full power. The ends of radials are particularly vulnerable points if you don't pay a lot of attention at installation.

Fig 13 shows what I call the "turkey-buz-

15 Meters: Nov., Jamaica (Kingston), for SSN = High, Sigs in S-Units. By N6BV, ARRL.

Zone	UTC --> 00	01	02	03	04	05	06	07	08	09	10	11	12	13	14	15	16	17	18	19	20	21	22	23
KL7 = 01	9	9	3	-	-	-	-	-	-	-	-	-	-	-	-	-	4	8	9	9	9+	9+	9+	9+
VO2 = 02	9	7	3	1	1	1	1	-	-	-	-	2	6	9+	9+	9+	9+	9+	9+	9+	9+	9+	9+	6
W6 = 03	4	9	6	1	-	-	-	-	-	-	-	-	-	-	5	9+	9+	9+	9+	9+	9+	9+	9+	9+
W0 = 04	9+	9+	9	4	-	-	-	-	1	-	-	-	9	9+	9+	9+	9+	9+	9+	9+	9+	9+	9+	9+
W3 = 05	9+	8	2	-	-	-	-	-	-	-	-	-	9+	2	8	9	9	8	8	8	8	6	-	9
XE1 = 06	4	9+	9+	9+	8	6	2	2	1	-	-	-	5	-	9+	9+	9+	9	8	8	8	8	7	2
TI = 07	8	3	-	-	-	-	-	-	-	-	-	-	-	9	9+	9+	9+	9+	9+	9+	9+	9+	9	9
VP2 = 08	5	2	1	-	-	-	-	-	-	-	-	7	9+	9+	9+	9+	9+	9	9	9	9	9	7	8
P4 = 09	9	6	4	1	-	-	-	-	-	1	-	-	2	9+	9+	9+	9|	9+	9	9+	9+	9	8	9+
HC = 10	9+	9+	9+	9+	9+	6	-	2	-	-	-	1	9+	9+	9+	9+	9+	9+	9+	9+	9+	9+	9+	9+
PY1 = 11	9+	9+	9+	9+	9+	9+	7	1	-	-	1	9	9+	9+	9	9	9	9	9+	9+	9+	9+	9+	9+
CE = 12	9+	9+	9	9+	9+	9+	9+	9	1	-	-	6	9+	9+	9+	9	9	9	9	9	9+	9+	9+	9+
LU = 13	9+	9+	9+	9+	9+	9+	9	7	-	-	-	9	9+	9+	9	9	9	9	9	9+	9+	9+	9+	9+
G = 14	-	-	-	-	-	-	-	-	-	-	-	2	8	9+	9+	9+	9+	9+	9	9	8	2	-	-
I = 15	-	-	-	-	-	-	-	-	-	-	-	3	9	9	9	9	9	9	9	9	4	-	-	-
UA3 = 16	-	-	-	-	-	-	-	-	-	-	-	6	9+	9	9	9	9	4	-	-	-	-	-	-
UN = 17	-	-	-	1*	3*	1*	1	-	-	-	-	-	1	9+	9	6	-	-	-	-	-	-	-	-
UA9 = 18	-	-	4*	2*	2*	1*	-	1	-	-	-	-	2	-	-	-	-	-	-	-	-	-	-	-
UA0 = 19	9+	8	4	1*	-	-	-	-	-	-	-	1*	-	-	-	-	-	-	-	-	-	5	9+	9+
4X = 20	1	2	1	-	1*	1*	6	-	-	-	5	9	9	8	8	8	9	9	9	7	6	-	1	-
HZ = 21	1	-	-	1*	2	5	3	-	-	-	3	8	8	8	8	8	8	9	5	5	2	1*	1*	3
VU = 22	1	2	2*	3*	1*	-	-	-	-	-	4	9	9	8	3*	1*	-	-	-	-	-	-	-	1
JT = 23	4	8	2	2*	1*	-	-	-	-	-	-	5*	1*	-	-	-	-	-	-	-	-	-	-	-
VS6 = 24	9	6	2	1*	2*	-	-	-	-	-	1*	6	5	2*	1*	-	-	-	-	-	-	-	-	9+
JA1 = 25	9	8	5	1*	1*	-	-	-	-	2	-	4*	3*	3*	1*	-	-	-	-	-	1	9	9	9
HS = 26	9	5	4*	3*	1*	-	-	-	-	-	-	-	9+	9+	9	6	4	1	1	1	-	-	-	1
DU = 27	9	8	5*	1*	-	-	-	-	-	-	-	3*	4*	9	5	1*	1*	1*	-	-	-	-	9	9
YB = 28	9	7	2*	2*	2*	-	-	-	-	-	-	1*	5	9+	9	9	8	8	8	9	5	-	1	9+
VK6 = 29	8	9	8	8	8	8	8	9	8	5	1	4	8	8*	5*	4*	2*	1*	-	-	-	-	4	8
VK3 = 30	7	8	8	8	9	9+	9	8	7	2	-	2*	3	9	7	-	-	-	-	2	7	7	6	6
KH6 = 31	9	9	8	8	6	3	-	2	2	1	-	-	-	-	-	-	-	9	9	8	8	8	9	9
KH8 = 32	8	9	9+	9+	9+	9	8	5	2	-	-	3*	4*	9+	9	4	9	8	8	7	8	8	8	8
CN = 33	-	-	-	-	1	-	-	-	-	-	5	9	9+	9+	9	9	9+	9+	9+	1	9	8	-	-
SU = 34	4	7	6	-	1*	1*	6	2	-	-	5	9	9	8	8	9	9	9	9	9	8	7	5	2
6W = 35	9	6	5	2	2	1	-	-	-	8	9+	9+	9	9	9	9	9	9+	9+	9+	9+	9+	9+	9
D2 = 36	9+	9+	9	9	9	8	7	1	-	6	9	8	8	8	6	8	9	9	9+	9+	9+	9+	9+	9+
5Z = 37	9+	8	8	6	7	8	6	-	-	5	8	6	6	6	7	8	9	9	9+	9+	9+	9+	9+	9+
ZS6 = 38	9	7	2	-	5	6	3	-	-	4	7	6	6	6	5	6	8	9	9	9+	9+	9+	9+	9+
FR = 39	7	3	-	8	8	7	2	-	-	1	6	5	5	6*	5	6	8	9	9	9+	9+	9+	9	8
FJL = 40	2	2	1	-	-	-	-	-	-	-	1	3	3	4	5	5	6	4	2	-	-	-	-	3
Zone	00	01	02	03	04	05	06	07	08	09	10	11	12	13	14	15	16	17	18	19	20	21	22	23

UTC -->

Expected signal levels using 1500 W and 4-element Yagis at 60 feet at each station.

Fig 12—Page from The ARRL Antenna Book CD-ROM, 18th Edition, showing propagation prediction from Jamaica to 40 Zones around the world for the month of November, at a High level of solar activity. Note signals levels followed by an asterisk (*), which indicates long-path predictions.

zard-wing" (TBW) radial system, in honor of our omnipresent feathered companions. (Most folks would probably call them "gull-wing" designs, but I'm fond of the term TBW. Curiously, we didn't see many gulls on Jamaica. Maybe the turkey buzzards intimidated them.) We supported the ends of each radial with pieces of driftwood, most often bamboo, that washed up on the shore. The relatively short radials used on 20 meters are pretty much self-supporting in the arrangement shown in Fig 13. However, the longer radials used on 80 and 160 meters required intermediate supports, since the radials started out typically about 8 to 10 feet above the ground at the vertical element. Sag in any long span of unsupported wire would cause them to droop down onto the coral and volcanic rock, which was washed constantly by salt water.

One evening before the contest K7CO/6Y5 was operating on 75-meter phone when I took a stroll out in the moonlight. I walked past the 80-meter array and noticed a peculiar flashing near the end of one of the reflector radials. This radial had been propped up near its end with a piece of semi-wet driftwood. Close (but careful) examination showed that the wood was arcing and actually smoking each time there was a transmission! I asked the operator to stop transmitting and performed an emergency repair, consisting of putting lots of black vinyl tape at the point where the wire ran over the driftwood. By the way, all the driftwood pieces used for such supports were either held up by placing them in natural holes in the volcanic rock or by placing a pile of coral and rock around the base. Not all the beaches on Caribbean islands are made of pure white sand like the ads show.

Another example of how high the RF voltage can get was vividly demonstrated on the half-wave dipoles used on 15 and 10 meters. Vertical dipoles have a high-voltage point at their top and bottom ends. The 10-meter arrays were located within 10 feet of the ocean and were regularly washed by salt spray when the wind picked up, as it often did. The bottom of the aluminum tubing used to make each half-wave dipole was perhaps a foot off the rock. In broad daylight I observed arcing at the bottom insulator of the 10-meter JA/USA driver element. The insulator itself was about six inches long, made of solid fiberglass rod. The arcing created a permanent carbon track that had to be carved off the

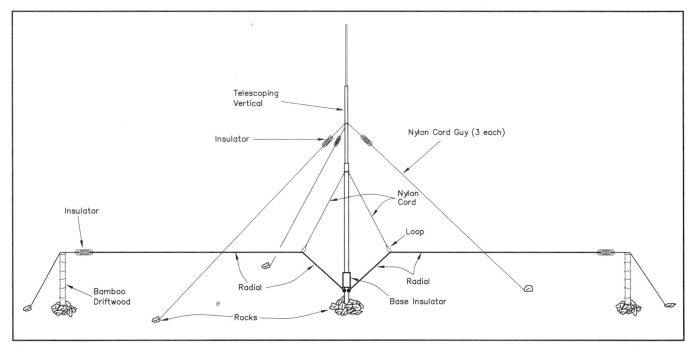

Fig 13—Drawing of 20-meter quarter-wave high vertical system, including the two "gull-wing" shaped radials used to fine-tune the resonant frequency. At 6Y2A, rocks were piled up at the insulated base of the verticals to help hold them vertical, along with nylon "parachute cord" used as guys.

insulator with a knife and the insulator washed with fresh water before operation could resume. The reason I was out investigating such a phenomenon was that the arcing in the 10-meter array created a broadband noise that interfered with both the 20 and 15-meter radios during the contest.

Another place where the RF voltage can rise to surprising levels is in the loading system used to tune the 80 and 160-meter verticals. See **Fig 14**. I refer to this scheme as "Deltoid Loading," rather than "linear loading" since the shape of the wires resembles the Greek uppercase Delta symbol (Δ), rather than the usual form of linear loading made with two parallel wires. The Deltoid Loading wires are at a high-impedance point, although not as high an impedance as the end of radial wires. Every morning we would walk the "vertical forest" to see what damage the wind, salt and RF had wrought overnight, especially while we were operating on 80 and 160 meters, where the radials were long and the Deltoid Loading was necessary.

For several days before the contest, we struggled with arcing at the Deltoid insulators due to salt-spray accumulation. Then we finally resorted to a home-grown solution—we used *Red Stripe* beer bottles as insulators! Tie-wraps, overlaid with black vinyl tape to make sure they didn't drift, were used around each end of these improvised insulators and they worked just fine. *Red Stripe* bottles also served as excellent coil forms for the hairpin-match inductors at the 80 and 160-meter feed points.

Incidentally, we standardized on the *Red*

Stripe bottles after a smaller bottle we found on the beach (it looked like some sort of medicine bottle) broke at one of the Deltoid loading points. Apparently, this occurred as a result of RF heating of the Deltoid wire, which in turn cracked the glass. The broken medicine bottle was discovered when the 160-meter array began putting broadband noise into the other radios. Although it was dangerous to do so, N6BT walked out at night onto the jagged coral and found the 160-meter vertical was acting like a flame-thrower!

Another word of caution: You don't want to fall down on coral, day or night. Not only do you get instant nasty cuts and bruises, but you usually get a nasty infection later.

Tuning the 20, 15 and 10-Meter Arrays

As alluded to previously, the vertical arrays were all designed by computer. Actually implementing the antennas required a disciplined approach in the field, or rather, on the beach. The following procedure describes how we tuned the 20-meter two-by-two array (a reflector and a driver in each "cell" of the two cells). In essence, each reflector is tuned without the presence of the driver, which is physically installed, but the feedpoint is left open. Once a reflector is tuned, its vertical element and radials are shorted together to make it into a parasitic reflector and then the associated driver is resonated. Finally, each driver/reflector cell is impedance-matched at the desired frequency for the array. (With a 0.6-λ spacing between the two parasitic reflector/driver systems, the mutual coupling between each

reflector/driver cell can be ignored—each system is tuned independently and then the phasing harness is connected.)

All of the antennas consisted of telescoping aluminum tubing sections that were pop-riveted with aluminum rivets. This made for secure electrical connections that could survive the rigors of the salt-spray environment. We used WD-40 to "grease" the sections so that they'd go together and come apart easily; WD-40 is marvelous stuff. (And yes, we had to drill out the rivets when we disassembled the antennas after the contest was over. A battery-operated drill was essential to the 6Y2A operation.)

Computer modeling shows that a vertical with radials can be tuned by varying the length of the vertical radiator and/or the length of the radials. What I didn't realize (until N6BT showed me) was that a variable TBW radial design (Turkey-Buzzard-Wing, or "gull-wing radial" if you insist) can be used to fine-tune the radials and hence the system. See Fig 13 again. The radial wires were supported from the vertical element by nylon cords ending in a loop made with a plastic tie-wrap. By sliding the loop along the radial wire, the effective height of the radial could be varied slightly, fine-tuning the radial/vertical system.

We coarse-tuned the radials by connecting them as a dipole (a rather low dipole, to be sure) and tuning them to resonance using an MFJ-259B *SWR Analyzer* connected through a multi-bead Force 12 choke balun. The closer this pseudo dipole was brought to the very lossy volcanic rock, the broader

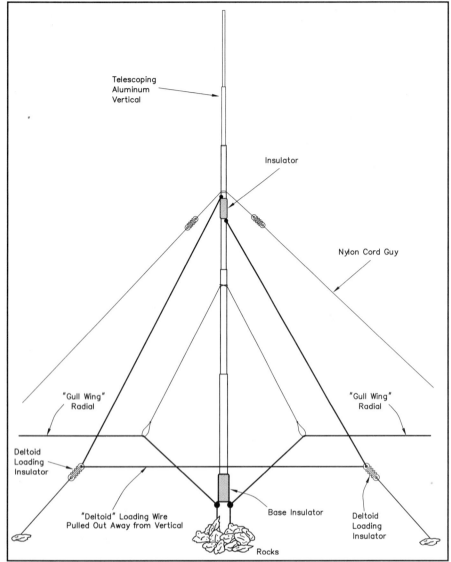

Fig 14—Drawing of one of the 80-meter vertical systems, including the two "gull-wing" shaped radials and the "Deltoid Loading" system used to bring the 37-foot-high vertical radiator to resonance. The insulators attached to the bottom of the Deltoid Loading wires were changed to beer bottles when other insulators failed under the high voltages present on this loading system when salt spray from the ocean was blown onto the wires.

Labels in figure: Telescoping Aluminum Vertical; Insulator; Nylon Cord Guy; "Gull Wing" Radial; "Gull Wing" Radial; Deltoid Loading Insulator; Deltoid Loading Insulator; "Deltoid" Loading Wire Pulled Out Away from Vertical; Base Insulator; Rocks

and shallower the resonant "dip" became. At radial heights greater than about two feet off the rock on 20 meters the dip was sharp and distinct and the feed-point impedance was close to the theoretical value for that height.

For the reflector, the frequency was set to the resonant frequency determined in the computer model when the driver was removed from the model. This was to eliminate the effect of the strong mutual coupling that occurs between the driver and the reflector, which are spaced apart by about 0.25 λ. Once a reflector radial pair was coarse-tuned, the two radials were shorted together at the base of the vertical and the resonant frequency of the vertical/radial system was fine-tuned, using the gull-wing height, to the desired reflector frequency.

Then the vertical reflector and its radials were shorted together.

Next we connected the MFJ-259B to the driver radials and resonated them to the desired array operating frequency. For example, on the 20-meter arrays this was at 14.05 MHz. Finally, we connected the driver radials to the base of the driver vertical and fine-tuned this system (which now included mutual coupling to the parasitic reflector) using the gull-wing radial height again. Impedance matching to bring the feed-point impedance to 50 Ω was done using a small "hairpin" coil at the drive point.

Then the second driver/reflector cell was tuned. Finally, the phasing harness was connected and the SWR at the feed-point tee was verified to make sure the whole two-by-two

was properly configured. This procedure sounds complicated, but we managed to build, install and fine-tune a 20-meter two-by-two array in about six hours from start to finish, using a crew of two people most of the time, supplemented by a few others during the actual installation phase.

Installation and tuning of the half-wave dipole arrays on 10 and 15 meters took less time, since they didn't have radials with which to contend. Imagine, however, how much time it would have taken to install three or four 60 to 100-foot towers and rotatable Yagis.

The 160 and 80-Meter Arrays

The verticals for 160 and 80 meters were custom designs by Force 12. The 80-meter verticals were 37 feet long and weighed a mere 9 pounds. These were made up of pop-riveted, telescoping aluminum tubing that was strong and supple, yet light enough to be hoisted to the vertical position by a single person. We used nylon parachute cord for guys, attached about halfway up the vertical element with small egg insulators and tie-wraps.

The same tuning procedure outlined above was used for each 80-meter element in each two-by-one array, except that the vertical element was tuned (after its two resonant radials had been separately resonated) with the Deltoid loading system.

The 160-meter array was truly a thing of beauty. Tom Schiller had TIG-welded aluminum tubing and rod to create what I like to call "Rohn 12 and a half" mini-tower sections that fit inside the golf-bag carriers and yet connected together to form a sturdy 20-foot high base for each 57-foot long vertical radiator. The face of each triangular mini-tower section was about 6 inches wide and each element weighed just 25 pounds. A pair of Deltoid loading systems were used with each vertical radiator, along with the now-standard pair of gull-wing radials. Six men were required to install each vertical—three on the top guys, two at the base and one pushing upward along the mast as it rose to a vertical position. Each vertical went up with surprising ease thanks to such a coordinated effort. **Fig 15** is a photograph looking up from the base of one of the 160-meter "mini-towers."

We installed a single 160-meter vertical and tested it out for the first few nights we were there on the island. The reports from all around the USA indicated that we were *very* strong. One W7 in Arizona said that we were louder than most of the W6s that he heard calling us! So we were confident that when the reflector was added to steer the beam North we would have a really outstanding signal on Top Band. The numbers tell the story: During the contest 1161 QSOs were made on 160 meters, with 22 Zones and 86 countries. Not bad for a couple of short verticals on the beach, don't you think?

The 40-Meter ZR Arrays

As promised, I'll try to describe the 40-meter antennas used at 6Y2A, which are the same arrays used so successfully in 1997 at 6Y4A. "ZR" stands for "Z-Axis Radiator," Tom Schiller's unique name for what amounts to a vertically positioned, loaded half-wave dipole. To me, the ZR looks like a rather large box kite, without paper on the ribs, of course. It is 15 feet high and 8 feet wide, and is fed in the center through a current-mode ferrite-bead balun. At the top and the bottom, both ends of the short dipole are wound into a sort of spiral. Although they superficially resemble a classic "top hat," the top and bottom is really a continuous conductor extending the electrical length of the dipole.

We set up two ZRs pointed into Europe as a reflector/driver pair, with another pair pointed into Japan/USA. They were placed at the edge of a small embankment about 8 feet above sea level and about 20 feet from the ocean. Did they work? You bet they did—W9QA had 3976 QSOs, with 36 Zones and 134 Countries during the contest. After the contest we pulled Dave's chain, telling him that in both 1997 and 1998 he had definitively proved that it's impossible to work 4,000 QSOs on 40-meter CW...

And If We Do It AGain?

It's hard to imagine topping the exhilaration of making 19,100 QSOs (18,000 after dupes) in a weekend and ending up with a raw (unchecked) score that is about 20% higher than the existing world's record. Perhaps we'll all simply rest on our laurels and sit out the next competition, but then again maybe not. . .

What would we do differently if we were to make a new assault on the world's record? One obvious thought is to seek a three-point location; one that is easy to get to and that has a lot of ocean-front property in the right directions. We're convinced that vertical arrays on-the-beach are the right way to go.

We're also convinced that there are a *lot* of reliability problems associated with any antenna located where salt spray can get directly to it. The amount of corrosion we found on the antennas after taking them down was pretty astounding—and these antennas had only been up in the air for about a week. It would be useful to know exactly how far from the

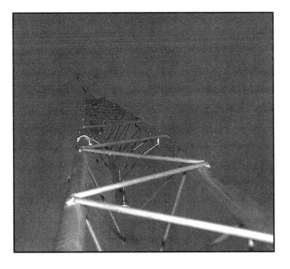

Fig 15—A view looking up from the base of one of the 160-meter "mini-towers" constructed by N6BT especially for this DXpedition. The overall height of each radiator is 57 feet and the tower face is about 6 inches across. All the welds were made with a TIG-welding system.

ocean's edge you can move (to get away from the direct spray) without losing the advantage of the over-the-saltwater shot. Preliminary modeling indicates that it may be possible to move back from the shoreline some, but not too far. The main effect appears that the wide "window" of elevation angles illuminated by a vertical array from the horizon up to about 30° in elevation is narrowed the further you move from the ocean's edge. The surprising part is that the model shows that the higher elevation angles are the most affected, not the lower angles as intuition would indicate.

Another interesting aspect of the modeling for verticals located back from the ocean is that the actual front-to-back ratio is higher than if the array were located directly over saltwater in all directions. The difference is due to the poor ground characteristics in the back of the antenna compared to the saltwater in the foreground. We experienced a sort of "double whammy" due to this effect during the contest. The cliffs toward the south have been mentioned previously. Add in an increased front-to-back ratio due to the poorer ground in the rearwards direction and that means that South American signals were weaker than a glance at Fig 9 or Fig 11 would seem to indicate.

Groundwave measurements done in the salt flats of San Francisco Bay a couple of years ago don't seem to follow part of what the computer model is showing, however. We're not sure whether to believe the models in this regard, although the models certainly seem to

mirror reality for how well verticals can do right at the shoreline. To make a very bad pun, stay tuned. More experimental work needs to be done in this area.

While the antennas and the location were major factors in the success of the 6Y2A operation in the 1998 CQ World Wide CW DX contest, other factors were equally important. It's hard to imagine putting eleven "Type-A" personalities together in the same room without friction and bickering. You know the old saw about "Put 5 contesters in the same room and there'll be 6 opinions," don't you? But this team worked and played together exceedingly well.

The leadership and planning were superb. Kenny Silverman, K2KW, is an incredibly detail-oriented manager who kept things on track for the entire year it took to plan and execute this operation. Not incidentally, having a year to plan everything down to the last detail gave us a material advantage over other teams we knew we were going to be competing against—detailed planning for 6Y2A started as soon as the 1997 6Y4A operation ended.

Having team members who were versed in many different aspects of contesting was another crucial element in the success too. If something broke down, there were many willing hands capable of fixing it.

And what did my Dad think of all this? He had a *great* time and would do it again at the drop of a hat! The raw numbers for the contest from 6Y2A were:

Band	QSOs	Zones	Countries	Band Captain	Antennas
160 m	1161	22	86	N6BT	2×1 Vertical, 57' high
80 m	1913	29	107	N6BV	2×1 Europe, 2×1 JA/USA, 37' high
40 m	3976	36	134	W9QA	2×1 Europe, 2×1 JA/USA, 15' high ZR arrays
20 m	4213	38	151	N6TV, W4SO	2×2 Europe, 2×1 JA/USA, λ/4 high, 2-ele. Yagi @30'
15 m	3508	39	151	AG9A, KE7X	2×2 Europe, 2×1 JA/USA, λ/2 high, 2-ele. Yagi @25'
10 m	3228	33	126	K2KW	2×2 Europe, 2×1 JA/USA, λ/2 high, 2-ele. Yagi @15'

VHF/UHF Antennas

The Expanded Quad (X-Q) Antenna for 144 MHz

By Fred Smith, W6DV (SK)

More about the expanded, bi-square quad antenna, with a simple, practical system.

The expanded quad (X-Q) antenna is a quad-type array that has a loop perimeter of two wavelengths—twice that of the conventional quad antenna. The driven element loop is also known as a bi-square antenna.[1] In addition, the elements are not continuous loops, but are divided into two one-wavelength sections, insulated at the top. The X-Q antenna can be derived from the Lazy-H array or four-element array by folding the ends of the H back to form a square with each side equal to $1/2$ wavelength.[2] The crossover feed system between the top and bottom elements of the Lazy-H is eliminated, and the resulting array is fed at the middle point of the bottom side, as shown in **Fig 1**.

A gain of 5 dBi is claimed for the quad loop, and 9.5 dBi if a parasitic element is added. The maximum gain occurs at an element spacing of 0.125λ with a variation of 0.5 dB with spacing from 0.1 to 0.25λ. The driven-element impedance falls in the range of 2 to 4 kΩ.

The X-Q array with a parasitic element provides somewhat greater gain than a traditional three-element Yagi parasitic array. It is also less expensive to construct, since its supporting structure is made of wood rather than aluminum. I've used this antenna for 2-meter SSB work, but it has enough bandwidth to cover the entire 2-meter band with a low SWR. I've built four, five and six-element X-Q antennas for 2 meters. A six-element X-Q antenna has been used at 220 MHz. The antenna is inexpensive to build and easy to adjust with an SWR meter and a simple field strength meter.

The 2-meter X-Q antenna is based on the X-Q antenna designed for lower frequencies discussed in *All About Cubical Quad Antennas.*[2] It consists of five quad elements: a reflector, driven element, and three direc-tors. These elements are mounted on a 7-foot boom. The reflector is tuned for maximum front-to-back ratio and the three directors for maximum gain, using stubs. A coaxial transmission line is matched to the driven element using a parallel-resonant circuit. *All About Cubical Quad Antennas* gives a discussion of other feed methods, and a table of dimensions for 6 through 40 meters.

Construction

The basic quad element uses four lengths of $5/8$ inch-diameter wood dowel for the spreader arms and a wooden hub, and shown in **Fig 2**. The arm lengths, designated A1, A2, A3 and A4, are given in **Table 1** for the each element. The X-Q loop wires are made from #18 wire. The half-loop lengths are as follows: reflector, $81^{1}/_{2}$ inches; driven element, $78^{15}/_{16}$ inches; directors, $75^{1}/_{4}$ inches. These dimensions include $1/2$ inch for solder-lug connections and $1^{1}/_{2}$ inches for looping and twisting at the top insulator.

Arm A1 is slightly longer than the others so that the feed-point insulator can be moved outward from the hub to put tension in the loop wires. The dimensions of the feed-point and top insulators are shown at the bottom of Fig 2. They are made from $1/4$-inch plastic. They are fastened to the ends of arms A1 and A3 by long #4-40 machine

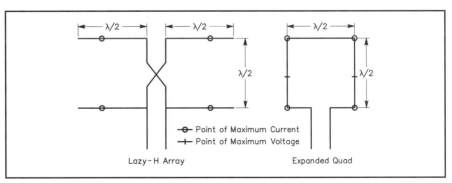

Fig 1—A pictorial showing the evolution of the X-Q array from the lazy H.

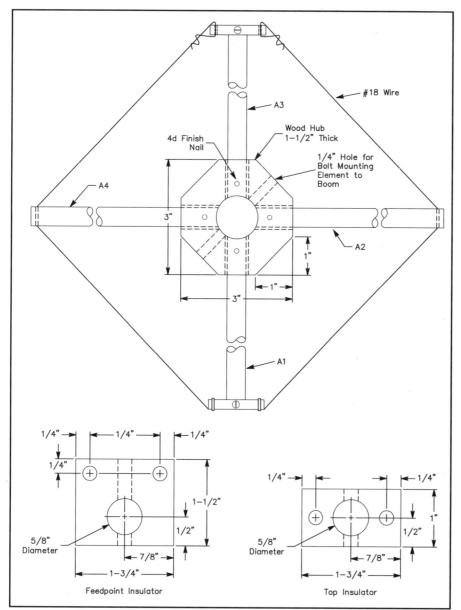

Table 1
Spreader Arm Lengths

(All dimensions are in inches).

Spreader	Reflector	Driven Element	Directors
A1	28$^1/_8$	27$^3/_8$	26
A2	28$^5/_{16}$	28	26$^5/_8$
A3	27$^5/_8$	26$^7/_8$	25$^1/_2$
A4	28$^5/_{16}$	28	26$^5/_8$

Fig 2—Details of the X-Q element structure. The spreaders, A1-A4, are made of wood. Dimensions are given in Table 1 for these pieces.

wood-dowel mast is secured to the boom with U bolts and a $^1/_8$-inch-thick aluminum plate 5$^1/_2$ × 3$^3/_4$ inches. The length of the wood dowel depends on the particular installation.

The wooden hubs for the quad elements should be mounted on the boom, and the holes drilled in the boom, before the arms are installed. The hubs can be positioned along the boom at the specified locations, and each one temporarily secured using a hose clamp on the boom, a small angle iron, and a C clamp. The bolt holes should be drilled in the hubs before mounting them on the boom. The rotational position of the hubs can be set by inserting 6-inch lengths of $^1/_4$-inch dowel in the bolt holes and sighting down the boom. Once the holes have been drilled in the boom, the hubs can be removed and the arms inserted into the hubs. Be sure that arm A1 is located in the same orientation on each hub. The arms are secured to the hub using water-resistant glue and a finishing nail driven through the hub, as shown in Fig 2. Coat all wood parts at least twice with spar varnish or other protective material before intalling the antenna.

Element Tuning

You will need the following items to tune this antenna: an SWR meter, a 2-meter hand-held transceiver (or other RF source sufficient to drive the SWR meter) and a simple field-strength meter. A long piece of small coax can be used to connect the field-strength meter circuit with the indicating meter, so that you can locate the meter where you can see it during tune-up. Here's the tune-up process I use:

1. Locate the antenna at least 5 or 6 feet above the ground, and the field-strength meter circuit and its antenna at least 30 or 40 feet from the antenna.
2. Adjust the driven-element capacitors for minimum SWR at the center of the desired band.
3. Position the antenna so that it faces directly away from the field-strength meter antenna, and slide the aluminum foil along the twin lead on the reflector to obtain minimum field strength indica-

screws or small wood screws.

The three director elements and the reflector are tuned by stubs made from pieces of 300-Ω twin lead, each 15 inches long. A piece of aluminum foil 2 inches wide is wrapped around the twin-lead stub as shown in **Fig 3** to tune the stub. The #18 wire loop ends are connected to the twin lead with solder lugs and 6-32 machine screws through the holes in the element insulators.

The driven element is matched to the 50-Ω transmission line by a parallel-resonant circuit, as shown in **Fig 4**. This circuit is mounted in a 2$^7/_8$ × 1$^5/_8$ × 1$^5/_8$ inch clear plastic box mounted on the feed-point insulator on arm A1 of the driven element. Two 6-32 machine screws secure the plastic box to the feed-point insulator and provide con-

nections between the split-stator capacitor and the #18 wires forming the quad loop. This box may have to be larger, depending on the size of the split-stator capacitor. Inductor L1 consists of six turns of #14 wire, and is $^3/_4$ inch long and $^1/_2$ inch in diameter. Capacitor C1 is 10 pF per section. Inductor L2 has 2$^3/_4$ turns close-wound and is 1 inch in diameter. Capacitor C2 has a 50 pF maximum value.

The five quad elements are mounted on the 84-inch boom made from 1$^1/_8$-inch aluminum tubing. A single 3$^1/_2$-inch hex bolt, $^1/_4$ inch in diameter, secures each quad element to the boom. The element spacing is shown in **Fig 5**. For horizontal polarization, arm A1 should extend vertically downward from the boom. For vertical polarization, arm A1 should be horizontal. The 1$^3/_8$-inch

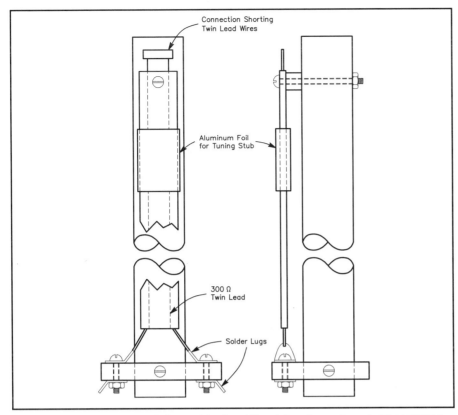

Fig 3—Stub attachment and element tuning. The elements are tuned using sliding sections of aluminum foil, then permanently shorted with soldered connections once tune-up is complete.

tion. Check the SWR and adjust the capacitors as necessary.

4. Aim antenna directly at the field-strength meter and slide the aluminum foil along the twin-lead stub on the first director to maximize the field-strength reading. Check the SWR and adjust as necessary.

5. Repeat step 4 for directors 2 and 3, each time checking the SWR and adjusting the match if necessary.

The X-Q array has an SWR under 1.5:1 over the 144-148 MHz range. An approximate measurement of the azimuthal beamwidth (and the assumption that the horizontal and vertical-plane beamwidths are similar) yield a calculated gain of about 12 dBi. This matches closely the gain predicted in computer simulation over ground.[3]

The aluminum foil should be taped to the twin lead, or (preferably) a short soldered across the twin-lead conductors, once the tuning is complete.

References
[1] R. Straw, *The ARRL Antenna Book,* 17th Edition (Newington: ARRL, 1994), p 8-43.
[2] W. Orr and S. Cowan, *All About Cubical Quad Antennas,* 3rd Edition (Wilton, CT: Radio Publications, Inc, 1982), pp 53-54.
[3] R. Bibby, "The K5BO Bi-Square Beam," *The ARRL Antenna Compendium, Vol 5* (Newington: ARRL, 1996), pp 55-56.

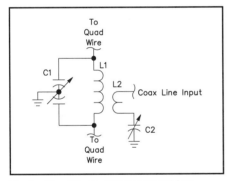

Fig 4—The driven-element matching network brings the antenna's high (2 to 4 kΩ) driving impedance down to 50 Ω. C1 should be a split-stator capacitor with 10 pF per section. C2 should have a 10 to 50-pF range. You may want to remove the variable capacitors, measure their values, and replace them with fixed, dipped-mica capacitors after the array is tuned. Choose an appropriate voltage rating for your capacitors based on the power level you plan to use with the antenna.

Fig 5—X-Q element spacing along the 7-foot boom. The mast mounts at the mechanical balance point. Be sure to attach the feed line before deciding where to attach the mast, as this shifts the balance point significantly toward the driven-element end.

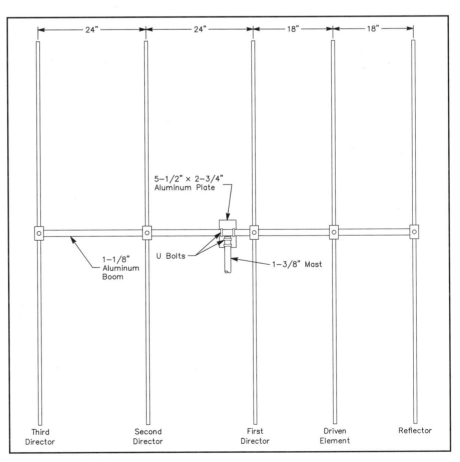

A Portable 900-MHz Corner Reflector Antenna

By Jack Warren, WB4MDC
4 Tomahawk Dr
Merrimack, NH 03054-2335

Need an antenna for 900 MHz that is simple to build and requires little or no tuning? WB4MDC shares his design for a Field Day ATV-station antenna.

S ome time ago, I found myself in need of a portable antenna for 900 MHz. For Field Day our local radio club tries to put a CW station and a phone station on every band. We decided to do ATV for the phone part of the 33 cm band. I didn't have any test equipment that covered this band, so I decided the antenna should be easy to construct, the materials should be easy to work with using simple hand tools, it should require little or no tuning and provide some gain. That sounded like a corner reflector to me.

Why Use a Corner Reflector?

Corner reflector antennas have been around for a very long time. In fact, in the early 1950s, I watched the local TV service shop owners, Ray Coover, W3ESV, and his brother Leon, W3JKZ, install what they called a bow-tie antenna for my parents. The antenna had two reflectors mounted at right angles to each other, made from a series of closely spaced aluminum rods and a bow-tie shaped dipole positioned half way between the reflectors. The halves of the dipole were connected to one end of a piece of 300-Ω twin lead. The other end of the twin lead eventually ended up at the TV set's antenna terminals. The dipole was tapered like a bow tie to increase the bandwidth of the antenna to cover the entire UHF TV band stretching from 470 MHz to 890 MHz.

I was planning to use my corner reflector for TV, but I only needed enough bandwidth to radiate all of my ATV signal sidebands. I could get that much bandwidth from a folded dipole. Folded dipoles are easy to build and tune, but they require a balun to couple their balanced feed point to the unbalanced coaxial transmission line. By placing the dipole in the middle of a conductive 90° reflector, the antenna would

have some gain and directivity. I just had to find the right dimensions for the antenna parts. I checked the reference material I had lying around the shack and found a good description of the corner reflector antenna in *Antennas* by Kraus.[1]

Putting the Theory into Practice

According to Kraus, if I spaced the dipole between $1/4$ λ and $1/2$ λ away from a 90° corner reflector, I could realize a gain of approximately 10 dB over a dipole in free space. *The ARRL Antenna Book*[2] states that the terminal impedance of a two-wire folded dipole changes more slowly with a change in frequency than that of a single-wire dipole. This implies that the SWR would remain relatively constant for a larger change in frequency. This benefits the broad-band characteristics of a TV signal. A folded dipole has a balanced feed point. Its impedance is also about four times the value of commonly available coaxial cable, so I decided to use a $1/2$ λ, 4:1 coaxial balun to match the balanced dipole feed-point impedance to the unbalanced 50-Ω coax.

I determined the relative size of the antenna, starting with the driven element. One wavelength at 915 MHz is nearly 13 inches

long, which means the $1/2$-λ dipole should be almost $6^1/2$ inches long. In the end, I shortened my folded dipole to $5^1/2$ inches to make it resonant at that frequency. According to the drawings in the reference text, each reflector should be 1 λ long on each side and the dipole should be mounted $1/2$ λ from the corner. These dimensions certainly meet my portability requirement. Also, with this driven-element-to-corner spacing the gain is very close to 10 dB over a single $1/2$-λ dipole.

The Corner Reflector Construction Details

The small size of this antenna lends itself to simple construction techniques. For the reflectors, I found two 12-inch-square sheets of 1/16-inch-thick double-sided copper-clad glass-epoxy circuit board material. I wanted 13-inch-square reflectors, but *free* was the operative word here. Single-sided cladding might have worked, but I was worried about sunlight warping the board because of the unequal stresses caused by having copper on only one side of the board. Copper makes a really good heat sink, and with cladding on both sides, warping is minimized. I rounded all the corners of each reflector panel to reduce the chance of personal injury. I drilled four equally spaced holes, $^7/_{16}$ inch from one edge of each panel and large enough to pass #8 sheet-metal screws. The holes are used to attach the reflector panels to a corner spine.

I constructed the corner spine from a piece of wood 12 inches long, 2 inches wide, and 1 inch thick. When assembled, the spine holds the reflectors rigid and at 90° to each other. I beveled the 1 inch sides of the spine lengthwise at a 45° angle so that when I screwed the reflectors to the $^7/_8$-inch wide beveled edges, the included angle would be 90° and I would have a flat surface on which to attach the driven element mounting post. I drilled a hole in the exact center of the 2 inch side of the spine, large enough to pass the mounting post's $^3/_8$-inch-diameter threaded bushing.

I assembled the corner by attaching a piece of adhesive-backed copper foil to the back surfaces of the wooden spine, sticky side to the wood. I placed the two pieces of copper-clad glass-epoxy board against the copper foil and fastened them using eight #8 sheet-metal screws. The copper foil electrically connects the two reflectors. I punched a hole in the foil to expose the hole for the mounting post. These details can be seen in **Fig 1**.

The Mounting Post

The driven-element mounting post is constructed from a $^3/_8$ inch outside diameter, 2 inch long threaded brass bushing purchased from the electrical supply store, two $4^1/_2$ inch long pieces and one $3^1/_2$ inch long piece of brass tubing purchased from the

hobby shop. The threaded bushing is of the type normally used to attach a lamp socket to the lamp. The outside diameter of the middle sized brass tubing is the most critical. I selected it by taking the bushing to the hobby shop and finding a size that would just slip into it. Tubing with an outside diameter of $^9/_{32}$ inch was a very snug fit into the $^3/_8$ inch bushing. Cleaning off the slight burr on the inside edge of the bushing would make this fit a little easier. I then selected two other sizes of tubing: one to go inside the $^9/_{32}$ inch tubing ($^1/_4$ inch) and one to go outside ($^5/_{16}$ inch). The outside tubing, which is $3^1/_2$ inches long, should provide a tight friction fit because that piece is not soldered to the other tubing.

The $4^1/_2$ inch long pieces of brass tubing are telescoped together and soldered into one end of the bushing. The double wall of the telescoped tubing provides the added strength needed during rough handling of the portable antenna.

I attached the mounting post to the corner by pushing the brass bushing of the driven-element mounting post through the copper foil and the hole in the corner spine, and then secured it with a brass nut and washer on each side. The brass tubing soldered into the brass bushing sticks out into, and bisects, the 90° corner.

The Folded Dipole

The feed antenna is a folded dipole, made from a length of #12 copper house wire. I prepared the dipole wire by placing one end of a 14 inch long piece of the wire in my bench vise and stretched it a little bit using a pair of pliers. This takes the kinks out of the wire and gives

it a somewhat springy quality.

I placed two 180° bends in the wire about $2^3/_4$ inches from the center to form the folded dipole. The internal dimensions of the dipole are $5^1/_2$ inches long and $^1/_4$ inch wide. A wire-bending jig helps make good clean bends.

The copper dipole has to be supported mechanically in a way that allows it to be attached to the mounting post. I constructed a center insulator from a $^7/_8$ inch long, $^1/_2$ inch wide piece of $^1/_{16}$ inch thick single-sided glass-epoxy board. I drilled a hole in the center of the insulator to accommodate a #6 machine screw. I drilled two more holes, $^1/_8$ inch from the long edge of the insulator, $^1/_2$ inch apart and centered on the machine screw hole to allow passage of the #12 wire. After the holes were drilled, I removed a $^1/_4$ inch wide piece of copper cladding that covered the two holes just drilled for the wire. I bent the feed point wires 90° so that when they were pushed through the two holes in the insulator and crimped against the insulator, the dipole would be laying flat against the insulator. After crimping the wire ends, I cut off the excess wire that stuck out past the insulator. I soldered the top of the folded dipole to the remaining copper cladding. These details can be seen in **Fig 2**.

To provide a rugged attachment between the dipole assembly and the mounting post, I constructed a dipole support tube. I cut the third piece of brass tubing to a length of $3^1/_2$ inches using a small tubing cutter. Since my tubing cutter wasn't very sharp, it rounded the cut end of the tubing. I found this to be an advantage because the deformed edge of the tubing held a #6 machine nut inside while I soldered it in place. I cleaned up the other end of the tubing with

Fig 1—This view of the 900 MHz corner reflector shows the construction from the back side of the antenna.

Fig 2—Here is a close-up view of the folded dipole driven element. The machine screw attaches the double-sided glass-epoxy circuit board material to the brass-tube antenna support. The copper circuit material is removed from the bottom half of this side, allowing the dipole antenna wires to go through the board and connect on the other side without danger of being shorted.

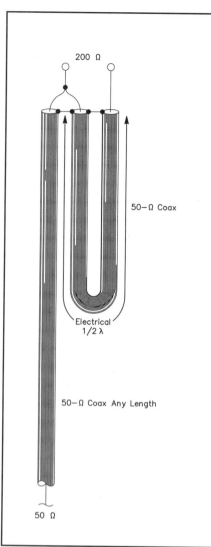

Fig 3–This balun provides a 4:1 impedance step-up ratio. The electrical length of the U-shaped section of coax is $\frac{1}{2} \lambda$.

a file so it would slip onto the driven element mounting post. Using a #6 machine screw, an outside-toothed star lock washer, and an inside-toothed star lock washer, I attached the support tube to the dipole insulator so that the screw head and outside-toothed lock washer are on the same side of the insulator to which the dipole is soldered and the inside-toothed lock washer is between the insulator and the support tube.

Feed Line Jumper and Balun

The next items I constructed were the coaxial jumper that goes between the dipole and the main feed line and the 4:1 coaxial balun that matches the feed line to the dipole. See **Fig 3** for a diagram of the balun. I practiced my coax stripping skills by making the feed line jumper first. I used a piece of RG-58 coax to connect the dipole and balun to the main feed line, but I limited its length to 18 inches because most small coax exhibits very high attenuation characteristics at 900 MHz. I began by stripping a $\frac{7}{8}$ inch long piece of outside insulation off of the coaxial cable, while trying to keep the braid from fraying. Using a solder pot and some liquid flux, I quickly tinned the exposed braid and was careful not to move the coax until it cooled. I removed a $\frac{5}{8}$ inch length of the braid, leaving $\frac{1}{4}$ inch of it sticking out from the outside insulator. I stripped the center insulator back until I had a $\frac{1}{8}$ inch long piece of it sticking out from the braid. This left a $\frac{1}{2}$ inch long piece of center conductor for connection to the dipole and balun. I cut another piece of RG-58 coax to a length of $5\frac{1}{2}$ inches to use for the balun. Using the same dimensions I used for the dipole feed line, I prepared both ends of the balun coax, making sure I ended with a

total shield length of $4\frac{1}{4}$ inches. This is the most critical dimension of the entire antenna because it has to be electrically $\frac{1}{2} \lambda$ long at 915 MHz, taking into consideration the coax velocity factor, which was 66% in my case.

Assembling the folded dipole, balun, and feed line pigtail requires a bit of manual dexterity. Refer to **Fig 4** to gain a better understanding of the next several details. I began by bending the jumper's center conductor 90° where it comes out of the center insulator. I placed the coax jumper beside one end of the balun so their shield ends were even and parallel, and I carefully wrapped the jumper's center conductor around the balun's center conductor and soldered the connection. I bent the balun coax into a U shape so all of the shields would line up with each other. When looking at the end of the coaxial bundle, the balun ends are at 4 and 8 o'clock, with the jumper at 6 o'clock. Holding the three coaxial ends together with their shields lined up, I wrapped a small-gauge piece of bare wire around the shields to hold them together while I soldered them. This operation left two center conductors sticking straight out of the end of the soldered bundle. At this point I slipped a short length of $\frac{3}{4}$ inch diameter heat shrinkable tubing over the coax ends, but I didn't shrink it yet.

To connect the balun to the dipole, I bent the two coax center conductors away from each other so they were pointing in opposite directions. I placed the jumper coax in line with the support tube so that the center conductors laid against the crimped ends of the folded dipole and soldered each conductor to its respective dipole feed point. Then I placed a piece of heat shrink tubing over the coaxial jumper and support tubing. Finally, I shrank all the tubing to hold the pieces together.

Fig 4—The completed driven element with $\frac{1}{2} \lambda$ coaxial cable balun is secured with a piece of heat shrinkable tubing, and the whole assembly is fastened to the antenna-support tubing with a length of heat shrinkable tubing over both the coaxial feed line and the support tubing.

Fig 5—A pair of wooden blocks are used to mount the corner reflector to a support mast. By loosening the wing nut on the right the antenna can be rotated 90° to produce horizontal polarization.

Fig 6—Here is the completed 900 MHz corner reflector antenna ready to go. The solder connections on the ends of the folded dipole driven element are the result of having to shorten the dipole from the original dimensions.

Antenna Performance

I was fortunate to have the SWR for this antenna measured on a network analyzer and found it to have a 2:1 SWR bandwidth of about 150 MHz, centered at 916 MHz. I haven't had the opportunity to measure the gain, but it exhibits very good front-to-back ratio. I attribute this to the solid reflector.

I was also rather amazed at the change in signal strength when changing the polarization of the corner reflector. When I loosened the wing nut and rotated the entire antenna through a 90° arc, the ATV signal strength went from a P5 signal to a very snowy P1 on my TV monitor. This demonstrates in practice the theory that says cross-polarized signals will be down as much as 20 dB as compared to both stations using the same polarization.

Some Observations

I haven't made significant adjustments to the antenna's dimensions. This is because I don't have access to the necessary test equipment to verify the results of changes in the dimensions. I did, however, have to shorten the length of the driven element from my original design to get the antenna to resonate in the middle of the 33 cm band. Fig 6 shows this modification, where you can see solder joints at the ends of the folded dipole. The dimensions given in this article represent my final version.

I was not too sure that I should have used soft copper wire for the driven element, but have found from several portable operations that having to bend the dipole back into alignment is better than having to reconstruct it from scratch as I would have to do if I had used a stiffer material such as brass tubing.

All in all, I am very pleased with the performance of this antenna and am considering building one for the 70 cm ATV band. Large diameter copper wire is too heavy for the folded dipole so I'm considering using the copper-plated aluminum center conductor from a piece of CATV Hardline. For the reflectors, I'd use ³/₁₆ inch aluminum rods attached to a pair of ³/₄ inch aluminum U channels. I haven't worked out the exact details yet.

Notes
[1] J. D. Kraus, *Antennas*, McGraw-Hill Book Company, Inc, New York, 1950, pp 328-336.
[2] R. Dean Straw, N6BV, ed, Folded Dipoles, *The ARRL Antenna Book*, The American Radio Relay League, Newington, CT, 1998, p 6-1 ff.

To complete the corner reflector antenna assembly, I crimped the end of the antenna support tube slightly, then slipped it over the driven element mounting post. This provides enough friction that it stays in place and still allows movement for adjustment. It also allows me to remove the dipole element for transporting the antenna. The folded dipole is positioned ¹/₂ λ from the apex of the corner (about 6¹/₂ inches). You can slide the antenna closer and farther away and experiment to determine the best operation of your antenna.

Mounting the Completed Antenna

There are various ways to mount this antenna. I wanted a method that provides convenient no-tools setup because I use it for portable operations. I devised what I call my *universal* mount.

The universal mount is nothing more than a 5 inch long 1¹/₂ × 1¹/₂ inch wooden block with a hole centered on one of the 1¹/₂ inch faces that's large enough to pass a 4 inch long ⁵/₁₆ inch carriage bolt. Both ends of the hole are counterbored to allow the bolt head and nut to be recessed into the block. The nut keeps the bolt from rotating during the adjustment of the wing nut. **Fig 5** shows how the block is attached to the back of the antenna's wooden spine using drywall screws.

My portable operations usually involve the use of a two-piece 6 foot long pole that attaches to a round base. To attach the corner reflector antenna to the pole, I use another wood block that has ⁵/₁₆ inch holes through the narrow face at both ends and a 1¹/₂ inch hole drilled through the wide face at one end. I made a saw cut from the end of the wood block into the large hole and use a ¹/₄ inch bolt, washer, and wing nut to clamp the block to the pole. The corner reflector attaches to the other end by slipping the carriage bolt through the hole and adding the wing nut. Using the two bolts with wing nuts, I can rotate the antenna for azimuth and polarization.

The completed 900 MHz corner reflector antenna is shown in **Fig 6**. The antenna is positioned for vertical polarization.

Building Log-Periodic Antennas for VHF and UHF Applications

By James Watterson, Ph.D, KBØRJG
3280 S Meridian
Colorado Springs, CO 80929
jmwphd@rmi.net

Introduction

After much research I determined that a Log Periodic Dipole Array (LPDA) was the best way to create the antenna of my dreams. But when I checked out the prices for commercial models I reeled from sticker shock—the commercially made antenna I wanted would cost almost $400!

My needs seemed simple enough: I just wanted a 130 through 1300 MHz, high-gain, low-SWR antenna that was also physically small and cost effective... There were few offerings in the retail market (and they were expensive) and I was skeptical about some of the gain claims. So, like any good ham, I decided to strike out on my own and build my own antenna.

The chapter on LPDAs in *The ARRL Antenna Book* looked incredibly daunting but a third reading brought enlightenment.[1] The LPDA is simply a series of half-wave dipoles electrically joined together in a continuous array. This allows you to operate across many bands with a single antenna. Best of all, the LPDA provides almost constant SWR, gain and front-to-back ratio over the entire design bandwidth. As mentioned in the *Antenna Book*, no other antenna can do this.

The magic of an LPDA occurs when an active region becomes energized for a frequency of interest. This happens automatically, using nearby combinations of elements. Those elements that are too short or long electrically are not used by the active region. The high and low frequency extremes of the antenna set the limits of the operational bandwidth for the whole antenna.

Imagine a smooth flow between the longest and shortest elements as the various frequencies are received or energy is transmit-

ted, as shown in **Fig 1**. Since this is an article geared toward building and using the LPDA, if you want to get into the really technical details you should get a copy of *The ARRL Antenna Book*. I will first discuss the software I created for designing the LPDA. Then I will discuss the construction of the antenna,

along with materials, assembly and use.

Software Description

I decided to write a BASIC program to design an LPDA. It allowed for multiple trial designs and gave me a printout of all the required design specifications after I

Commercial antennas that cover a wide portion of the VHF/UHF bands aren't inexpensive. KBØRJG tells you how to design and build a rugged Log Periodic Dipole Array using copper tubing and brass elements.

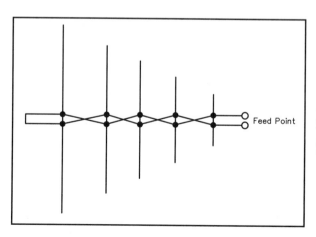

Fig 1—A log-periodic dipole array (LPDA). All elements are driven. The forward gain of the array as drawn here is to the right.

Feed Point

234

was satisfied with the results.[2] The *LPDA BASIC* program incorporates all of the mathematics from Chapter 8 of *The ARRL Antenna Book*. I've verified the program for accuracy, which can be used to design LPDAs over a wide range of frequencies. It runs in DOS as an executable file on all machines. I've included the BASIC source code, which can be run using *QBASIC.EXE*. (Note that *QBASIC.EXE* may not be included in the root directory of machines running *Windows 95* or later.)

After you load and start *LPDA*, the first thing you will be asked to do is to enter a high and a low frequency of interest, in MHz (decimals can be included but do not type in "MHz" after the frequency values). Next, you have to choose τ (Greek letter tau) and σ (Greek letter sigma). The letter τ represents a design constant and σ represents the relative spacing constant. In brief, the intersection of these values from **Fig 2** allows you to choose the desired gain of the antenna. Keep in mind that as τ increases so do the number of elements, and as σ rises the boom will lengthen. Experiment with these values to reach the compromise you like.

I wanted a design that covered 130 to 1300 MHz with an approximate free-space gain of about 7.5 dBi. I eventually chose 0.84735 for τ and 0.15 for σ. This gave me a final design with 18 elements, a boom length of just over 7 feet and a longest element just shy of 4 feet total length (2 feet on each side of the boom).

I decided to forgo the 6-meter band when I realized that an antenna that would cover 50 to 1300 MHz would have been 9 feet long with a maximum element length of more than 9 feet. With a 130 to 1300 MHz antenna I could work multiple amateur bands, satellites, and also receive FM/TV and multiple-band scanner signals over the entire bandwidth.

The next thing the software will do is ask for the diameter of the shortest element, element n. This is an empirical decision and you need to consider readily available materials. I chose to make my booms of 1-inch copper pipe and my elements of 3/32-inch brass welding rod. You could also choose to use brass tubing, which only comes in 12-inch lengths. You will find, however, that you will have to telescope various diameters of tubing together to make elements suitable for the longer elements.

Welding rod, on the other hand, comes in 36-inch lengths and it's cheap. Using rods increases strength, decreases the work and cost, and only marginally affects the SWR over the band. (By the way, my entire antenna cost less than $50.) At the prompt from the *LPDA* program asking for the diameter of the smallest element, I enter 0.09375 inch, the diameter of welding rods.

The next prompts in the software are the feed-point impedance and the diameter of the feeder conductor. You don't need to use these parameters directly for VHF/UHF applications, but I included them for HF LPDA use. At VHF/UHF, the feeder spacings become ridiculously small so I decided to go with the straight 72-Ω feeder design I will describe shortly. For HF or VHF use refer to *The ARRL Antenna Book* for a description of the feed-point and feeder dimensional values and the construction of a phased feeder system. For my VHF antenna I enter 72 for the feed-point value and 0.403 inch (RG-11 size) for the conductor value. The calculations will not effect the elements or their spacings, the values that you are really interested in knowing.

The program will prompt you if you want a hard copy printout. You will probably answer "Y," once you've experimented with different values for σ and τ. Most of Section 1 of the printout contains summaries and values that are technical in nature. However, the overall boom length and number of elements are there. When you buy copper pipe for your boom, include the extra length (in inches) obtained from the Section 1 listed as "Distance of Stub... Behind Longest Element" and add an extra 1/4 inch to this number. This allows you to connect the feedline to the booms and gives a bit of room to drill for the first (short-end) element.

Section 2 in the printed report covers several things. Column 1 shows the full size of each half-wave element, in inches, from the longest (element 1) to the shortest (element n). Column 2 is the half wavelength in centimeters (used for measuring and cutting elements precisely, very important at VHF/UHF work). Note that in my design, one-half of each element length in Column 1 or 2 is mounted on each boom half. Column 3 gives you the actual half-wave resonant frequency for each of the element pairs. If you divide 492 by Column 3 you will get Column 1 (492/f = resonance of a half wave in feet).

Section 3 gives you the spacings between each successive element pair running down the boom from the longest to the shortest elements. Column 1 is in inches, Column 2 is in millimeters and Column 3 is in feet (useless for precision work at VHF/UHF, but fine for HF use).

Section 4 of the printout shows you the element diameters you've chosen, together with the computed length-to-diameter ratios for each element. I included this information to give any perfectionists among you the ability to determine the ideal length-to-diameter ratios of each element. Keeping a constant length-to-diameter ratio would result in constant electrical characteristics (that is, SWR) across the entire bandwidth of the antenna. As I said, I decided to be practical and used welding rod!

Construction Details

Get some 3/4 or 1-inch copper pipe for your boom. You will need two pieces the same length. I used 1-inch pipe, but 3/4-inch pipe is workable if you use RG-59 feed line, as explained below. You can roughly figure this from the second and third sections of the printout. Take the centimeter column lengths of Section 2 and cross-reference them with each element pair diameter from Section 4.

Now, multiply cm times 10 (to obtain mm) and divide by 2. This gives you the length of one side of the element pair. Carefully measure the length of the element and add 5 mm (for a mounting stub). Cut the element pairs using wire cutters or a small

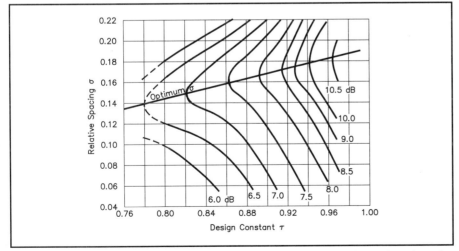

Fig 2—LPDA directivity (gain over isotropic, assuming no losses) as a function of τ and σ, for a length to diameter ratio of 125 for the element at the feed point. For each doubling of length-to-diameter the directivity decreases by about 0.2 dB for ratios in the range of 50 to 10,000. (*After Carrel, followed up by Butson and Thompson.*)

tubing cutter. I stuck each pair vertically in green floral styrofoam, with a numbered label of masking tape to indicate which element pair was which.

Once all of your elements are cut, slide a circle template just over one end of the copper boom pipes and make a mark at 0° and at 180°. Then lay a board against the pipe or use a door frame and line the edge up with the mark you made. Run a line down the entire length of the pipe on both sides with a permanent marker while having someone hold the pipe firm to the board or door frame. Using the element spacings from Section 3 and the stub distance from Section 1, make your first mark beginning at one end of the pipe plus 1 inch. Using a mm scale, mark off each spacing running down the line on the pipe until you get to the last element. You should have a small bit left after the last mark. Do this on the other side and repeat for the other section of pipe.

Now, referring to **Fig 3**, run down one side of the pipe and mark all of the even-numbered element holes with a permanent marker (these are the "keepers" for drilling). On the opposite side, mark all of the odd-numbered holes. Repeat this on the second boom pipe also. You can go back and erase the unused holes on each side of the two boom pipes if it confuses you. Place the pipes vertically and side-by-side and make sure the respective sides' holes match closely, if not perfectly.

Get a drill (or better yet use a drill press) and begin to drill out the holes using the correct drill bit. I found the best way to work was to use a machinist's V-block to hold the pipe while drilling and soldering. If you can't find a V-block, you can fashion one out of a 2 by 2 with two opposing 45° angled pieces of thin wood tacked to the ends.

Once the booms are done it's time to solder. I used lead-free 4% silver solder from Radio Shack. It's strong stuff and easy to use. Get several tubes and use it liberally around the bases of each element pair. You

will need a propane torch and soldering tip or the small torch extension with feed tube and regulator. (Forget the tips that come with this extension; there's not enough heat transfer.) The best way to attack this job is to purchase two wooden dowels. One is approximately 5 mm smaller in diameter than the inside diameter of the boom. The second dowel should be 10 mm smaller than the boom diameter. Slide the larger dowel into the pipe several feet and insert each element into its respective hole.

Then apply your heat and coat the area with a good ring of silver solder. After you have a puddle of solder tight against the perimeter of the element, reheat it, true up the element with pliers and then allow the solder to set. Cool the area with a wet towel or sponge and move on. You don't need to be overly precise making the elements true at this point as they will get bent a bit as you work. However, make sure they are basically perpendicular to the boom drilling line and parallel to each other as you work down the line.

Sight down the row from time to time and ensure that the elements all lie in a fairly true plane. If not, reheat the solder on the offending element and reset it. Wear gloves when working—the boom conducts heat very quickly.

When you finish one side rotate the boom in the V-block and clamp it down to complete the other side. At this point I used spring clamps to hold the boom ends onto two sawhorses. Slide the thinner wood dowel into the boom to ensure equal depth for the opposite side elements. Set the entire affair down flat when you finish to avoid dropping it, something that could ruin your whole day.

When both booms are done, you need to polish and clean the entire unit. I used Tarnex metal cleaner, fine steel wool and some applications of flux remover. Be careful around the thin elements and polish them by drawing the steel wool in one direction away from the boom. When you finish, give

each boom a couple coats of quality spray polyurethane to keep corrosion at bay.

To secure one boom to the other you will need some hardware. Get six 6/32×3 inch brass panhead screws and nuts. I used brass because it is nonferrous and holds up well in weather. To insulate the two booms from each other, I used some nylon "shoulder washers" I found in a bin at a local Home Base Superstore. Mine were 1/2-inch long and the 6/32 screws slid through them easily. If you use a 3/4-inch boom, you will need shorter shoulder washers. Get 24 shoulder washers (four for each bolt).

For the end of the booms you will need two insulators, made of 1/4-inch thick Plexiglas, 2 inches wide by 6 inches long. From the end of each boom, mark holes at 2 inches and 5 inches. Drill completely through each boom at these points (perpendicular to the elements), using a 1/4-inch bit so that the shoulder washers fit in these holes. Line up the Plexiglas insulators at the end of the booms and drill corresponding holes through them.

Slide one shoulder washer over a screw and place it in the hole at the end of one boom. Place another shoulder washer over the screw protruding from the boom, followed by the Plexiglas spacer and another shoulder washer. Place the end of this screw through the second boom, followed by the last shoulder washer and a nut to secure everything. Then do the same thing at the other end of the two booms.

Now lift the antenna and find the balance point. Mark points on one of the booms 1 inch on each side of the balance point and drill holes through the booms, making sure that they are perpendicular to the elements. Prepare another piece of 1/4-inch thick Plexiglas about 4 inches wide by 12 inches long. This will be the center insulator and the boom-to-mast plate. Position this Plexiglas plate between the two booms so that the top of the plate is 1 inch above the two booms. Drill through the plate using the previously drilled holes as guides. Secure the plate sandwiched between the two booms as before, using screws and shoulder washers. You will probably have to loosen the hardware at the ends of the booms. When you finish, check with a multimeter to make sure there is no continuity between the booms.

Feed a length of RG-59U (for a 3/4-inch boom) or RG-11 (for a 1-inch boom) through one of the booms, leaving several feet sticking out of the smallest-element end and several inches out the back. This takes some patience and twisting to snake the coax past the screws holding the two booms together but it can be done. Strip 2 inches of the outer insulation off the coax at the back of the LPDA and separate the shield. Cover all but a 1/2 inch of the shield with shrink tubing. Strip about 3/4 inch of

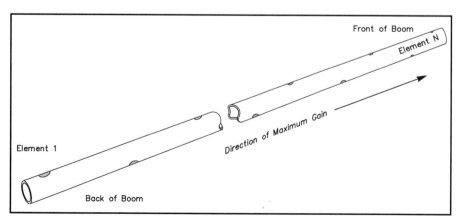

Fig 3—Boom drilling details for KB0RJG's LPDA. Both booms should be identical.

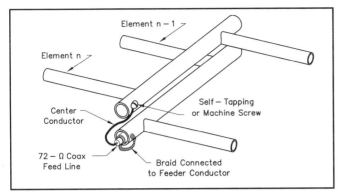

Fig 4—Schematic drawing of feed system used with dual-boom LPDA for VHF/UHF designs.

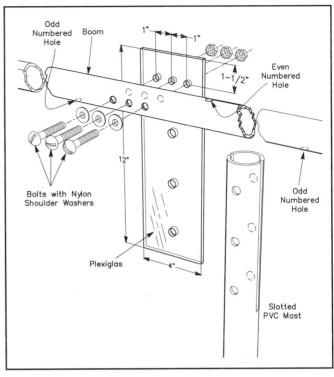

Fig 5—Mounting details for KBØRJG's LPDA. The Plexiglas boom-to-mast plate is sandwiched between the two booms and also acts as an insulator. The elements are mounted vertically.

Table 1

SWR Readings for the LPDA Using Cross-Needle SWR/Power Meter

Frequency (MHz)	SWR	Frequency (MHz)	SWR
144	1.9:1	430	1.8:1
145	1.8:1	435	1.1:1
146	1.6:1	440	1.9:1
147	1.3:1	445	1.9:1
148	1.8:1	450	2.0:1

foam off the center conductor.

Fig 4 shows the feed mechanics. I used a sheet-metal screw to tap into the top boom for the center conductor, but I used a 1/8-inch screw and nut through a hole drilled 1/4 inch from the end of the bottom boom to attach the shield. This prevents cutting into the outer insulation of the coax. I used a small crimped lug for the shield. Prepare your coax and attach the shield and center conductor.

You can attach a BNC or N connector to the free end of the feed coax. Use good quality coax, Belden 9913-F or RG-214-U to the shack. The RG-59U coax running through the boom creates a balun that delivers 72 Ω at the feed point, but this will only work for VHF/UHF antennas. HF log periodics require baluns and special feeders that cannot use the boom. The small 72 to 52-Ω mismatch will not harm your efforts.

Finally, take a piece of 2-inch PVC pipe about 3 feet long and cut a 1/4-inch wide slot down its center for the Plexiglas boom-to-mast plate to slide into. The slot should be deep enough so that the entire antenna rests on the top of the pipe, while the bottom of the Plexiglas plate rests on the bottom of the slot. See **Fig 5**.

Drill three centered holes through the pipe and Plexiglas and secure with 1/4 × 3 1/2 inch brass bolts, nuts and lock washers. You can now mount the mast to the rotator directly, although you may want to run a

Fig 6—Photograph of KBØRJG's completed LPDA.

wooden dowel secured with wood screws through the PVC mast to make sure it isn't crushed when the rotator clamps are tightened. Remember to use a nonconducting mast to make sure that it doesn't interact electrically with the vertical elements.

When you are finished, gently true up the elements. If your drilling was slightly off, don't try to force the elements too much or you will crack a solder joint. Your antenna is now ready to go to work!

Results

After all the assembly came the moment of truth. How would my antenna work? After hooking up with an N connector and Belden 9913, I plugged the other end into my dual-bander. The results for 2 meters and 440 MHz are shown in **Table 1**. Not bad at all.

Reception for my scanner showed an improvement of three to four S-units all across the bandwidth, although one should not assume 24 dBi of gain from such a measurement, given the nonlinearities involved with most S-meters!

Not only did my new antenna fulfill all of my needs but it looks so similar to a TV antenna that the neighbors didn't notice it. **Fig 6** is a photograph of the finished antenna. It is satisfying to realize that there is nothing mystifying nor difficult about building and using log periodic antennas in the VHF/UHF spectrum.

My Elmer, Bill Berendt, WØHNI, was instrumental in the consultation phase of this project.

Notes

[1] *The ARRL Antenna Book*, 17th Ed. (Newington: ARRL, 1994), pp 10-1 through 10-6.

[2] The BASIC program *TAPER* is also required for LPDA design using telescoping tubing elements. A compiled version is included here. It is also available from ARRL as part of *The Antenna Book*, 17th Edition, software.

[3] P. C. Butson and G. T. Thompson, "A Note on the Calculation of the Gain of Log-Periodic Dipole Antennas," *IEEE Trans Ant Propag*, Vol AP-24, No. 1, Jan 1976, pp 105-106.

[4] R. L. Carrel, "The Design of Log-Periodic Dipole Antennas," *1961 IRE International Convention Record*, Part 1, Antennas and Propagation.

Notes

Notes

Notes

FEEDBACK

Please use this form to give us your comments on this book and what you'd like to see in future editions, or e-mail us at **pubsfdbk@arrl.org** (publications feedback). If you use e-mail, please include your name, call, e-mail address and the book title, edition and printing in the body of your message. Also indicate whether or not you are an ARRL member.

Where did you purchase this book?

☐ From ARRL directly   ☐ From an ARRL dealer

Is there a dealer who carries ARRL publications within:

☐ 5 miles   ☐ 15 miles   ☐ 30 miles of your location?   ☐ Not sure.

License class:

☐ Novice   ☐ Technician   ☐ Technician Plus   ☐ General   ☐ Advanced   ☐ Amateur Extra

Name _____   ARRL member? ☐ Yes ☐ No

_____ Call Sign _____

Daytime Phone (   ) _____ Age _____

Address _____

City, State/Province, ZIP/Postal Code _____

If licensed, how long? _____ e-mail address: _____

Other hobbies _____

_____

Occupation _____

From _____

_____

_____

EDITOR, ANTENNA COMPENDIUM VOL 6
AMERICAN RADIO RELAY LEAGUE
225 MAIN STREET
NEWINGTON CT 06111-1494

— — — — — — — — — — — — — — please fold and tape — — — — — — — — — — — — — — —